Tritium-Labeled Molecules
in Biology and Medicine

AMERICAN INSTITUTE OF BIOLOGICAL SCIENCES

and

U. S. ATOMIC ENERGY COMMISSION

MONOGRAPH SERIES ON
RADIATION BIOLOGY

JOHN R. OLIVE, *Series Director*

AMERICAN INSTITUTE OF BIOLOGICAL SCIENCES

ADVISORY COMMITTEE

AUSTIN M. BRUES, *Argonne National Laboratory*
LEO K. BUSTAD, *Pacific Northwest Laboratory*
ERNEST C. POLLARD, *Pennsylvania State University*
CHARLES W. SHILLING, *Biological Science Communications Project*

MONOGRAPH TITLES AND AUTHORS

RADIATION, RADIOACTIVITY, AND INSECTS
R. D. O'BRIEN, *Cornell University*
L. S. WOLFE, *Montreal Neurological Institute*

RADIATION, ISOTOPES, AND BONE
F. C. McLEAN, *University of Chicago*
A. M. BUDY, *University of Chicago*

RADIATION AND IMMUNE MECHANISMS
W. H. TALIAFERRO, *Argonne National Laboratory*
L. G. TALIAFERRO, *Argonne National Laboratory*
B. N. JAROSLOW, *Argonne National Laboratory*

LIGHT: PHYSICAL AND BIOLOGICAL ACTION
H. H. SELIGER, *Johns Hopkins University*
W. D. McELROY, *Johns Hopkins University*

MAMMALIAN RADIATION LETHALITY: A DISTURBANCE IN
CELLULAR KINETICS
V. P. BOND, *Brookhaven National Laboratory*
T. M. FLIEDNER, *Brookhaven National Laboratory*
J. O. ARCHAMBEAU, *Brookhaven National Laboratory*

IONIZING RADIATION: NEURAL FUNCTION AND BEHAVIOR
D. J. KIMELDORF, *U. S. Naval Radiological Defense Laboratory*
E. L. HUNT, *U. S. Naval Radiological Defense Laboratory*

TISSUE GRAFTING AND RADIATION
H. S. MICKLEM, *Radiobiological Research Unit, Harwell*
J. F. LOUTIT, *Radiobiological Research Unit, Harwell*

THE SOIL–PLANT SYSTEM IN RELATION TO INORGANIC
NUTRITION
M. FRIED, *International Atomic Energy Agency, Vienna*
H. BROESHART, *International Atomic Energy Agency, Vienna*

TRITIUM-LABELED MOLECULES IN BIOLOGY AND MEDICINE
L. E. FEINENDEGEN, *Services de Biologie, Euratom*

(IN PREPARATION)

RADIOISOTOPES IN THE HUMAN BODY: PHYSICAL AND BIO-
LOGICAL ASPECTS
F. W. SPIERS, *University of Leeds*

Tritium-Labeled Molecules in Biology and Medicine

LUDWIG E. FEINENDEGEN

Services de Biologie
Euratom, Brussels, Belgium

presently at

Kernforschungsanlage Jülich
Germany

Prepared under the direction of the American Institute of Biological Sciences for the Division of Technical Information, United States Atomic Energy Commission

ACADEMIC PRESS • New York and London 1967

ACADEMIC PRESS, INC.
111 Fifth Avenue, New York, New York 10003

United Kingdom Edition published by
ACADEMIC PRESS INC. (LONDON) LTD.
Berkeley Square House, London W.1

LIBRARY OF CONGRESS CATALOG CARD NUMBER: 67–23155

PRINTED IN THE UNITED STATES OF AMERICA

244531

FOREWORD TO THE SERIES

This monograph is one in a series developed through the cooperative efforts of the American Institute of Biological Sciences and the U. S. Atomic Energy Commission's Division of Technical Information. The goal in this undertaking has been to direct attention to biologists' increasing utilization of radiation and radioisotopes. Their importance as tools for studying living systems cannot be overestimated. Indeed, their application by biologists has an added significance, representing as it does the new, closer association between the physical and biological sciences.

The association places stringent demands on both disciplines: Each must seek to understand the methods, systems, and philosophies of the other science if radiation biology is to fulfill its promise of great contributions to our knowledge of both the normal and the abnormal organism. Hopefully, the information contained in each publication will guide students and scientists to areas where further research is indicated.

The American Institute of Biological Sciences is most pleased to have had a part in developing this Monograph Series.

JOHN R. OLIVE
Executive Director
American Institute of Biological Sciences

PREFACE

The great impact of nuclear technology on the life sciences was first summarized by G. von Hevesy in his book *Radioactive Indicators* (Interscience Publishers, 1948). With the expanded use of radioactive tracer techniques, tritium, the radioactive isotope of hydrogen, has been in increasing demand. Its favorable half-life of about 12.3 years and its relatively low cost is matched by more specific advantages, but it also poses considerable disadvantages.

Its advantages and disadvantages stem partly from the fact that hydrogen is abundant in living matter and that its molecular bond often participates in biochemical reactions. It may seem difficult at first to comprehend the role of tritium (like deuterium) as an ideal isotopic marker of metabolites. Still, replacement of a "stable" hydrogen in a molecule by tritium is relatively easy and obviously may yield high specific activities that are at times impossible to obtain with other radioactive labels. Any compound may be tritiated, even one whose structure is unknown. In addition, the advantages and disadvantages of using tritium as a tracer derive from its low energy radiation. Its range of only a few microns makes its quantitative detection dependent on equipment more sensitive than the commonly used counting devices, but by virtue of just this feature photographic fine grain emulsions (nuclear track emulsions) are ideally suited to localize tritium in biological specimens of subcellular dimensions.

Moreover, the radiation from tritium is absorbed within a volume sphere having a radius of a few microns, at most, around the decaying nuclide. Thus, accumulation of tritium in a cell nucleus, for example, leads to highly selective irradiation, making proper dosimetry difficult. One may compare tritium radiation with the Compton electrons of lower energy range that are produced by X-rays.

The potential usefulness of tritium as a tracer has been evaluated with caution. A great deal of work has resulted in the development of specific techniques for the labeling of molecules, for measuring tritium efficiently, and for applying autoradiographic methods, all of which have become valuable tools for the cytologist and biochemist. In the evolution of modern biology and medicine, tracer techniques using tritium have now certainly achieved a firm place, although their refinement is far from perfect. In recent years the respective literature has accumulated greatly and continues to grow rapidly.

The monograph tries to function not only as a mediator between the research worker and the original literature but also attempts to explain in a condensed and coherent manner various topics with which one should be acquainted prior to using tritium-labeled compounds. These topics, in six chapters, cover: the physics of tritium; the production of tritiated compounds and their characteristics; gas counting and liquid scintillation counting; autoradiography; and the biological toxicity of tritium β-radiation. A discussion of general factors which influence the cellular incorporation of a precursor, mainly for nucleic acids, has been included in Chapter 5. It is self-evident that many of the points raised apply as well to isotopic tracers other than tritium.

Throughout the chapters cross references help to bridge the diverse topics and to exemplify the relationship between data and methods. A supplementary list of references, grouped according to the type of labeled compound used, has been added. This list should be sufficient to guide the interested reader to the additional literature in his field of interest. Although some valuable information, which continued to appear after completion of the manuscript, could not be included, this monograph does give a nearly complete survey of the present-day basic knowledge and evaluation of the technology employed in the use of tritium as a tracer. It should meet the needs of the undergraduate student as well as those of the research scientist in biology and medicine. Specific terms, if used, are explained in the text. The Subject Index should be of help in clarifying terminology.

The first part of the work was done in Brussels at the administrative seat of the European Atomic Energy Community, and the author expresses his gratitude to the Commission of EURATOM and to the Director of the biology division, Dr. Appleyard, for the support provided. The work was completed in Paris at the Institute du Radium, and the author is indebted to Professor Latarjet for his welcome to his laboratory and for his hospitality.

The author is particularly indebted to Drs. Bond, Cronkite, and Hughes, and the staff of the Medical Department of Brookhaven National Laboratory for their constantly helpful advice and the fruitful discussions with the late Dr. H. Quastler of Brookhaven are remembered with affection. It is to them the author owes most.

The reviewers were Drs. W. L. Hughes and H. Cottier whose valuable suggestions for improvement were deeply appreciated. The author acknowledges his indebtedness also to Professor Minder from the University of Bern, who kindly consented to assist Professor Cottier; he helped considerably in writing the chapter on "Physics of Tritium." The author expresses also his appreciation and gratitude to the editorial staff of the American Institute of Biological Sciences for unswerving patience, cooperation, and advice. Since the decision on the final form of the manuscript was left to the author, he must be held solely responsible for possible errors or omissions.

L. E. FEINENDEGEN

June, 1967

CONTENTS

CHAPTER 1

Physics of Tritium

1. Introduction

This chapter discusses briefly the physical properties of tritium, its natural occurrence, and its production by man-made nuclear reactions in order to familiarize the reader with this nuclide and to point out its particular advantages and disadvantages when used as a label of molecules in biological tracer studies.

2. The Isotopes of Hydrogen

The hydrogen atom is characterized chemically by one single electron orbiting around the nucleus, which thus has one positive charge, but which can have different masses. The simplest form of the hydrogen nucleus is a single proton; the next heavier form is composed of a proton and a neutron (the deuteron); then follows the triton, which consists of a proton and two neutrons, with a mass of 3.01645 atomic units. Hydrogen with a single proton, the simplest nuclide, is sometimes called protium, and it amounts to 99.98% of naturally occurring hydrogen. The name hydrogen is conventionally synonymous with protium. The next heavier isotope is named deuterium, and the hydrogen isotope thereafter is called tritium. There is no other family of isotopes with such relatively great mass differences. The mass differences largely determine the effects of isotopes in chemical and physical reactions (see Chapter 2).

In tritium, the binding energy between the three elementary nuclear particles is relatively low, with the result that the nucleus is not stable. The nucleus remains unstable until the emission of an electron (β-particle) of varying energy to 18.6 kev[20,22,34] and a neutrino, whereby one neutron is changed to a proton. The nuclide hence acquires an additional charge which can hold a second electron in orbit. The tritium thus transmutes by β-decay to a new chemical entity, namely, helium with a mass of 3. On the average, about 11 ev of excitation may be added to the helium ion in this process.[37] In deuterium, on the other hand, the nuclear binding forces are strong; hence this nuclide is stable. The three isotopes are schematically shown in Fig. 1.1.

1

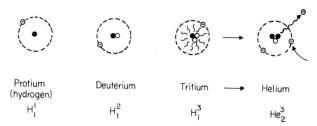

Protium
(hydrogen)
H_1^1

Deuterium
H_1^2

Tritium
H_1^3

Helium
He_2^3

FIG. 1.1. Schematic presentation of the isotopes of hydrogen: ●, proton; ○, neutron; ⊖, electron.

3. Tritium Production

Tritium was discovered together with He³ in 1939 by Alvarez and Cornog[1] upon the bombardment of deuterium with nuclei of deuterium (deuterons) in a cyclotron. The following nuclear reactions occurred:

$$H_1^2 + H_1^2 \nearrow He_2^3 + n_0^1 + 4.04 \text{ Mev}$$
$$\searrow H_1^3 + H_1^1 + 3.26 \text{ Mev}$$

shown schematically in Fig. 1.2. For convenience, these two reactions may be written as:

$$H^2(d,n)He^3 \quad \text{and} \quad H^2(d,p)H^3$$

where d is a deuteron; n, neutron; p, proton. The tritium thus produced may react again with deuterons to produce helium with a mass of 4.

$$H^3(d,n)He^4$$

The exposure of deuterium to deuterons therefore leads finally to a steady state between tritium formation and tritium reaction to yield increasing amounts of helium nuclides, with masses of 3 and 4.

A great number of nuclear reactions yielding tritium have been studied with the help of accelerators,[18] which permit the bombardment of virtually every possible nuclide with high-energy protons, deuterons, or α-

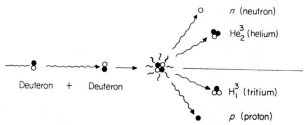

n (neutron)

He_2^3 (helium)

Deuteron + Deuteron

H_1^3 (tritium)

p (proton)

FIG. 1.2. Schematic presentation of the nuclear reactions $H^2(d,n)He^3$ and $H^2(d,p)H^3$.

particles (the nuclei of helium with a mass of 4). These reactions give information on nuclear binding forces, but the amount of tritium produced is too small to provide an adequate supply for biological tracer experiments. For large-scale productions, therefore, these reactions are not practical, mainly for economic reasons.

Tritium is now produced on a large scale in reactors, where any nuclide can easily be exposed to a high flux of neutrons under controlled conditions. Among the various possibilities it was found that lithium is a particularly favorable nuclide because of its high "cross section" for thermal neutrons. This means that the lithium nucleus splits easily when exposed to neutrons of an energy lower than molecular bond energies yielding tritium and a helium nucleus (with a mass of 4, conventionally called an α-particle):

$$Li^6(n,\alpha)H^3$$

schematically shown in Fig. 1.3. This reaction is most widely used now to produce tritium in large quantities.[7,10,15,17,24,29-31]

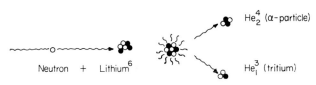

FIG. 1.3. Schematic presentation of the nuclear reactions $Li^6(n,\alpha)H^3$.

There are various technical designs for obtaining pure tritium efficiently. For example, solid lithium fluoride is exposed in a reactor to a proper flux of thermal neutrons and the tritium generated is subsequently recovered from the gaseous radiation products.[24] Alternatively, lithium may be placed in the reactor beam as lithium hydroxide or lithium mixed with nickel oxide.[31] The flux and energy of the neutrons must be optimal for highest yield and purity.

4. Naturally Occurring Tritium

Nuclear reactions occur at high altitudes by the bombardment of the atmosphere with cosmic radiation.[11,38] Neutrons thus generated may interact with deuterium to produce tritium with the emission of γ-radiation:

$$H^2(n,\gamma)H^3$$

Neutrons may interact especially with the abundant nitrogen to yield, besides C^{14} and protons $[N^{14}(n,p)C^{14}]$, C^{12} and tritium also:

$$N^{14}(n,t)C^{12}$$

where t is triton. Or deuterons may interact as shown in Section 3. There is therefore a continuing production of "natural" tritium by a variety of nuclear reactions in high altitudes owing to cosmic radiation.

Tritium is produced primarily in the form of its ion (the triton), which in the atmosphere combines with hydroxide ions to form tritium water:

$$H^{3+} + OH^- = H^3HO \qquad \text{also written as THO}$$

Tritium water descends from the atmosphere with rain or snow. Thus tritium is found in small amounts in place of hydrogen (protium) throughout nature as a "natural tracer" of water.

One tritium atom per 10^{18} hydrogen atoms has been defined as 1 tritium unit and, prior to the commencement of thermonuclear explosions in the atmosphere, natural rain water contained about 6 tritium units. The concentration has risen by varying degrees since about 1954–1955 in some areas of the earth by a factor of even more than 100.[4,28] This increased tritium content of atmospheric water permits the comparison of tritium concentration in terrestrial water, as in oceans, rivers, glaciers, springs, and subterrestrial structures, to gain new information on the turnover of surface and underground water depots.[3,5,6,8,16] In such calculations the natural rate of tritium decay (its half-life) must, of course, be taken into account.

5. Tritium Radiation

As mentioned above, the tritium nucleus decays by the emission of an electron (β-particle) and a neutrino, in which process one of the neutrons changes into a proton. Since this is a random process, it is best characterized by the time required for one-half of the tritium atoms in a sample to decay. According to Jones,[25] this half-life is 12.262 ± 0.004 years; according to others, the half-life is held to be 12.4 years.[23,33] On the basis of a half-life of 12.26 years, the decay constant λ equals 0.0565 per year, or 1.791×10^{-9} per second.

$$A_t = A_0 e^{-\lambda t} \qquad \text{and} \qquad \lambda = \frac{\ln 2}{\text{half-life}} = \frac{0.693}{\text{half-life}}$$

where A_t is the specific activity at any given time; and A_0 is the specific activity at time zero.

The product of the decay of tritium is a helium ion, the nucleus of which has a mass of 3 and is stable. The decay of tritium is therefore a simple one-step process:

$$H^3 \rightarrow He^{3+} + \beta^-$$

Beta-radiation from a nuclide always occurs in a characteristic spectrum; the spectrum of tritium is shown in Fig. 1.4, according to Robertson

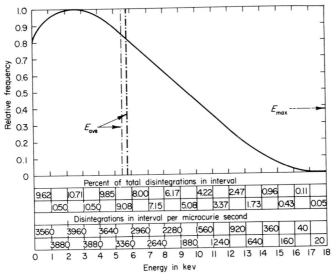

FIG. 1.4. The spectrum of the β-radiation from tritium. Courtesy of Robertson and Hughes, *Proc. 1st Natl. Biophys. Conf., Columbus, Ohio, 1957.*[35]

and Hughes.[35] Besides the relative frequencies of the various levels of energy of the β-particles, the frequencies with which the various levels of energy occur within 1 second in an amount of tritium corresponding to 1 μc are also listed.

The spectrum, like all β-spectra, is continuous from a maximum energy to zero. The maximum energy is 18.6 kev[20,22,34] and the average energy is close to 5.6 kev, as can be seen from Fig. 1.4. The average energy, $\bar{E}$, is obtained mathematically by integrating the spectrum over all increments $N_E dE$, where N_E is the number of β-particles between the energies E and $E + dE$:

$$\bar{E} = \frac{1}{N} \int_0^{E_{max}} N_E \, dE$$

In other words, the areas under the curve on both sides of the "average energy" are equal. Expressed in terms of ergs, an average energy of 5.6 kev = 8.96×10^{-9} erg (1.6×10^{-6} erg/Mev).

Of importance is the fact that the most frequent single energy has the value of 2–3 kev, and about 85% of the emitted particles have energies below 10 kev. An emission of a particle with an energy as low as 1 kev occurs nine times more frequently than one with a higher energy of 14 kev. Only 0.05% of the particles have an energy above 17 kev.

With the ejection of the β-particle, recoil energy is imparted to the nucleus of the helium ion. Owing to the low energy of the β-particle and the relatively large mass of the nucleus, however, this recoil energy is less than 0.05% of the mean energy of the ejected electrons, i.e., from 0 to about 3 ev. Besides this recoil energy of the helium nucleus an excitation energy of about 11 ev average is added to the ion owing to the sudden change of charge in the course of transmutation.[37] This change of charge and added excitation energy alone or together affects the molecule to which the decaying tritium is bound and thus may result in "damage" to a biological system different from the radiobiological effect of the β-particle.

6. The Range of β-Particles in Matter

The energy, mass, charge of a particle, and characteristics of the matter traversed determine the distance the particle can travel.

The over-all stopping power of various materials for low-energy electrons may be determined experimentally.[12-14,27] But it must be considered that the range measurements of electrons with the low energy of β-particles from tritium are not easy to perform. The electrons penetrating a foil of aluminum, for example, may be measured by scintillating material directly placed on the foil or by biological detectors such as radiosensitive enzymes. The penetration of β-particles from tritium through aluminum foils of various thickness is exemplified in Fig. 1.5.[14] It is seen from Fig. 1.5 that in an aluminum foil of a thickness of 0.3 mg/cm², corresponding to a sheet of 3-μ thickness of material of unit density, more than 99% of the β-particles are absorbed.

Actually, the path and the track length of the electrons in matter are

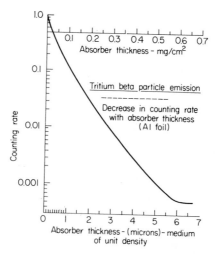

Fig. 1.5. Measurements of the range spectrum of tritium electrons in aluminum. Courtesy of Fitzgerald et al., Science.[14]

a function of quite complicated interactions, which will not be discussed here. In all, it may be said that there is sufficient evidence to ascribe the interactions of low-energy β-particles with matter, i.e., the absorption (or attenuation) to nearly completely electronic processes.[13] In other words, the reduction in intensity (or flux) of low-energy β-particles in a unit volume of attenuating matter is proportional to the number of electrons per unit volume. For low electrons of less than 10 kev it has been shown that considerable scattering and straggling must be taken into account to describe the experimental data by a proper range-energy equation.[12] Due to the scattering, particularly at the end portions of tracks, the low-energy electrons may be visualized to follow a tortuous and zigzag path in an absorbing material, and practically none of the particles traverse the absorbing matter in a forward direction without deviation.

For an attenuating material of relatively low atomic number (such as biological material of approximately 7.4 average), the absorption of the low-energy β-particles may be described by a simple exponential expression:

$$I_{(x)} = I_0 e^{-\mu^* x}$$

where $I_{(x)}$ is the intensity of the β-radiation after penetration of a sheet of material of thickness x; I_0, the intensity of the β-radiation at the same point without the absorbing material; and μ^*, the absorption (or attenuation) coefficient of the β-radiation in the material.

The intensity of the radiation is conventionally expressed as the radiation traversing per unit time a surface of 1 cm^2 perpendicular to the radiation direction. But since the very low-energy β-particles are scattered in all directions soon after entry into absorbing matter (already within a fraction of a micron), the radiation intensity may be better expressed by the term flux, i.e., the number of particles entering per unit time a volume of 1 cm^2 cross section.

The absorption coefficient expresses the relative reduction in intensity (or flux) by a material layer of unit thickness:

$$\mu^* = -\frac{1}{I_{(x)}} \frac{dI}{dx}$$

Since the absorption of low-energy β-particles in matter is almost completely an electronic process, it must depend on the number of electrons per cubic centimeter, namely, $NZ\rho/A$, where N is Avogadro's number (6.025×10^{23}/mole); Z, atomic number; A, atomic weight; and ρ, density of the material traversed. Thus the absorption coefficient may also be written:

$$\mu^* = S(E) \ \frac{NZ\rho}{A}$$

where $S(E)$ is a rather complicated term which takes into account the energy of the moving electron.

For matter with a relatively low atomic weight, such as biological material, the expression Z/A approximates a constant of 0.5. If the density is assigned a value of unity, and if $S(E)$, the function of energy dependence, is taken as a fixed value with the material traversed, μ^* may be assumed here for the purpose of calculation to be a constant for low-energy β-radiations in any material with relatively low atomic weight.

It is generally agreed that the absorption coefficient μ^* should be expressed in square centimeters per milligram, which means penetration by β-particles $(1/\mu^*)$ is measured in milligrams per square centimeter, i.e., in mass per unit surface of the absorbing material. Since 1 cm²/mg of water corresponds to a layer thickness of 10 μ/cm², the linear absorption coefficient may also be expressed per μ-layer thickness of unit density.

The mean absorption coefficient μ^* for biological material may thus be determined to be 17.85 cm²/mg or 1.785 μ^{-1} for low-energy tritium β-particles. With this coefficient a semilogarithmic absorption curve can be constructed which shows for the assumed conditions that: (1) the mean range of the β-particles from tritium in matter of unit density is 0.56 μ which equals 0.056 mg/cm²; (2) 50% of the β-particles are absorbed in a thickness of about 0.4 μ of the same material (the so-called half-value layer); and (3) the maximum range of the particles in this material is about 6 μ, corresponding to 0.6 mg/cm².

Actually, the above calculation is a simplified approximation because of the difficulty in determining accurately the degree of scattering and straggling of the electrons from the various ranges of the spectrum. A calculated mean value for the absorption coefficient should therefore be erroneous. Thus, it has been assumed valid to assign to the electrons above 3 μ an absorption coefficient[26, 36] of 1.5–2.1 μ^{-1} and for electrons below the range of about 3 μ an absorption coefficient[26] of 0.75–0.8 μ^{-1}. The application of this latter value tends to increase the mean range of all H^3 β-particles to approximately 0.9 μ in material of unit density.

Various range calculations have been performed for biological material, particularly with the purpose of interpreting in a quantitative manner autoradiographic data (see Chapter 4) and evaluating the biological effect of the β-radiation (see Chapter 6). Figure 1.6 gives a recent range calculation for tritium electrons corrected for their curbed paths in matter of a density 1.1 (methacrylate),[9] which is close to the density of biological material. It can be seen that 50% of the particles are calculated to be absorbed already by a layer only 0.3 μ thick, 80% of the particles are

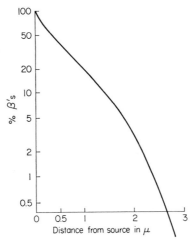

FIG. 1.6. Calculation of the range spectrum of tritium electrons in matter with a density of 1.1 (methacrylate). Courtesy of Caro, *J. Cell Biol.*[9]

calculated to be absorbed within 1 μ from the source, and 99% of the radiation does not reach beyond 2.5 μ, which appears hence to be practically a maximum range in biological matter. These calculations have been found to agree closely with experimental data.[9,14,21,32]

7. Implications of the Low Energy of the β-Particles from Tritium

It is evident from the above range calculations that it is possible to localize tritium in biological material with great accuracy by using, for example, the autoradiographic technique. In Chapter 4, the possible resolution in an autoradiogram will be shown, in fact, to depend mainly on the size of the silver halide crystals in the photographic emulsion if the tissue section or cell smear can be kept relatively thin.

It must, however, also be considered that biological material in subcellular dimensions in tissues does not possess uniform density, as it was assumed for reasons of easy calculation. In a single cell, for example, various structures may differ in their stopping power for low-energy electrons. Thus, an electron traversing biological material may actually loose energy in an irregular manner in a succession of energy traps. These subcellular "islands of increased density" or energy traps around the position of incorporated tritium in a cell are distributed presumably at random and are therefore of little practical consequences. Few structures such as cellular membranes have an increased density and can be defined morphologically.[19] More clear-cut is the situation in dry biological material, for example, in histological tissue sections. Thus, various absorption coefficients for the cytoplasm, the chromatin portion of the nucleus, and the nucleolus of liver cells in sections have been described as function of mass per unit area by Maurer and Primbsch.[32] The variation in absorption of low-energy electrons in single cells in histological preparations must be kept in mind when attempting to interpret quantitatively autoradiographic data (see Chapter 4).

The very short ranges of the emitted electrons impose obstacles for the quantitative measurement of the nuclide even when it is contained in the thinnest layer of material, and preparing appropriate standards is difficult. The measurement from an "infinitely thick" layer of labeled material, however, circumvents some of the difficulties. In an infinitely thick layer, the radioactivity contained in the superficial stratum only is registered; in biological material this thickness is for tritium β-particles not more than 6 μ, for 99% of the β-particles approximately 2.5 μ only. Measurements from an infinitely thick layer have the advantage that the data correspond to the specific activity in the sample, and unevenness in the layer is less apt to cause counting errors. In addition, through an infinitely thick layer the scattering of the radiation from the back of the supporting structure, such as a planchet, is eliminated.

The counting efficiency from an infinitely thick layer is low as expected. For example, one may calculate the number of β-particles leaving a material layer of certain thickness, uniformly loaded with the radiating nuclide, if the specific activity and the absorption coefficient in the given material is known. Thus, if it is assumed that a material of density 1, loaded uniformly with tritium, has a specific activity of 1 mc/cm³, it is calculated with an absorption coefficient of 1.785 μ^{-1} that 1036 β-particles leave per second per square centimeter surface of an infinitely thick layer.

Because of the very considerable degree of absorption of the tritium β-particles, it is obvious that cheap and conventional radiation detectors such as Geiger-Muller counters are inapplicable for tritium measurements, unless the labeled material is directly introduced into the counter. For greatest accuracy and highest efficiency, tritium is measured best in gaseous or liquid form in direct contact with the detector device (see Chapter 3).

It is also clear from the very short ranges of the tritium electrons that energy is deposited at average only within a sphere of about 1-μ radius around the disintegrating nuclide. Hence, external radiation hazards are certainly reduced as compared to those expected from higher energy particles. On the other hand, immediate radiation effects from incorporated tritium are strictly localized, and they may be expected to vary greatly according to the radiation sensitivity of the structure to which tritium is attached or adjacent. For example, one may estimate on the basis of the energy per ionization of water (approximately 30 ev) that a β-particle of average energy (range about 1 μ) may produce approximately 190 ion pairs in liquid water. A tritium β-particle of maximum energy would cause about 60 ionizations over the first micron of the track.[2] This means that a sizable radiation dose is delivered to the relatively small volume around the disintegrating nuclide. With these considerations in mind, it can be predicted that, for example, in mammals, tritiated water with its general distribution is much less radiotoxic than tritiated thymidine which is specifically incorporated into a cell nucleus (known to be highly radiosensitive). Absorbed dose, "linear energy transfer," and the biological toxicity of tritium are treated in Chapter 6.

For the storage of tritium-labeled molecules, it is obvious that separation of the single molecules will greatly minimize radiochemical effects. Tritium-labeled substances are preferably stored in an appropriate solution, or perhaps absorbed on a feasible material (see Chapter 2).

8. Conclusions

The advantages of tritium as a label for molecules in biological reactions are severalfold. The relatively long half-life permits the use of this nuclide in studies over extended time periods. The extremely short range of the β-radiation allows high autoradiographic resolution and precision to localize the tracer in single cells and subcellular structures, however, with the concomitant difficulty in arriving at quantitative data. The methods of gas counting and liquid scintillation counting have been adapted and perfected to give a reliable and high efficiency and to suit any demand in the course of tracer work with tritium in chemical fractions and even in whole tissue. Labeling molecules with tritium is rather simple by appropriate techniques of hydrogen–tritium exchange and can be applied to practically any class of compounds, even those with unknown structures. Thus, tritium may be most beneficial as the only possible label. Tritium in the place of hydrogen offers the further advantage for the study of reaction mechanisms of hydrogen exchange in pure chemical or biological systems. On the other hand, the short range of the β-radiation from tritium may deceive one in the attempt to assess the possible toxicity, which varies greatly with the type of molecule and its pathway in metabolic reactions.

9. Appendix

Before closing this short survey, the degree of radioactivity of some substances containing tritium may be calculated.

(1) One cubic centimeter of pure tritium gas, H_2^3 (at normal temperature and pressure), contains 2.69×10^{19} molecules or 5.38×10^{19} atoms, giving 1.06×10^{11} disintegrations per second, which corresponds to 2.86 c $(1 \text{ c} = 3.7 \times 10^{10} \text{ disintegrations/second})$.

(2) One gram of pure tritium water, H_2^3O, contains 2.74×10^{22} molecules or 5.48×10^{22} tritium atoms, giving 1.08×10^{14} disintegrations per second, which corresponds to 2.92×10^3 c. It thus happens that 1 mm³ of pure tritium water is practically as radioactive as 1 cm³ of tritium gas.

(3) One mole of substance contains 6.025×10^{23} molecules. If in each molecule one hydrogen only is replaced by tritium, 6.025×10^{23} tritium atoms are present in 1 mole of labeled substance, giving 1.20×10^{15} disintegrations per second, which corresponds to 3.2×10^4 c. Hence, the specific activity of the substance would be 3.2×10^4 c/mole, or 32 c/mmole.

(4) The β-radiation dose delivered within a uniformly labeled substance can be calculated according to the following equation, if it is assumed that the total radiation is absorbed in the substance. (This is true except for a thin surface layer, the thickness of which is equal to the range of the β-particles):

$$D = \frac{3.7 \times 10^7 \times 3600 \times 1.6 \times 10^{-6} \times \bar{E}}{100 \times g} \ (\text{rad/mc/hour})$$

where 3.7×10^7 equal the disintegrations per millicuries per second; 3600, seconds per hour; 1.6×10^{-6}, ergs per millielectron volts; 100, ergs per gram per rad; $\bar{E}$, average β-energy in millielectron volts; and g, gram of substance.

Resolving the constants, the equation becomes:

$$D\beta = 2130\bar{E} \ \text{rad/mc/hour}$$

If the specific activity of tritium-labeled material is 1 mc/g, the dose-rate delivered to a gram of this material will be approximately:

$$D\beta = 2130 \times 0.0057 = 12.14 \ \text{rad/hour}$$

It should, however, be remembered that this value is true only for homogenous distribution of the label within the material. To predict radiation effects in volumes of cellular dimensions the local specific activity and the "discrete distribution" of ionizations from tritium electrons, as indicated in Section 7 of this Chapter, should be taken into account.

With decreasing volumes, the relative loss of β-radiation from the volume edge increases, of course, and proper corrections need to be made for calculation of dose, for example, in a cell nucleus. This will be discussed in Chapter 6.

REFERENCES

1. L. W. Alvarez and R. Cornog, Helium and Hydrogen of Mass 3, *Phys. Rev.,* **56:** 613 (1939).

2. S. Apelgot and R. Latarjet, Marque d'un acide d'oxyribonucleique bacterien par le radiophosphore, le radio carbone et le tritium, comparaison des effets letaux, *Biochim. Biophys. Acta,* **55**: 40–55 (1962).
3. A. E. Bainbridge and B. J. O'Brien, Levels of Tritium in a Variety of New Zealand Waters and Some Tentative Conclusions from These Results, in *Tritium in the Physical and Biological Sciences, Symp. Intern. At. Energy Agency,* **1**: 33–39 (1961).
4. E. W. Barrett and L. Huebner, Atmospheric Tritium Analysis, *Tech. Progr. Rept. No. 2.* Chicago University Press, Chicago, Feb. 1960.
5. F. Begemann, Redetermination of the Decay Rate of Natural Tritium and Origin of "Natural" Tritium, *Z. Naturforsch.,* **14a**: 334–342 (1959).
6. F. Begemann, The Natural Tritium Economy of the Earth and the Question of Its Variation with Time, *Chimia (Aarau),* **16**: 1–10 (1961).
7. C. V. Cannon, E. M. Shapiro, G. H. Jenks, J. Boyle, L. T. McClinton, N. Elliott, C. J. Borkowski, H. S. Pomerance, and R. P. Metcalf, *The Production and Purification of Tritium,* Clinton Laboratories, Oak Ridge, Tenn., Feb. 1957.
8. C. W. Carlston and L. L. Thatcher, Tritium Studies in the U.S. Geological Survey, in *Tritium in the Physical and Biological Sciences, Symp. Intern. At. Energy Agency,* **1**: 75–81 (1961).
9. L. G. Caro, High Resolution Autoradiography. II. The Problem of Resolution, *J. Cell. Biol.,* **15**: 189–199 (1962).
10. N. Chellew, J. McGuire, W. Olsen, and A. H. Barnes, *Tritium Production Process,* Argonne National Laboratory, Illinois, March 1960.
11. H. Craig and D. Lal, The Production Rate of Natural Tritium, *Tellus,* **13**: 85–105 (1961).
12. M. Davis, Range Measurement of Low-voltage Electrons, *Phys. Rev.,* **94**: 243–245 (1954).
13. C. Feldman, Range of 1–10 kev Electrons in Solids, *Phys. Rev.,* **117**: 455–459 (1960).
14. P. J. Fitzgerald, M. L. Eidinoff, J. E. Knoll, and E. B. Simmel, Tritium in Radioautography, *Science,* **114**: 494–498 (1951).
15. P. W. Frank, *Determination of the Effective Neutron Flux for Production of Tritium from LiOH in Primary Coolant of PWR,* Westinghouse Electric Corp., Bettis Atomic Power Div., Pittsburgh, Dec. 1958.
16. J. R. Gat, U. Karfunkel, and A. Nir, Tritium Content of Rain Water from the Eastern Mediterranean Area, in *Tritium in the Physical and Biological Sciences, Symp. Intern. At. Energy Agency,* **1**: 41–54 (1961).
17. General Nuclear Engineering Corp., *A Study of Reactor Systems for the Production of Tritium and Radioactive Cobalt,* Dunedin, Florida, June 1959.
18. J. Gonzalez-Vidal and W. H. Wade, Survey of Tritium-Producing Nuclear Reactions, *Phys. Rev.,* **120**: 1354–1359 (1960).
19. C. R. Goodheart, Radiation Dose Calculation in Cells Containing Intranuclear Tritium, *Radiation Res.,* **15**: 767–773 (1961).
20. D. P. Gregory and D. A. Landsman, Average Decay Energy of Tritium, *Phys. Rev.,* **109**: 2091 (1958).
21. D. K. Hill, Resolving Power with H^3-autoradiographs, *Nature,* **194**: 831–832 (1962).
22. J. M. Hollander, I. Pearlman, and G. T. Seaborg, Table of Isotopes, *Rev. Mod. Phys.,* **25**: 469–651 (1953).

23. G. H. Jenks, J. A. Ghormley, and F. H. Sweaton, Measurement of the Half-life and Average Energy of Tritium Decay, *Phys. Rev.*, **75**: 701 (1949).
24. G. H. Jenks, E. M. Shapiro, N. Elliott, and C. V. Cannon, Production of Tritium, U. S. Patent 3,079,317, Feb. 1963.
25. W. M. Jones, Half-Life of Tritium, *Phys. Rev.*, **100**: 124–125 (1955).
26. A. L. Koch, A Distributional Basis for The Variation in Killing Efficiencies by Different Tritiated Compounds Incorporated into *Escherichia coli, Radiation Res.*, **24**: 398–411 (1965).
27. R. O. Lane and D. J. Zaffarano, Transmission of 0–40 kev Electrons by Thin Films with Application to Beta-ray Spectroscopy, *Phys. Rev.*, **94**: 960–964 (1954).
28. W. F. Libby, Tritium Geophysics: Recent Data and Results, in *Tritium in the Physical and Biological Sciences, Symp. Intern. At. Energy Agency*, **1**: 5–32 (1961).
29. J. G. Linhart, Improvements Relating to Thermonuclear Reactors, British Patents 855857, 855858, Dec. 7, 1960.
30. C. B. Magee, J. E. Fulenwider, G. J. Rotariu, and R. P. Petersen, *A Study of the Feasibility and Economics of Radioisotope Production in Power Reactors*, Booz-Allen Applied Research, Inc., Glenview, Ill., Feb. 1960.
31. C. Mantescu and T. Costea, Tritium Release from the Neutron Irradiated Lithium Doped Nickel Oxide, *Can. J. Chem.*, **40**: 1232–1233 (1962).
32. W. Maurer and E. Primbsch, Grösse der beta-Selbstabsorption bei der H³-Autoradiographie, *Exptl. Cell Res.*, **33**: 8–18 (1964).
33. W. L. Pillinger, J. J. Hentges, and J. A. Blair, Tritium Decay Energy, *Phys. Rev.*, **121**: 232–233 (1961).
34. F. T. Porter, Beta Decay Energy of Tritium, *Phys. Rev.*, **115**: 450-453 (1959).
35. J. S. Robertson and W. L. Hughes, Intranuclear Irradiation with Tritium-Labeled Thymidine, *Proc. 1st Natl. Biophys. Conf. Columbus, Ohio, 1957*, pp. 278–283 (1959).
36. F. S. Stewart, The Calculation of Radiation Dose from Distributed Sources of Tritium, *Intern. J. Rad. Biol.*, **8**: 545–549 (1965).
37. S. Wexler, Dissociation of Molecules by Nuclear Decay of Constituent Atoms, in *Chemical Effects of Nuclear Transformations*, pp. 115–145. Symp. Intern. At. Energy Agency, Prague, 1960.
38. A. T. Wilson and G. J. Fergusson, Origin of Terrestrial Tritium, *Geochim. Cosmochim. Acta,* **18**: 273–277 (1960).

CHAPTER 2

Organic Molecules Labeled with Tritium

1. Introduction

The advantages of tritium as a tracer, as indicated in Chapter 1, would not have become applicable to such a wide extent if it were not relatively easy to label organic molecules with tritium at high specific activities, and in a versatility that is not obtained with any other isotopes. Hydrogen–tritium exchange by exposure of an organic substance to tritium gas, as developed by Wilzbach,[224] undoubtedly was monumental in making countless compounds of limitless complexity available for tritiation. Progress was so rapid that there was talk in 1958 of the tritium revolution. A large variety of tritium-labeled organic substances is now available from commercial sources at relatively low prices, most of which are within the budget range of any research laboratory.

The commercially available tritiated compounds often can be used in a biological experiment without further preparation. However, the easy availability of tritium-labeled precursors may tempt the investigator to put too much trust in their purity and identity and thus he may use them uncritically; or he may forget that a molecule, labeled with tritium in a chemically stable position, may yet lose its tracer in the course of unrecognized metabolic reactions. In addition, a labeled compound may, prior to the experiment, partially decompose during storage, even though it was radiochemically pure upon arrival from the supplier. Even a small amount of decomposition by-product with high specific activities may disturb the outcome of an experiment. Furthermore, the investigator must be aware of the so-called isotope effect. The mass of tritium is three times that of hydrogen. This difference in the atomic masses may lead to differences in reaction rates of labeled versus nonlabeled molecules, so that the specific activity of a reaction product does not indicate the reaction rate of the nonlabeled counterpart.

This chapter attempts to provide the biologist who works with tritium-labeled compounds with a basic understanding of the nature of this special tool, for guidance and introduction. Therefore, the isotope effects of tritium, the various methods of labeling organic molecules, the stability of the tritium on molecules in the course of metabolic reactions, and, finally, the radiochemical stability of labeled organic substances under various conditions, particularly those suitable for storage, will be reviewed shortly. This condensed survey cannot possibly do justice to all of the excellent reports, particularly those which have appeared over the past few years. The selection of references has by necessity been an arbitrary one. There is hardly any class of organic molecules which has not been labeled with tritium by one or the other method. Therefore, a supplementary list of references pertaining to tritium-labeled organic molecules used in biological work will be added at the end of the volume in addition to those references which are verbally discussed. It is hoped that the interested reader will find the addition of these references useful in specific instances.

2. Isotope Effects

When the chemical reaction rate or physical behavior of an isotopically labeled molecule is different from that of its unlabeled sister molecule, one observes an isotope effect. Directly or indirectly, this effect is mainly due to the difference in mass which is introduced to the molecule by the isotopic label. Since the mass of tritium is three times that of "normal" hydrogen (protium), isotope effects in molecular reactions may become rather large, depending on the type of molecule to which the tritium is bound and on the type of the reaction.[127] Isotope effects, if not recognized, may lead to erroneous conclusions. On the other hand, these effects provide a valuable tool in the study of reaction mechanisms. The effect is relatively small when the isotopic bond is not directly involved in the reaction (secondary isotope effect), but, in general, it is large if the isotopic bond is engaged in the rate-determining step (primary isotope effect). Numerically, isotope effects are expressed in the ratio of the reaction rate of labeled molecules to the rate of unlabeled ones (K^x/K).

2.1. PRIMARY ISOTOPE EFFECTS

The mass of an element determines in part the stability of its bond to another element. The lower the masses, the weaker is the bond owing to a higher vibrational energy residing in the bond between the elements to be visualized as part of an oscillator. This vibrational energy, at a temperature of absolute zero, for practical purposes also at room temperature, is called "zero-point" energy. According to the quantum theory, the zero-point energy equals Planck's constant h times a vibration frequency v. This characteristic frequency of vibration in a bond is inversely proportional to the masses of the elements participating in the oscillation.

The energy necessary to split a bond must be higher, the lower the "zero-point" energy is, that means the larger the masses are of the participating atoms. Applied to the carbon-hydrogen bond, for example, it is known that the carbon-tritium bond is more difficult to separate than that of carbon-deuterium, and this bond again is stronger than the bond of carbon-hydrogen.

The energy to split the bond of carbon-tritium is approximately 0.065 ev/molecule higher than that necessary to break the carbon–hydrogen bond, which is approximately 3.793 ev.* In the case of molecular hydrogen, the energy to dissociate two hydrogen nuclides (each with a mass of 1) is 4.476 ev. But 0.11 ev more energy, namely, 4.59 ev, is needed to split two tritium nuclides.[45] Since bond energies are temperature dependent, isotope effects are likewise affected and they become smaller with increasing temperatures.[45,222]

When tritium ions recoiling from a nuclear reaction [$He^3(n,p)H^3$] were allowed to bombard a 1:1 mixture of hydrogen gas and deuterium gas, H—H^3 was produced 1.55 ± 0.06 times more frequently than D—H^3. In other words, the bond between the deuterium nuclides is stronger than the bond between the light hydrogens.[114] An important isotope effect may be observed in the combustion of tritium-labeled organic substances. If the combustion is not carried out to completion, the resulting water does not have the specific activity which reflects the specific activity of the labeled material: the "normal" hydrogen combines with oxygen more readily than the tritium does.

A similar example is the isotope effect observed in the reaction of H^3-formaldehyde with periodate. For obtaining H^3-formalydehyde to be used as the tritium donor for labeling of organic molecules, tritiated glucose was split with periodate. When periodate was added in excess, the oxidation continued beyond the optimal yield of formaldehyde and the specific activity of the H^3-formaldehyde was higher than that of the glucose. This indicates that formaldehyde when tritiated is less readily oxidized. In this reaction there was no exchange of the tritium with the solvent.[177]

Effects of isotope in or very close to a functional bond on reaction kinetics provide an important analytical tool for describing reaction mechanisms in organic chemistry. If an isotopic bond breaks in the reaction, the effects on the reaction rate are greater than when a cleavage does not occur. In a series of investigations, Isbell and co-workers thus

* One electron volt per molecule equals 23.060 kcal/mole.

analyzed the oxidation by halogens of various aldoses labeled with tritium in position 1.[99-102] In the reaction with sodium chlorite, ten different 1-H^3-aldoses gave relatively low values of isotope effects and indicated therefore that here the C-1–H bond was not ruptured in the rate-determining step. In another analysis of reaction mechanisms, the tritium isotope effect was needed to identify the sequence of enolization of ketones by acid catalysis.[194]

Isotope effects in radiation chemistry during radiolysis of compounds labeled with tritium or deuterium were critically reviewed in work with biphenyl-molecule ions and methanol.[38] These molecules were subjected to excitation and the resulting dissociation and reaction of secondary radicals were analyzed. Träger and associates[203] investigated the effect of ultraviolet irradiation at 254 mμ on tritium-labeled uracil (5,6-H^3) compared with uracil labeled with C^{14}. With increasing radiation energy to uracil (from 1.2 $\times$ 10^6 erg/mm^2 to 5 $\times$ 10^6 erg/mm^2), various proportions of dimerization to hydrogenation (5,6-dihydro-6-hydroxyuracil) were observed in which the latter increased with higher energy relatively more than the first. A strong isotope effect was seen in that during hydrogenation at higher UV energy and subsequent dehydration the tritium was shown to be bound more firmly than the hydrogen. With regard to the relative chemical stability, the tritium in position 5 was found to be more labile than that in position 6. As expected, tritium in position 6 was stable even in concentrated perchloric acid at 100°C for 1 hour; and in cytosine, because of the amino group in position 4, the tritium in position 5 was a little more stable than in the corresponding position of uracil.

Substitution of deuterium or tritium in hydrogen bonds of enzymes may have a profound effect on tertiary structure and enzyme activity. Thus, it was shown that deuteration of poly-γ-benzyl-L-glutamate, as a model, lowered the transition temperature by about 11°C. This indicates that the helix formation from random coil proceeded more rapidly than in the nonlabeled polypeptide.[42]

Primary isotope effects may also influence chemical equilibrium.[25] Thus, in the vaporization of water, formation and rupture of hydrogen bonds are involved and add to the effect of alteration of molecular velocities induced by the isotope. The vapor pressure of tritiated water at different temperatures is shown in Table 2.1. At a temperature of 25.7°C the tritiated water has a vapor pressure of 0.77, the value of ordinary water,[147] and the boiling points for the two waters differ by 1°–2°C. In consequence, diluted tritiated water may be concentrated by distillation.[180,184] As expected, the difference in vapor pressure of ordinary hydrogen gas and tritium gas is greater than that of ordinary

TABLE 2.1

VAPOR PRESSURES OF TRITIATED WATER[a] AND ISOTOPIC HYDROGEN MOLECULES

1. Ratio of vapor pressures of tritiated water (THO) and "normal" water at various temperatures

Temperature (°C)	Vapor pressure THO/ vapor pressure H_2O
25.7	0.77
27.84	0.81
39.98	0.84
55.02	0.88
75.60	0.89

2. Vapor pressures of isotopic hydrogen molecules at the boiling point of H_2 (-252, 6°C)

Molecule[b]	Vapor pressure (mm Hg)
H_2	760
HT	254 ± 16
DT	123 ± 6
T_2	45 ± 10

[a] Reproduced with permission: (1) from Libby and Barter, *J. Chem. Phys.*[117]; (2) from Price, *Nature.*[147]

[b] Deuterium, D; tritium, T.

water and tritiated water (see Table 2.1). The vapor pressure of pure tritium gas at the boiling point of hydrogen is only 45 ± 10 mm Hg, whereas that of ordinary hydrogen gas is approximately 17 times higher.[117] Another example is the lower vaporization pressure of tritiated formaldehyde compared with the normal compound.[178] But this might be also a chemical effect due to a differential oxidation of the labeled versus unlabeled compound. Different vapor pressures may be held also partly responsible for the isotope effect observed when tritiated cyclohexane was purified by gas–liquid chromatography.[153,225]

Hydrogen–tritium exchange in the course of labeling molecules does not always lead to a complete dissociation of the hydrogen bond during the reaction. As an example, the isotope effects which were observed in reactions of recoiling tritium ions with deuterium-labeled isopropyl benzoate will be mentioned. Other exchange reactions proceed similarly as will be discussed later in this chapter.

The energy of tritium ions produced by nuclear reactions, for example, upon bombardment of helium with thermal neutrons, $He^3(n,p)$

H^3, or upon bombardment with neutrons of lithium, $Li^6(n,\alpha)H^3$, may activate C—H bonds and facilitate tritium exchange with a hydrogen. Recoiling tritium ions were allowed to react with isopropyl benzoate labeled with deuterium in the ring or the side chain.[36] It was found with unlabeled molecules that the tritium went preferentially to positions in the benzene ring over those in the methyl group of the side chain by a factor of 2.66. But when the hydrogen was replaced by deuterium in the molecule, tritium exchange occurred less readily and the distribution to the ring was 3.78 times higher than to the side chain. For the benzene ring this preferential exchange with hydrogen over that with deuterium was expressed by a factor of 1.6, and in the side chain the tritium exchanged with the hydrogen 1.41 times more readily than with the deuterium atoms in the same methyl group. The preferential substitution of hydrogen by tritium in the aromatic ring was explained by tritium capture by probability into the position followed by preferential explusion of the hydrogen without rupture of the bond. But in the saturated chain the tritium–hydrogen exchange was held to involve a weakening of the C—H bond.

2.2. SECONDARY ISOTOPE EFFECTS

Secondary isotope effects in chemical reactions are mediated by a variety of factors which are little understood. Influences on the steric condition by the mass of the isotope are especially important and may lead to isotopic fractionation in reactions, in which the isotopic bond is not directly involved.

Alterations in the mean configuration of isotopically labeled molecules can be determined by optical methods,[35] and they may change the electron distribution and the electron-releasing ability of the molecules.[87,176] However, electronic effects were, on theoretical ground, surmised to be of significance in organic reactions[216]; but changes in steric configuration due to isotopic substitution are known to have chemical effects. For example, an isotope effect was observed in the fractional recrystallization of D-mannose-1-H^3-phenylhydrazone from 60% aqueous ethanol because the labeled compound showed a different rate of isomerization in water than the unlabeled molecules. Thus, the crystals that separated initially had a lower specific activity than those which formed later.[219] No isotopic separation, however, occurred during the fractional recrystallization of 1-H^3-α-D-glucose[98] under conditions ordinarily used for purification of the sugar. In another study, a secondary isotope effect due to a resistance of change in conformation of the molecule could be observed separately from the primary isotope effect due to rupture of the isotopic bond in direct oxidation in the reaction of 1-H^3-aldoses with bromine.[101] The value for the primary isotope effect was 0.14 (K^x/K), while it was 0.80 for the secondary effect.

2.3. ISOTOPE EFFECTS IN BIOCHEMICAL REACTIONS

It is obvious that biochemical reactions directly or indirectly involving hydrogen bonds may be altered by the substitution of tritium for hydrogen. In the following section some isotopic effects in biochemical reactions will be reviewed with no intent of elaborating on theories of underlying mechanisms. It should be the aim here to point out that experimental results may differ according to the choice of the isotope and its molecular position.

2.3.1. Tritiated Water

The principal recognition of effects of deuterium in place of hydrogen on reaction rates was well advanced prior to the application of tritium as a tracer.[106,127]

A more recent investigation, for example, showed that the mitotic apparatus in cleaving eggs of Arabacia punctulata, when exposed to 90% deuterated sea water, became markedly resistant to disorganizing effects of high pressure.[123] For this kind of study tritium is not suitable because of its effects from radiation and transmutation.

When tritiated water became available for studies in biological systems, isotope effects were soon reported. In one of the earlier investigations, Eidinoff and co-workers[56] found a different distribution of deuterium and tritium in rats after administration of water labeled with the two isotopes. Deuterium was preferentially incorporated into glycogen and fatty acids from the liver, 8–18% above the amount of tritium found there. Similar to the fatty acids of the liver, the cholesterol was found to have retained more deuterium than tritium.[58]

Working with tritiated water in various mammals, Siri and Evers[183] determined the degree of exchange from the body water to the tissue solids. Twenty-four hours after administration of labeled water, the nonexchangeable tritium bound by metabolism in the tissue accounted for approximately 2% of the total tritium dose. An isotope effect between total-body water and tissue solids could not be observed, probably because it was immeasurably small. An isotope effect, however, was seen when the specific activity of the expired water vapor was compared with the specific activity of the tritiated water in urine and blood. Without the isotopic effect the specific activities of the expired water vapor and that of the tritiated water in the urine and blood should be equal, but it was found in humans that the specific activity of the breath water was lower by a factor of 0.78–0.96. In pigeons the specific activity of the expired water was lower by a factor of about 0.5 of the water in the blood. This enhanced isotope effect may perhaps be due to the different vaporization pressures of labeled and unlabeled water. The higher effect in pigeons is unexplained. Yet it is to be recalled that the metabolism of water varies, of course, in different tissues and also with the age and the stage of health of the experimental animal (see Chapter 5).

2.3.2. *Tritiated Methyl Groups*

Isotope effects from tritium in methylation reactions were recognized and carefully interpreted.[149,207,208,210] When labeled methanol was used as a donor for the methyl groups of choline and creatinine, labilization of hydrogen of the methyl group was obvious. When methanol labeled with C^{14}, deuterium, and tritium was administered, the ratio of deuterium to C^{14} and of H^3 to C^{14} in the methyl groups of choline and creatinine was only 22% and 69–75%, respectively, of that in the administered methanol.[207] In other words, more tritium than deuterium (3:1) remained associated with the methyl group donated by methanol.

The transfer of the methyl group from methionine labeled with C^{14} and H^3 to choline, creatinine, and adrenaline was also observed to involve hydrogen labilization contrary to findings with formate as methyl donor.[150] Although the H^3/C^{14} ratio in the choline was found to be identical to the one of the methionine, the methyl group of adrenaline and creatinine had a much higher H^3/C^{14} ratio than that of the donor.[208] Indeed, it was concluded that a secondary oxidation of the transferred methyl group occurred. It was again obvious that deuterium in place of tritium led to a different relationship of the isotope ratios. When the single methyl groups were doubly labeled with C^{14} *and* deuterium, the rate of oxidation of methionine in the whole animal was reduced to 60–80% of the control labeled only with C^{14}. It is clear, then, that different experimental results may be obtained, depending on which isotope is chosen as a tracer. On the other hand, the differences in the data provide the evidence for the type of reactions.

2.3.3. *Other Reactions*

Many other biochemical reactions have been studied with the help of deuterium or tritium isotope effects. Using deuterium, glucose 6-phosphate dehydrogenase was found to discriminate against the hydrogen isotope, and the deuterium-labeled substrate reacted more slowly than the control which was labeled with C^{14} only. With this effect, the respective rate-limiting step in the multiple enzyme sequence of reactions in the metabolism of labeled glucose could be distinguished.[160] The conversion of glucose 6-phosphate to 6-phosphogluconate showed an isotope effect lowering the reaction rate when the tritium was in position 1 instead of position 6.[29] The fact that the recovery in glycogen of tritium versus C^{14} from position 1 of glucose was lower than that of tritium versus C^{14} from position 6[77] indicated an isotope effect. There is evidence, in addition, that the hydrogen in position 6 partially exchanges during glucose transfer into or out of the cells.[52] Also the triose–phosphate–isomerase reaction discriminated against tritium when the conversion was allowed to proceed in tritiated water.[158] Also the enzymatic oxidation of succinic acid with deuterium in the methyl groups was observed to proceed at a slower rate, and here the affinity of succinic oxidase was shown to be altered. It was 1.45 times higher for normal succinic acid than for deuterium-labeled substrate (77% D in methylene groups).[199] Deuterated sarcosine (in the methyl group) was oxidized by dehydrogenase at a rate of only two-thirds that of nonlabeled sarcosine,[1] probably also indicative of reduced binding forces between enzyme and substrate. A similar effect might be responsible for a tritium isotope effect observed to reduce the rate of thymidine phosphorylation *in vitro* with liver extracts. The reaction was studied with 6-H^3-thymidine and with 2-C^{14}-thymidine as reference in different concentrations.[85]

During the oxidation in *Acetobacter suboxidans* of polyhydroxyl alcohols, as mannitol to fructose and glucitol to sorbose, various degrees of isotope effects could be observed with tritium, depending on the molecular position of the label.[99] Thus, 1-H^3-D-mannitol was oxidized to 1-H^3-D-fructose and 6-H^3-D-fructose or 1,6-H^3-fructose (see Fig. 2.1); 2-H^3-D-mannitol gave 5-H^3-D-fructose; and 3-H^3-D-mannitol gave 3 or 4-H^3-D-fructose. The corresponding isotope effects in the various reactions are shown in Table 2.2.

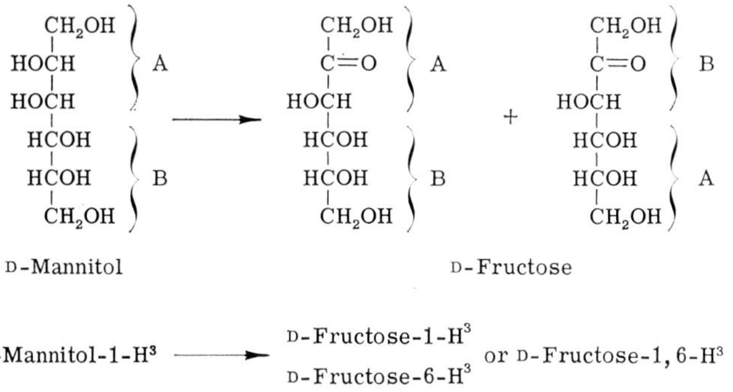

FIG. 2.1. Oxidation of D-mannitol to D-fructose. Courtesy of Isbell *et al.*, *Symp. Intern. At. Energy Agency.*[99]

TABLE 2.2

ISOTOPE EFFECTS IN OXIDATION OF LABELED D-MANNITOL[a]

Reactant	Product	Isotope effect (K^x/K)[b]
1-H³-D-Mannitol	1,6-H³-D-fructose	1.02
2-H³-D-Mannitol	5-H³-D-fructose	0.23
3-H³-D-Mannitol	3,4-H³-D-fructose	0.70

[a] Reproduced with permission of Isbell et al., Symp. Intern. At. Energy Agency.[99]
[b] Reaction rate of labeled substrate, K^x; reaction rate of unlabeled substrate, K.

2.4. DETERMINATION OF ISOTOPE EFFECTS

Isotope effects (K^*/K) become recognizable by comparing reaction rates of unlabeled and labeled reactants or substrates. The use of a reference isotope placed in a molecular position remote from the site of molecular reaction facilitates the technique of measurement. In the double-labeling technique, one tracer identifies the functional bond in a reaction directly or indirectly and the other tracer monitors the reactants or substrates without the functional isotope. The two labels are thus carried on different molecules of the same species. For measuring isotopic exchange during a reaction, however, a reference tracer might be bound better to the same molecule. The necessity for placing two different labels in the same molecular group in transfer reactions is obvious.

With the single-tracer technique, isotope effects in organic reactions are recognized mainly by three methods.[159] In one, the specific activity of the accumulated product of a partial reaction may be compared with the specific activity of the initial reactant. In another, the specific activity of a residual reactant may be compared with the specific activity of the initial reactant or total product. In the third, the specific activity of small increments of the product formed during a given time interval is compared with the specific activity of the starting material or final accumulated product. The latter two values are equal when the reaction has gone to completion without side reactions.

If

$$r = \frac{\text{molar specific activity of accumulated product}}{\text{molar specific activity of initial reactant}} \qquad (1)$$

and f equals the fraction of the starting material that has reacted, then

$$\frac{K^*}{K} = \log (1 - rf)/\log (1 - f) \qquad (2)$$

and if

$$r' = \frac{\text{molar specific activity of the residual reactant}}{\text{molar specific activity of the initial reactant}} \qquad (3)$$

and f equals the fraction of the starting material that has reacted, then

$$\frac{K^*}{K} = 1 + [\log r'/\log(1 - f)] \qquad (4)$$

The above approach is direct and convenient if the purification and measurement of a labeled reactant or reaction product is easy, as is the case of reactions yielding tritiated water.[100]

When the reactants and the reaction product are not easy to isolate quantitatively, the double-labeling technique becomes the method of choice.[99] Thus, tritium may be used as tracer to identify the functional molecular bond, and C^{14} may act as reference isotope for reaction rates without the functional isotope.

According to Isbell *et al.*,[99,101] if

$$p^0 = \frac{\text{amount of tritium (functional isotope)}}{\text{amount of } C^{14} \text{ (reference isotope)}}$$

in the initial reactant (p, above ratio in the residual reactant; p', above ratio in the product), then the term r in eq. (1) and r' in eq. (3) becomes:

$$r = \frac{p'}{p^0} \quad \text{and} \quad r' = \frac{p}{p^0}$$

and

$$\frac{K^*}{K} = \log\left[1 - \left(\frac{p'}{p^0}\right)f\right] \Big/ \log(1 - f)$$

and

$$\frac{K^*}{K} = 1 + \left[\log\left(\frac{p}{p^0}\right) \Big/ \log(1 - f)\right]$$

Thus, by simply measuring the H^3/C^{14} ratios in reactants and products, isotope effects can be accurately determined and analyzed for their mechanisms.

While the above equations have proved useful and valid for first-order reactions in organic chemistry, enzymatic reactions are not amenable to this approach, but should be analyzed in terms of reaction velocity versus substrate concentration, i.e., in terms of the Michaelis equation.

2.5. CONCLUSIONS

From the few examples of isotope effects involving deuterium and tritium which have been referred to, the reader may become aware of the importance of this phenomenon in chemical and biological investigations. For further and more detailed information on isotope effects the reader is referred to the monograph by Melander.[127]

When tritium or deuterium is chosen as tracer for studying the fate of metabolites rather than reaction mechanisms, it is essential to assure the retention of the label in the molecule during the reaction and to clarify the question of possible isotopic effects on reaction rates. In case of doubt, a check for generation of labeled water in the reaction and the double-tracer technique should ascertain the validity of data and should conform to expectations from the specific label position in the molecule.

3. Labeling of Organic Molecules with Tritium

In organic compounds hydrogen is bound mainly to carbon, nitrogen, oxygen, or sulfur, and each of these hydrogen bonds, depending on its position in the molecule, is characterized by a rate constant of exchange for a given solvent. Hydrogens in —OH, —COOH, —NH$_2$, =NH, —SH groups, and in the *ortho* and *para* positions of phenol exchange very rapidly in water. Hydrogens that are shared by two molecular groups, however, as in the hydrogen bonds of proteins or nucleic acids in helical configuration, or that are inaccessible in the core of a protein have a slower rate of exchange. Hydrogen bound to carbon is stable under normal conditions. In order to label a molecule for tracer studies, the tritium (or deuterium) needs to be introduced to those bonds which are stable and remain so also during metabolic reactions. A variety of chemical hydrogen-exchange reactions are known to suit this purpose and have been applied to labeling molecules with deuterium as well as tritium.

The substitution of a hydrogen atom by its isotope tritium (or deuterium) prior to 1956 was achieved mainly by catalytic exchange or reduction from tritiated (deuterated) water, or acid, or tritium (deuterium) gas over platinum or another noble metal. Biosynthesis of labeled organic molecules was also used by growing yeast, bacteria, algae, or other organisms in a medium containing tritiated (deuterated) water or other labeled small molecular precursors.

It was learned more recently that the energy of recoiling tritium from a nuclear reaction[163] or the radiation of tritium in gaseous form in large quantities may activate a molecule sufficiently to facilitate an exchange of hydrogen for tritium. Particularly the last method, by simply exposing any compound to tritium gas, has found wide applicability in various modifications and has led to a greatly increased popularity of tritium in many fields—from the chemical industry to biology.

The recoil technique and the gas-exposure method are, however, limited by some disadvantages. Thus, with these methods, the tritium exchanges with hydrogen to different degrees in many, if not all, possible sites in the molecule. Both techniques further lead to large amounts of by-products with high specific activities, requiring extensive purification steps. Moreover, the yield of specific activities is frequently too low for biological studies with autoradiography. Selective tritium labeling and high specific activities are achieved by chemical hydrogen-exchange techniques and synthesis combining various labeling methods, including enzymatic hydrogen transfer as an intermediate step. Therefore, the trend in recent years is toward these more specific labeling techniques. In the following, the various labeling techniques citing yield, specific activity, and purity will be considered briefly.

3.1. RECOIL LABELING TECHNIQUE

3.1.1. *Principle*

A compound exposed to recoiling tritium ions from a nuclear reaction such as $Li^6(n,\alpha)H^3$ may exchange hydrogen for tritium. The application of this technique to the study of C—H bonds[36,114] has already been mentioned in Section 2.1 (primary isotope effects) of this chapter. Indeed, the recoiling tritium ions constitute a powerful tool in radiation chemistry. To facilitate tritium exchange for hydrogen in organic molecules the recoiling tritium ion is used at the same time to activate a "stable" C—H bond and to replace the hydrogen.

The principle of the method is rather simple.[163] Thus, a lithium salt mixed with the compound to be labeled is exposed to thermal neutrons from a nuclear reactor. The nuclear reaction $Li^6(n,\alpha)H^3$ produces recoiling α-particles with an energy of 2.1 Mev and recoiling tritium nuclei with an energy of 2.7 Mev. By collision and by causing ionization and excitation, the recoiling tritium loses energy to reach finally the level of chemical bond energies (approximately 4 ev) at the end of the recoiling track. The range of recoiling tritium is about 50 μ, that of the α-particle about 10 μ. If the energy from the recoiling tritium excites a molecule sufficiently to break or weaken a carbon–hydrogen bond, the tritium may be substituted for hydrogen. Thus, as much as 50% of the tritium produced may enter the molecules. The activation of the molecular bond and the replacement of hydrogen by tritium last an extremely short period of time only, perhaps within one vibration cycle.[200]

Where the substitution takes place in the molecule depends on the bond energy involved. In general, ring positions are more easily taken than those in side chains, and on the ring *ortho* and *para* positions are preferred over *meta* positions. In benzoic acid the *meta* position showed 20% less tritium than the *ortho* and *para* positions. Carbon–carbon double bonds are easily saturated. Unequal distribution of tritium with preference for the side chain over that in the aromatic ring was reported for toluene.[2] Steroids were labeled by this method,[34] and the major part of the tritium was found in positions 11, 20, and 22, while there was less tritium in position 17 and 21 of the steriod molecule. Yet, as expected, minor amounts of tritium were also introduced, scattered in all other positions. When L-alanine in crystals was exposed to recoiling tritium, the hydrogen exchange on the asymmetric C atom did not alter the optical configuration at all; however, a 15% change was observed when the reaction occurred in the methyl group.[108]

The specific activity yields are about 1 mc/mg for a radiation of 1-day's duration. The specific activity obtained depends not only on the percentage of lithium salt present, the neutron flux, and the duration of the exposure, but also on the molecule to be labeled (permitting a characteristic "rate of entry" of tritium). Additional radiation effects on the molecules exposed are caused by the tritium ion, the recoiling α-particle, and the γ-radiation from the reactor, resulting in a decomposition of part of the molecules or in polymerization, isomerization, and so forth. Chain lengthening of hydrocarbons could be eliminated or decreased when iodine was present.[61,84] With prolonged exposure of the molecules to the neutron beam, the damage increases the yielding of all sorts of labeled by-products of interest to the radiation chemist.

3.1.2. *Methodology*

Lithium carbonate (Li_2CO_3) may be used as a lithium salt, and it is mixed with the compound to be labeled in a ratio of 0.1 to 0.3 to 1 and enclosed in a wrapping such as aluminum foil. The mixture is then exposed in a reactor to a flux of thermal neutrons, approximately 1 to 5×10^{12} n/sec/cm^2.[163] The time of exposure varies from a few seconds to several days. A kilogram and more of a compound can be labeled that way. The technical problems include a proper size of the reactor facility, optimal temperature control of 40°–50°C, and a gas exhaust. Other lithium salts may be used such as lithium sulfate ($Li_2SO_4 \cdot H_2O$) or lithium chloride (LiCl), which is soluble in organic liquids but has the disadvantage that its Cl$^-$ ion may participate in a nuclear reaction. A wide variety of compounds has been labeled with tritium that way, when chemical synthesis would have been inapplicable or too long and too costly, as in the case of alkaloids and complex molecules of unknown configuration.

3.2. Gas Exposure Technique (Wilzbach)

It has already been stated that hydrogen in a stable position may not be replaced by tritium or deuterium without addition of energy to weaken the C—H bond, i.e., to activate it. In case of recoiling tritium from a nuclear reaction, the required activation energy is delivered in abundance. In 1957 it was reported by Wilzbach[224] that the β-decay of tritium present in curie amounts over several days also provides sufficient activation energy to effect the substitution of "stable" hydrogen by tritium, resulting in labeled compounds with moderately high specific activities. Similar to the tritium recoil-labeling method, the gas-exposure technique leads to a tritium incorporation in all possible positions, and the distribution is not uniform. In addition, a considerable number of by-products is obtained owing to molecular damage from the radiation. The simplicity of the actual labeling process by exposure of a compound to curie amounts of tritium gas and the versatility of application are somewhat counterbalanced by the problem of properly purifying the labeled compound from radiochemical contaminants. Soon after Wilzbach's announcement, many investigators confirmed the results, and a number of various modifications were introduced.

It is appropriate to consider here the energy liberated in tritium gas. As was mentioned in Chapter 1, the decay of 1 cm^3 of pure tritium gas at normal temperature and pressure corresponds to 2.86 c. If 1 cm^3 of pure tritium gas is adsorbed by 1 g of substance to be labeled, the radiation dose to the substance is about 30,000 rads/hour. The radiochemical reactions induced are complex, including excitations, ionizations, fragmentations, etc. Some will be discussed in the following sections.

3.2.1. Principle

The process by which energy from the decay of tritium affects the activation and labeling of the molecule is complex and, in principle, very similar to the hydrogen exchange caused by recoiling tritium atoms. The internal (vibrational) energy of the molecule to be labeled must be raised above a critical value specific for the molecule in order for bond dissociation to occur. This may then lead to a replacement of hydrogen by tritium. Therefore, also in the gas-exposure method, the tritium serves two functions in one operation: it activates and replaces. The tritium-hydrogen exchange reactions following tritium decay ($H_2^3 \rightarrow$ $HeH^{3+} + e^-$) may be initiated by the ejected electron, causing excitation and ionization of molecules both of the tritium gas and the organic compound. They may also result from ionic reactions of the tritium-helium ion which carries a strongly positive charge. The importance of both components for the labeling process was quantitatively examined using toluene[4] and vapors of saturated hydrocarbons.[229]

Similar to the tritium recoil-labeling technique, the efficiency of labeling is highest for aromatic compounds. With increasing concentration of tritium and with prolongation of the reaction, the labeling yield increases linearly or exponentially,[4] depending on the molecular group involved, until it is overtaken by radiation damage. The labeling yield in gases is independent of the gas pressure.[51] Since the energy available from the tritium gas is 0.88 ev per atom per day (i.e., approximately 1.8×10^{19} ev/c of tritium per day) and since the energy needed to rupture a carbon–hydrogen bond is about 4 ev (that needed to split a H^3—H^3 is 4.59 ev),[45] one should expect a high yield of exchange. However, the actual energy liberated per useful exchange (one tritium atom into an intact organic molecule) is about 1000 ev. Thus, there is much wasted energy relative to useful tritium labeling. Usually 10–100 molecules are damaged permanently or destroyed for each one successfully labeled. Damage can be kept within limits by allowing 1 ev per molecule, which corresponds to 30 c/mmole/day or 1 c/mmole for 30 days. The degree of damage can also be decreased by modifications of the gas-exposure method, as will be discussed below. With this technique, about 1 tritium atom is introduced per 1000 carrier molecules, resulting in specific activity of about 1–100 mc/g of substance.

The labeling proceeds in an apparatus such as that shown in Fig. 2.2. Up to several grams of organic substances (liquid or powder) are exposed in a glass reaction vessel (of about 6 ml volume for 1 g) to tritium gas (up to 5 c or more, 5 c in 2 ml) at room temperature. The substance may be present also as a vapor. The tritium gas is pumped from a storage vessel or a depot where it is bound as uranium tritide and from which it can be liberated upon heating. The tritium gas is left with the substance to be labeled for several days or weeks at room temperature. In the case of liquids, the reaction vessel is shaken. If there are solids to be labeled, they should be powdered or finely dispersed over the wall by rotating the vessel which should be disconnected from the apparatus. The optimal reaction time is often chosen by experience since the radiation sensitivity of many molecular entities is not known.

3.2.2. Modifications of the Principle

Various modifications of the method were tried to shorten the exposure time of the organic compound to tritium and increase the labeling efficiency by introducing additional activation energy to the molecules to be labeled and to the tritium gas. Such additional energy may be

Apparatus for labeling by
exposure to tritium

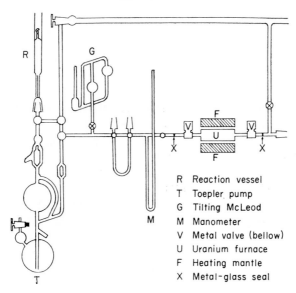

R   Reaction vessel
T   Toepler pump
G   Tilting McLeod
M   Manometer
V   Metal valve (bellow)
U   Uranium furnace
F   Heating mantle
X   Metal-glass seal

FIG. 2.2. Apparatus for labeling by exposure to tritium gas. Courtesy of Wilzbach, *Symp. Intern. At. Energy Agency.*[226]

supplied, for example, by γ-radiation, ultraviolet radiation, mercury photosensitization, microwave radiation, and electrical discharge.

The use of γ-irradiation from Co^{60} (5×10^6 r) to a reaction mixture of hydrocarbon vapor and tritium gas indeed increased the labeling yield, but it aslo produced a greater degree of destruction than the original method.[6,116]

Prior to the description of the Wilzbach method, attempts had already been made to label organic molecules with tritium by externally inducing a low kinetic energy in tritium gas (ions) similar to the final energy of recoiling tritium ions. This was done with an electrical current of 500 volts and 100 μa.[228] The principle was reapplied to the gas-labeling method by Lemmon et al.[116] With an alternating current of 20 kv and 1 ma for 1 hour, the benzene used in testing decomposed only slightly, while the labeling yield increased by a factor of 10^4. Upon prolonging the discharge, destruction of the benzene increased. Atropine and cocaine were labeled by this method to a specific activity of 2.5 and 16.5 mc/mmole.[166] Dorfmann and Wilzbach[51] used an electrical discharge from a Tesla coil leak tester—1000 volts, 100 μa for 3–10 minutes. In this manner the necessary amount of tritium gas was reduced by a factor of 10 and the exposure time was shortened from days to minutes. This modification was further altered[103] by the construction of a technically convenient cell specially bent, allowing a silent discharge from a Tesla coil for 5–30 minutes at a peak potential of about 25 kv.

Another mode of activating the exchange reaction in Wilzbach's method was described by Ghanem and Westermark.[78] They used microwaves (approximately 2425 millicycles per second at various watts) and thus reduced the necessary amount of tritium gas to millicuries, instead of using curies in the labeling of polystyrene, polyethylene glycol, serum albumin, and benzene. They obtained specific activities of 5 mc/g for albumin, 87 mc/g for polyethylene glycol, 400 mc/g for polystyrene, and 218 mc/g for benzene. These authors also tested ultraviolet light radiation (at 2537 A, 50 watt) and obtained, from 100 mc tritium gas with an exposure time of 24 hours, a specific activity of 31.1 mc/g of polymethacrylate. A shorter wavelength of about 2000 A perhaps would increase the efficiency.

Cacace and associates[41] added a small amount of mercury to the reaction sample (the organic compound and the tritium in a silica ampule) and irradiated it with ultraviolet light (2537 A). Both tritium gas and organic molecules were excited and dissociated by the action of the mercury vapor, which absorbs photons having a wavelength of 2537 A.

The admixture of a noble gas to the reaction has been tested. Noble gases have an increased ionization potential over tritium, and they may act as an amplifier in the gas-exposure reaction by transferring part of their charge to both the tritium and the organic molecule. They therefore increase the ratio of ionized to excited reactants. Argon added to the reacting system caused a higher labeling efficiency in n-hexane, and the specific activity was increased from 71 to 92 mc/ml without affecting the tritium distribution in the molecule.[132] Xenon but not helium increased the labeling efficiency in benzoic acid by 50%, but the byproducts from radiation damage showed a three- to fourfold rise simultaneously.[226] Platinum as catalyst added to the reaction mixture was found useful by Meshi and Takahashi.[128]

In the various gas-exposure methods the labeling yield depends, in part, on the access the tritium has to the organic substance to be labeled. Thus, solid substances are best when powdered to a fine grain or when well spread over the walls of the reaction vessel. To assure a high surface exposure, the compounds to be labeled in milligram amounts have also been adsorbed on granulated charcoal of a particle size of 0.1–0.3 mm.[214,107] For a variety of compounds the specific activities were increased by this method by a factor of approximately 3–100. There

were no signs of concomitant increase in the by-products, perhaps because of their firm adsorption to charcoal. A few milligrams of ecdyson,
the hormone of the metamorphosis in silkworm pupae, was thus labeled
with tritium to a specific activity of several hundred microcuries per
milligram, and the hormone retained its full activity.[107]

More recently, the charcoal adsorption method was again modified to
use, in addition, platinum as a catalyst (as $H_2PtCl_6 \cdot 6H_2O$). That way
the specific activity yield (of digitogenin) was improved threefold and
the labeling time was reduced about 100 times from the original gas-
exposure technique.[126]

A surface was also utilized by labeling organic compounds with
tritium directly from uranium tritide, in which form tritium is stored
and from which it can be generated as gas. Felter and Curie[72] thus heated
vapors of various hydrocarbons (n-pentane and ethylene) with uranium
tritide for about 30 minutes to 12 hours. The rate of tritium incorporation was 0.2–10% per hour of the initial tritium. There were very few
decompositions. The specific activity varied according to the conditions,
and it was 32 μc/mg for tritiated ethylene after an exposure for 30 minutes at a temperature of 75°C.

Although the gas-exposure technique of Wilzbach, similar to the tritium-recoil technique, results in a diverse but nonuniform distribution
of tritium in the molecule, specific labeling may still be achieved by
taking advantage of the distinct radiosensitivity of the carbon–iodine
bond as compared to carbon–hydrogen bond.[73] It was shown that the
exposure of iodinated benzoic acid (in *para* and *ortho* positions) to
tritium gas, according to Wilzbach, led to the specific tritiation in *para*
position and a high degree of specificity in *ortho* position. Another
advantage of the method is the possibility of a rather easy chemical
separation of the labeled compound in a carrier-free form since it is
chemically different from the starting material.

Iodine, by virtue of its strong acceptance of electrons, may exert a
"scavenger effect" on the reaction in the gas-exposure technique, as it
does in the reaction of methane with recoiling tritium ions. In the latter,
the lengthening of hydrocarbon chains as a result of radiation effects
was prevented.[61,84] Indeed, the addition of molecular iodine to methane
during the gas exposure amplified by γ-rays from cobalt led to a drop
in the yield of higher chain hydrocarbons.[6] Addition of high concentrations of iodine to a mixture of toluene vapor and tritium gas was reported
to prevent tritiation of the side chain, whereas the tritium distribution
in the ring positions was specifically influenced (see Fig. 2.3).[3] Furthermore, the total labeling yield was increased by a factor of 100 above
control without iodine.

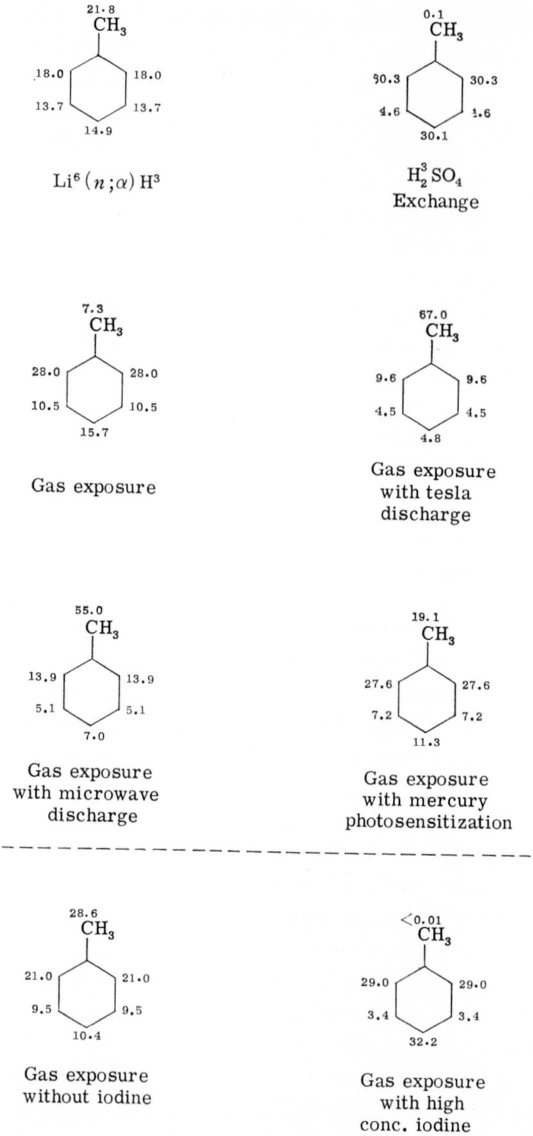

Fig. 2.3. Tritium exchange on toluene by different techniques. The numbers denote relative distribution of tritium in per cent. Courtesy of Ache *et al., Symp. Intern. At. Energy Agency,*[2] and *Angew. Chem.*[3]

3.2.3. *Purification*

The gas-exposure method, as well as the tritium-recoil technique, is applicable to a practically limitless number of molecular species. The most difficult problem with these methods is the purification of the labeled compounds from the labeled by-products. As already mentioned, as many as about 10–100 molecules may be expected to become permanently altered or destroyed for each tritium that is bound to an intact carrier molecule in the gas-exposure technique. The molecular alterations involve fragmentation or addition of fragments to the mother compound, rearrangements, exchanges, reductions, oxidations, and polymerizations. Jellinck and Smyth[104] subjected tritium-labeled 1,6-dihydroxyhexosterol repeatedly to the Wilzbach procedure and found each time, after renewed labeling, impurities with high specific activities. Since the by-products are likely to be labeled in the course of their formation, these impurities may contain the major part of the incorporated tritium, i.e., often 10–100 times as much as the mother compound. For example, gas-exposure labeling of L-phenylalanine mustard resulted in a specific activity of 450 μc/mg total substance; after purification by repeated recrystallization it was 4.3 μc/mg.[130] It is obvious that even the slightest contamination with labeled by-products of high specific activities makes a labeled compound useless for tracer experiments.

Radiolysis of labeled molecules continues during their storage depending on the type of molecule or the specific activity and the storage condition. Such self-irradiation decomposition of tritiated compounds will be discussed later in this chapter.

Repeated crystallizations of the compound mixture after exposure to tritium in a solvent containing exchangeable hydrogen will remove the tritium that is bound in an exchangeable position such as —OH, —COOH, —NH₂, =NH. But such procedures may not remove all by-products. Further purification steps may include all of the current methods of chromatography, electrophoresis, ultracentrifugation, and the preparation of chemical derviatives. Obviously, the ultraviolet absorption spectrum may prove a poor guide to purity since the impurities, due to their high specific activity, need be present in only infinitesimal amounts. Paper chromatography in several solvent systems is frequently the best technique for detecting such impurities (see also Section 2.5 in this Chapter).

3.2.4. *Exchange Specificity*

Although the labeling techniques by exposure to tritium gas result usually in a diverse pattern of labeling, the distribution is not truly random.[221]

In the case of compounds containing unsaturated double bonds of carbon, C=C, reduction may be the predominant reaction as in the tritiation of cyclohexene, where in liquid phase a free cyclohexyl radical was observed as an intermediate.[136] Exposure of methyl oleate to tritium gas resulted, after purification by gas chromatography, in labeled methyl stearate containing nearly all the tritium. Scarcely any labeled methyl oleate or other by-products were obtained.[53]

Configurational inversion may also occur during tritiation by the Wilzbach method as exemplified by the inversion of (–)-inositol.[8] After tritiation, the relative amounts of *myo-*, *allo-*, and *muco*inositol increased to various specific activities. The inversion was greater when the inositol was tritiated in the noncrystalline form than when it was exposed to tritium gas in the form of crystals. The tritium in the inversion product *myo*inositol was shown to be localized solely in position 1,[9] indicating that a hydrogen–tritium exchange was likely accompanied by inversion. Tartaric acid has only two stable hydrogens which are both in optically active positions. "Wilzbach" substitution of these stable hydrogens by tritium altered the configuration, and 60 times more tritium was exchanged in the hydroxyl groups than in the stable position and malic acid was also formed.[179]

Ache and associates[2] compared various tritium-labeling methods using toluene, and the possible labeling mechanisms were critically considered. With the different techniques, including various modifications of the gas-exposure method, different intermediates were probably formed. The resulting tritium distribution is shown in Fig. 2.3. In no case was there a random distribution of tritium, and remarkable specific differences were seen as a result of the modifications of the gas-exposure technique. Thus, the tritium in the methyl group of the toluene increased greatly over that on the aromatic ring when the gas exposure was carried out with the addition of an electrical discharge or microwave radiation; less tritium went into the methyl group with the mercury-photosensitized reaction, causing with prolonged exposure tritium distribution similar to that obtained with the original gas-exposure method. Nearly exclusive labeling of the toluene ring was found following tritium gas exposure in the presence of high concentration of iodine, similar to the pattern resulting from exchange in tritium sulfate. The tritium-recoil labeling again gave another tritium distribution involving all positions, but in a specific manner.

A remarkable nonuniformity of tritium distribution between the various positions was also reported in carbohydrates.[179] For example, approximately 90% of the total tritium on D-glucose was found to be in position 3, independent of the gas-exposure time or the purification steps. However, in D-mannose, different from D-glucose at C-2, 80–90%

of the tritium occupied positions 4 and 5. On D-ribose, 95% of the tritium was in position 3; however, D-ribose 5-phosphate showed a less specific distribution: C-1, 10.7%; C-2, 40%; C-3, 15.8%; C-5, 12.2%; C-5, 19.5%. Nonuniformity of tritium distribution following the Wilzbach technique was also reported for steroids, as expected.[76]

With purines and pyrimidines, a relationship between molecular structure and position of tritium exchange was not observed after the gas-exposure technique.[204]

3.2.5. Macromolecules

The gas-exposure method has been used to label innumerable organic compounds of practically any class. Only a few examples will be mentioned here with comments on their biological activity after labeling. Digitoxin was labeled by Wilzbach[224] to give a specific activity of 90 mc/g without significant alteration in the pharmacological action. Steinberg and colleagues[190] labeled two enzymes, lysozyme and ribonuclease, with tritium by the Wilzbach technique. After chromatographic purification, a specific activity of 3.6×10^5 counts per minute per milligram was found for lysozyme, and 90% of the enzymatic activity was preserved. Similarly, the tritiated ribonuclease retained 82% of its enzymatic activity. Also, with a higher specific activity of about 50 mc/mmole, lysozyme was found to have retained its enzymatic activity.[19] In 1958, Holt and Holt[95] labeled insulin according to Wilzbach and found a specific activity of 4.6 μc/mg, and the biological activity (blood-sugar assay in rats) was indistinguishable from the nonlabeled insulin. The individual amino acids of the molecule were all labeled, but to different degrees, more tritium being in the aromatic amino acids. After Wilzbach labeling, gonadotropin became physiologically inactive and the isolated amino acids showed various degrees of labeling, but tyrosine and phenylalanine after hydrolysis were completely devoid of tritium.[115] The metamorphosis hormone in silkworms (ecdyson), after tritiation purified by thin-layer chromatography, had a specific activity of about 250 μc/mg and retained full hormonal activity when tested by the specific puff development in chromosomes, which precedes metamorphosis.[107] Tetanus toxin tritiated by the Wilzbach procedure (5 c tritium gas; 2.5 day exposure in deep-freeze cabinet) was still highly toxic in mice, but the addition of tetanus antitoxin did not completely neutralize the toxin.[188] The material had a specific activity high enough so that it could be used in mice for autoradiographic studies on cellular distribution. On the other hand, the γ2-globulin fraction retained a rather nonspecific antibody titer after tritiation by the gas-exchange method despite increased molecular heterogeneity.[151] Deoxyribonucleic acid (DNA) from human leukocytes was tritiated and purified on ecteola columns; it had a specific activity of 0.86 mc/mg with a distribution of tritium among the bases: adenine = 1, thymine = 9.8, guanine = 1.4, and cytosine = 2.4.[31] The tritiation caused a drop in the average molecular weight from 5.2 to 1.3×10^6. There was also some aggregation in addition to the degradation. But the twin-stranded configuration of the molecule remained. This labeled DNA was also used for autoradiographic work, and its penetration into HeLa tissue culture cells was described. Ribonucleic acid (RNA) and DNA from various sources such as bacteria and mammalian tissue were tritiated by Wilzbach's method, fractionated, and purified by DEAE-cellulose paper chromatography.[113] The separation into 12 different fractions lasted only about 3 hours. Radiation decomposition of the labeled compounds was very slow as observed over 3–7 months. An interesting approach to the study of the development of malignancies utilized tritiated carcinogenic hydrocarbons, which are polycyclic aromatics. The hydrocarbons (phenantrenes, benzanthracenes, benzypyrenes, cholanthrenes) of high-grade purity were tritiated by the gas-exposure method, isolated from by-products by chromatography on Florisil columns and acetylated or paraffinized paper, and finally carefully stored in benzene at low temperature. The specific activities ranged from 0.04 to 2.40 mc/mg.[82] The purification was carried out rapidly in the dark and under nitrogen in order to minimize decomposition.

3.2.6. Conclusion

The application of the gas-exposure method and its modifications, as well as the tritium recoil-labeling technique, is practically limitless and especially useful when other techniques for labeling are not available, too difficult, or too costly.

The preservation of the biological activity of hormones, enzymes, vitamins, etc., depends not only on proper chemical treatment but also on the degree of radiolysis, which is determined by the nature of the compound, its specific activity, its concentration, and other storage conditions. Tritiated compounds with specific activities below 500 mc/ mmole do not exhibit serious decomposition when they are stored under the best conditions for at least 1 year. This level of radioactivity is not reached with the methods discussed so far. Storage conditions and self-decomposition of tritiated compounds will be discussed in more detail at the end of this chapter.

3.3. LABELING BY CONVENTIONAL CHEMICAL MEANS

Labeling with tritium may be facilitated by a variety of chemical reactions involving hydrogenation commonly used in organic chemistry.

Some of these procedures lead to a more specific tritiation than others; and some introduce tritium without exchange for hydrogen, others involve hydrogen–tritium exchanges. Most of these reactions utilize tritium ions dissolved in water.

Before the major exchange and hydrogenation (or tritiation) procedures are discussed, the radiation dose from tritium in tritiated water will be evaluated briefly. As mentioned in Chapter 1, 1 g of pure tritium water having 5.48×10^{22} tritium atoms yields a decay rate of 2.92×10^3 c or 35.45×10^6 rads/hour. In 1 mc/g giving 12.14 rads/hour there is only 1 tritium atom in about 1.5×10^6 water molecules. The desired specific activity is obtained by appropriate dilution with a suitable solvent. Without going into detail concerning the β-irradiation of the water, it is pointed out here that approximately 3.6 molecules will undergo chemical alterations per 100 ev absorbed radiation. Since 1 rad equals 6.24×10^{13} ev, 1 rad will alter 2.25×10^{12} water molecules. Hence, in tritiated water with 1 mc/g about 2.7×10^{13} out of 2.74×10^{22} molecules will undergo chemical changes per hour, i.e., 1 in 10^9 molecules (1 g of H_2O has 2.74×10^{22} molecules under normal conditions). With time, an equilibrium is reached between breakdown of tritiated water molecules and recombination of the resulting radicals and ions. As to the potential hazards in work with tritiated water, the reader is referred to Chapter 6.

3.3.1. *Acid Catalysis*

Strong acids without an additional catalyst exchange hydrogen with organic compounds resistant to the acid. Schoenheimer and associates, in 1937,[168] labeled organic compounds with deuterium from concentrated deuterated sulfuric acid ($DHSO_4$) by heating 100°C for 24 hours. The deuterium was thus exchanged for hydrogen in stable positions, for example, in DL-alanine and D-leucine. The label was not lost upon boiling the amino acids in 20% sulfuric acid for 48 hours. Certain compounds which are resistant to strong acids can thus be labeled with tritium or tritium and deuterium simultaneously.

A promising modification has been described by Yavorsky and Gorin[230] who added borofluoride to tritiated phosphoric acid ($H_2^3PO_4 \cdot BF_3$). The substance to be labeled is mixed with the reagent and allowed to react for a few hours to a few days at desired temperatures. Whereas aromatic compounds react readily, nonbranched aliphatics do not exchange hydrogens with this reagent. Since hydrocarbons are insoluble in the reagent, they can be separated easily after the labeling process. Side reactions are rare; thus a rather pure labeled product is obtained. The labeling yield can be varied with the specific activity of the phosphoric acid. The position of the tritium is nonspecific and statistical among the exchangeable hydrogens. Tritium fluoroacetate in perchloric acid was employed to label the starting compound in the synthesis of chloramphenicol labeled exclusively in the aromatic nucleus to a specific activity of 800 μc/mmole.[143] Tritium iodide (hydriodic acid), produced from iodine and tritiated water in the presence of red phosphorous, was used to label thyroxine and its derivatives to a specified activity of 90–150 mc/mmole.[157]

3.3.2. *Metal Catalysis*

(*a*) One of the most useful hydrogen–tritium exchange methods is the catalytic exchange of organic chemistry. The advantage of this method is its efficiency, wide applicability, and the relative absence of degradation of the substances to be labeled. Certain compounds, however, sensitive to higher temperatures are not suitable for this technique. Generally, relatively few by-products are obtained. Another advantage lies in the possibility for double labeling with tritium and deuterium, which can be carried out easily in a one-step procedure. Furthermore, this method, if applicable, can yield much higher specific activities than those obtained by the gas exposure or recoil-labeling technique. Tritiated compounds with particularly high specific activities, i.e., 500 mc/mmole and more, are often desired for autoradiographic work.

(*b*) The mechanism of hydrogen–tritium exchange[79,80] probably involves the simulatenous adsorption of the organic compound and tritium ions on the surface of a metal catalyst such as activated platinum, rhodium, palladium, or Raney nickel. Subsequently, a hydrocarbon radical is formed by rupture of a C—H bond, which leads to the exchange of a hydrogen with tritium. Although direct hydrogen substitution may take place also without rupture of the C—H bond, in general, substitution occurs more readily in bonds with more ionic character. If a compound is adsorbed too strongly on the surface of the catalyst, the exchange efficiency may decrease, i.e., the catalyst becomes "poisoned," perhaps by displacement of adsorbed water. Catalyst "poisoning" is observed thus by sulfur-containing compounds, those which have iodine, or other certain functional groups such as NO_2. Different catalysts are poisoned to different degrees.

(*c*) The catalytic exchange method is rather simple and applies to the scale of microchemistry. It involves, for example, the enclosure in a sealed tube of the organic substance to be labeled (dissolved in a solvent if solid) plus the tritium, usually as tritiated water, and a proper catalyst such as activated platinum. The mixture is then heated, even to 200°C if necessary, or the compound to be labeled may be refluxed with tritiated water in the presence of the catalyst. The substance to be labeled and the tritiated water are brought preferably into a solvent which has no easily exchangeable hydrogen, although occasionally solvents such as acetic acid have proved necessary. The method has also been used with the reactants in the vapor state. In this manner Harris[90] labeled the ethyl ester of valine with tritium gas in the presence of platinum. In general, the specific activity of the products depends on the specific activity of the tritium donor, such as tritiated water, assuming equilibrium is reached. Equilibrium may not be achieved, however, either because the rate is too slow or because the catalyst is "poisoning" during the exchange. The yield of activity in the product at equilibrium obviously depends on the relative sizes of the exchangeable pools of tritium for donors and products. The catalytic exchange method first developed for deuteration of organic compounds is widely used. For example, purines were labeled with tritium from tritiated water in glacial acetic acid over platinum.[57] In a similar manner thymidine was tritiated.[197,209]

Tritium in gas form may easily exchange, in the presence of certain metal catalysts, with labile hydrogens of organic compounds in a solvent without exchangeable hydrogen. Thus, a carboxyl group can be tritiated, and the label may be stabilized by subsequent transfer into a stable position by decarboxylation. With this technique tritiated acetic acid was prepared from labeled malonic acid, and tritiated methylpyrrole was prepared from labeled N-methylpyrrole-2-carboxylic acid.[118,185] Rhodium as a catalyst was preferred in the reactions because it was less readily "poisoned." Organic acids labeled with tritium in the carboxyl group were also successfully used as a tritium donor, with 5% rhodium or alumina as a catalyst, to exchange with hydrogen specifically in unsaturated linkage without concomitant reduction of the unsaturated linkage in the course of the labeling process.[185]

3.3.3. Catalytic Reduction

Tritium may be placed specifically in organic molecules by catalytic reductions of carbon double bonds. This reaction is also called catalytic hydrogenation. Instead of hydrogen, tritium is added. Platinum, palladium, or another appropriate metal catalyst is employed in this technique. As in catalytic exchange, the combination of the reactants is facilitated by their adsorption on the active surface of the catalyst. This method is applicable to practically all unsaturated hydrocarbons, and it is one of the most widely used methods in the labeling of organics by chemical synthesis for the reason of avoiding high temperatures. For example, steroids were labeled this way at high specific activities.[83,105,]

[140,182] Verly *et al.*[211] used Myleran labeled specifically in position 2 and 3 of the butanediol moiety by catalytic reduction and subsequent esterification with methanesulfonyl chloride. Myleran is dimethanesulfonyl oxybutane.

Catalytic reduction may be coupled with subsequent dehydration, however, with the concomitant loss of some activity. Still, the isotope effect favors the retention of tritium on the carbon atom. Tritiated styrene was thus obtained with a specific activity of 0.66 mc/mmole.[24]

Partial reduction of carbon triple bonds is feasible with specially prepared catalysts, for example, in the form of palladium partially inactivated with heavy metal salt and quinoline (Lindlar catalyst). With partial reduction in tritiated water unsaturated fatty acids can be specifically labeled with tritium.[193,206]

Reduction with desulfuration over Raney nickel was employed by Buu-Hoi *et al.*[39,40] for labeling specifically various saturated aliphatic hydrocarbons.

Catalytic dehalogenations with tritium are also widely used for specific labeling, especially of aromatic compounds. With a proper metal catalyst such as palladium, hydrogen (tritium) exchanges specifically for the halogen. Thus iodination of oxytocin and subsequent deiodination in the presence of tritium led to specific labeling of the tyrosine in the peptide.[5] After careful iodination, proteins can likewise be labeled to relatively high specific activities.[135] With this method aromatic amino acids were tritiated in specific positions to specific activities of 10 and more curies per millimole.[27,28,92] By carrying out the exchange reaction in the last step of the chemical synthesis radiation decomposition of intermediate products is avoided. Synkavit [methylnaphthaquinolbis(disodium phosphate)] was labeled specifically in the aromatic component by this method up to a specific activity of 83 c/mmole (i.e., 2 or 3 tritium atoms per molecule) for therapeutic purposes in malignant disease.[7,122] Catalytic dehalogenation with tritium gas was used to label salicylic acid for autoradiographic studies.[129] Another example is the tritiation by catalytic dehalogenation of steroids to a specific activity as high as 3.4 c/mmole.[140]

3.3.4. *Other Reduction Methods*

All methods in chemical syntheses involving hydrogenation may be used to introduce tritium instead of hydrogen; examples are shown in Table 2.3.

A valuable method of tritiation takes advantage of the reactions of borotritides and H^3-organoboranes.[97,119,137] Thus, tritium labeling can be achieved by coupling the compound with lithium borotritide ($LiBH_4^3$) and splitting it again subsequently.[186] With sodium borotritide, D-glycer-

TABLE 2.3

A SUPPLEMENTARY LISTING OF HYDROGENATION REACTIONS SUITABLE FOR LABELING
WITH TRITIUM (T)

1. $Ca_2 + 2T_2O \rightarrow TC{\equiv}CT + Ca(OT)_2$
2. $KCN + 2T_2O \rightarrow TCOOK + NT_3$
3. $Cl_3CCHO + NaOT \rightarrow Cl_3CT + HCOONa$
4. $R'-MgX + THO \rightarrow R'-T + HOMgX$
5. $SOCl_2 + THO \rightarrow SO_2 + 2TCl$ "Grignard" reactions
   $R'-MgX + TCl \rightarrow R'-T + ClMgX$
6. $R'-COCHN_2 \xrightarrow{T_2O/Ag_2O} R'-CHTCOOT + N_2$ "Arndt-Eistert" reaction

7.[a]

$$\underset{\text{COOH}}{\overset{\text{COOH}}{C}}\underset{\text{NHCO—CH}_3}{\overset{R'}{\big|}} \xrightarrow{T_2O/CH_3COOH} \underset{R'}{\overset{\text{COOH}}{T-C-NH_2}}$$

[a] From Hempel.[92]

---

aldehyde was reduced to H^3-3-glycerol[29] and 7-ketodeoxycholic acid to H^3-7β-cholic acid.[165] Nystrom *et al.*[137] evaluated various tritioboration procedures to label unsaturated hydrocarbons. The organoborane as tritium donor can be labeled by any technique applicable, such as catalytic exchange or the Wilzbach method.

3.3.5. Chromatographic Columns

Easily exchangeable hydrogen may be replaced by tritium on chromatographic columns for studying hydrogen exchange rates. For example, sorbitol (hexa-OH-hexane) was adsorbed on silica gel columns in a gas chromatograph and charged with tritiated water. Subsequent passage through the column of organic compounds in vapor state led to the exchange of the labile hydrogen with tritium.[60] For specific tritiation calcium tritide (CaH_2^3) was adsorbed on a gas chromatographic column. Subsequent injection into the column of halogenated aliphatic or aromatic volatile compounds at a temperature of 100°–200°C led to the exchange of the halogen with the tritium for the more stable metal halogen compound.[192] The technique has limited applicability, but yields specific labeling.

3.3.6. Synthesis

The usefulness of tritium in many biological and biochemical studies and in research on reaction mechanisms (radiochemistry, nature and role of reaction intermediates, stereospecificity, etc.) requires a specific rather than random positioning of tritium on the molecule. Several tritiation methods discussed in the previous sections fulfill this requirement, whereas others, such as the recoil-labeling technique and the gas-exposure technique, do not satisfy. Catalytic exchange also may lack complete specificity and in any case requires subsequent demonstration of the location of the label. Much effort is therefore being placed on the development of proper synthetic techniques for producing compounds specifically labeled in the desired position and with a reasonably high specific activity. Several such examples were given in the foregoing sections and need not be repeated here. Organic synthesis with isotopes, furthermore, is treated in the book by Murray and Williams.[133] All available labeling methods including biosynthesis, which is discussed below, may be used to provide a starting or intermediate compound according to the requirements of the steps of synthesis. The final yield may represent only a small fraction of the initial radioactivity. The starting compound may be tritiated according to Wilzbach, as, for example, in the synthesis by Verly et al.[212] of tritiated DL-carnitin, labeled in all positions except for the methyl group. The suitable precursor (β-hydroxy-γ-aminobutyric acid) was tritiated according to Wilzbach and after purification was methylated (without tritium) to DL-carnitin. This again could be converted to tritiated β-crotonic acid. As another example, specifically tritiated colchicine was prepared by methylation of colchicine with diazomethane in tritiated water. A specific activity of 2.5 c/mmole was obtained.[196] For hydrogenation reactions, tritiated formaldehyde may be used. It can be generated from glucose or urotropin labeled according to Wilzbach.[177]

Of particular biological interest is the labeling of biologically active proteins to yield relatively high specific activities without the need of wasteful and laborious purification steps. If possible, labeled polypeptides can be synthesized, as was oxytocin containing H³-leucine.[15] The use of catalytic dehalogenation for the tritiation of proteins has already been mentioned.[135] Various coupling reactions have been used also. Thus, porcine γ-globulin was labeled with tritium by coupling the protein with H³-aniline monohydrochloride to yield a specific activity of 6.4 mc/0.1 g.[156] Antibodies were tritiated by coupling with labeled ethylmethanesulfonate, an acylating agent, which attaches to carboxyl groups and amino acids at a pH above 8. The immunological activity was retained.[162] Potentially useful is the conjugation of proteins with haptenic groups, e.g., ribosides, for preparing labeled antigens. The protein riboside complexes caused specific antibodies against denatured DNA in the rabbit.[64]

Many specifically tritiated organic compounds are now commercially available where the demand warrants it. In other cases the collaboration of the biologist with an experienced chemist will be mutually beneficial.

3.4. LABELING BY BIOSYNTHESIS

Biosynthesis of tritiated compounds has the advantage of highly selective labeling of stereospecific molecules. But often the yield in quantity is very small and the specific activity is rather low, in contrast to the chemical techniques discussed in the preceding paragraphs. Still, a variety of useful tritiated compounds have been prepared biosynthetically from simpler molecules and also from more complex intermediates prepared by chemical synthesis. Biosynthesis may utilize plants, animals, unicellular organisms, and bacteria, or isolated parts of them, as well as purified enzyme preparations.

3.4.1. Enzyme Preparations

Since isolated enzymes perform essentially one stereospecific reaction on one or a very limited number of substrates, excellent specificities may be achieved. Even crude preparations, including tissue homogenates, have proved useful. Thus, tritiated progesterone was incubated with placental homogenates for the preparation of 17-OH corticoids (cortisone, cortisol).[146] Tritiated cholesterol was conjugated to serum lipoproteins simply by incubating it with serum *in vitro*. The lipoprotein prepared in this way behaved like one obtained after *in vivo* injection of the labeled cholesterol.[16]

Pure and crude enzyme preparations were used for the synthesis of stereospecifically labeled cholesterol[165] in studying hydrogen transfer during the biosynthesis, with C^{14} being the reference isotope. Thus, farnesyl pyrophosphate labeled with C^{14} was first anaerobically converted with H^3-NADP (nicotinamide adenine dinucleotide phosphate) and with rat liver microsomes to tritiated squalene, which in a second step was then incubated with the soluble supernatant of liver homogenate in an oxygen atmosphere to yield cholesterol labeled specifically in positions 12β and 11 (with uncertainty concerning the α- or β-position). The isolated cholesterol was further converted to cholic acid. H^3-NAD (nicotinamide adenine dinucleotide) was the tritium donor in the specific labeling of L-lactic acid (H^3 at C-2) by coupled enzyme reactions.[215] The preparation occurred in a single reaction mixture consisting of tritiated water as starting material, and of disodium fumarate, NAD, fumarate hydratase, lactate dehydrogenase, malate dehydrogenase, sodium pyruvate, in phosphate buffer at pH 7.3.[215] The reaction time lasted about 4 hours. Mevaldate specifically labeled with tritiated NAD from tritiated farnesol served as parameter for the stereochemical hydrogen transfer from H^3-NAD catalyzed by mevaldate reductase.[50]

H-NAD, tritiated water, and an enzyme preparation from *Aerobacter aerogenes* were used by Hanson and Rose[89] to label specifically 6-H^3-quinic acid from 5-dehydroshikimate. Further oxidation yielded 4-H^3-citric acid. Citric acids were also labeled from isocitrate and tritiated water or tritiated succinic acid via tritiated isocitrate with aconitate hydratase.[89,161] In a study with deuterium, monodeuterium citrate was synthesized stereospecifically using fumarase.[63] Tritium could, however, not be transferred to citrate from tritiated acetyl coenzyme A in the reaction with oxalacetate.[32]

The tritium in positions 2 and 3 of succinate was donated to long-chain fatty acids by isolated mitochondria probably via succinic dehydrogenase, flavin, and NAD.[220]

Fructose was tritiated in various positions stereospecifically with the help of glucose 6-phosphate isomerase, aldolase, and triose phosphate isomerase by carrying out the reaction in tritiated water.[179] Triose phosphate isomerase was also utilized to study the inversion of dihydroxyacetone phosphate and glyceraldehyde 3-phosphate in tritiated water with the result of obtaining specifically labeled dihydroxyacetone phosphate.[152] During the reaction of phosphoriboisomerase and ribulose-5-phosphate-3-epimerase in tritiated water, tritium was transferred specifically to the substrates.[121]

Many other purified enzymes have been successfully used to introduce tritium into specific molecular positions, mainly to study the mechanism of enzymatic hydrogen transfer. The systems employed can be equally suitable for labeling organic molecules for other metabolic tracer studies.

In the field of nucleic acid biochemistry, the methylation reaction of thymidine, studied by Pastore and Friedkin,[144] could be useful in labeling specifically thymidine in the methyl group from the H^3-leucovorum factor. The tetrahydrofolate was tritiated enzymatically from H^3-glucose 6-phosphate or from H^3-isocitrate and NADP with the appropriate dehydrogenases. Specific thymidine labeling was also obtained by first labeling thymine, which was then enzymatically coupled by thymidine phosphorylase with 2-deoxyribose.[172,223] Deoxycytidine diphosphate was tritiated in position 2 of the deoxyribose from cytidine diphosphate by reductase in tritiated water.[111] Tritiated thymidine triphosphate was enzymatically obtained from H^3-thymidine by the appropriate enzyme system.[26]

Likewise, macromolecular RNA and DNA can be enzymatically synthesized from labeled precursors. For example, Bollum and Potter[30] labeled DNA *in vitro* specifically with H^3-thymidine with a primer DNA and a polymerase system from homogenates of regenerating rat liver.

3.4.2. *Tissue Culture*

Biosynthesis may be achieved with isolated tissue in a culture of short duration. Chemically synthesized 16-H^3-progesterone, having a specific activity of 13.4 c/mmole, was used as a precursor for specifically labeled cortisol, corticosterone, and aldosterone by incubating it *in vitro* with adrenal glands. The specific activity was between 5 and 11 mc/mg.[17]

Similarly, H^3-arachidonic acid, labeled by partial catalytic reduction to a specific activity of 9 µc/mg, was incorporated by vesicular glands of sheep into the hormone prostaglandin with an efficiency of about 30% and more.[23,206]

3.4.3. *Intact Organisms*

In intact organisms, tritium-labeled precursors of simpler structure, including tritiated water, were used for the biosynthesis of complex structures. Microorganisms have long proved particularly suitable in work with deuterium and can serve similarly for labeling with tritium, as long as the radiation damage is kept low. The antibiotic paromomycin (Humatin) was labeled to a specific activity of 1 µc/mg by fermentation of *Streptomyces* in a medium containing tritiated water.[138] This degree of labeling sufficed to allow degradation studies on the molecule in rats. The isolation of the antibiotic from the mold was easier than the purification, which followed the gas-exposure technique of Wilzbach.

Erythromycin was synthesized from tritiated propionate in *Streptomyces*,[86,195] and it was indicated that erythromycin consisted of seven units of propionate.[86]

In *Trichoderma viride*, gliotoxin was labeled by addition to the medium of H^3-phenylalanine and other amino acids labeled with C^{14}.[227] All nine carbon atoms of phenylalanine were found to be incorporated into the gliotoxin structure with tyrosine as an intermediate. In *Torula utilis*, Eidinoff *et al.*[55] synthesized nucleic acid derivatives from tritiated acetate added to the culture medium. The tritium was found in various positions of the purine and pyrimidine rings and expectedly showed different degrees of chemical stability and resistance to isotopic exchange.

Tritiated fatty acids were obtained from soybeans, which were grown in a nutrient solution containing tritiated water.[54] Root cultures of the tobacco plant converted H^3-nicotinic acid to H^3-nicotine, except when the tritium was in position 6.[48]

Tritiated water and a variety of tritiated amino acids were used to label biosynthetically egg protein in chickens.[167] The specific activities obtained varied with the specific activity of the amino acids. Lysozyme, with a specific activity of about 23 mc/mmole still was enzymatically intact. It appeared in these studies that amino acids were preferentially incorporated into egg white over the proteins in the egg yolk or other parts of the body. In the rabbit, antibody to bovine serum albumin was weakly labeled with tritium by administering H^3-valine to the animal. The isolated antibody had a specific activity of 1.5 $\mu c/g$ only.[47] Labeled RNA, DNA, and proteins can obviously be biosynthesized by a variety of whole organisms such as bacteria, suitable plant tissue, and mammalian tissues, which include liver, thymus, ascites tumor cells, or tissue culture cells. In modern molecular biology macromolecules labeled biosynthetically are of growing interest in a wide array of metabolic and genetic studies.

3.4.4. Outlook and Conclusion

Tritium may be less efficient than C^{14} in labeling biosynthetically a large variety of compounds. For example, in photosynthesis $C^{14}O_2$ may label plants essentially quantitatively, whereas tritiated water can only be incorporated to a slight degree because of the necessity of a large excess of water always being present.[131] Also, the tritium radiation constitutes a limiting factor. Still, using simple tritiated precursors, some algae such as Chlorella which are highly radioresistant, may, contrary to higher organisms, also yield higher specific activity compounds. Since certain hormones, alkaloids, and other biological substances cannot be synthesized chemically as yet, biosynthesis is the only mode to date by which a specific label distribution is provided. The combined use of chemical and biosynthetic labeling methods, particularly also the use of pure enzymes or tissue homogenates, gives good prospects for the future.[43]

As in all other techniques, a most important step in obtaining the labeled molecules is the proper extraction and purification from the biological material. This may be a simpler and less laborious procedure than labeling by gas exposure or tritium recoil and, in any event, can usually be accomplished by the same techniques already developed in detail for the isolation of the unlabeled compound. The degree of final radiochemical purity should be carefully assessed before the labeled compound is used in an experiment.

4. Biological Stability of the Label

Following the brief account on the principles of labeling organic molecules with tritium, the question of the biological stability of the label will be considered. In biological investigations with tritium-labeled compounds, it has occasionally been erroneously assumed that the label served as a true tracer of a substrate, providing data for the calculation of the kinetics of metabolic processes. A radiochemically pure and stable compound does not necessarily exhibit a corresponding stability in a biological system; moreover, chemically "not exchangeable" hydrogens, such as in C—H bonds, frequently become labile in a biological reaction, as was illustrated by various examples in the preceding paragraph. In fact, the labilization is the reverse phenomenon of tritiation by biosynthesis.

In order to guard against misinterpretations, it is important to consider, with respect to possible tritium labilization, all alterations in molecular configuration in the course of metabolism and to measure the labeling intensities which may be expected in all respective metabolic products.[189] Of course, often the labilization and metabolic transfer of the tritium label and the recognition of possible isotope effects are the main purpose of a biological experiment.

Methods of assaying "biological stability" may have different meanings for different situations. Most frequently, with normal metabolites, biological stability of the label means that the portion of the molecule bearing the label has not been chemically altered or activated during the biological experiment. In the case of antimetabolites, biological stability of the label may mean that the original molecule is inert and can be recovered unaltered and having the same specific activity. Proof of inertness, however, requires that no radioactivity can be found in fractions of the system except in association with the original compound.

The use of another isotope as reference parallel to tritium helps greatly to distinguish those molecular sites which participate directly in metabolism. The usefulness of tritium as a label for certain investigations may thus be established easily. Likewise, isotope effects are recognized, as was discussed in Section 2 of this chapter. Carbon-14 has been used most frequently as a reference isotope. Also I^{131} or I^{125} was conveniently employed for that purpose; for example, to distinguish the reutilization pathway of DNA-thymidine.[69,70,96]

Attempting to verify data from tritium-labeled compounds with another tracer in parallel control experiments, it must, of course, be kept in mind that certain metabolic functions are subject to periodic variation in single cells, cell groups, and entire organisms, and may change with the time of day, with age, with an altered basal metabolism, fat content, water content, and so forth. It is therefore important to coordinate parallel experiments as closely as possible.

In this section a few examples will be discussed in which information concerning the biological stability of tritium label has become avail-

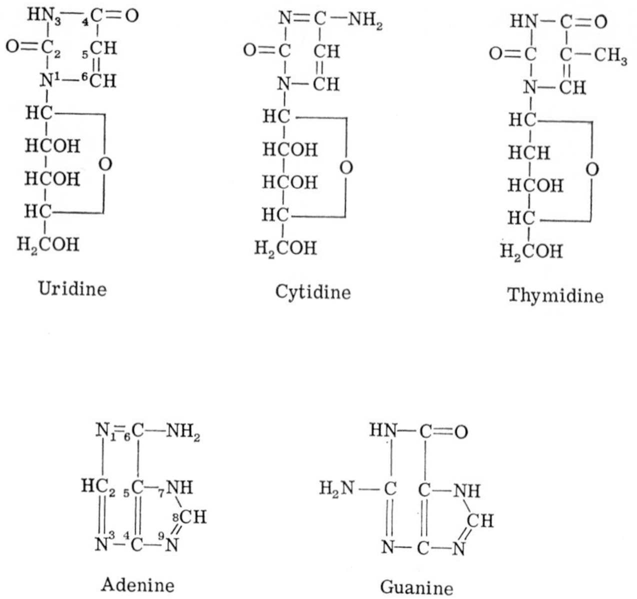

Uridine   Cytidine   Thymidine

Adenine   Guanine

FIG. 2.4. Structural formulas of uridine, cytidine, thymidine, adenine, and guanine.

able, such as in the course of metabolism of nucleic acid and its components, proteins and amino acids, carbohydrates, lipids, and some other biochemical compounds.

4.1. NUCLEIC ACIDS AND THEIR PRECURSORS

Figure 2.4 shows the structures of the five common precursors, the pyrimidine bases, but not the purine bases, linked to ribose or deoxyribose. The precursors are easily incorporated in this form by higher developed cells. In microorganisms the pyrimidine bases are utilized as well. In the purine rings the tritium in position 8 is considered to be stable, both chemically and biologically.[55] In the pyrimidine bases tritium in position 6 only may be considered biologically stable, since during methylation of cytosine or uracil to thymine, tritium in position 5 exchanges. Pyrimidine ribosides may also be labeled in the ribose moiety to study, for example, the reduction of cytidine to deoxycytidine.[198] No loss of tritium occurred during the incorporation of thus labeled cytidine into DNA. Hence, carbonyl or unsaturated intermediates were not involved in this conversion.

In most biological systems the methyl group of thymine does not exchange. In *Neurospora crassa*, for example, thymidine is a precursor for uridine, which in turn may be remethylated to thymidine. Therefore, the tritium in the methyl group of thymine is totally lost in this organism.[74] Also in *Paramecium aurelia* thymidine was found to be readily converted to uridine as a precursor for RNA.[21]

Various labeled nucleic acid precursors are commercially supplied with different label specifications. It is important to be aware of these specifications and also to remember, as it has been reported, that specifications concerning the tritium position may not always be correct. Different shipments of cytidine and uridine were found to have various distributions of tritium between position 5 and 6. Some tritiated cytidine had 10% of the label in position 6, whereas that of another shipment had only 5%. Some of the tritiated uridine had only 2% of the label in position 6.[74] In work with *Drosophila* embryos different results were obtained with various shipments of H³-thymidine; one caused considerable cytoplasmic labeling, whereas another did not do so. Probably various amounts of labeled impurities or different label positions in the molecule, unrecognized in the various samples of H³-thymidine, could be held responsible.[134] Tritiated thymidine (labeled in the methyl group) in the reutilization pathway after DNA breakdown, as studied in rat bone marrow by double-tracer technique, did not exchange the label, which attests to the inertness of the thymine during DNA catabolism and resynthesis.[71]

Specification of label position is also important in preventing misinterpretations of radiochemical data. Thus, the tritium in position 5 in uracil and cytosine may exchange upon acid hydrolysis (in uracil more than in cytosine) whereas that in position 6 does not. If only 2% of the tritium in uridine is bound to position 6 of uracil, acid hydrolysis could result in the labilization of nearly 98% of the total tritium. Biochemical extraction and isolation methods employing hot acid treatments may be expected, therefore, to cause a considerable loss of label which varies for the different bases.[69,203]

There has been no indication thus far that a biological tritium exchange occurs in intact macromolecular nucleotide chains such as DNA and RNA, aside from those instances involving labile hydrogens, such as in interstrand hydrogen bonds. These hydrogens appear to exchange in the native nucleic acids probably by local opening and closing of the molecular strands, as shown for RNA[62] and DNA.[148] Stability of tritium in DNA has been repeatedly demonstrated,[70,71] and it is the prerequisite for using labeled DNA precursors for permanently marking a cell. After RNA-labeling from H³-cytidine in HeLa cells, the tracer was nearly totally retained in the cells and the ratio of H³-uracil/H³-cytosine remained constant for at least 2 days, indicating the lack of measurable tritium exchange in native RNA over this period of time.[68] In rat reticulocytes tritium-labeled RNA continued to appear for several days after a single injection of H^3-cytidine, but reticulocytes themselves did not synthesize RNA.[69] This again implies the stability of the label in the native RNA molecule.

4.2. PROTEINS AND AMINO ACIDS

In amino acids, aliphatic tritium is biologically stable. However, enzymatic reactions involving side groups such as the amino, sulfhydryl, or hydroxyl group may labilize tritium on the corresponding C atom. Tritium in α-position may become labilized when, during incorporation into proteins, deamination and reamination occur as shown for H^3-valine.[46] In the β-position tritium was not exchanged. In the α-position tritium may lose its stability also during reactions with D-amino acid oxidase.[66]

Tritium in aromatic rings of some amino acids, such as tyrosine[125] or Dopa (dioxyphenylalanine),[92] is chemically relatively labile. But double-labeling checks with C^{14} during the conversion of Dopa to catechol amines of the adrenals indicated the biological stability of the tritium on the aromatic ring in this amino acid.[92] In studies on the formation of the matrix of bone, various tritiated amino acids were used and they were found to become stable components of the collagen so that the rate of apposition as well as the degree of amino acid reutilization could be observed.[202] The complete loss of tritium from H^3-hydroxylysine injected into rats indicated that lysine is the chief source of hydroxylysine in the collagen.[181]

Interconversion or catabolism of the various amino acids must finally lead to tritium labilization, the extent of which depends, of course, on the particular molecular position of the label. Hankes and Segel[88] used tritiated DL-kynurenine to demonstrate the metabolic conversion to quinolinic acid and N^7-methylnicotinamide; only 6.86% of the precursor was excreted unchanged over a 24-hour period. The tritium activity of the N^7-methylnicotinamide was the same as the ring activity of the injected kynurenine.

Analogous to the nucleic acids, proteins probably exchange hydrogen (or tritium) in chemically stable positions only upon catabolism. Labile hydrogens are also those in peptide bonds and hydrogen bonds between peptide strands. Their exchange rate varies with secondary factors such as protein configuration and pH changes.[91,109,124] Hydrogen exchange rates in proteins are important for studies on protein structure.

Enzymes and substrates which participate in hydrogen-transfer reactions must have labile hydrogen, of course, at their active site as, for example, H-NAD and H-NADP, that is also used to donate tritium during enzymatic hydrogenation, as mentioned above.

Tritiated oxytocin synthesized with H^3-leucine was, after injection into rats, rapidly excreted in the urine; 30–35% appeared within 2 hours. Two additional metabolites were also recovered.[15]

4.3. CARBOHYDRATES

The rapid turnover of carbohydrates in energy-yielding reactions in a living system limits tritium stability in these molecules. Moreover, the tritium–hydrogen exchange in the course of carbohydrate metabolism helps to identify enzymatic reaction mechanisms. As was pointed out in the previous section glucose donates hydrogen, for example, to glycogen and fatty acids.

Hydrogen from position 1 of glucose and hydrogen from position 2 of lactate were compared as two sources of hydrogen for the synthesis of fatty acids in animals.[120] The lactate hydrogen was more readily utilized and was less readily converted into water than the tritium from positions 1 and 6 of glucose.[174] The respective yields were lower in patients with diabetes. Using glucose labeled intermolecularly with C^{14} and H^3, it was shown that over the generation of H^3-NADP and H^3-NAD the tritium of position 1 in glucose was less readily converted to water than the one in position 6.[77] Tritium in position 6 of glucose was held to become partially labilized probably during the transfer into or out of cells.[52]

Between 75 and 85% of the injected tritium in position 1 of glucose disappeared from the circulation within 3 hours, and 65–80% of the injected dose could be recovered with water.[81] Although approximately 0.5–1% of the administered activity converts to fatty acid, the rest of the dose was unaccounted for, but a major part of it may have contributed to glycogen.

Until its disappearance from the bloodstream tritium in position 1 (and probably also 6) of glucose does not exchange, as exemplified by the double-labeling technique with C^{14} (see Table 2.4).[171] Breakdown

TABLE 2.4

TRITIUM STABILITY (H^3/C^{14} RATIO) IN POSITION 1 OF GLUCOSE IN THE CIRCULATING BLOOD OF OBESE, NONDIABETIC HUMANS[a]

Experiment	Hours after injection		
	1	2	3
1	1.28	1.30	1.02
2	1.08	1.03	1.00
3	1.02	1.06	1.07

[a] Reproduced with permission of Schwartz, Thesis.[171]

and significant resynthesis from lactate and cycling back into circulation may perhaps involve about 10% of the injected glucose over the period of 1–2 hours. The stability of tritium in positions 1 and 6 of glucose verifies the experiment of Peterson and Leblond,[145] who could demonstrate autoradiographically the distinct localization of the label in the Golgi region of intestinal cells within minutes after administration regardless of whether the tritium was in position 1 or 6.

4.4. LIPIDS

What has been said in general for the carbohydrates in metabolism is also applicable to the group of lipids. There are less OH groups, however, in these molecules and, hence, more stable positions for tritium.

In studies with cholesterol, double-labeled molecules were used to verify the biological half-life of the injected compound in animals. With both labels, identical slopes were thus obtained which indicated the stability and true tracer behavior of tritium-labeled cholesterol.[139] Since interconversion and catabolism can render tritium labile, depending upon its position in the molecule, tritium has been used to study such specific enzymatic reactions also in steroids. Figure 2.5 shows the position in various steroids where tritium becomes labile during specific metabolic reactions.[142] In a number of studies on the degradation of cholesterol and the formation of deoxycholate from cholic acid, stereospecifically labeled molecules gave information on the intermediates and their conversions during the reactions, indicating that hydrogen specifically in 6β- and 7α-position was lost.[22,164,165] The tritium stability on hexoestrol during conjugation to glucuronide and sulfate was shown in female sheep.[37] In the urine of normal individuals,[175] H^3-androsterone glucuronoside (randomly labeled) was excreted unchanged, but not H^3-estradiol-3-sulfate.[18] The metabolic conversion of testosterone double labeled with C^{14} and H^3 proved helpful in the diagnosis and management of a variety of endocrine and metabolic diseases in humans.[44] Lecithins were labeled with P^{32}, C^{14}, and H^3 to study the position distribution of saturated and unsaturated fatty acids in lipid cores of biological membranes.[205] Thus, misinterpretations from tracer labilization were prevented.

4.5. OTHER COMPOUNDS

A large number of tritiated compounds other than those discussed above have been studied in metabolic reactions and have been checked for tritium labilization and labeled catabolites. Only a few examples should serve to represent tritiated alkaloids, antibiotics, cytotoxic agents, and hormones.

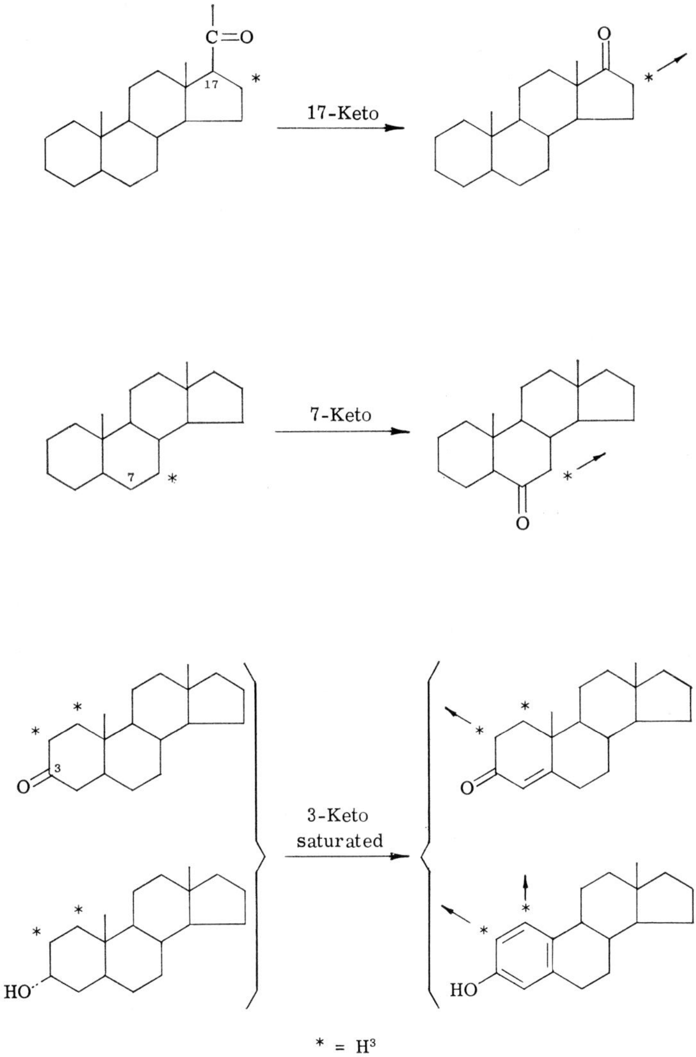

FIG. 2.5. Labilization of hydrogen (tritium) in different positions, during conversions of steroids. Courtesy of Osinski, *Conf. Methods Preparing Storing Marked Molecules*.[142]

Tritium-labeled paromomycin (Humatin), an antibiotic similar in structure to neomycin and kanamycin, did not lose more than 0.05% of the administered radioactivity into the volatile fraction over a period of 20 hours following the injection. Ninety-six per cent of the tritium remained associated with the nonvolatile substances excreted.[138] Erythromycin was not broken down in resistant strains of *Bacillus subtilis*.[195]

Labeled actinomycin was seen to be bound specifically to DNA in rat liver,[49] and its specificity served to identify DNA in yolk platelets in amphibian eggs.[33]

The rapid breakdown of Endoxan, a nitrogen mustard derivative, was studied in normal and diseased tissues of humans suffering from malignancy. By using the molecule labeled specifically in various positions with tritium, differences in the catabolic pathways in neoplastic tissue versus normal tissue could be observed.[154,155]

Tritiated methotrexate was used in man[94] and monkeys, dogs, rats, and mice[93] without evidence of a metabolic alteration. Up to nearly 90% of the dose was excreted in the urine during the first 24 hours in man. Injection into tumor-bearing rats of H^3-L-phenylalanine mustard, tritiated by the Wilzbach technique, was distributed throughout the body, and 20% was excreted within 48 hours. No label was detected in tumor protein or the nucleic acids.[130]

A rather complete analysis of the labeled metabolic products of tritium-labeled epinephrine (in position 7) excreted in the urine of man accounted for about 97% of the tritium dose injected.[110] Only 6.8% of the tritium was bound to unaltered epinephrine.

4.6. CONCLUSION

It is reemphasized, in conclusion, that chemical stability of tritium on a molecule does not necessarily imply a likewise preservation during molecular alterations in the course of enzymatic reactions. It is, hence, necessary to assure oneself of the proper position of tritium in a molecule chosen for tracer work. Alterations of radioactively labeled compounds during storage, due mainly to radiation effects, are discussed in the following paragraph.

5. Radiation Decomposition of Tritium-Labeled Compounds

Radioactively labeled compounds may decompose upon storage. The degree and type of decomposition depend largely on the specific activity of the compound if decomposition due solely to inherent molecular instabilities or chemical interactions with the solvent, the atmosphere, or the storage vessel is minimized or excluded. Decompositions due to radiation occur by various mechanisms. In the case of tritium there is the effect of the emitted β-particle and the transmutation effect of the remaining helium.

During the transmutation of tritium, recoil energy is imparted to the resulting helium nuclide. This energy ranging from near 0 to about 3 ev is obviously too small to cause the breaking of a molecular bond. But chemical changes still may occur as a result of the sudden change of charge with concomitant molecular excitation.[218] In addition, the chemically inert helium leaves a carbon atom positively charged. The ion thus produced may capture a negative charge, perhaps revert to the original molecule, or the ion may dissociate further, aggregate, or undergo other rearrangements similar to those occurring in consequence of the interaction of the β-particle. Thus tritiated methane converts to methyl ions,[187] and tritiated ethane in an analogous manner leads to ethyl ions and numerous other decomposition products,[217] such as C_2H_4, C_2H_3, C_2H, C_2, CH_4, H, He, and H_2; tritiated propane led to 25 different fragments.[218] Some of these ions may be obviously very reactive. In most tritium-labeled compounds transmutation effects are hardly observable during a limited period of storage, since the relative number of molecules affected is very small. For example, if a labeled substance has a specific activity of 1c/ mmole, a total of about 1 out of 600 molecules only will be involved over a period of one year. Transmutation effects have, however, considerable importance when the carrier molecule is incorporated into biological structure; this will be discussed in Chapter 6. The term transmutation effect is synonymous with "internal primary effect."

By far more important are the radiochemical effects from the β-particle on the compound in storage (external primary effect). The ejected β-particle with a mean energy of 5.6–5.7 kev may cause within the labeled or unlabeled molecules, in the neighborhood of less than 6 μ away from the decaying tritium, excitation and ionization with all possible consequences typical of direct radiation effects. The molecule hit by the charged particle absorbs part of the energy and converts it within an extremely short period of time to rotational and vibrational energy. An electron may be knocked off the molecule, another may be absorbed to form a negative ion, or another electron may react with a positive ion to form an excited neutral molecule. Radicals may form. Breaking of a bond that has a relatively low binding energy may occur. The place where the bond breaks in the excited molecule need not be identical with the initial place of impact of the charged particle. Various compounds have different radiosensitivities.

These initial events follow secondary reactions mainly with excited molecules, ions, or radicals of the solvent. The final outcome then may be molecular fragmentation, or rearrangements within the molecule may occur, or several molecules may polymerize. These secondary effects, called also indirect effects, depend on the nature of the molecule and on the milieu in which the molecules are situated—whether it is in a polar or nonpolar solvent perhaps with impurities present, or whether it is in a dry state with or without oxygen, or whether it is spread out on a surface, which itself may also contribute to indirect effects. The temperature also is important.

In order to keep radiation damage as low as possible, the labeled compound must be stored optimally. It is clear that secondary or indirect effects can be prevented by inert solvents or addition of radical traps such as R—SH to a radiochemically reacting solvent. Also, dilution decreases the chance of a radical to find a labeled molecule, and, furthermore, it decreases direct radiation effects by separating labeled molecules beyond the range of the β-particle. The best storage temperature is usually low, although freezing obviously crowds molecules together,[13] increasing both direct and indirect effects unless the temperature is chosen below the point where no liquid phase is present. Then indirect effects should vanish, except, of course, that radicals produced by the radiation may also be "frozen" and produce damage when rewarmed.

Storage of labeled substances in very thin films should reduce radiation effects by letting the radiation interact mainly with the supporting structure. Optimally, the film should at least be thinner than the range of the β-particle. The support then must not be able to transfer radicals back to the compound via moisture or gas. Paper, resins, or clay have been used to adsorb labeled material for storage, at times *in vacuo* instead of in air. Storage in dry form is occasionally indicated when a proper solvent is not available. Thus, enzymes may often be stored better dry than in solution and, for example, DNase I was shown to be protected against X-irradiation by adsorption on powdered cellulose.[75] Finally, a chemically labile compound may be converted to a stable derivative.

5.1. RADIOSENSITIVITY OF MOLECULES

The fraction of radiation absorbed by a compound needs to be known in order to determine the specific sensitivity or radiation damage. This is conveniently expressed in the so-called destruction coefficient or G-value, i.e., the number of irreversibly altered molecules per 100 ev of energy absorbed by the substance. If the specific activity of a tritium-labeled substance is 1 mc/g, the dose rate delivered to this material will be approximately 12.14 rads/hour (see Chapter 1). Assuming this substance to be pure thymidine labeled with tritium, the energy absorbed by 1 mmole corresponds to approximately 3 rads/hour (1 mmole thymidine = 242.24 μg). The self-irradiation dose of tritiated compounds with various specific activities over extended time periods is shown in Table 2.5 as calculated by Tolbert.[201] For thin layers of labeled substance, the fraction of energy absorbed can be calculated, according to Bayly and Weigel,[20] from the density of the substance in milligrams per square centimeter, the mean range of the β-particle, and the thickness of the even layer.

The specific radiation sensitivity, in terms of the destruction coefficient, has been evaluated for various classes of compounds by Tol-

TABLE 2.5

CALCULATED SELF-IRRADIATION OF TRITIATED COMPOUNDS[a]

Specific activity (mc/g)	Extent of self-irradiation[b]		
	1 Day	1 Month	1 Year
1	2.9×10^2	9×10^3	1.1×10^4
10	2.9×10^3	9×10^4	1.1×10^5
100	2.9×10^4	9×10^5	1.1×10^6
1000	2.9×10^5	9×10^6	1.1×10^7
1[c]	2.3×10^3	5.5×10^5	8.3×10^6

[a] Reproduced with permission of Tolbert, Nucleonics.[201]
[b] Data given in rads.
[c] Activity given in mc/mmole (125).

bert.[200,201] Simple aromatic substances, saturated hydrocarbons, halides, alcohols, and aliphatic α-amino acids were all quite stable, whereas unsaturated hydrocarbons were quite unstable. Among the amino acids cystine, methionine, phenylalanine, and histidine are highly radiosensitive.[173] The radiosensitivity of proteins varies with the amino acid composition and steric conditions in solution.[191] For example, lysozyme and α-chymotrypsin were affected quite differently by γ-irradiation (Cs[137]); in the latter the conformation was less readily disrupted than in the former, as determined by enzyme activity and hydrogen-deuterium exchange. Scholes and associates[170] determined the G-value for DNA in a 0.1% solution in the presence of oxygen and they found that 6–7 hydrogen-bond pairs were broken per 100 ev of absorbed energy and 14–15 bond pairs were broken per main scission. It was also indicated in these studies that 20% of the radicals produced reacted with the sugar moiety and 80% with the base moieties of the molecule. Irradiation of deoxyribonucleoprotein alters mainly the protein which exerts a protective effect on the DNA. With increasing irradiation doses (to 7200 rad), the protein progressively detached itself from the DNA and liberated the DNA so that it had a greater capacity for serving as template for RNA synthesis.[213]

For practical purposes, the radiation sensitivity of labeled compounds in various storage conditions, which allow the indirect radiation effects to operate also, is represented by the degree of purity of the compounds found after various durations of storage.

5.2. DECOMPOSITION AND STORAGE OF LABELED COMPOUNDS

Evans and Stanford[65] examined a great number of tritium-labeled compounds under various storage conditions. Table 2.6 gives a sum-

TABLE 2.6

SUMMARY OF DECOMPOSITION RATES OF TRITIATED ORGANIC COMPOUNDS
STORED UNDER VARIOUS CONDITIONS[a]

Compound class	Specific activity (mc/ mmole)	Storage state	Temperature (°C)	Decomposition rate (maximum % per annum)
Acids				
Aliphatic	100	Solid	Room	5
	60,000	Solid	0	100
Aromatic	200	Solid	Room	5
Alkaloids	250	Solid	Room	10
	200	Solid	0, −40	5
	200	Aqueous solution	0, −40	5
	500	Aqueous solution	−40	10
	2,000	Aqueous solution	Room	30
	5,000	Aqueous solution	0	30
Halides, alkyl or aryl	25	Liquid/solid	−40	5
Hydrocarbons, aliphatic or aromatic	200	Gas, liquid, or solid	Room	5
Nucleosides	100	Solid	Room	20
	100	Solid	−40	10
	200	Solid	−40	20
	400	Solid	Room	40
	400	Solid	−40	30
	700	Aqueous solution	−40	5
	4,000	Aqueous solution	0	10
	4,000	Aqueous solution	−40	10
	14,000	Aqueous solution	−40	30
Purines	100	Solid	Room	5
	500	Solid	−40	5
Pyrimidines	100	Solid	Room	5
	1,000	Aqueous solution	0, −40	5
	3,000	Solid	−40	15
	17,000	Solid	−40	30
Steroids	100	Benzene solution	Room	5
	200	Solid	Room	10
	300	Benzene solution	Room	10
	3,000	Solid	Room	15
	3,000	Benzene solution	Room	5
Sugars	500	Solid	0	10
	500	Aqueous solution	0	5
	500	Aqueous solution	−40	5

[a] Reproduced with permission of Evans and Stanford, *Nature*.[65]

mary of the decomposition rates in per cent per year of various classes of compounds, indicating the storage conditions, temperature, state of compound, and specific activity. The authors kept the compounds in a solution having a concentration of 1–5 mc/ml, as solids in crystalline form, or freeze-dried. As can be seen from Table 2.6, most compounds are stored optimally in a suitable solvent below room temperature rather than in the dry state. The table also indicates that in many instances storage at −40°C did not offer any advantage over storage at 0°C. In general, tritiated compounds with specific activities below 500 mc/mmole stored optimally do not appear to decompose at a rate greater than 10% per year. With higher specific activities, the rates of decomposition increased. For example, nucleosides with a specific activity of 14 c/mmole in solution at −40°C decomposed at a rate of 30% per year. Additional data are listed in Table 2.7, according to Evans and Stanford.[65]

5.2.1. *Thymidine*

The decomposition of H^3-thymidine upon storage deserves additional comments. At a storage temperature of 0°C, a decomposition rate of about 1% per month was observed for specific activities of 2.5 c/mmole.[67] The data suggested, however, that at a temperature below 0°C the decomposition rate increased, as can be seen from Tables 2.7 and 2.8.

Thymine and deoxyribose are decomposition products in solution but not in the freeze-dried state, in consequence of a fission of the N-glucosidic linkage. While reporting upon γ-irradiation of thymidine in solution, Ekert[59] noted the isolation of hydroxymethyluracil, glycols (*cis* and *trans*), and dihydrothymine, in addition to thymine and deoxyribose, which confirmed the known formation of hydroperoxides of nucleic acids upon X-irradiation in aqueous systems.[169]

Apelgot *et al.*[10] examined further the decomposition products of tritiated thymidine (specific activity 1.9 c/mmole) after 37 months of storage in aqueous solution of 1 mc/ml, and they found 5.4% of the total thymidine in the form of peroxides (*cis* and *trans*) and 24.4% in the form of glycols (*cis* and *trans*). The structural formulas of these substances are shown in Fig. 2.6. The delivered radiation from the β-particles over the 37 months of storage was calculated to have been 274,000 r.

These studies were extended to thymidine, labeled specifically in position 6 with specific activities up to 9 c/mmole.[11,12] The decomposition in aqueous solution was greater when the tritiated thymidine was stored at −20°C instead of at 0° or −75°C, similar to the data reported by Evans and Stanford.[67] There was a linear relationship between per cent decomposition and accumulated radiation dose to about 300–400 krad,

TABLE 2.7

DECOMPOSITION OF TRITIATED ORGANIC COMPOUNDS STORED UNDER VARIOUS
CONDITIONS[a]

Compound	Specific activity (mc/ mmole)	Age (months)	Storage condition	Temperature (°C)	Radio-chemical purity (%)
Tritiated amino acids					
DL-Alanine-T (G)	1,130	4	Aqueous solution	Room	100
DL-Alanine-T (G)	1,130	12	Solid	0	90
DL-Alanine-T (G)	36	30	Solid	Room	100
L-Arginine-T (G)	27	15	Solid	Room	100
DL-3,4-Dihydroxyphenyl-alanine-T (G)	223	7	Solid	0	100
Glycine-2-T	176	17	Solid	0	100
Glycine-2-T	176	17	Aqueous solution	0	100
Glycine-2-T	176	21	Aqueous solution	0	100
DL-5-Hydroxytrypto-phan-T (G)	927	3	Aqueous solution	0	94
DL-Leucine-T (G)	105	18	Solid	Room	93
DL-Leucine-T (G)	102	7	Solid	Room	100
L-Leucine-T (G)	197	12	Solid	0	96
DL-Leucine-4,5 T	151	3	Aqueous solution	0	100
DL-Leucine-4,5 T	5,400	—	Aqueous solution	0	75
DL-Leucine-4,5 T	576	10	Aqueous solution	−40	90
DL-Methionine-T (G)	28	8	Solid	Room	86
DL-Methionine-T (G)	28	8	Solid	−40	90
DL-Methionine-T (G)	148	11	Solid	0	83
DL-Methionine-T (G)	148	11	Aqueous solution	0	100
DL-Methionine-T (G)	148	13	Solid	−40	97
DL-Methionine-T (G)	145	16	Solid	−40	97
DL-β-Phenylalanine-T (G)	126	25	Solid	Room	97
DL-β-Phenylalanine-T (G)	1,800	7	Aqueous solution	Room	85
DL-β-Phenylalanine-T (G)	1,800	16	Aqueous solution	Room	73
L-Proline-T (G)	141	7	Solid	0	100
DL-Serine-T (G)	138	12	Solid	0	100
DL-Serine-T (G)	138	14	Solid	0	96
DL-Tryptophan-T (G)	658	3	Solid	Room	100
DL-Tryptophan-T (G)	658	9	Solid	Room	97
DL-Tryptophan-T (G)	658	18	Solid	Room	94
DL-Tryptophan-T (G)	658	24	Solid	−40	95
DL-Tyrosine-T (G)	242	23	Solid	Room	100
DL-Tyrosine-T (G)	434	10	Aqueous solution	−40	95
L-Tyrosine-T (G)	163	10	Solid	0	97
DL-Tyrosine-T (G)	69	28	Solid	0	100
Tritiated nucleosides					
Adenosine-T (G)	199	10	Solid	−40	83
Adenosine-T (G)	199	24	Solid	−40	75

TABLE 2.7—*Continued*

Compound	Specific-activity (mc/mmole)	Age (months)	Storage condition	Temperature (°C)	Radiochemical purity (%)
Adenosine-T (G)	680	13	Aqueous solution	−40	97
5-Bromodeoxyuridine-6-T	552	2	Aqueous solution	0	100
Cytidine-T (G)	159	7	Solid	0	100
Deoxyadenosine-T (G)	627	14	Aqueous solution	−40	100
Deoxyuridine-T (G)	385	14	Aqueous solution	−40	85
Guanosine-T (G)	407	4	Solid	Room	87
Guanosine-T (G)	407	4	Solid	−40	90
Thymidine-T (G)	72	9	Solid	Room	83
Thymidine-T (G)	82	17	Solid	−40	98
Thymidine-6-T	2,500	15	Aqueous solution	0	85
Thymidine-6-T	4,400	10	Aqueous solution	Room	100
Thymidine-6-T	4,400	1	Aqueous solution	−40	95
Thymidine-6-T	4,400	5	Aqueous solution	0	85
Thymidine-6-T	4,400	10	Aqueous solution	0	92
Thymidine-6-T	14,100	1.5	Aqueous solution	−40	90
Thymidine-6-T	14,100	3.5	Aqueous solution	Room	100
Uridine-T (G)	1,080	2	Aqueous solution	0	98
Uridine-T (G)	1,080	5	Aqueous solution	0	91
Uridine-T (G)	3,000	2	Aqueous solution	−40	85
Uridine-T (G)	3,000	10	Aqueous solution	−40	75
Tritiated purines and pyrimidines					
Adenine-2,8-T	82	8	Solid	Room	95
Adenine-2,8-T	82	36	Solid	Room	100
Adenine-2,8-T	439	11	Solid	−40	100
Caffeine-T (G)	1,280	9	Solid	0	100
Cytosine-5,6-T	117	20	Solid	Room	100
Pteroylglutamic acid-T (G) (folic acid)	166	18	Solid	Room	95
Orotic acid-5-T	115	4	Solid	Room	96
Orotic acid-5-T	115	4	Solid	Room	96
Uracil-5,6-T	123	8	Solid	Room	99
Uracil-5,6-T	870	13	Aqueous solution	−40	95
Uracil-5,6-T	870	21	Aqueous solution	0	94
Thymine-6-T	125	11	Solid	Room	100
Thymine-6-T	324	10	Solid	Room	83
Thymine-6-T	2,600	5	Solid	−40	96
Thymine-6-T	3,140	18	Solid	−40	80
Thymine-6-T	17,000	5	Solid	−40	86
Tritiated steroids					
Δ⁴-Androstenedione-T (G)	3,400	6	Benzene solution	Room	96
Δ⁴-Androstenedione-T (G)	3,400	20	Benzene solution	Room	90
Δ⁴-Androstenedione-T (G)	3,400	20	Solid	Room	76

TABLE 2.7—*Continued*

Compound	Specific activity (mc/ mmole)	Age (months)	Storage condition	Temperature (°C)	Radiochemical purity (%)
Cholesterol-T (G)	110	13	Benzene solution	Room	88
Cholesterol-T (G)	110	16	Benzene solution	Room	90
Cholesterol-T (G)	314	7	Benzene solution	Room	95
Estradiol-6,7-T 17β-acetate	3,200	4	Solid	0	100
Estrone-T (G)	180	21	Solid	Room	100
Estrone-T (G)	180	8	Benzene solution	Room	98
Progesterone-T (G)	118	9.5	Benzene solution	Room	100
Progesterone-T (G)	118	18	Benzene solution	Room	100
Miscellaneous tritiated compounds					
Acids					
Adipic acid-T (G)	58,000	2.5	Solid	0	14
Benzoic acid-T (G)	30	14	Solid	Room	100
1-Naphthylacetic acid-T (G)	180	9	Solid	Room	100
Stearic acid-9,10-T	98	13	Solid	Room	96
Alkaloids					
Atropine-T (G)	246	28	Solid	Room	85
Nicotine-T (G)	41	13	Liquid	−40	90
Amines					
Aniline-T (G)	40	15	Liquid	Room	87
Esters					
Glyceryl tristearate-9,10-T	397	3	Solid	Room	100
Halides					
Ethyl iodide-2-T	25	34	Liquid	−40	94
Hydrocarbons					
Benzene-1-T	30	24	Liquid	0	95
n-Decane-1,2-T	210	28	Liquid	Room	90
Sugars					
D-Glucose-6-T	468	2	Aqueous solution	0	100
D-Glucose-6-T	468	7	Solid	0	96
D-Glucose-6-T	468	11	Solid	0	100
D-Glucose-6-T	468	15	Aqueous solution	0	96
D-Glucose-6-T	468	7	Aqueous solution	−40	100
Vitamins					
Pyridoxine-T (G) hydrochloride	331	27	Solid	−40	85
Pyridoxine-T (G) hydrochloride	331	17	Solid	−40	80
Vitamin B_{12}-T (G)	2,570	7	Solid	−40	99

[a] Reproduced with permission of Evans and Stanford, *Nature*.[65]

TABLE 2.8

DECOMPOSITION OF THYMIDINE TRITIATED IN THE METHYL GROUP OR THE 6-POSITION OF THE THYMINE RING UNDER VARIOUS STORAGE CONDITIONS[a]

Sample	Specific activity (c/mmole)	Activity in ampule (mc)	Volume of solution (ml)	Weight of thymidine (μg)	Age (months)	Temperature of storage (°C)	Radiochemical purity (%)
Decomposition of thymidine-5-methyl-H³ in aqueous solution
1	1.06	1	1.4	230	2	0	100
2	1.52	1	2	160	3	0	95
3	3.20	2	0.53	150	14	−40	85
4	4.70	2	0.5	100	8	−40	92
Decomposition of 6-H³-thymidine in aqueous solution
1	2.5	2	0.29	200	12	−40	72
2	2.5	2	0.29	200	7	−40	90
3	2.5	2	0.29	200	8	0	90
4	1.14	0.5	0.25	90	10	Room (20)	100
5	14.1	2	0.5	34	1.5	−40	90
6	14.1	2	0.5	34	12	−40	55
7	14.1	2	0.5	34	3.5	Room (20)	100
8	14.1	1	0.5	17	5	Room	97
9	3.6	0.2	0.2	134	10	−40	80
10	1.4	1	0.5	170	10	−40	90
11	12.1	0.5	0.5	10	10	0	65
12	4.8	0.2	0.5	10	10	0	70

[a] Reproduced with permission of Evans and Stanford, *Nature*.[67]

as illustrated in Fig. 2.7. The decomposition could be markedly reduced in the presence of cysteamine, and at −196°C no decomposition at all was reported to take place. A 10% glycerol solution was similarly protective as was cysteamine.[14] The temperature effect on the degree of radiation decomposition of H³-thymidine in solution was further analyzed by Apelgot et al.[13] and could be attributed to crowding of thymidine molecules during freezing. When the solution was frozen rapidly to −75° or −196°C, the crowding effect was less; i.e., the thymidine in solution remained distributed more uniformly and less radiation damage occurred than at −20°C. Parallel studies with C¹⁴-thymidine confirmed this finding in that the crowding effect was minimal owing to the wider range spectrum of the C¹⁴ β-particles. The mechanism of peroxidation of pyrimidines upon irradiation and the role of possible protectors (mainly that of the efficient mercaptoethylamine) and its biological implication for radiolesions of nucleic acids were discussed by Latarjet et al.[112]

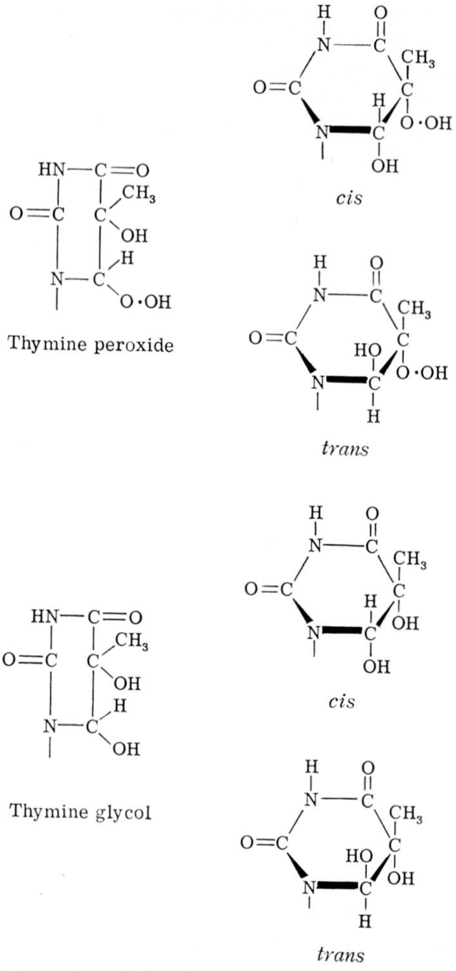

Fig. 2.6. Strctural formulas of thymine peroxide and thymine glycol, both radio-decomposition products of thymine. Courtesy of Apelgot et al., J. Chim. Phys.[10]

In conclusion, H^3-thymidine decomposes least readily in aqueous solution at $-196°C$. The addition of cysteamine appears effective in keeping the decomposition rate similarly low at $0°C$. Since the relatively high concentration of cysteamine may be unwanted in biological experimentation, other protective agents were looked for, and it was found that glycerol added to the solution at $0°C$ exerts a protective effect practically as good as a temperature of $-196°C$.[14] The radiation decomposition rate of H^3-thymidine in solution at $0°C$ without added protector is approximately 1% per month, when the specific activity is 2.5 c/mmole

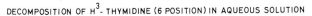

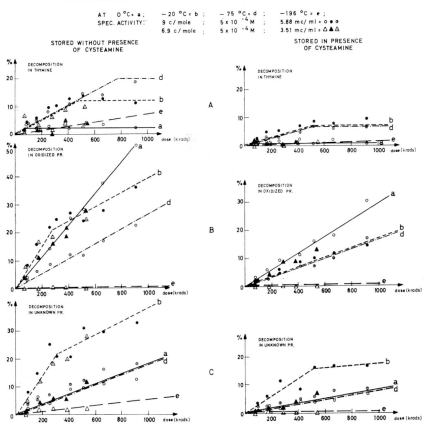

FIG. 2.7. Decomposition rate of H³-thymidine to thymine; thyminic glycols, peroxides, and unknown products, in aqueous solution (5 × 10⁻⁴ M; specific activity, 9 c/mmole(I) and 6.9 c/mmole(II) at 0°, −20°, −75°, and −196°C. Addition of cysteamine (10 molecules cysteamine for 1 molecule thymidine) depresses the rate of decomposition. Courtesy of Apelgot et al., J. Chim. Phys.[11]

and the concentration is about 6 mc/ml. The rate of radiation decomposition is also low at room temperature, but this might be less preferable because of the danger of microbial contamination. Also, other nucleosides are stored properly in aqueous solution at 0°C.

5.2.2. Amino Acids

The decomposition of various tritiated amino acids with specific activities up to about 5 c/mmole is also indicated in Table 2.7. In addition, Hempel[92] examined compounds having very high specific activities of 12 c/mmole and more. He first confirmed the chemical stability of the label on the aliphatic C atoms, also in the α-position, by subjecting the compounds to 5% hydrochloric acid at 100°C for 10 hours. There was no liberation of tritium except for that bound to the aromatic rings unless it was stabilized by a nitro group (NO_2). The tritium was also stable on the phenylanaline ring, but it was unstable in tyrosine in the position *ortho* to the hydroxyl group.[125] Ten different storage conditions were tested with the amino acids in solid form or solution. Radiation effects were barely observed in solutions having a concentration of approximately 3 mc/ml. The best storage condition proved to be a solution of the amino acids in 80% ethanol in 0.1 N HCl or 0.1 N NaOH at −15°C. Storage in physiological saline at −15°C was detrimental to lysine, for example. In general, the amino acids in solution were less rapidly decomposed than those stored in dry form, whether on paper or quartz. Table 2.9 gives a comparison of various storage conditions for a few amino acids selected. The very labile DOPA (dihydroxyphenylalanine) became less sensitive in presence of vitamin C. The chemical instability of various amino acids in alcoholic solution was also examined. Ethyl esters of the amino acids were the most common by-products, and they were not caused by radiation effects. These esters can be easily separated again to yield the original amino acids.

TABLE 2.9

DECOMPOSITION OF TRITIATED AMINO ACIDS WITH HIGH SPECIFIC ACTIVITY 10 C/MMOLE AND MORE UNDER VARIOUS STORAGE CONDITIONS[a]

Storage conditions			Months until H³ of impurities reaches 5% of total H³			
Solvent	H³ concentration (mc/ml)	Temperature (°C)	Phenylalanine	Lysine	DOPA	Amino adipic acid
1. 80% Ethanol 20% Water	3	−15	9	4–5	0.2	2
		+20	6	3–4	0.2	<0.1
2. 80% Ethanol 20% Water 0.1 N HCl	3	−15	9	11	0.5	1
		+20	0.5	1	0.2	0.1
3. 80% Ethanol 20% Water 0.1 N NaOH	3	−15	9	3–4	—	4–5
		+20	4	2–3	—	1
4. Physiologic NaCl	6	−15	9	1	0.2	1

[a] Reproduced with permission of Hempel, *Conf. Methods Preparing Storing Marked Molecules, Euratom, Brussells*, 1963.[92]

TABLE 2.10

DECOMPOSITION OF TRITIATED CORTISOL AND CORTICOSTERONE (ABOUT
2 C/MMOLE; 100 μC/ML) UNDER VARIOUS STORAGE CONDITIONS[a]

Solvent	Temperature (°C)	Per cent of substance chemically pure after 6 months	
		Cortisol	Corticosterone
Dioxane	37	50	52
	0	90	86
	−25	97	96
Benzene	37	54	65
	0	78	89
	−25	80	100
Methanol	37	0	0
	0	87	80
	−25	98	88
Water	37	0	0
	0	85	97
	−25	94	91
Solid	37	0	13
	0	76	76
	−25	71	86

[a] Reproduced with permission of Osinski and Deconinck, *Conf. Methods Preparing Storing Marked Molecules, Euratom, Brussells*, 1963.[141]

5.2.3. *Steroids*

Attention has also been given to the decomposition of, and the storage conditions for, steroids.[141] Breakdown varied more with the solvent than with the specific activity in the range of 4–12 μc/μg at 37°C. Table 2.10 shows the influence of various solvent systems at different temperatures on the stability of H^3-cortisol and H^3-corticosterone. Testosterone, prednisolone, triamcinolone, and tetrahydrocortisol were similarly examined. Testosterone was the more resistant compound. Decomposition at 37°C could be greatly reduced in a solution of benzene or dioxane; and, at a temperature of 0°C or below, the nature of the solvent system was less crucial. The decomposition products owing to β-radiation were not identified. As seen from Tables 2.6 and 2.7, a variety of tritiated steroids can be stored in benzene at room temperature with remarkably little decomposition.

5.2.4. *Compounds with Extremely High Specific Activities*

Drugs similar in structure to Synkavit [methylnaphthaquinolbis (disodium phosphate)] were labeled for therapeutic purposes with tritium up to 83 c/mmole; that means about two to three tritium atoms were exchanged for hydrogen per molecule. These extremely highly labeled compounds could still be stored in aqueous solution for several months and remain radiochemically pure.[7] On the other hand, tritiated adipic acid, with a specific activity of 58 c/mmole and stored as a solid for 2.5 months, showed an 86% decomposition (see Table 2.7).

5.3. Determination of Radiochemical Purity

The principles outlines in this section and the data presented should make the investigator aware of the necessity of checking from time to time the radiochemical purity of labeled precursors in storage. This may be done simply with the help of paper chromatography in various solvent systems. Yet any proper chromatographic procedures may serve this purpose. Evans and Stanford[65] used paper chromatography and have listed the solvent systems they employed for checking the data given in Table 2.7. In the following, these solvent systems are reproduced according to some common compound classes for which they apply.

Nucleosides, Purines, and Pyrimidines

    n-butanol saturated with water
    n-butanol/water/ammonia, 172:18:10
    isopropanol/water/hydrochloric acid, 130:37:33
    ethyl acetate saturated with phosphate buffer at pH 6.0
but orotic acid
    n-butanol/acetic acid/water, 120:30:50
    ethanol/ammonia/water, 80:4:16
    n-butanol/ethanol/3 N ammonia, 120:30:150
and adenosine
    also n-butanol/acetic acid/water, 120:30:50
and thymidine
    also isopropanol/ammonia/water, 100:5:10

Amino acids

    n-butanol/acetic acid/water, 120:30:50
    ethanol/ammonia/water, 80:4:16
    n-butanol/pyridine/water, 1:1:1
and L-arginine
    also phenol/ethanol/ammonia, 150:40:10
and L-leucine and DL-leucine
    also tertiary butanol/water/methyl ethyl ketone/diethylamine, 80:80:40:8
but DL-hydroxytryptophan
    n-butanol/acetic acid/water, 120:30:50
    n-butanol/pyridine/water, 1:1:1
    tertiary butanol/formic acid/water, 140:30:30
    isopropanol/ammonia/water, 100:5:10

Glucose

isopropanol/water, 160:40
ethyl acetate/pyridine/water, 120:50:40
isopropanol/*n*-butanol/water, 140:20:40
n-butanol/pyridine/water, 1:1:1

Alkaloids

n-butanol/acetic acid/water, 120:30:50
n-butanol/1 *N* sodium acetate/ 1 *N* hydrocholoric acid, 7:120:60
n-butanol/5% aqueous citric acid, 180:20
isoamyl alcohol/5% citric acid, 180:20

Cholesterol

90% acetic acid/paraffin, 100:1
ethoxyethanol/*n*-butanol/methanol/water, 35:10:30:25
n-propanol/methanol/water, 15:82:3

Pyridoxine-HCl

n-butanol/acetic acid/water, 120:30:50
ethanol/ammonia/water, 80:4:16
n-butanol/pyridine/water, 1:1:1
n-butanol/dioxane saturated with 2 *N* ammonia, 4:1

Vitamin B₁₂

sec-butanol/water/acetic acid (trace of KCN), 50:18:1

Progesterone

xylene/methanol, 225:75, on paper, impregnated with 5% paraffin in ether
petroleum ether (b.p. 100°–120°C) on paper, impregnated with 10% ethylene glycol.

For all systems listed, the paper was Whatman No. 1, the run was ascending for a period of 12–16 hours, at room temperature; 20–50 μg per spot was analyzed.

6. Conclusion

In this chapter the principle characteristics of tritium-labeled organic compounds were surveyed: the peculiarity of the tritium position in the molecule with regard to isotope effects, the general method of introducing tritium into a hydrogen position in a molecule, the stability of the label in biological systems and enzymatic reactions, and the radiation decomposition of tritiated molecules and storage conditions which should be observed for them. A limited number of references was necessary to substantiate the problems and to help the reader who might wish to do more work on his own. Further information may be obtained by consulting the references in a supplementary list at the end of the book.

REFERENCES

1. R. H. Abeles, W. R. Frisell, and C. G. Mackenzie, A Dual Isotope Effect in the Enzymatic Oxidation of Deuteromethyl Sarcosine, *J. Biol. Chem.*, **235**: 853 (1960).
2. H. J. Ache, W. Herr, and A. Thiemann, Study on the Position of Tritium in Aromatic Molecules Labeled by Different Methods, in *Tritium in the Physical and Biological Sciences, Symp. Intern. At. Energy Agency*, **2**: 21–35 (1961).
3. H. J. Ache, A. Thiemann, and W. Herr, Katalytische Wirkung von Jod bei der H³-Markierung nach Wilzbach, *Angew. Chem.*, **73**: 707 (1961).
4. H. J. Ache and W. Herr, Uber den Mechanismus des β-Zerfall-induzierten Einbaues von Tritium in das Toluol-Molekül, *Z. Naturforsch.*, **17a**: 631–638 (1962).
5. Y. Agishi and J. F. Dingman, Specific Tritiation of Oxytocin by Catalytic Deiodination, *Biochem. Biophys. Res. Commun.*, **18**: 92–97 (1965).
6. R. W. Ahrens, M. C. Sauer, Jr., and J. E. Willard, Hydrogen Labeling of Hydrocarbons Using Ionizing Radiations, *J. Am. Chem. Soc.*, **79**: 3285–3286 (1957).
7. K. J. M. Andrews, F. Bultitude, E. A. Evans, M. Gronow, R. W. Lambert, and D. H. Marrian, A Radioactive Drug 2-methyl-6-tritio-1,4-naphthaquinol-bis-(disodium phosphate) and 2-methyl-5,6,7-tritritio-1,4-naphthaquinol-bis-(disodium phosphate), *J. Chem. Soc.*, pp. 3440–3446 (1962).
8. S. J. Angyal, J. L. Garnett, and R. M. Hoskinson, Occurrence of Configurational Inversion during Tritiation by the Wilzbach Method, *Nature*, **197**: 485–486 (1963).
9. S. J. Angyal and C. Fernandez, Specific Tritium Labeling by the Wilzbach Method, *Nature*, **202**: 176–177 (1964).
10. S. Apelgot, B. Ekert, and A. Bonyat, Autodécomposition de thymidine tritiée en solution aqueuse, *J. Chim. Phys.*, **60**: 505 (1963).
11. S. Apelgot, B. Ekert, G. Tham, and A. Tordjman-Bouyat, Autodecomposition et radiolyse, a basse température, de thymidine tritiée en solution aqueuse, *J. Chim. Phys.*, **62**: 845–852 (1965).
12. S. Apelgot, B. Ekert, and M. Frilley, Etude de l'autodecomposition de la thymidine tritiée conservée en solution aqueuse, *Biochim. Biophys. Acta*, **103**: 503–505 (1965).
13. S. Apelgot, M. Frilley, and A. Defaux, Etude de l'hétérogénéité de solutions congolées de thymidine, *J. Chim. Phys.*, **62**: 838–844 (1965).
14. S. Apelgot, personal communication 1965.
15. J. P. Aroskar, W. Y. Chan, J. E. Stouffer, C. H. Schneider, V. V. S. Murti, and V. du Vigneaud, Renal Excretion and Tissue Distribution of Radioactivity after Administration of Tritium-Labeled Oxytocin to Rats, *Endocrinology*, **74**: 226–232 (1964).
16. J. Avigan, A Method for Incorporating Cholesterol and Other Lipids into Serum Lipoproteins *in Vitro*, *J. Biol. Chem.*, **234**: 787 (1959).
17. P. J. Ayers, The Biosynthesis of (16-H³) Steroids by Isolated Adrenal Cortex Tissue, in *Tritium in the Physical and Biological Sciences, Symp. Intern. At. Energy Agency*, **2**: 132–137 (1961).
18. E. E. Baulieu, R. Emiliozzi, M. C. Lebeau, C. Corpechot, and P. Robel, Studies on the Secretion and the Metabolism of Steroid Conjugates: Synthesis, Analysis and Use of Doubly Labeled Compounds, *Advan. Tracer Methodol.*, in press.
19. W. Bayens, G. Zamorani, and L. Ledoux, Stability of Tritiated Lysozyme and

Ribonuclease, *Conf. Methods Preparing Storing Marked Molecules, Euratom, Brussels, 1963*, p. 1191.

20. R. J. Bayly and H. Weigel, Self-decomposition of Compounds Labeled with Radioactive Isotopes, *Nature*, **188**: 384–387 (1960).

21. J. Berech and W. J. Van Wagtendonk, An Autoradiographic Study of the Macro-nuclear Changes Occurring in *Paramecium aurelia* during Autogamy, *Exptl. Cell Res.*, **26**: 360–372 (1962).

22. S. Bergström, S. Lindstredt, B. Samuelsson, E. J. Corey, and G. A. Gregoriou, The Stereochemistry of 7 α-hydroxylation in the Biosynthesis of Cholic Acid from Cholesterol, *J. Am. Chem. Soc.*, **80**: 2337–2338 (1958).

23. S. Bergström, H. Danielsson, and B. Samuelsson, The Enzymatic Formation of Prostaglandin E₂ from Arachidonic Acid. Prostaglandins and Related Factors 32, *Biochim. Biophys. Acta*, **90**: 207–210 (1964).

24. I. A. Bernstein, W. Bennet, and M. Fields, Tritiation of Multiple Bond-Synthesis of Tritiated Styrene, *J. Am. Chem. Soc.*, **74**: 5763–5764 (1952).

25. J. Bigeleisen, Chemistry of Isotopes, *Science*, **147**: 463–471 (1965).

26. D. Billen, Sedimentation of a DNA-Polymerase Component from Bacterial Extracts, *Biochem. Biophys. Res. Commun.*, **7**: 179 (1962).

27. L. Birkhofer and K. Hempel, Eine neue Lysin Synthese, besonders geeignet zur Darstellung von Tritium-markiertem Lysin, *Chem. Ber.*, **93**: 2282–2284 (1960).

28. L. Birkhofer and K. Hempel, Synthese Tritium markierter Aminosäuren hoher spezifischer Aktivität, *Chem. Ber.*, **96**: 1373–1381 (1963).

29. B. Bloom and D. W. Foster, Hexose Synthesis in Liver and Muscle Studied with Glycerol-3-H³, 1,3-C¹⁴, *J. Biol. Chem.*, **239**: 967–970 (1964).

30. F. J. Bollum and V. R. Potter, Incorporation of Thymidine into Deoxyribo-nucleic Acid by Enzymes from Rat Tissues, *J. Biol. Chem.*, **233**: 478–482 (1958).

31. E. Borenfreund, H. S. Rosenkranz, and A. Bendich, Studies on Deoxyribonucleic Acid after Exposure to Tritium Gas, *J. Mol. Biol.*, **1**: 195–203 (1959).

32. J. Bove, R. O. Martin, L. I. Ingraham, and P. K. Stumpf, Studies of the Mechanism of Action of the Condensing Enzyme, *J. Biol. Chem.*, **234**: 999 (1959).

33. J. Brachet and A. Ficq, Binding Sites of ¹⁴C-Actinomycin in Amphibian Ovocytes and an Autoradiography Technique for the Detection of Cytoplasmic DNA, *Exptl. Cell Res.*, **38**: 153–159 (1965).

34. H. L. Bradlow, D. K. Fukushima, and M. Tsutsui, Specific Incorporation of Tritium into a Steroid Molecule with Recoil Tritium, *Chem. Ind. (London)*, p. 1124 (1959).

35. J. K. Brody and F. S. Tomkins, Optical Methods of Isotope Ratio Determination, *Proc. U.N. Intern. Conf. Peaceful Uses At. Energy, Geneva*, **28**: 639–645 (1958).

36. W. G. Brown and J. L. Garnett, Recoil Tritium Labeling of Deuterated Compounds, *Intern. J. Appl. Radiation Isotopes*, **5**: 114 (1959).

37. J. Burgos-Gonzalez and R. F. Glascock, Identity of the Metabolites of Hexoestrol Accumulated by the Genital Organs of Sheep, *Biochem. J.*, **74**: 33 (1960).

38. J. G. Burr, Isotope Effects Accompanying Use of Tritium and Deuterium in the Study of Organic Radiation Chemistry, in *Tritium in the Physical and Biological Sciences, Symp. Intern. At. Energy Agency*, **1**: 137–152 (1961).

39. N. P. Buu-Hoi and N. D. Xuong, The Influence of Deuterium on the Properties of Some Biologically Active Organic Molecules, *Proc. U.N. Intern. Conf. Peaceful Uses At. Energy, Geneva*, **25**: 223 (1958).

40. N. P. Buu-Hoi, N. D. Xuong, and N. V. Bac, Methods of Desulphurizing and Dehalogenating Hydrogenolysis of Organic Molecules as Applied to the Synthesis of Deuterated and Tritiated Compounds, *Conf. Methods Preparing Storing Marked Molecules, Euratom, Brussels, 1963.* p. 1237.

41. F. Cacace, A. Guarino, and G. Montefinale, Labeling of Organic Compounds by Mercury-Photosensitized Reaction with Tritium Gas, *Nature,* **189:** 54–55 (1961).

42. M. Calvin, J. Hermans, Jr., and H. A. Scheraga, Effect of Deuterium on the Strength of Hydrogen Bonds, *J. Am. Chem. Soc.,* **81:** 5048 (1959).

43. J. R. Catch, Biological Preparation of Labeled Compounds, *Conf. Methods Preparing Storing Marked Molecules, Euratom, Brussels, 1963.* p. 293.

44. W. S. Coppage, Jr. and A. E. Cooner, Testosterone in Human Plasma, *New Engl. J. Med.,* **273:** 902–907 (1965).

45. T. M. Cottrel, *The Strength of Chemical Bonds,* Butterworth, London, 1958.

46. J. C. Crawhill and D. G. Smyth, The Synthesis of Tritio Valine and Its Incorporation into Rat Visceral Proteins, *Biochem. J.,* **69:** 280 (1958).

47. J. C. Crawhill, J. D. Hawkins, and D. G. Smyth, The Biosynthesis of a Tritium Labeled Antibody, *Biochem. J.,* **69:** 286–287 (1958).

48. R. F. Dawson, D. R. Christmann, A. D'Adamo, M. L. Solt, and A. P. Wolf, The Biosynthesis of Nicotine from Isotopically Labeled Nicotinic Acid, *J. Am. Chem. Soc.,* **82:** 2628 (1960).

49. C. W. Dingman and M. B. Sporn, Actinomycin D and Hydrocortisone. Intracellular Binding in Rat Liver, *Science,* **149:** 1251–1254 (1965).

50. C. Donninger and G. Popjak, The Stereochemistry of Hydrogen Transfer Catalysed by Mevaldate Reductase, *Biochem. J.,* **91:** 10 (1964).

51. L. Dorfman and K. E. Wilzbach, Tritium Labeling of Organic Compounds by Means of Electric Discharge, *J. Phys. Chem.,* **63:** 799 (1959).

52. A. Dunn and S. Straps, A Comparison of ^{3}H and ^{14}C-Glucose Metabolism in the Intact Rat, *Nature,* **205:** 705–706 (1965).

53. H. J. Dutton, E. P. Jones, L. H. Mason, and R. F. Nystrom, The Labeling of Fatty Acids by Exposure to H^3 Gas, *Chem. Ind. (London),* 1176 (1958).

54. H. J. Dutton, E. P. Jones, C. R. Scholfield, W. Chorney, and N. J. Scully, Counter Current Distribution of Soy Bean Fatty Acids with Methyl Esters Biosynthetically Labeled with H^3 and C^{14}, *J. Lipid Res.,* **2:** 63–67 (1961).

55. M. L. Eidinoff, H. C. Reilly, J. E. Knoll, and D. H. Marrian, Hydrolysis Products of Nucleic Acids Labeled with Tritium, Preparation by Biosynthesis, *J. Biol. Chem.,* **199:** 511–551 (1952).

56. M. L. Eidinoff, G. C. Perri, J. E. Knoll, B. J. Marano, and J. Arnheim, The Fractionation of Hydrogen Isotopes in Biological Systems, *J. Am. Chem. Soc.,* **75:** 248 (1953).

57. M. L. Eidinoff and J. E. Knoll, The Introduction of Isotopic Hydrogen into Purine Ring Systems by Catalytic Exchange, *J. Am. Chem. Soc.,* **75:** 1992 (1953).

58. M. L. Eidinoff, Tritium in Biochemical Studies, *Advan. Tracer Methodol.,* **1:** 222–226 (1963).

59. B. Ekert, Effect of Gamma-Rays on Thymine in De-aerated Aqueous Solutions, *Nature,* **194:** 278–279 (1962).

60. H. Elias, The Labelling of Organic Compounds in Gas Chromatographic columns, *Conf. Methods Preparing Storing Marked Molecules, Euratom, Brussels, 1963,* p. 1205.

61. M. F. A. El Sayed and R. Wolfgang, Chemical Reaction of Recoil Tritium with Gaseous Alkanes, *J. Am. Chem. Soc.*, **79**: 3286 (1957).
62. S. W. Englander and J. J. Englander, Hydrogen Exchange Studies of s-RNA, *Proc. Natl. Acad. Sci. U. S.*, **53**: 370–378 (1965).
63. S. Englard, Studies on the Mechanism of the Citrate Condensing Enzyme Reaction, *J. Biol. Chem.*, **234**: 1004 (1959).
64. B. F. Erlanger and S. M. Beiser, Antibodies Specific for Ribonucleosides and Ribonucleotides and Their Reaction with DNA, *Proc. Natl. Acad. Sci. U.S.*, **52**: 68–74 (1964).
65. E. A. Evans and F. G. Stanford, Decomposition of H^3 Labeled Organic Compounds, *Nature*, **197**: 551–555 (1963).
66. E. A. Evans, R. H. Green, J. A. Spanner, and W. R. Waterfield, Labilization of the Alpha-Hydrogen Atom of Generally Labeled Tritiated L-alpha-amino Acids in the Presence of Renal D-amino Acid Oxidase, *Nature*, **198**: 1301–1302 (1963).
67. E. A. Evans and F. G. Stanford, Stability of Thymidine Labeled with Tritium or Carbon-14, *Nature*, **199**: 762–765 (1963).
68. L. E. Feinendegen, V. P. Bond, and W. L. Hughes, RNA Mediation in DNA Synthesis in HeLa Cells Studied with Tritium Labeled Cytidine and Thymidine, *Exptl. Cell Res.*, **25**: 627–647 (1961).
69. L. E. Feinendegen, V. P. Bond, E. P. Cronkite, and W. L. Hughes, RNA Turnover in Normal Rat Bone Marrow, *Ann. N.Y. Acad. Sci.*, **113**: 1009–1019 (1964).
70. L. E. Feinendegen, V. P. Bond, E. P. Cronkite, and W. L. Hughes, Reutilization of DNA-thymine, and Conversion of RNA-pyrimidines for DNA-thymine, in Normal Rat Bone Marrow, *Proc. IXth Congr. European Soc. Hematol., Lisbon, 1963*, pp. 1527–1532.
71. L. E. Feinendegen, V. P. Bond, W. L. Hughes, and E. P. Cronkite, unpublished data, 1964.
72. R. E. Felter and L. A. Currie, Tritium Labeling by Means of Uranium Hydride, in *Tritium in the Physical and Biological Sciences, Symp. Intern. At. Energy Agency*, **2**: 61–67 (1961).
73. P. Y. Feng and T. W. Greenlee, Specific Tritium Labeling of Organic Compounds by the Gas Exposure Method, in *Tritium in the Physical and Biological Sciences, Symp. Intern. At. Energy Agency*, **2**: 11 (1961).
74. R. M. Fink and K. Fink, Relative Retention of H^3 and C^{14} Labels of Nucleosides Incorporated into Nucleic Acids of *Neurospora*, *J. Biol. Chem.*, **237**: 2889–2891 (1962).
75. G. Fletcher and S. Okada, Effect of Adsorbing Materials on Radiation Inactivative of DNase I, *Radiation Res.*, **11**: 291–298 (1959).
76. J. R. Florini, Isolation and Characterization of a Tritium Exchange Labeled Synthetic Corticosteroid, *J. Biol. Chem.*, **235**: 367–370 (1960).
77. D. W. Foster and B. Bloom, A Comparative Study of Reduced Di- and Triphosphopyridine Nucleotides in the Intact Cell, *J. Biol. Chem.*, **236**: 2548–2551 (1961).
78. N. A. Ghanem and T. Westermark, Unspecific Tritium Labeling Accelerated by Microwave, Alternating Current and Direct Current Electrical Discharges and by U. V. Radiation, *J. Am. Chem. Soc.*, **82**: 4432–4433 (1960).
79. J. L. Garnett, Catalytic Tritium Labeling Attractive for Organics, *Nucleonics*, **20**: 86–91 (1962).

80. J. L. Garnett, L. E. Henderson, and W. A. Sollich, The Synthesis of Tritium
    Labeled Aromatic Compounds by Platinum Catalyzed Exchange with Tritium
    Oxide, in *Tritium in the Physical and Biological Sciences, Symp. Intern. At.
    Energy Agency*, **2**: 47–59 (1961).
81. A. Ghose, W. W. Shreeve, Y. Shigeta, and S. L. Schwartz, Incorporation of Trit-
    ium into Human Plasma Triglycerides from Glucose-1-H^3 and Lactic Acid-2-H^3,
    Nature, **201**: 722–723 (1964).
82. B. C. Giovanella, C. W. Abell, and C. Heidelberger, The Preparation and Purifi-
    cation of Tritiated Carcinogenic Hydrocarbons, *Cancer Res.*, **22**: 925–930
    (1962).
83. R. F. Glascock and G. S. Pope, The Preparation and Purification of Tritium-
    Labeled Hexoestrol of Very High Specific Activity on the 5 mg Scale. *Biochem.
    J.*, **75**: 328–335 (1960).
84. A. A. Gordus, M. C. Sauer, Jr., and J. E. Willard, Evidence on Mechanisms of
    Halogen and Tritium Recoil Labeling Reactions, *J. Am. Chem. Soc.*, **79**: 3284–
    3285 (1957).
85. R. Goutier, L. Baugnet-Mahieu, and M. Semal, A Comparison of the *in vitro*
    Enzymatic Phosphorylation of Thymidine Labeled with ^{3}H or ^{14}C, *Proc. Intern.
    Congr. Biochem., 4th, New York, 1964*, abstracts.
86. H. Grisebach, H. Achenbach, and W. Hofheinz, Studies in the Biogenesis of Mac-
    rolides by Means of Propionic Acid (1-C^{14}-3-T), in *Tritium in the Physical and
    Biological Sciences, Symp. Intern. At. Energy Agency*, **2**: 137–145 (1961).
87. E. A. Halevi, The Secondary Hydrogen Isotope Effect, *Intern. J. Appl. Radiation
    Isotopes*, **7**: 192 (1960).
88. L. V. Hankes and I. H. Segel, Synthesis and Metabolism of Tritium labeled DL-
    kynurenine, *Proc. Soc. Exptl. Biol. Med.*, **97**: 568–571 (1958).
89. K. R. Hanson and I. A. Rose. The Absolute Stereochemical Course of Citric Acid
    Biosynthesis, *Proc. Natl. Acad. Sci. U.S.*, **50**: 981 (1963).
90. H. Harris, The Relationship Between the Synthesis of Protein and the Synthesis
    of Ribonucleic Acid in the Connective Tissue Cell, *Biochem. J.*, **74**: 276–279
    (1960).
91. D. J. Hartshorne and A. Stracher, Deuterium-Hydrogen Exchange of Muscle
    Proteins, *Biochemistry*, **4**: 1917–1923 (1965).
92. K. Hempel, Preparation and Storage of Tritiated Amino Acids of High Specific
    Activity. *Conf. Methods Preparing Storing Marked Molecules, Euratom, Brus-
    sels, 1963*, p. 1009.
93. E. S. Henderson, R. A. Adamson, C. Denham, and V. T. Oliverio, The Metabolic
    Fate of Tritiated Methotrexate. I. Absorption, Excretion, and Distribution in
    Mice, Rats, Dogs, and Monkeys, *Cancer Res.*, **25**: 1008–1017 (1965).
94. E. S. Henderson, R. H. Adamson, and V. T. Oliverio, The Metabolic Fate of
    Tritiated Methotrexate. II. Absorption and Excretion in Man, *Cancer Res.*, **25**:
    1018–1024 (1965).
95. Cl. v. Holt and L. v. Holt, Markierung von Insulin mit Tritium, *Naturwissen-
    schaften*, **45**: 289 (1958).
96. W. L. Hughes, S. L. Commerford, D. Gitlin, R. C. Krueger, B. Schultze, V. Shah,
    and P. Reilly, Deoxyribonucleic Acid Metabolism *in vivo*: I. Cell Proliferation
    and Death as Measured by Incorporation and Elimination of Iododeoxyuridine,
    Federation Proc., **23**: 640–648 (1964).
97. H. S. Isbell and J. D. Moyer, Tritium-Labeled Compounds. II. General Purpose
    Apparatus, and Procedures for the Preparation, Analysis, and Use of Tritium

Oxide and Tritium Labeled Borohydride, *J. Res. Natl. Bur. Stand.*, **63A**: 177–183 (1959).

98. H. S. Isbell, H. L. Frush, and N. B. Holt, Absence of an Isotope Effect in the Fractional Recrystallization of Alpha-D-glucose-1-t, *Anal. Chem.*, **33**: 225 (1961).

99. H. S. Isbell, H. L. Frush, and L. T. Sniegoski, Utilization of Tritium and C^{14} in Studies of Isotope Effects, in *Tritium in the Physical and Biological Sciences, Symp. Intern. At. Energy Agency*, **2**: 93–100 (1961).

100. H. S. Isbell and L. T. Sniegoski, Tritium Labeled Compounds. IX. Determination of Isotope Effects in Reactions Yielding Water-t from Nonvolatile Reactants. Oxidation of Aldoses-1-t with Iodine, *J. Res. Natl. Bur. Stand.*, **67A**: 569–572 (1963).

101. H. S. Isbell and L. T. Sniegoski, Tritium Labeled Compounds. X. Isotope Effects in the Oxidation of Aldoses-1-t with Bromine, *J. Res. Natl. Bur. Stand.*, **68A**: 145–151 (1964).

102. H. S. Isbell and L. T. Sniegoski, Tritium Labeled Compounds. XI. Mechanism for the Oxidation of Aldehydes and Aldoses-1-t with Sodium Chlorite, *J. Res. Natl. Bur. Stand.*, **68A**: 301–304 (1964).

103. F. L. Jackson, G. W. Kittinger, and F. P. Krause, Efficient Tritium Labeling with an Electric Discharge, *Nucleonics*, **18**: 102 (1960).

104. P. H. Jellinck and D. G. Smyth, Molecular Changes in Exchange Labeling with Tritium, *Nature*, **182**: 46 (1958).

105. D. Jerchel, S. Henke, and K. Thomas, Preparation and Thin Layer Chromatography of 1,2,4,-H³-dexamethason. *Conf. Methods Preparing and Storing Marked Molecules, Euratom, Brussels, 1963*, p. 1115.

106. M. D. Kamen, *Isotopic Tracers in Biology. An Introduction to Tracer Methodology*, 3d ed., Academic Press, New York, 1957.

107. P. Karlson, R. Maurer, and M. Wenzel, Eine Micromethode zur Markierung von Steroiden und von Ecdyson mit Tritium, *Z. Naturforschung.*, **18b**: 218–224 (1963).

108. J. G. Kay, R. P. Malson, and F. S. Rowland, Recoil Tritium Reaction at an Asymmetric Carbon: L (+)-alanine, *J. Am. Chem. Soc.*, **81**: 5050 (1959).

109. I. M. Klotz and B. H. Frank, Deuterium-Hydrogen Exchange in Amide N—H Groups, *J. Am. Chem. Soc.*, **87**: 2721–2728 (1965).

110. E. H. La Brosse, J. Axelrod, I. J. Kopin, and S. S. Kety, The Metabolism of Tritium Labeled Epinephrine in Man, in *Tritium in the Physical and Biological Sciences, Symp. Intern. At. Energy Agency*, **2**: 407–412 (1961).

111. A. Larsson, Enzymatic Synthesis of Deoxyribonucleotides. VII. Studies on the Hydrogen Transfer with Tritiated Water, *Biochemistry*, **4**: 1984–1993 (1965).

112. R. Latarjet, B. Ekert, and P. Demerseman, Peroxidation of Nucleic Acids by Radiation: Biological Implications, *Radiation Res.*, **3** (Suppl.): 247–256 (1963).

113. L. Ledoux, C. Davila, R. Huart, and P. Charles, Preparation, Properties, and Storage of Nucleic Acids. *Conf. Methods Preparing Storing Marked Molecules, Euratom, Brussels, 1963*, p. 1123.

114. J. K. Lee, B. Musgrave, and F. S. Rowland, Intermolecular Isotope Effect in Recoil Tritium Reactions with Hydrogen, *J. Chem. Phys.*, **32**: 1266–1267 (1960).

115. J. Legault-Demare and P. Jolles, Repartition de la radio-activite dans l'hydrolysate d'une proteine marquee au tritium, *Bull. Soc. Chim. Biol.*, **44**: 445–450 (1962).

116. R. M. Lemmon, B. M. Tolbert, W. Strohmeier, and J. M. Whittemore, Ionizing

Energy as an Aid in Exchange Tritium Labeling, *Science*, **129**: 1740–1741 (1959).

117. W. F. Libby and C. A. Barter, Vapor Pressures of the Tritium Liquid Hydrogens in Dependence of Hydrogen Vapor Pressure on Mass of the Molecule, *J. Chem. Phys.*, **10**: 184–186 (1942).

118. M. W. Lindauer and H. A. Smith, A Method of Tritium Labeling, *J. Org. Chem.*, **27**: 2245 (1962).

119. H. C. Brown, *Hydroboration*, W. A. Benjamin, Inc., New York, 1962.

120. J. M. Lowenstein, The Pathway of Hydrogen in Biosynthesis. I. Experiments with Glucose-1-H^3 and Lactate-2-H^3, *J. Biol. Chem.*, **236**: 1213 (1961).

121. M. W. Mc Donough and W. A. Wood, The Mechanism of Pentose Phosphate Isomerization and Epimerization Studied with T_2O and H_2O^{18}, *J. Biol. Chem.*, **236**: 1220–1224 (1961).

122. B. Marrian, B. Marshall, I. S. Mitchell, and J. Simon-Reuss, The Treatment of Cancer by a Radioactive Drug: Tritium-Labeled Tetrasodium 2-methyl-1:4-naphthaquinol Diphosphate, in *Tritium in the Physical and Biological Sciences, Symp. Intern. At. Energy Agency*, **2**: 211 (1961).

123. D. Marsland and A. M. Zimmermann, Structural Stabilization of the Mitotic Apparatus by Heavy Water, in the Cleaving Eggs of *Arabacia punctulata*, *Exptl. Cell Res.*, **38**: 306–313 (1965).

124. R. B. Martin, *Introduction to Biophysical Chemistry*, McGraw-Hill, New York, 1964.

125. R. B. Martin and V. J. Morlino, Exchange of Carbon-Bound Hydrogen Ortho to the Hydroxyl Group in Tyrosine, *Science*, **150**: 493 (1965).

126. R. Mauer, M. Wenzel, and P. Karlson, Tritium-Labeling of Natural Products, *Nature*, **202**: 896–898 (1964).

127. L. Melander, *Isotope Effects on Reaction Rates*, The Ronald Press Company, New York, 1960.

128. T. Meshi and T. Takahashi, Studies on Tritium Labeled Compounds. VI. The Platinum Catalyzed Exposure Technique, *Bull. Chem. Soc. (Japan)*, **35**: 1510 (1962).

129. R. Michel and R. Truchot, Synthesis of Various ^{3}H-labelled Radioisomers of Salicylic Acid, *Conf. Methods Preparing Storing Marked Molecules, Euratom, Brussels, 1963*, p. 1171.

130. A. N. Milner, O. Klatt, S. E. Young, and J. S. Stehlin, Jr., The Biochemical Mechanism of Action of L-Phenylalanine Mustard. I. Distribution of L-Phenylalanine Mustard-H^3 in Tumor Bearing Rats, *Cancer Res.*, **25**: 259–264 (1965).

131. V. Moses and M. Calvin, Photosynthesis Studies with Tritiated Water, *Biochim. Biophys. Acta*, **33**: 297–312 (1959).

132. A. Y. Mottlau, Effect of a Noble Gas on the Labeling of *n*-Hexane by Exposure to Tritium, *J. Phys. Chem.*, **64**: 931–933 (1960).

133. A. Murray and D. L. Williams, *Organic Synthesis with Isotopes*, John Wiley and Sons (Interscience), New York, 1958.

134. V. Nigon and S. Gillot, L'incorporation de la thymidine au cours de l'ovogenese et du developpement embryonnaire chez la drosphile, *Exptl. Cell Res.*, **33**: 29–38 (1964).

135. J. Nunez and J. Pommier, New Method of Iodination and Tritiation of Proteins, *Advan. Tracer Methodol.*, in press.

136. R. F. Nystrom and N. S. Rajan, Radiation Induced Addition of Tritium to Carbon-Carbon Double Bonds, *Chem. Ind.* (London), p. 1165 (1961).

137. R. F. Nystrom, N. G. Nam, and A. J. Russo, Preparation of Marked Olefinic Substances by Tritioboration Procedures, *Conf. Methods Preparing Storing Marked Molecules, Euratom, Brussels, 1963*, p. 47.

138. R. E. Ober, S. A. Fusari, G. L. Coffey, G. W. Gwynn, and A. J. Glazko, Preparation of H^3 Labeled Paromomycin (Humatin) by Fermentation in a Medium Containing HTO, *Nature*, **193**: 1289–1290 (1962).

139. G. T. Okita and J. L. Spratt, Determination of Radiotracer Stability of Tritium Labeled Compounds in Biological Studies, in *Tritium in Physical and Biological Sciences, Symp. Intern. At. Energy Agency*, **2**: 85–91 (1961).

140. P. A. Osinski, The Synthesis of Tritium Labeled Adrenal and Gonadal Hormones, in *Tritium in Physical and Biological Sciences, Symp. Intern. At. Energy Agency*, **2**: 113–118 (1961).

141. P. A. Osinski and J. M. Deconinck, Autoradiolysis of High Specific Activity Tritium Labelled Steroids, *Conf. Methods Preparing Storing Marked Molecules, Euratom, Brussels, 1963*, p. 931.

142. P. A. Osinski, Synthesis of Tritiated Steroids, *Conf. Methods Preparing Storing Marked Molecules, Euratom, Brussels, 1963*, p. 1177.

143. Ph. H. L. Otto, Synthesis of Tritiated Chloramphenicol, Exclusively Labelled in the Aromatic Nucleus, *Conf. Methods Preparing Storing Marked Molecules, Euratom, Brussels, 1963*, p. 799.

144. E. J. Pastore and M. Friedkin, The Enzymatic Synthesis of Thymidilate, II. Transfer of Tritium from Tetrahydrofolate to the Methyl Group of Thymidylate, *J. Biol. Chem.*, **237**: 3802–3810 (1962).

145. M. R. Peterson and C. P. Leblond, Uptake by the Golgi Region of Glucose Labeled with Tritium in the 1 or 6 Position, as an Indication of Synthesis of Complex Carbohydrates, *Exptl. Cell Res.*, **34**: 420–423 (1964).

146. F. Polvani, G. D. Roversi, and R. Silvestrini, Employment of the H^3-progesterone in the Examination of the Synthesis of 17-OH-cortico-steroids by Human Placental Tissue, in *Tritium in the Physical and Biological Sciences, Symp. Intern. At. Energy Agency*, **2**: 121–130 (1961).

147. A. H. Price, Vapor Pressure of Tritiated Water, *Nature*, **181**: 262 (1958).

148. M. P. Printz and P. H. Von Hippel, Hydrogen Exchange Studies of DNA Structure, *Proc. Natl. Acad. Sci. U. S.*, **53**: 363–370 (1965).

149. J. R. Rachele, E. J. Kuchinskas, F. H. Kratzer, and V. du Vigneaud, Hydrogen Isotope Effect in the Oxidation *in vivo* of Methonine Labeled in the Methyl Group, *J. Biol. Chem.*, **215**: 593–601 (1955).

150. J. R. Rachele and H. Aebi, The Utilization *in vivo* of Deuterio-C^{14}-formate, Labeled Intramolecularly, *Arch. Biochem. Biophys.*, **81**: 63 (1959).

151. P. C. Rajan and A. L. Jackson, Labeling of Antibody Against the Erlich Ascites Carcinoma with Tritium (H^3), *J. Lab. Clin. Med.*, **55**: 46–54 (1960).

152. S. V. Rieder and I. A. Rose, The Mechanism of the Triosephosphate Isomerase Reaction, *J. Biol. Chem.*, **234**: 1007 (1959).

153. P. Riesz and K. E. Wilzbach, Labeling of Some C_6 Hydrocarbons by Exposure to Tritium, *J. Phys. Chem.*, **62**: 6 (1958).

154. F. Ritzl, W. Bolt, and H. Nahrmann, Untersuchungen über Abbau, Verteilung und Ausscheidung von Tritium-markiertem Cyclophosphamid im menschlichen Organismus. I. Verteilung und Auscheidung des an verschiedenen Stellen im Molekül markierten Cytostaticums, *Klin. Wochschr.*, **40**: 834–837 (1962).

155. F. Ritzl, W. Bolt, and H. Nahrmann, Untersuchungen über Abbau, Verteilung und Ausscheidung von Tritium—markiertem Cyclophosphamid im menschli-

chen Organismus. II. Umbau des Cytostaticums *in vivo, Klin. Wochschr.,* **40:** 837–842 (1962).

156. A. N. Roberts, Quantitative Cellular Distribution of Tritiated Antigen in Immunized Mice, *Am. J. Pathol.,* **44:** 411–430 (1964).

157. J. Roche, J. Nunez, Cl. Jacquemin, and J. Pommier, Saturation of Double Bonds with Tritium Marked Hydriodic Acid: Preparation of Thyroxine and Its Tritium Marked Analogues, *Conf. Methods Preparing Storing Marked Molecules, Euratom, Brussels, 1963,* p. 813.

158. R. Rognstad, R. C. Kemp, and J. Katz, Enzymic Synthesis of Glucose-4-Tritium and Glucose-3-Tritium, *Arch. Biochem. Biophys.,* **109:** 372–375 (1965).

159. G. A. Ropp, Studies Involving Isotopically Labeled Formic Acid and Its Derivatives. V. Studies on the Decarbonylation of Formic, Benzoyl-formic and Triphenylacetic Acids in Sulfuric Acid, *J. Am. Chem. Soc.,* **82:** 842 (1960).

160. I. A. Rose, The Use of Kinetic Isotope Effects in the Study of Metabolic Control, *J. Biol. Chem.,* **236:** 603 (1961).

161. I. A. Rose, E. L. O'Connell, and Z. B. Rose, Direct Conversion of Citrate to Isocitrate with Aconitase, *Federation Proc.,* **21:** 245 (1962).

162. C. G. Rosen, L. Ehrenberg, and G. Ahnström, Tritium Labelling of Antibodies, *Nature,* **204:** 796–797 (1964).

163. F. S. Rowland and R. Wolfgang, Tritium Recoil Labeling of Organic Compounds, *Nucleonics,* **14:** 58–61 (1956).

164. B. Samuelsson, Bile Acids and Steroids, *J. Biol. Chem.,* **234:** 2852–2856 (1959).

165. B. Samuelsson, Synthesis of Stereospecifically Marked Sterols and Bile Acids and Their Use in Studies of Biosynthetic Mechanisms, *Conf. Methods Preparing Storing Marked Molecules, Euratom, Brussels, 1963,* p. 251.

166. H. L. Schmidt and G. Werner, Wilzbach Markierung von Atropin und Nor(−) cocain, *Ann. Chem.,* **656:** 149 (1962).

167. A. G. Schnek, J. Leonis, L. Ledoux, and M. Rappoport, Biosynthetic Labelling of Hen Egg Proteins, *Conf. Methods Preparing Storing Marked Molecules, Euratom, Brussels, 1963,* p. 1083.

168. R. Schoenheimer, D. Rittenberg, and A. S. Keston, Exchange Reaction of Organic Compounds with D_2SO_4, *J. Am. Chem. Soc.,* **59:** 1765 (1937).

169. G. Scholes, J. J. Weiss, and C. M. Wheeler, Formation of Hydroperoxides from Nucleic Acids by Irradiation with X-rays in Aqueous Systems, *Nature,* **178:** 157 (1956).

170. G. Scholes, J. F. Ward, and J. J. Weiss, Mechanism of the Radiation Induced Degradation of Nucleic Acids, *J. Mol. Biol.,* **2:** 379–391 (1960).

171. S. L. Schwartz, A Metabolic Balance Study in Man. Through the Use of Glucose-1-C^{14}, H^3, and Lactic Acid-2-C^{14}, H^3, Ph.D. Thesis, University of Cincinnati, 1964.

172. T. Sekigouchi and H. Yoshikawa, Enzymatic Synthesis of C^{14} Labeled Thymidine, *J. Biochem. (Japan),* **46:** 1505 (1959).

173. F. Shimazu and A. L. Tappel, Comparative Radiolability of Amino Acids of Proteins and Free Amino Acids, *Radiation Res.,* **23:** 203–209 (1964).

174. W. W. Shreeve, R. C. De Meutter, Y. Shigeta, and A. Ghose, Formation of $C^{14}O_2$ and H^3—OH from Labeled Lactate, Pyruvate, and Glucose in Diabetic and Obese Patients, *Diabetes,* **12:** 360 (1963).

175. P. K. Siiteri and S. Lieberman, *In vivo* Studies with Radioactive Steroid Conjugates. I. The Fate of Randomly Tritiated Androsterone Glucuronoside in Humans, *Biochemistry,* **2:** 1171–1177 (1963).

176. H. Simon and D. Palm, Untersuchungen über Isotopen Effekte bei der Phenylhydrazon Bildung verschiedener an der Carbonyl Gruppe C^{14} bzw.T-markierter Aldehyde, *Chem. Ber.*, **93**: 1289 (1960).

177. H. Simon and G. Heubach, Analyse und Synthese von H^3 markietem Formaldehyd, *Z. Naturforsch.*, **18b**: 159 (1963).

178. H. Simon and G. Heubach, Isotopen Effect bei der Distillation wässriger Lösungen von Tritium-markiertem Formaldehyd, *Z. Naturforsch.*, **18b**: 160 (1963).

179. H. Simon, G. Müllhofer, and H. D. Dorrer, The Tritium Marking of Sugars and Certain Carboxylic Acids with Enzyme Reactions and/or Wilzbach Marking. *Conf. Methods Preparing Storing Marked Molecules, Euratom, Brussels, 1963*, p. 997.

180. J. D. Simpson and J. R. Greening, Preparation of Tritiated Water Samples by Distillation, *Nature*, **186**: 467–468 (1960).

181. F. M. Sinex, D. D. Van Slyke, and D. R. Christman, The Source and State of the Hydroxylysine of Collagen. II. Failure of Free Hydroxylysine to Serve as a Source of the Hydroxylysine or Lysine of Collagen, *J. Biol. Chem.*, **234**: 918–921 (1959).

182. F. M. Singer, J. P. Januszka, A. Taft, E. Yiacas, L. J. Lerner, and A. Borman, Radioactive Distribution of Tritium Labeled Acetophenone Derivative of 16α, 17α-Dihydroxyprogesterone, *Proc. Soc. Exptl. Biol. Med.*, **118**: 1051–1054 (1965).

183. W. F. Siri and J. Evers, Tritium Exchange in Biological Systems, in *Tritium in the Physical and Biological Sciences, Symp. Intern. At. Energy Agency*, **2**: 71–84 (1961).

184. D. B. Smith and D. S. Rawson, The Reconcentration of Tritium by Distillation, in *Tritium in the Physical and Biological Sciences, Symp. Intern. At. Energy Agency*, **1**: 105–120 (1961).

185. H. A. Smith and M. W. Lindauer, Tritium Labelling by Catalytic Exchange. *Conf. Methods Preparing Storing Marked Molecules, Euratom, Brussels, 1963*, p. 171.

186. N. H. Smith, K. E. Wilzbach, and W. G. Brown, The Synthesis of Tritium Labeled Methyliodide and Acriflavine, *J. Am. Chem. Soc.*, **77**: 1033–1035 (1955).

187. A. H. Snell and F. Pleasonton, The Atomic and Molecular Consequences of Radioactive Decay, *J. Phys. Chem.*, **62**: 1377–1382 (1958).

188. R. S. Speirs, Distribution of Tritiated Tetanus Toxin Following an Intraperitonal Injection in Immunized and Non-immunized Mice, in *Tritium in the Physical and Biological Sciences, Symp. Intern. At. Energy Agency*, **2**: 419–528 (1961).

189. J. L. Spratt and G. T. Okita, The Use of a "Self-radiation" Labeled Tritium Compound in Biological Experimentation, *Proc. Intern. Conf. Peaceful Uses At. Energy, U.N., Geneva*, **25**: 186–189 (1958).

190. D. Steinberg, M. Vaughan, C. B. Anfinsen, and J. D. Gorry, Preparation of Tritiated Proteins by the Wilzbach Method, *Science*, **126**: 448 (1957).

191. C. O. Stevens, L. E. Henderson, and B. M. Tolbert, Radiation Chemistry of Proteins. II. Enzymic Activity and Deuterium Exchange Properties of Lysozyme and α-Chymotrypsin, *Arch. Biochem. Biophys.*, **107**: 367–373 (1964).

192. G. Stöcklin, F. Schmidt-Bleek, and W. Herr, Spezifische Tritium Markierung über einen heterogenen Austausch auf gas-chromatographischen Säulen, *Angew. Chem.*, **73**: 220 (1961).

193. W. Stoffel, Synthesis of ^{14}C- and ^{3}H-Labelled Polyunsaturated Fatty Acids. *Conf. Methods Preparing Storing Marked Molecules, Euratom, Brussels, 1963*, p. 843.

194. C. G. Swain, E. C. Stievers, J. F. Reuwer, Jr., and L. J. Schaad, Use of Hydrogen

Isotope Effects to Identify the Attacking Nucleophile in the Enolization of Ketones Catalized by Acetic Acid, *J. Am. Chem. Soc.*, **80**: 5885 (1958).

195. S. B. Taubman, F. E. Young, and J. W. Corcoran, Antibiotic Glycosides. IV. Studies on the Mechanism of Erythromycin Resistance in *Bacillus subtilis*, *Proc. Natl. Acad. Sci. U.S.*, **50**: 955 (1963).

196. E. W. Taylor, The Mechanism of Colchicine Inhibition of Mitosis. I. Kinetics of Inhibition and the Binding of H^3-Colchicine, *J. Cell Biol.*, **25**: 145–160 (1965).

197. J. H. Taylor, P. S. Woods, and W. L. Hughes, The Organization and Duplication of Chromosomes as Revealed by Autoradiographic Studies Using Tritium Labeled Thymidine, *Proc. Natl. Acad. Sci. U.S.*, **43**: 122–128 (1957).

198. R. Y. Thomson, G. T. Scotto, and G. B. Brown, On the Conversion of Cytidine to Deoxycytidine in the Rat, *J. Biol. Chem.*, **237**: 3510–3512 (1962).

199. M. B. Thorn, Studies on the Enzymic Oxidation of Succinic Acid, Containing Deuterium in the Methylene Groups, *Biochem. J.*, **49**: 602–609 (1951).

200. B. M. Tolbert and R. M. Lemmon, Radiation Decomposition of Pure Organic Compounds, *Radiation Res.*, **3**: 52–67 (1955).

201. B. M. Tolbert, Self-destruction in Radioactive Compounds, *Nucleonics*, **18**: 74 (1960).

202. E. A. Tonna, Protein Synthesis in Cells of the Skeletal System in *The use of Radioautography in Investigating Protein Synthesis, Symp. Intern. Soc. Cell Biol.*, Montreal, Canada, September, 1964.

203. L. Träger, A. Kornhauser and A. Wacker, The Tritium Isotope Effect in Pyrimidines, *Conf. Methods Preparing Storing Marked Molecules, Euratom, Brussels, 1963*, p. 1217.

204. L. Träger and A. Wacker, Zusammenhang zwischen Molekülstruktur und Tritium Einbau bei der Wilzbach-Markierung, *Advan. Tracer Methodol.*, in press.

205. H. Van Den Bosch and L. L. M. Van Deenen, The Synthesis of P^{32}, C^{14}, H^3 Labeled Lecithins and their Use in the Studies of Lipid Metabolism, *Advan. Tracer Methodology*, in press.

206. D. A. Van Dorp, R. K. Berthuis, D. H. Nugteren, and H. Vonkeman, The Biosynthesis of Prostaglandins, *Biochim. Biophys. Acta*, **90**: 204–207 (1964).

207. W. G. Verly, J. R. Rachele, V. du Vigneaud, M. L. Eidinoff, and J. E. Knoll, A Test of Tritium as a Labeling Device in a Biological Study, *J. Am. Chem. Soc.*, **74**: 5941–5943 (1952).

208. W. G. Verly, Contribution a l'etude du metabolisme du groupe methyle labile, *Arch. Intern. Physiol. Biochim.*, **64**: 309–416 (1956).

209. W. G. Verly and G. Hunebelle, Preparation of H^3-Thymidine, *Bull. Soc. Chim. Belges*, **66**: 640 (1957).

210. W. G. Verly, Tritium, Dosage, Preparation des molecules marquées et applications biologiques, *Intern. At. Energy Agency, Tech. Rept. Ser.* **2** (1960).

211. W. G. Verly, A. Dewandre, and J. and M. Moutschen-Dahmen, Study of Genetic Targets with Labeled Mutagens. The Action of Myleran on the Resistance to Streptomycin of *Chlamydomonas eugametos*, *J. Mol. Biol.*, **6**: 175–181 (1963).

212. W. G. Verly, P. A. Flamee, and Ch. J. Fallais, The Synthesis of Tritium Labelled *dl*-carnithine and Croton Betaine. *Conf. Methods Preparing Storing Marked Molecules, Euratom, Brussels, 1963*, p. 1043.

213. J. J. Weiss and C. M. Wheeler, Effect of γ-Radiation on Deoxyribonucleoprotein Acting as a Primer in RNA Synthesis, *Nature*, **203**: 291–292 (1964).

214. M. Wenzel, H. Wollenberg, and P. E. Schulze, Specific Activity of Charcoal Adsorbed Compounds after H^3-Labeling by the Wilzbach Procedure, in *Tritium*

in the Physical and Biological Sciences, Symp. Intern. At. Energy Agency, 2: 37–45 (1961).

215. 215. M. Wenzel and T. Günther, Enzymatic Conversions in Tritium Water. I. Enzymatic Synthesis of Specifically Tritiated L-lactic Acid from THO, Conf. Methods Preparing Storing Marked Molecules, Euratom, Brussels, 1963, p. 971.

216. R. E. Weston, Jr., The Magnitude of Electronic Isotope Effects, Tetrahydron, 6: 31–35 (1959).

217. S. Wexler and D. C. Hess, Dissociation of C_2H_5 T and 1,2-C_2H_4 $BrBr^{82}$ by β-Decay, J. Phys. Chem., 62: 1382–1389 (1958).

218. S. Wexler, Dissociation of Molecules by Nuclear Decay of Constituent Atoms, Symp. Intern. At. Energy Agency, Prague, 1960, pp. 115–145.

219. I. Weygand, H. Simon, K. D. Keil, H. S. Isbell, and L. T. Sniegoski, Isotope Effect in the Recrystallization of D-mannose-1-t phenyl Hydrazone, Anal. Chem., 34: 1753–1755 (1962).

220. A. F. Whereat, Incorporation of Tritium from Succinate-2,3-H^3 into Long Chain Fatty Acids by Aortic Mitochondria, Proc. Soc. Exptl. Biol. Med., 118: 888–892 (1965).

221. M. L. Whisman and B. H. Eccleston, Gas-exposure Labeling of Organics with Tritium, Nucleonics, 20: 98–101 (1962).

222. K. B. Wiberg, The Deuterium Isotope Effect, Chem. Rev., 55: 713–743 (1955).

223. D. L. Williams, Synthesis of Carbon^{14} Labeled Deoxyribonucleosides, Can. J. Chem., 40: 1742 (1962).

224. K. E. Wilzbach, Tritium Labeling by Exposure of Organic Compounds to Tritium Gas, J. Am. Chem. Soc., 79: 1013 (1957).

225. K. E. Wilzbach and P. Riesz, Isotope Effects in Gas-Liquid Chromatography, Science, 126: 748–749 (1957).

226. K. E. Wilzbach, Gas Exposure Method for Tritium Labeling, in Tritium in the Physical and Biological Sciences, Symp. Intern. At. Energy Agency, 2: 3 (1961).

227. J. A. Winstead and R. J. Suhadolnik, Biosynthesis of Gliotoxin. II. Further Studies on the Incorporation of Carbon-14 and Tritium Labeled Precursors, J. Am. Chem. Soc., 82: 1644–1647 (1960).

228. R. Wolfgang, T. Pratt, and F. S. Rowland, Production of Labeled Organic Material with Accelerated Tritium, J. Am. Chem. Soc., 78: 5132 (1956).

229. K. Yang and P. L. Gant, Reactions Initiated by β-decay of Tritium. IV. Decay and β-labeling, J. Phys. Chem., 66: 1619–1622 (1962).

230. P. M. Yavorsky and E. Gorin, New Reagent for Labeling Organic Compounds with Tritium, J. Am. Chem. Soc., 84: 1071 (1962).

CHAPTER 3

The Counting of Tritium

1. Introduction

The increasing availability of tritium-labeled compounds and the recognition of their usefulness in many fields of science led to the modification and adaptation of detection devices suitable for the low-energy β-radiation of tritium. Since the range of the tritium β-particles in matter does not surpass 0.6 mg/cm²—in air this is about 6 mm and it is approximately 1 μ in aluminum—even a thin window, for example, of a Geiger-Müller counter shields practically completely against the radiation from tritium. The window counter, the easiest and cheapest instrument for detecting and counting radioactivity, is thus not useful for tritium. For this reason, conventional monitoring devices which are carried by the personnel in the laboratory do not detect tritium, and considerable contamination may occur without being noticed, except by the aid of special equipment. To be detected, tritium must be in closest contact with the detection device.

1.1. SURVEY OF DETECTION DEVICES

Radioactivity is measured by its interaction with matter. The resulting alterations in atomic and molecular structure lead to secondary chemical consequences governed by the physicochemical state of the interacting matter. It is the amplification of the initial event by these secondary effects which permits radiation detection.

Interaction of radiation with molecules in living organisms may trigger such secondary consequences in metabolic functions that morphological and physiological changes (i.e., "radiation damage") become obvious, such as mutations, chromosomal breaks, disturbances of cellular proliferation, atrophy of tissue, pyknotic nuclei, bizarre or giant cells, or death. Each of these changes may serve as parameters of dosimetry in the living system. Tritium with its low-enery β-radiation can affect directly only those biological structures and systems of which it has itself become an integral part, i.e., into which it has been incorporated.

Hence, the degree of biological toxicity of tritium depends greatly on the metabolic pathway of the molecule to which it is bound. Some molecules carry tritium to very sensitive structures, such as tritiated thymidine to DNA. Other tritium-labeled molecules may randomly bypass particularly sensitive structures, as tritiated water does for the most part. The question of tritium toxicity, the tolerable doses in living systems, and the related health-physics problems will be discussed in Chapter 6.

Specific chemical radiation decomposition products, discussed briefly in the preceding chapter, vary with the state and radiosensitivity of the irradiated molecules. The amount of the characteristic by-products reflects the radiation dose absorbed by the molecules at times rather accurately. Thus, ferrous sulfate is a popular compound in chemical dosimeters. The iron oxide produced by radiation can be measured spectrophotometrically. Chemical dosimeters are reasonably accurate with relatively high-energy radiation, but they are inadequate for use with low-energy radiation, such as that from tritium.

The simpler the molecule, the narrower is the spectrum of possible alterations induced by radiation. If the detector molecules are a gas or in the vapor state, the production of ions is easily measured in an electrical field. Thus, if tritium is brought into close contact or is mixed with a proper gas, the short-range β-particles have a good chance to produce ions and free electrons which reduce the charge applied to the electrical field. Gas-counting devices are most efficient for measuring radiation.

In liquids and solids, ions produced by radiation are difficult to detect, but the accompanying process of activation absorbs energy by raising electrons in molecules above their ground state. Some substances then return to the ground state by emitting photons of characteristic energy. Thus, a variety of crystals and conjugated hydrocarbons with a high degree of molecular symmetry emit energetic photons upon excitation. The photon yield per absorbed energy is comparatively small, but it is registered by photomultiplier tubes and appropriate electronic equipment. The method of counting tritium preferably in solution in close contact with scintillating molecules (scintillation counting) is now widely employed.

Finally, silver halide crystals in photographic emulsions should be mentioned as the most popular detection device of radiation. Silver halide crystals upon exposure to electromagnetic or particle radiation can store energy in metallic silver which, when subsequently exposed to proper reducing agents, initiates chain reactions resulting in the reduction to metallic silver in the whole crystal. Black silver grains in a photographic emulsion after development thus give testimony of the interaction of radiation with an intact crystal. The application of photographic emulsions to detect tritium in biological structures by the autoradiographic technique has been most rewarding, and autoradiography will be treated in Chapter 4.

1.2. THE PROPER CHOICE

In making a choice among the various tools of radiation detection one needs to consider efficiency, accuracy, and expense of available equipment applicable to the form in which tritium is to be measured. Tritium may be bound to a solid substance, a liquid or a gas, and it may be worth the effort to convert the labeled material into a readily countable form. One method is often so much superior that the choice is obvious. For example, a large number of samples which can be readily and simply introduced into a liquid scintillating system is assayed best by liquid scintillation counting. However, the equipment is expensive. The absolute counting efficiency is highest in gas-counting systems which cost relatively little, but sample preparation is more tedious. Since often a larger amount of substance can be measured per sample by liquid scintillation counting than by gas counting, the overall efficiency of the latter may be lower than that of the first. Special adaptations for counting devices to be used in connection with chromatography have been developed, such as scanners for paper chromatograms or thin-layer chromatograms or counters for liquid or gaseous effluents for chromatographic columns. Whatever the choice, in all counting of tritium it is necessary to assure the closest contact of the tritium with the detector.

Supplementary to textbooks[51,77,109,116,138,171] and several reviews, the various counting devices, their principle mode of operation, and application to work with tritium will be discussed in this chapter. Since scintillation counting has become such a potent tool for biological and medical investigators, it is presented in more detail in the second part of the chapter. Emphasis will be placed on the main features of handling samples for counting and on possible sources of error and misinterpretation.

2. Measurement by Gas Ionization

2.1. THE PRINCIPLE OF GAS COUNTING

The group of gas counting devices includes the ionization chamber, the proportional counter, and the Geiger-Müller counter, all measuring ions produced in gases by radiation (see Fig. 3.1). The charges generated are detected in an electrical field of certain voltage. Each gas will require appropriate combinations of pressure and voltage for optimal results. Figure

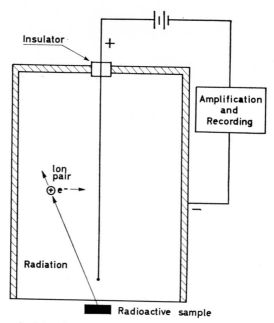

FIG. 3.1. The principle of a conventional gas-counting device. Courtesy of Overman and Clarke, *Radioisotope Techniques.*[109]

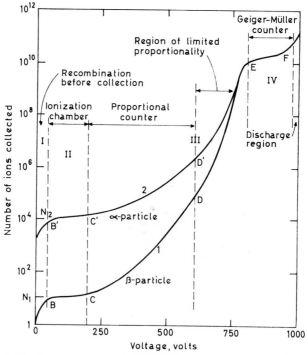

FIG. 3.2. Ionization response in gas-counting devices depending on the voltage of the electrical field and on the energy of the incident particle (for example, α- and β-particle). Courtesy of Overman and Clarke, *Radioisotope Techniques.*[109]

3.2 shows the principal responses in terms of "counts per minute" in relation to the applied voltage and will be discussed subsequently.

2.1.1. *Theoretical Considerations*

Nearly all types of gases can be used with low voltages in the ionization chamber. The gas is situated between the plates (or equivalent of plates) of a condenser carrying an electrical charge of a few hundred volts. Incident radiation produces in the gas one or more ions and free electrons which move in the electrical field to discharge the condenser partially. This change in the charge can be recorded, for example, by a sensitive electrometer.

In proportional counters the voltage is increased. The primary ions become accelerated in the electrical field, and by collision with other atoms or molecules cause secondary ions and free electrons. Thus, a burst of ions and free electrons is generated as an amplified pulse of the initial event in a part of the gas volume. The reaction depends on the gas composition, and a noble gas with a high ionization potential such as argon (27.8 ev) is often added in these higher voltage regions. The size of the burst of ions and free electrons depends upon the energy of the incident particle (i.e., the number of primary ions) and the applied voltage. Photons are also produced by excited gas atoms and recombination of electrons with positive ions. The photons are, however, too weak to cause more ionizations. The ions move relatively slowly to the cathode, and the electrons move relatively quickly to the anode. The current thus produced is measurable through electronic amplification, and it is registered on a recorder. With resumption of a neutral state, the gas is ready for another event. The time required for the gas and the instrument to become responsive again to another incident radiation is called dead time. The shortest interval between two responses of the instrument is approximately 10^{-6} seconds for the high voltage in the range where there is proportionality between applied voltage and burst of ionization for a given energy and charge of radiation. The response of the instrument reaches a plateau at an optimal region over several hundred volts (see Fig. 3.2). The plateau varies also with the nature and the pressure of the filling gas.

The dead time is longer, about 10^{-4} seconds, in Geiger-Müller counters where the voltage is further increased. Then, the ions become more accelerated and the photons, generated during the event of the interaction, have a higher energy. As a result, ionization spreads through the entire gas and leads to a prolonged discharge. Actually, the perpetual excitation and ionization in the noble gas used at this highest voltage would last as long as the electrical field exists and as long as there are gas molecules to become ionized. But one does not need to interrupt the applied voltage. Simple addition to the noble gas of another gas of higher molecular weight and with a lower ionization potential (methane, ether, ethylamine, or an alcohol) absorbs a great part of the energy, mainly the energetic photons, and thus quenches the burst of discharge. The quenching gas itself becomes ionized and exchanges charge with the cathode of the instrument by capturing electrons. This process is accompanied by partial dissociation of the molecules, and in case of long-term measurements it is therefore necessary to renew the quenching gas from time to time. The composition, pressure, and temperature of the gas are particularly important in this highest voltage region of the instrument for reproducible performance. The large burst of ionizations each time one or more gas atoms or molecules become ionized is no longer dependent on the number of primary ions, i.e., on the energy and charge of the incident radiation. At these highest voltages the discharge response in the gas becomes nearly an "all or none effect."

2.1.2. Instrument Design

The gas is usually kept in a cylindrical or bell-shaped container of metal or glass lined with metal. The wall of the container is placed on the circuit as a cathode. Insulated from the wall of proportional or Geiger-Müller counters, usually a fine wire of tungsten, less than 0.1 mm in diameter, is held in place by springs inside the metal envelope. The wire is connected directly to the high voltage as the anode from which impulses are recorded over an amplifier system, as schematically indicated in Figs. 3.3 and 3.4. In ionization chambers the charge-collecting device usually consists of a metal rod or small plate. The various devices may be designed to suit any experimental requirement and can easily be constructed for assaying gas flowing through the equipment. Flow chambers and flow counters will be discussed further below.

The volumes of such devices may range from a few cubic centimeters to several liters. The various types of instruments, particularly ionization chambers and proportional counters, can be made to operate at high temperatures of several hundred degrees Centigrade. The ionization chambers are the most versatile gas-counting devices, but they are slower in response and measure the radiation as a rate of charge or in impulses with a resistance leak circuit. Proportional counters and Geiger-Müller counters have a high sensitivity, a relatively low background, and can be operated with high-speed scalers. The details of such instruments and the electronic equipment necessary to operate them are contained in the appropriate books elsewhere[116,138] and the manuals of commercial manufacturers.

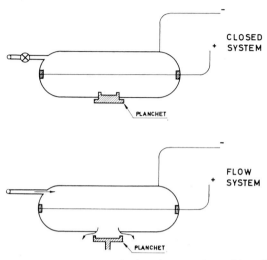

Fig. 3.3. The principal gas-counting devices for assaying tritium from solids in a closed system and a flow system.

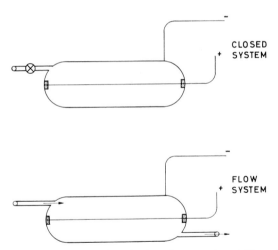

Fig. 3.4. The principal gas-counting devices for assaying tritium from gases or vapors in a closed system and a flow system.

Higher energy radiation penetrates easily through the wall of a counter or through a specially designed window of certain density to interact with the enclosed gas. Since tritium β-particles penetrate maximally 0.6 mg/cm² only (equivalent to approximately 1 μ of aluminum foil), ordinary instruments with a window or those that are dipped into a liquid containing isotopes cannot be used. For tritium, the counters must be constructed to allow the direct contact with the labeled substance, be it a solid, a liquid, or a gas. For the various forms of labeled material specific instrument adaptations are now available. They can be handled and decontaminated easily; they are reliable and not difficult to operate under normal circumstances and belong to the less expensive counting equipment. It will be seen in the subsequent discussion that each of these designs has advantages and disadvantages, and they must be weighed before a choice is made for use in an experiment. The gas-counting devices may reach 100% counting efficiency with a standard deviation of 1%.

2.2. Counting Solid or Liquid Substances

Isotopes emitting high-energy radiation are most easily measured from a solid substance. The low-energy β-particle of tritium, however, makes this mode of counting the least sensitive and least accurate of all available methods. Unless tritium is measured at "infinite thickness," the absorption of the β-particles must be corrected for.

The solid to be measured is introduced into the counter usually on a planchet (see Fig. 3.3). Liquids may be assayed in an ionization chamber. The counter or the ionization chamber is subsequently filled with the counting gas, or the counting gas in a windowless flow counter may be kept flowing through the counting chamber or tube during the assay. There is obviously a danger of contaminating the counter when the gas is introduced, and volatilization of a sample may occur. Repeated filling of proportional or Geiger-Müller counters with gas and the replacement of the air may also change the sensitivity of the instrument, unless it is done carefully.

Assaying thin films of solids by the gas-counting technique allows the counting of maximally one-half of the emitted β-particles. The other half of the β-particles radiates toward the planchet. Because of this geometry, these arrangements are called two-π counting systems. The counting is affected not only by the layer thickness, but also by back-scatter of the β-particles if the layer is thinner than the range of the β-particles. Since back-scatter is a function of the atomic number of the material, a planchet of platinum may lead to a higher back-scatter and hence higher counting rate than, for example, the light aluminum.[126] Seldom is the counting efficiency as high as 50%, usually it is considerably lower.[25,70]

2.2.1. Technique of Planchet Preparation

Isbell et al.[70] measured tritium in solids of various thicknesses up to an infinitely thick layer carefully prepared on a planchet with the help of a thickening agent. "Infinite thickness" for tritium means the solid layer must be thicker than 0.6 mg/cm² so that the β-particles from the lower ranges of the layer do not reach the detector, and hence the radiation measured is independent of sample size. The result of such measurement is directly porportional to the specific activity of the labeled compound. The counting efficiency from a thickness of 0.6 mg/cm² was approximately 4% (see Fig. 3.5). It was nearly 50% when the thickness was reduced to 1 μg/cm². It is clear that in order to obtain comparable data the samples must be prepared with great care so that they have reproducible thickness, and the planchet material should remain unchanged. Rydberg[126] achieved constancy of counting conditions by carefully bringing, with the help of a pipette, the substance to be measured in solution onto a planchet which was warmed to constant temperature on a heating block. A drop of the solution evaporated slowly and evenly

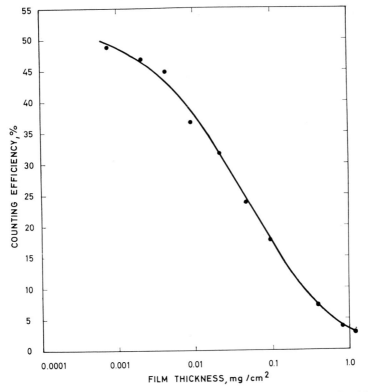

FIG. 3.5. The efficiency of counting tritium from solids, depending on the thickness of the layer, in milligrams per square centimeter. Courtesy of Isbell *et al., J. Res. Natl. Bur. Std.*[70]

from the periphery, and the result was a uniform layer of solid substance. Tritium bound to water may be transferred to a solid prior to gas counting. Thus, octadecene was reduced from tritiated water by the Grignard reaction to tritiated octadecane which is solid at room temperature.[99] From a proper solvent a uniform layer of solid octadecane was placed on the planchet and could be measured reproducibly with a two-π gas flow counter. There was linearity of counts per minute versus thickness of the sample up to approximately 150 μg/cm^2. At 600 μg/cm^2, as expected, infinite thickness was reached. Gas counting from a solid may be quick and efficient when the geometry of the solid layer can be easily controlled. This is true for work with whole bacteria which may be filtered on collodion membranes to be inserted into a gas counter. The "specific activity" thus measured from an "infinitely thick" bacterial layer can be converted easily to total activity, when the number of the bacteria per unit area is known.[3]

2.2.2. Measurement of Double-Labeled Compounds

Detection of another isotope in the presence of tritium in a solid sample is easy because the tritium β-particle can be shielded with a thin window. Although tritium and a second isotope, for example, C^{14}, are counted simultaneously in a windowless system, the second isotope can be counted alone after insertion of the window.[71]

2.2.3. Application to Paper or Thin-Layer Chromatograms

Tritium activity in paper chromatograms or thin-layer chromatograms may be assayed directly without prior elution with a windowless counting tube in which the gas is constantly renewed. The counting efficiency is greatly improved when the paper chromatogram is scanned simultaneously from both sides by a double counter.[105,170] For simple scanning of thin-layer chromatograms, Schulze and Wenzel[135] constructed a gas-flow proportional counter with an open narrow slit, under which the chromatogram can be drawn. Because a close contact of the counter to the surface of the thin-layer chromatogram can be maintained, the device has proved useful. The counting efficiency, however, was only approximately 0.3% with a layer thickness of 0.25 mm. An adaptation of this counter to scan paper chromatograms has been described.[8] The methods of evaluating the tritium activity in paper and thin-layer chromatograms will be treated further in a separate paragraph at the end of this chapter.

2.2.4. Conclusion

In conclusion, it may be said that gas counting of tritium in solid material is limited in efficiency by the two-π counting arrangement and the considerable absorption of the weak β-particle in the solid. Further, it is difficult to prepare reproducibly solid layers of a certain thickness. The method still has its usefulness in particular instances and for quickly checking substances containing a relatively high tritium activity. For most biological material better techniques exist which give higher efficiency and better reproducibility combined with ease of sample preparation.

2.3. Counting Gaseous Substances

The efficiency of gas-counting devices becomes optimal when tritium is assayed in gaseous form as a part of the counting gas. It has been the recent trend to replace this technique by liquid scintillation counting, which is simpler and of a high overall efficiency despite its lower signal to dose ratio. One of the advantages of the gas-counting technique lies in assaying gases at high temperatures. In particular, ionization chambers and proportional counters can be made to operate at high temperatures, even to several hundred degrees Centigrade. Although proportional counters and Geiger-Müller tubes are superior to ionization chambers because of their fast response and sensitivity, ionization chambers have the advantage of greater tolerance toward a larger variety of even corrosive gases, which therefore become suitable for assay.[18] The proportional counters are superior to the Geiger-Müller tubes in that they discriminate against weak background pulses and between various radiation qualities. They are, furthermore, less temperature dependent than Geiger-Müller counters, which require reproducible filling pressures. Figure 3.4 shows the two principle designs applicable for tritium in a "closed system" and in a "gas-flow system."

In the closed system, the gas or the gas mixture to be counted is introduced into the counting device, which, after a measurement, is flushed and used again; or the gas or the gas mixture may be kept flowing through the counting device while the measurements are taken. These devices are called gas-flow counters or gas-flow chambers. They are particularly useful in combination with gas chromatography. Wolfgang and Mackay[180] have presented various adaptations of proportional flow counters for assaying gases and vapors, yielding an efficiency of approximately 95%, with plateaus sufficiently wide to assure reproducible performance.

Although radioactive gases may be measured directly, a labeled solid or a liquid must be treated so that tritium emerges in the gaseous phase, in which form it can be added to the detector gas in the counter. Thus, tritium may be converted to tritium gas or may be assayed in the form of tritiated water vapor or a low molecular weight hydrocarbon such as tritiated butane, ethane, acetylene, or a mixture of these to be inserted together with argon or methane or a mixture of them into ionization chambers, proportional counters, or Geiger-Müller tubes. Tritium gas or hydrogen gas alone in large quantities is less suitable for proportional or Geiger-Müller counters, since it ionizes too readily. Likewise, a variety of other gases, because of easy ionizability or because of their corrosive action on the counting equipment, should be diluted with a proper counting gas. Ionization chambers are less sensitive in this respect and can be filled often directly with effluents from a gas chromatograph.

In case of low-level activity in gas mixtures, "pseudo-peaks" may interfere with the counting rate. Such interferring discharges, for example, in proportional counters, may be caused my minimal amounts (50 μliters) of a variety of hydrocarbons such as benzol, amyl alcohol, Methyl Cellosolve, ethylene dichloride, ethyl acetate, pyridine, formic acid, and acetic acid.[129]

In an ionization flow chamber, currents were observed from spurious amounts of isooctane, acetone, methanol, chloroform, ethyl acetate, and petroleum ether, added to argon as the carrier gas.[78]

Counting equipment may exhibit a "memory effect" when successive samples of tritium gas or tritiated water are assayed. This many-fold increase in the background counting rate is due to the easy interaction of water and hydrogen with the wall of the counter. A memory effect may also be due to trapping of tritium on the wall of such equipment in which tritium-labeled organic material is oxidized or combusted.[113,179] Glass gives rise to a high memory effect, and it is therefore an unsuitable material for counting tubes and any equipment employed in repeatedly combusting tritium-labeled material for gas counting. Decontaminating or flushing the equipment repeatedly with nonradioactive hydrogen gas reduces or abolishes this effect.[78,141]

Christman,[25] in his review on counting soft β-particles, discussed the criteria for choosing among the various counting devices. For a low sample load and where utmost efficiency is desired, particularly for very low counting rates, the more or less laborious preparation of the sample for gas counting is profitable. For most biological and medical investigations where a large number of samples has to be prepared, the simpler liquid scintillation counting is preferred, since it is sufficiently accurate and gives a high over-all efficiency.

2.3.1. The Generation of the Gas

Tritium water vapor may be generated in various ways.[51] Thus, organic material may be burned or combusted with various oxidizing substances according to the type of the material. Perchlorate, permanganate, copper oxide, or vanadium pentoxide have all proved useful. Also, the organic material may be burned in an atmosphere of oxygen in a furnace or bomb. Various combustion methods have been devised also in connection with liquid scintillation counting which is discussed later in this chapter. Peets and collaborators[113] described a special furnace which allows one to combust simultaneously three samples weighing as much as 2 g. In all combustion techniques it is important to assure the conversion of all hydrogen to water, otherwise the results are too low owing to tritium isotope effect (see Chapter 2).

The water generated by oxidation or combustion is trapped in the cold and is subsequently reduced to hydrogen gas at high temperature over metal, such as zinc, calcium, sodium, magnesium amalgam, or with lithium aluminum hydroxide.[144] Eidinoff[39] thus reduced tritiated water over zinc and measured the hydrogen gas in a mixture with argon and ethanol in a Geiger-Müller tube. Verly and collaborators[163] found a similar technique useful, but preferred methane as the quenching gas in mixture with argon. Besides tritiated water, carbon dioxide trapped separately after combustion can be assayed also by gas counting in case of double-tracer experiments.

The two-step preparation of organic samples for tritium gas counting as outlined above was combined into a one-step procedure by Wilzbach and co-workers.[178] By heating the organic substance in a sealed tube at 640°C in the presence of zinc and nickel oxide, the hydrogen emerged as hydrogen gas and was bound to methane. The composition of the gas generated in this way is not entirely known, but it may be used satisfactorily in an ionization chamber. Simon and collaborators[141] also investigated the "zinc fusion method" and found it to give excellent results if the nickel oxide catalyst had a nickel content of approximately 77%. This technique was further adapted for assaying effluent gases from a gas chromatographic column with a proportional counter. It was found that there were no difficulties with substances containing nitrogen as amino or nitro groups, sulfur as thioethers, with fluorine-, chlorine-, bromine-, and iodine-containing compounds, or with benzene, toluene, and water.[142] Compounds mixed with ammonium salts could not be measured, however, because the resulting gas contained a considerable amount of ammonia. When anhydrous sodium carbonate was added to the animal tissue in addition to metallic zinc powder, and nickel oxide was eliminated, upon heating to 650°C for 3 hours a gas mixture was generated that was largely free of nitrogen, sulfur, and halogens.[53] By mixing this gas with methane a 38% counting efficiency was obtained in a proportional counter. A microtechnique of the one-step combustion and reduction method was developed for assaying in gas-phase tritium bound to nucleic acids from single cells.[86]

Natural tritium levels in water have been measured by directly converting the water to molecular hydrogen (tritium), for example, over zinc or magnesium or in the reaction with lithium aluminum hydride ($LiAlH_4$).[144] The hydrogen (tritium) gas subsequently flows into counting tubes together with a noble gas and an additional quenching vapor. Östlund[106] thus measured hydrogen (tritium) gas in a 1-liter volume counting tube, with 1.3% pressure of propane as the quenching gas. The counting efficiency was 94.1%. In a similar technique, ethylamine and ether were found to be good quenchers in Geiger-Müller tubes when used together with hydrogen (tritium) gas and argon in various proportions.[101] A relatively huge Geiger-Müller tube with a 2.9-liter effective volume was used by Von Buttlar and Stahl[164] to assay low-level tritium in natural water, after reduction to tritium gas, with argon and ethylene as a quencher (in proportion of 400:40:30 mm Hg). Von Buttlar[165] extended this technique and concentrated the tritium by electrolysis and by letting the gas subsequently pass through thermal diffusion columns prior to measurement.

Tritium has been counted directly in the form of water vapor.[51] Merrit[98] used a heated proportional counter to measure water vapor together with methane with a filling pressure of 1 atm. An ionization flow chamber of 3-ml volume was tested by Dobbs[30] in which flowing water vapor was assayed for tritium at 190°C with nitrogen as the carrier gas.

Glascock,[51] in his book, gives various methods for preparing samples containing tritium for gas counting. Besides preparing the isotope in the state of tritium–hydrogen gas or vapor of tritiated water, it may also be bound, for example, by reduction or catalytic exchange to a lower molecular weight hydrocarbon, which may be used directly in proportional or Geiger-Müller counters in place of the quenching gas. These techniques are particularly useful for low-level counting such as that of "natural" tritium in rain water. Butane labeled with tritium can be prepared from tritiated water and butylmagnesium bromide. Similarly, tritiated methane may be generated from tritiated water and methylmagnesium iodide, or methane may be obtained from water and aluminum carbide; but because of an isotope effect a more quantitative method was found in the reaction of tritiated water over zinc with carbon dioxide to yield labeled methane.[4] Combustion in a bomb under oxygen pressure in the presence of aluminum carbide resulted in a gas mixture which could be filled directly into counting tubes.[112] Animal tissue as well as pure amino acids could thus be prepared for tritium counting. Bainbridge *et al.*[7] let hydrogen react with acetylene over a palladium catalyst and obtained labeled ethane, which could be used easily in proportional or Geiger-Müller counting tubes. Tritiated acetylene mixed with argon has also been assayed in proportional counters and Geiger-Müller tubes. Thus, a labeled organic specimen may be oxidized to water, which subsequently reacts with calcium carbide to give tritiated acetylene.[9,157] The resulting gas mixture may be purified by interposing various adsorbants prior to filling the acetylene with the carrier gas (CO_2) into the counter.[158] In another technique, tritium may be transferred to ammonia and counted as such with methane in a proportional counter.[90]

2.3.2. Application to Gas Chromatography

In conjunction with gas chromatography, proportional counters and ionization chambers offer the advantage that they can be readily applied to constantly flowing hot gas which, under favorable conditions, may subsequently be used for further experimentation. Since the proper composition and temperature of gas mixtures are more critical for proportional counters, ionization chambers are often more useful.[20,97,129,156,179]

Ionization chambers are relatively slow in response and have a relatively high background which can be reduced by trapping ions out of the gas prior to entry into the chamber.[156] Techniques have been developed also using proportional flow counters to obtain a faster response and higher efficiencies and which permit a minimum quantity of gas to be handled. When gases are kept flowing through the counter, it is possible to assay even slightly corrosive gases. Wolfgang and collaborators[180,181] devised and described the application of a proportional flow counter to monitor effluents from a gas chromatograph. The effluents with helium as a carrier were first analyzed as usual with a thermal conductivity cell; they were then injected into a stream of flowing methane, prior to passage through the proportional flow counter at a temperature of up to 200°C to prevent condensation. Thus, 50 disintegrations per minute ±5% error in a volume of 10–20 ml could be measured. With very low counting rates, however, certain impurities in the flowing gas may cause false impulses[78,129] or may reduce the counting efficiency. If nitro compounds are the only "poisons" interferring, addition to the flowing gas of nitrobenzene (4% of the counting gas) could stabilize their effect.[1] To avoid interferences from impurities when counting at low activity, the continuous combustion of the gases with generation of hydrogen-tritium gas in a combustion train was preferred.[78,142] A "memory effect" due to absorbed tritium activity on the wall of the equipment could be avoided by addition of nonradioactive hydrogen gas.[78] The hydrogen–tritium gas was assayed in a flow chamber or a proportional flow counter. In the case of very low tritium activity, Karmen and associates[78] condensed the gas, leaving the combustion train for scintillation counting.

3. Measurement by Liquid Scintillation Counting

Tritium that is bound to a liquid substance is best measured by liquid scintillation counting when the labeled liquid and the scintillator solution form a homogeneous phase. The homogeneity of the system assures a most intimate contact between the β-emitting tritium and the scintillating molecules and thus eliminates uncertainties imposed by the short range of the β-particles. The spacial distribution of radiating nuclide and detector molecules is practically as intimate as between isotope and gas molecules in the gas-counting technique described above. Nonhomogeneous scintillation-counting systems may have a relatively low efficiency, but still are very useful in particular instances.

In liquid scintillation counting, the detector molecules are conjugated aromatic hydrocarbons with nearly symmetrical molecular structure. These molecules have the characteristic property of emitting photons upon excitation. Usually the molecules are dissolved in a proper solvent, although they may also be embedded in plastic or may be used in crystal form, and powders of crystalline scintillators have been applied in measuring tritium activity in liquids immiscible with the solvent system. Large scintillating crystals, as they are used to measure γ-radiation, are, of course, least suitable for tritium.

3.1. THE LIQUID SCINTILLATION COUNTER

The equipment for monitoring scintillations is more elaborate than that needed to amplify and record the pulses generated in a gas-counting device. Figure 3.6 shows the principal arrangement of a liquid scintillation spectrometer with two phototubes in coincidence circuit. Some investigators prefer counters with a single phototube.

3.1.1. Optical Contact

Photons emitted from the scintillating molecules are "viewed" in the dark by one or two photomultiplier tubes. To avoid any losses of photons, the sample to be measured, whether it is mixed with a liquid or solid scintillator, is placed into optical contact with the phototubes. By proper arrangement of reflectors and "light pipers," about 90% of the photons are captured by the phototube.

3.1.2. The Phototube

The photons hitting the photomultiplier tube cause the emission of electrons which become accelerated in a high-voltage field. The respon-

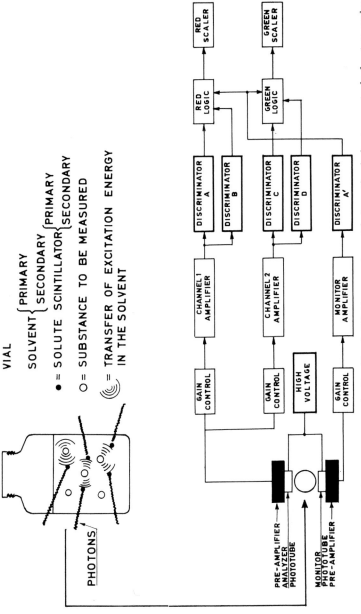

FIG. 3.6. The principal arrangement of a liquid scintillation counter with four discriminator controls for two pulse-height windows (314 EX Tri-Carb Spectrometer, Packard Instr.). Adapted from Kabara *et al.*, *Advan. Tracer Methodol.*[75]

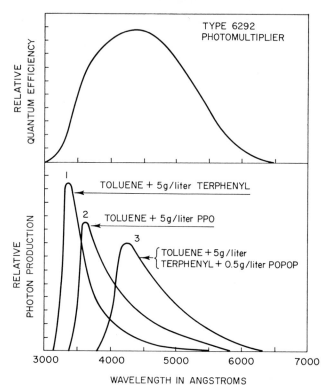

FIG. 3.7. Emission spectra of various scintillator solutions in comparison with the sensitivity range of a conventional photomultiplier tube (6292). Courtesy of Swank, *Liquid Scintillation Counting.*[153]

siveness of the phototube has its maximum at a certain region of the electromagnetic wave spectrum, conventionally around 4000 A. It is clear that in order to have an optimal yield of phototube electrons the emitted photons from the scintillator should have approximately the same wavelength. Figure 3.7 shows the emission spectra of three scintillators dissolved in toluene, together with the relative sensitivity of a phototube (type 6292 photomultiplier). The sensitivity varies with different types of tubes.

In a scintillating system composed of "PPO" and "POPOP" as scintillators dissolved in toluene (see below for scintillators and solvents), a tritium β-particle of an average energy (5.6 kev) causes the emission of 30–40 photons,[110] of which approximately 90% by close optical contact reach the phototube where, in response, two to four electrons are emitted. The relatively high energy of approximately 1.5–3 kev of β-radiation is therefore needed for the emission of one electron in the phototube.[153] If two phototubes are placed in front of one sample, the emitted photons are distributed between the two. Hence, the simultaneous emission of an electron in each of the two phototubes requires 3–6 kev of the β-particles. Since about 30–60% of the tritium β-particles have an energy of below 3–6 kev, the theoretical counting efficiency in a coincidence arrangement cannot be higher than about 50%.

There is a great deal of thermionic emission from the phototube at room temperature. This random emission of electrons is greatly reduced in the cold. Therefore, counting the samples in the cold substantially reduces background pulses and greatly improves the sensitivity. A cesium(Cs)–antimony(Sb) cathode thus reduces thermionic emission of electrons by a factor of 2 when the temperature is lowered by 13°C.[153] The lower range of the temperature is limited by the counting sample which must not freeze or show phase separation. Therefore, phototubes and samples are usually placed at a temperature of 0°–8°C. If phase separation in the scintillating sample occurs, the counting temperature must perhaps be increased. Exposure of a phototube to daylight ruins it for hours.

3.1.3. Pulse Amplification and Discrimination

The yield of electrons emitted by the phototube is optimal at a certain high voltage and is amplified to strong enough pulses to operate a scaler. The discriminator circuitry between amplifiers and scalers distinguishes between different pulse heights, allowing thus the selection of certain pulse heights only to become registered by the scaler, and too low or too strong pulse heights can be excluded. Background counts are thus considerably reduced. By setting a proper and optimal "pulse-height window" for one scaler characteristic for a section of the energy spectrum of the isotope and by setting a second window of different width for another scaler, interference from background pulses becomes easily recognizable. The use of two window settings by proper discriminators allows also the simultaneous determination of two isotopes, whose radiation energy is sufficiently different (like those of tritium and C^{14}).

Interference from background pulses is, furthermore, greatly depressed by the discriminators in coincidence circuit. By this arrangement, only those electronic pulses from the phototube are registered which are generated at exactly the same time in both tubes. It is clear that random pulses from background have thus a minimum chance only to pass through a set "window" of the discriminators in coincidence circuit. Of course, the counting efficiency is also lowered by this arrangement.

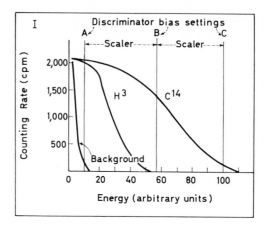

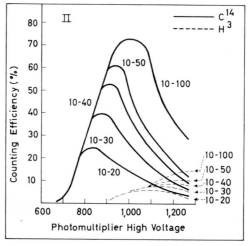

Fig. 3.8. I, The distribution of pulse heights from tritium and from C^{14} within two pulse-height windows (set in arbitrary units of energy) at a single high voltage applied to the phototube. II, Discriminator bias curves for pulses from tritium and C^{14}; i.e., the yield of various pulse heights as a function of the high voltage applied to the phototube. Courtesy of Okita *et al., Nucleonics.*[103]

Figure 3.8 helps to visualize the selection of pulse heights within two windows A–B and B–C. The resulting discrimination against pulses from background, tritium, and C^{14} is obvious.

The stability of operation of the counter is optimal at that certain high voltage at which the maximum counting rate is obtained within a chosen pulse-height window. This "balance point" is determined by constructing a discriminator bias curve, which differs with various scintillator solutions.

3.1.4. Summary

In summary, the signal to noise ratio of a liquid scintillation counter is greatly improved by (1) the proper optical contact of sample to phototube, (2) the proper sensitivity range of the phototube, (3) the reduction of thermionic emission in the phototube at low temperature, (4) coincidence arrangement of two phototubes monitoring one sample, and (5) a proper discriminator circuitry allowing for selected "window-settings" of pulse heights. It is needless to say that constancy of operation of the counter is a prerequisite for obtaining reproducible data. Under optimal conditions of scintillating sample and counter operation, a counting efficiency of approximately 15% for tritium is commonly obtained.

3.2. THE SCINTILLATOR SOLUTION

3.2.1. Energy Transfer

In order to understand the proper use of a liquid scintillator for tritium, it is desirable to consider in more detail the mechanism by which the energy from the tritium β-particle causes the scintillator molecule to emit photons.[76] The photon emission is not the result of a direct interaction with the charged particle. The first interaction occurs with the molecules of the solvent which results in molecular excitation and formation of radicals, ions, and free electrons. The reactions of free radicals and recombinations of free electrons with ions add to the excitation of the solvent molecules. If the solvent permits these electronic excitations to have a long enough life span, they continue to be transferred to neighbor molecules until there is a scintillator molecule which traps the energy. The transfer of energy from the moment of its absorption from the incident particle in the solvent until its absorption by the scintillating molecule lasts approximately 10^{-9} seconds.

3.2.2. The Scintillating Molecule

The scintillator molecule can trap the energy without decomposing in the process. But molecular electrons change orbitals, and in returning to the nonexcited state photons are emitted. Thus, the excitation energy is extinguished from traveling further in the solvent. A tritium β-particle with average energy of 5.6 kev leads to the emission of 30–40 photons in a toluene solution of the scintillators "PPO" and "POPOP" [110] (see below).

It is clear that the efficiency of a liquid scintillator[60] depends on the ability of the solvent to maintain an effective intermolecular energy transfer which can occur only if the excited solvent molecules are electronically more resistant, i.e., have a higher electron excitation energy than the scintillator molecules. Nonpolar solvents such as alkyl benzenes, free from impurities, possess this required quality. Impurities which are polar or have the capacity of absorbing the excitation energy and converting it to molecular alterations without emitting photons greatly decrease the efficiency of an optimal solvent system. The problem of quenching is discussed in a later section.

Figure 3.9 lists the most widely used scintillators, with their chemical names, their "short-hand names," their chemical formulas, and the

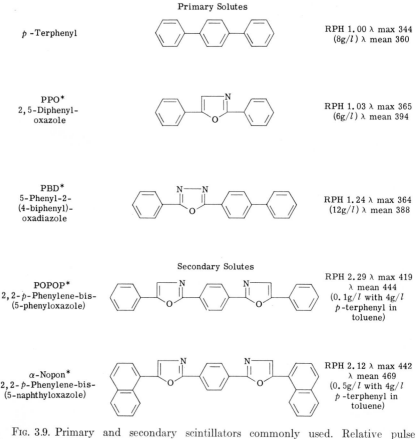

Primary Solutes

p -Terphenyl
RPH 1.00 λ max 344
(8g/l) λ mean 360

PPO*
2,5-Diphenyl-
oxazole
RPH 1.03 λ max 365
(6g/l) λ mean 394

PBD*
5-Phenyl-2-
(4-biphenyl)-
oxadiazole
RPH 1.24 λ max 364
(12g/l) λ mean 388

Secondary Solutes

POPOP*
2,2-p-Phenylene-bis-
(5-phenyloxazole)
RPH 2.29 λ max 419
λ mean 444
(0.1g/l with 4g/l
p-terphenyl in
toluene)

α-Nopon*
2,2-p-Phenylene-bis-
(5-naphthyloxazole)
RPH 2.12 λ max 442
λ mean 469
(0.5g/l with 4g/l
p-terphenyl in
toluene)

FIG. 3.9. Primary and secondary scintillators commonly used. Relative pulse height (RPH) compared to that emitted by p-terphenyl (see text). Adapted from Ott, *Liquid Scintillation Counting.*[107] Asterisked compounds coded as follows: P, phenyl; B, biphenyl; O, oxazole; D, oxadiazole; N, naphthyl.

pulse heights they yield, normalized to the pulse height given by p-terphenyl at a certain concentration in the solvent. Also listed are the maxima of the emission spectra and the mean emission spectra. The mean wavelength, or emission spectrum, is defined as that wavelength which divides the emission spectrum into two portions, each having an equal number of photons.[107] A distinction is made between primary and secondary scintillators.[57,58]

The primary scintillator should fulfill the practical requirements of a good and efficient scintillator—that it is economical and that it is reasonably soluble in the proper solvent. The primary scintillators are dissolved usually to a concentration of 5–10 g/liter. Although p-terphenyl is an excellent scintillator,[69,118,122] it suffers from a relatively low solubility particularly in the cold, where measurements are usually taken. Another disadvantage is the fact that it does not react well with naphthalene as a secondary solvent, which, as will be discussed below, renders the energy transfer in certain solvent systems more efficient.[49] Naphthalene together with p-terphenyl leads to a decrease in counting efficiency. Overall, PPO (2,5-diphenyloxazole) ranks highest because of its good solubility[55] and compatibility with naphthalene.[49] Another p-oligophenyl, such as tetramethylquaterphenyl (TMQP), was tested as a scintillator in comparison to PPO.[41] TMQP was found to be more efficient than PPO in toluene with POPOP as secondary solute; it was also found to be less sensitive to the quenching by acids. But similar to p-terphenyl, TMQP yielded a lower counting efficiency than PPO when naphthalene was added to the system. PBD [5-phenyl-2-(4-biphenyl) oxadiazole], as seen in Fig. 3.9, has a high efficiency, yielding a relative pulse height of 1.24; but it has the disadvantage of limited solubility, similar to the one of p-terphenyl. Furthermore, nearly twice as much PBD as PPO is necessary for obtaining the desired greater efficiency.

The secondary solutes, two of which are listed in Fig. 3.9, frequently (but not always) increase the counting efficiency[58] by shifting the wavelength of the photons toward the maximum sensitivity of the phototube. It is seen in Fig. 3.9 that the emission spectra of the secondary solutes have their maximum at a longer wavelength than that of the primary scintillators. The effect of POPOP in addition to p-terphenyl in toluene is exemplified in Fig. 3.7. Thus, the secondary solutes are also called wavelength shifters, and they increase the counting efficiency when colored substances are present in the system which absorb in the shorter wavelength region. Among the secondary scintillators, POPOP [2,2-p-phenylenebis(5-phenyloxazole)] is most popular, but dimethyl-POPOP was reported to exceed POPOP in solubility and to have a longer wavelength maximum.[19,61] Of the less popular secondary scintillators α-NOPON [2,2-p-phenylenebis(5-naphthyloxazole)] has the advantage of a relatively high mean wavelength of 469 mμ compared to 444 mμ for POPOP. However, it is used at higher concentration. The concentration of the secondary scintillators generally ranges around 0.5 g/liter of solvent, at which optimal efficiency is combined with optimal solubility and lowest expense. Although the presence of a secondary scintillator in the system is at times indispensable, often no benefit is gained from it unless its concentration is increased. Because of a great deal of uncertainty with regard to the sample in work with complex biological material, it is recommended that the secondary solute always be tried in combination with the primary scintillator to improve the counting efficiency. Various scintillating systems will be discussed below.

3.2.3. *The Solvent*

A useful solvent must not only allow an efficient intermolecular transfer of electronic excitation, but it must also be clear and transparent for the light that is emitted by the scintillator. Table 3.1 lists a variety of solvents and their efficiency in counting C^{14} with 0.3% PPO.

The solvents which offer the best characteristics are, in general, alkylbenzenes of which toluene and xylene are the most widely used (see Fig. 3.10). The disadvantage of these solvents is their low miscibility with water. Various combinations of primary and secondary solvents have been devised to improve the water-holding capacity. For example, by adding absolute ethanol, a labeled aqueous solution can be counted in a homogeneous phase with a PPO solution in toluene or xylene.[56] Thus, 2.5 ml of ethanol holds 0.2 ml of water in 10 ml of toluene without phase separation at 3°C.

Liquid scintillation counting made important progress when dioxane was found by Farmer and Berstein to be suitable as a solvent of the scintillator for assaying larger volumes of aqueous solutions.[42] As much as 30% water can be dissolved in dioxane; but dioxane is less efficient in transferring energy than xylene or toluene with ethanol, and it gives thus comparatively lower counting rates if used as the only solvent. Another disadvantage of dioxane as the sole solvent is the high freezing point (12°C) which can, however, be depressed by addition of xylene or ethanol. Dioxane, furthermore, is somewhat unstable on long standing, and peroxides, which are stronger quenchers, may result.[128] It was another step forward in liquid scintillation counting when the low efficiency of dioxane in transferring excitation energy, and thus the relatively low counting rates, could be improved by the addition of naphtha-

TABLE 3.1

SUITABILITY OF VARIOUS SOLVENTS FOR LIQUID SCINTILLATION COUNTING WITH
0.3% PPO[a]

C¹⁴-labeled compounds	Freezing point[b] (°C)	High voltage[c]	Counting efficiency[d] (%)
Toluene	−95	6	100
Methoxybenzene (anisole)	−37	7	100
Xylene (reagent, mixed isomere)	< −20	7	97
1,3-Dimethoxybenzene	−52	8	81
n-Heptane	−90	9	70
1,4-Dioxane	+12	9	70
1,2-Dimethoxyethane (ethylene glycol dimethyl ether)	−71	9	60
Benzyl alcohol	−15	9	38
Diethylene glycol diethyl ether (diethyl carbitol)	−44	10	32
Acetone	−94	10	12
Tetrahydropyran	−81	10	6
Ethyl ether	−116	10	4
1,1-Diethoxyethane	−100	10	3
Tetrahydrofuran	−65	10	2
1,3-Dioxolane	−95	10	0
Ethyl alcohol	−114	10	0
Diethylene glycol monoethyl ether	−76	10	0
Ethylene glycol monomethyl ether	−85	10	0
Diethylene glycol	−8	10	0
Ethylene glycol	−13	10	0
2,5-Diethoxytetrahydrofuran	−27	10	0
N,N-Dimethylformamide	−61	10	0
Diethylamine	−49	10	0
n-Methyl morpholine	−66	10	0
2-Ethylhexanoic acid	−117	10	0
Tri-n-butyl phosphate	< −80	10	0

[a] Reproduced with permission of Davidson, *Liquid Scintillation Counting*.[28]

[b] Approximate.

[c] Relative high voltage (in steps of 70 volts) on photomultipliers necessary to give highest counting rate; 10 represents 1250 volts which was the maximum that was practical at the 2°C counter temperature.

[d] Efficiency, on basis of counts per minute, relative to toluene equaling 100%.

lene as a secondary solvent.[49] Thus, naphthalene with dioxane as a solvent for PPO results in a counting efficiency nearly as good as that in toluene with PPO. Further additions of solvents to dioxane–naphthalene permit good counting efficiencies also at low temperatures, but the capacity of holding water is hardly improved. Naphthalene should not be

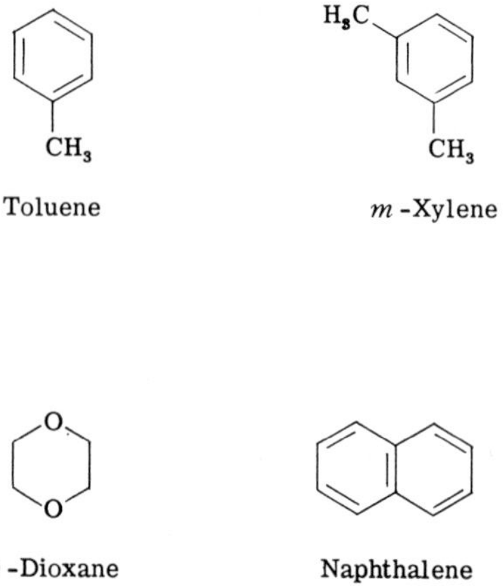

Toluene   *m*-Xylene

p-Dioxane   Naphthalene

Fig. 3.10. Structural formulas of solvents commonly used. Xylene is normally a mixture of *o*-, *m*-, and *p*-isomers.

added to solutions with *p*-oligophenyls and derivatives, since the energy transfer in such systems is inhibited causing the counting efficiency to drop considerably.

3.2.4. Optimal Composition of the Scintillating System

To achieve optimal counting efficiency, the volume of the scintillator solution used per given sample may be critical. It was thus demonstrated in work with C^{14}-testosterone dissolved in benzene that with increasing volume of toluene containing *p*-terphenyl, 4 g/liter, and POPOP, 0.2 g/liter, the counting efficiency rose rapidly as expected, but began to fall again steeply when a critical volume, in this case 5 ml, was surpassed.[152] The background-counting rate, however, continued to rise. Similar data were reported for C^{14}-benzoic acid dissolved in a system with xylene.[17] For low-level counting it is therefore advisable to test the optimal volume for a labeled sample in a pilot experiment.

Also important for optimal counting efficiency are the relative volumes of primary and secondary solvents used in one scintillator solution. A secondary solvent needed for blending an aqueous solution with the primary solvent usually exerts a quenching effect, such as in the case of ethanol,[56] dioxane,[42] or hyamine.[111]

With increasing concentration of the scintillating molecule in the solvent, the efficiency of the system rises toward a plateau, after which it may fall again with simultaneous increase in background counts. The declining counting efficiency with increasing concentrations of some scintillators is also called concentration quenching, and it has been examined and discussed for a variety of scintillators by Furst and Kallmann.[50] The most popular scintillators, however, are dissolved to a concentration below that at which concentration quenching is observed.

For optimal efficiency the concentration of a scintillator in the solvent may need adjustment when a secondary solvent is added or when heavy quenching is present. Although in toluene alone, 0.5% PPO is usually efficient, a concentration of 1% PPO is preferred when dioxane is added. The choice of the "scintillator cocktail" is made according to the type and amount of sample to be measured. The least errors arise and calculations are simplified if the composition of the liquid scintillator is kept unchanged throughout an experiment.

3.3. QUENCHING IN LIQUID SCINTILLATING SYSTEMS

Various compounds, when mixed with the liquid scintillator, cause the counting rate to rise; other compounds lower it. The latter are called quenchers. Any substance introduced into a liquid scintillating system is a potential quencher, and if unlabeled, its increasing concentration depresses the counting efficiency exponentially.[82]

3.3.1. Chemical Quenching

Quenchers may interfere with the process of radiation detection at different levels. If a substance is electronically activated more easily than the scintillator in solution, it will compete with the scintillator for the excitation energy transferred in the solvent and will trap and extinguish it without emission of photons. The quenching substance may also interact chemically with the scintillator, for example, as does trichloroacetic acid with oxazoles[82]; p-terphenyl is, on the contrary, inert. Substances interfering with the intermolecular energy transfer or interacting with the scintillator molecule are called chemical or primary quenchers. The degree of quenching expectedly varies with different scintillator solutions.

Polar compounds such as water, acids, or alkali are primary quenchers. Kerr et al.[82] have systematically investigated the quenching effect of many substances on counting C^{14} (see Table 3.2). General quenchers, besides acids and alkali, are peroxides, aldehydes, ketones, amines, ether, acyl halides, and heterocyclic compounds. A classification by the degree of quenching of functional groups in aliphatic compounds is shown in Table 3.3. Thus, strong quenchers and mild quenchers are distinguished from those groups which simply dilute but do not quench. Stitch,[152] also working with C^{14} in toluene with p-terphenyl plus POPOP, identified the following as relatively heavy quenchers: methylene dichloride, chloroform, acetone, and carbon tetrachloride; ethanol and

TABLE 3.2

COMPARISON OF THE DEGREE OF QUENCHING OF C^{14}-LABELED ORGANIC COMPOUNDS
IN THREE DIFFERENT SOLVENT SYSTEMS AT ROOM TEMPERATURE[a]

Compounds (20 g/liter)	Solvent systems		
	PPO–POPOP– toluene[b]	PPO–POPOP– naphthalene– dioxane[c]	PPO–POPOP– naphthalene– dioxane diluted with water to 150 g/liter[c]
Ethyl ether	1.00	—	—
Butyl phosphate	1.00	—	—
Cholesterol	—	0.98	0.94
Ethyl acetate	0.97	—	—
Fluorobenzene	0.96	—	—
Cholesterol	—	—	—
Glycerol	—	0.96	0.97
Furan	0.94	—	—
Ethyl benzoate	—	0.95	0.76
Sucrose	—	—	0.94
Dextrose	—	—	0.94
Ethanol	0.94	—	—
Ethyl malonate	0.94	—	—
Anisole	0.93	—	—
Water	—	0.92	—
L(+)-Arabinose	—	—	0.92
Butyl chloride	0.91	—	—
Acetic acid	0.89	0.83	0.72
Urea	—	—	0.89
Caffeine	—	0.87	—
Tristearin	0.83	0.82	—
Acetone	—	0.78	0.61
Ethyl bromide	0.76	—	—
Benzyl alcohol	0.70	—	—
Pyridine	—	0.64	0.54
Hydrogen peroxide	—	—	0.65
Chlorobenzene	0.60	—	—
Chloroform	0.51	0.58	0.59

[a] Tabulated with permission of Kerr *et al.*, *Intern. J. Appl. Radiation Isotopes.*[82]
[b] PPO, 4 g/liter; POPOP, 0.1 g/liter.
[c] PPO, 7 g/liter; POPOP, 0.5 g/liter; naphthalene, 50 g/liter.

methanol were medium quenchers, and benzene, diethyl ether, and ethyl acetate were examples of very light quenchers or simple diluters. A very similar scaling of chemical quenchers in a xylene–naphthalene–PPO system was reported by Brown and Badman,[17] who also worked with C^{14}. Oxygen may be a more powerful quencher than chloroform. For example, 0.001 mole of oxygen per liter of xylene was found suf-

TABLE 3.3

CLASSIFICATION BY DEGREE OF QUENCHING OF FUNCTIONAL GROUPS IN ALIPHATIC COMPOUNDS[a]

Diluters	Mild quenchers	Strong quenchers
R—H	R—COOH	R—SH
R—F	R—NH₂	R—OCOCO—R
R—O—R	R—CH=CH—R	R—CO—R
(RO)₃PO	R—Br	R—COX
R—CN	R—S—R	R—NH—R
R—OH		R—CHO
R—COO—R		R₂N—R
R—Cl		R—I
		R—NO₂

[a] Reproduced with permission of Kerr *et al.*, *Intern. J. Appl. Radiation Isotopes.*[82]

ficient to quench the excitation of xylene to one half of its value.[76] But simple oxygenation of the scintillator solvent, toluene or xylene plus naphthalene, lowered the counting efficiency by approximately 10%.[17,152] It is self-evident that the degree of quenching of energy transfer in the solvent changes with the nature of the solvent and the scintillator.

Quenching exerted by the scintillator itself when present in too high a concentration is called concentration quenching[50] and has already been mentioned. No such effect has been observed with the popular scintillator PPO in various solvents over the usual ranges of concentrations. Even 18 g of PPO per liter did not "self-quench" when tested in a solvent consisting of ethylene glycol, dioxane, anisole, and 1,2-dimethoxyethane in a relation of 2:6:1:1.[28] The low solubility of *p*-terphenyl precludes the possibility of self-quenching.

3.3.2. Color Quenching

Another form of quenching is due to absorption of the emitted photons. Yellowish colors, which absorb in the region of 400 mμ, are detrimental to the counting efficiency. Most colored substances cause quenching both by absorbing emitted photons and interfering with the energy transfer in the solvent. Color quenching is synonymous with secondary quenching. Many animal tissues, particularly blood, when prepared for scintillation counting with hyamine, cause an intense coloration of yellow to brown. Color quenching was quantitatively interpreted and correlated with the substance concentration and wavelength absorption by Ross.[124,125] It is noteworthy that colorless opacity may quench only slightly, probably because the tiny particles causing the "white opacity" act as mirrors and reflectors for the photons.

3.3.3. Prevention of Quenching

Quenching can rarely be prevented entirely, but it may be kept low by the proper choice and preparation of the scintillating system. The quenching of water in a dioxane-containing system is reduced or prevented by naphthalene,[49] if PPO is the solute scintillator. This effect is not obtained in conjunction with p-terphenyl[49] or its derivatives, such as tetramethylquaterphenyl.[41] It has, moreover, been observed that, depending on the acidity of the quenching substance in the solvent (toluene, PPO, POPOP), naphthalene may increase the quenching rather than eliminate it.[32]

Quenching can be diminished principally by diluting the scintillating sample with more solvent, since with diminishing concentration of an unlabeled quencher the counting efficiency rises exponentially.[52,114]

If color quenching is predominant, bleaching with hydrogen peroxide is effective.[65] However, hydrogen peroxide is itself a stronger quencher and, if necessary, can subsequently be decomposed by heating.[127] The use of hydrogen peroxide requires, however, assurance that no tritium oxide is lost with the evolution of gas. If quenching persists, for example, after decolorizing a tissue digest in hyamine, subsequent acidification may restore the counting efficiency.[65] The use of hyamine for digesting biological material in preparation for liquid scintillation counting will be discussed later. Another way of eliminating color quenching is the decoloration of the specimen with charcoal prior to preparation of the scintillating sample. Without such pretreatment with charcoal, urine may quench nearly 100%.[102]

The degree of quenching of acids can be controlled by the proper choice of the scintillator solution as well as by neutralization, if the isotope content in the sample is sufficiently high. For example, small volumes of 10% perchloric acid may be counted in a xylene (toluene)–ethanol system.[43] The quenching by the acid was not increased more than by a factor of about 1.3 beyond that caused by the ethanol alone. Larger volumes of acids can be counted with solvent systems containing dioxane and hyamine or 0.5 M ethanolic potassium hydroxide.[65,83] The system of Bray[16] appears especially useful. The preparation of counting samples for various substances will be discussed later in this chapter.

3.3.4. Correction for Quenching

Since quenching is usually not prevented entirely in the sample preparation, corrections for it need to be applied after the measurement. The presence and degree of quenching in a sample is detected generally by adding a known amount of isotope to the sample and by checking its counting efficiency. The presence of quenching can also be recognized by diluting the sample and observing the effect of the dilution on the counting rate. Quenching may be detected further by measuring the ratio of the counting rates in two different pulse-height "windows," since the pulse-height spectrum varies with different solvents and in the presence of quenchers. Finally, the degree of color quenching can be correlated to spectrophotometric absorption measurements. The first method, using an internal standard, is the most popular also in work with tritium.

The quenching factor can be easily determined by recounting the sample after addition of a known amount of radioactivity ("internal standard"), such as tritiated toluene. This applies to chemical and color quenching. Kaufmann and collaborators[79] suggested the use of Co^{57} attached to small needles as an internal standard; Ni^{63} was also found suitable.[21] These have the advantage of being easily removed from the counting sample after measurement for repeated use. Dobbs[33] preferred a small glass rod carrying a coating of C^{14}-labeled barium carbonate. With the transferable rod, the counting efficiency of H^3 in toluene–PPO–POPOP could be well determined in the presence of chemical and color quenching. On the other hand, the usefulness of internal standards other than the isotope being assayed is limited to certain ranges of the counting efficiency, and the internal standard technique should conform to the counting characteristics of the scintillating system. Thus, Bloom[13] found the counting efficiency of tritium but not of C^{14} to differ in two toluene–PPO systems, one of which contained a gel, the other hyamine, and it was recommended that a tritium standard only be used when assaying tritium.

Quenching may be corrected to the level of the counting rate of the internal standard in the basic scintillator solution without quenchers being present. However, it is obviously more satisfactory to know the absolute amount of activities present. Thus if the "internal standard" is known in absolute disintegrations per minute, the correction for quenching leads to the absolute amount of activity in the sample. In work with tritium, the "internal standard" added should have approximately 100,000–150,000 dpm.

Thus,

$$\text{disintegrations/minute (corrected)} = \text{net counts/minute of sample}$$

$$\times \frac{\text{disintegrations/minute of "internal standard," added}}{\text{counts/minute of "internal standard," measured}}$$

The expression

$$\frac{\text{disintegrations/minute of "internal standard," added}}{\text{counts/minute of "internal standard," measured}}$$

is also called the efficiency factor, while the true quenching factor in a given scintillator solution is

$$\frac{\text{counts/minute of "internal standard," added}}{\text{counts/minute of "internal standard," measured}}$$

Thus, for one determination four measurements are necessary: the sample, the sample plus "internal standard," the "internal standard" alone, and the appropriate background sample. Because of the high counting rate of the "internal standard," variations in the background rate, usually about 30–50 counts per minute, are of no consequence in the calculation of the efficiency factor.

When severe quenching also affects the background-counting rate, and when the sample data are close to those of the background, the quenching factor of the background must be determined too. Otherwise, the corrected net counting rate of the sample is too high. Scales[127] described a quick method for correcting the background count in unlabeled samples containing quenching substances. An "internal standard" was used for the construction of a standard reference curve. For example, comparable tissue samples, free from tritium activity, prepared with hyamine, and bleached with peroxide, were used as blanks for counting the background. Then, an internal standard was added and the counting efficiency of each sample was determined. A calibration curve was constructed from the data of the background-counting rates and the appropriate counting efficiency factors. The tissue samples containing tritium were then measured in the usual way, of course, in the same type of solvent system, and the efficiency factors were determined with internal standard. From the value of the efficiency factor the corresponding background rate for each sample could be read off the calibration curve. After subtraction of the corrected background rate from the gross counting rate of the sample, the resulting net counts per minute were then multiplied with the efficiency factor. Herberg[68] has examined statistically the variables in this type of correction for quenching by applying the propagation of error equation, taking into account the fractional errors in the various counting rates. This will be referred to again below.

Color quenching occurs at times without being accompanied by chemical quenching. This can be differentiated by comparing the quenching factor of the sample in question with that of the same scintillator solution without color quenching; internal standard is a small vial filled with the basic scintillator solution and the isotope. Thus, the measurement is not affected by chemical quenching.[125] If the quenching is caused by color alone, correction is a simple technique. Since color quenching occurs only at the wavelengths corresponding to the sensitivity of the phototube, normally around 400 mμ, absorbancy measurements in a spectrophotometer at this wavelength can be used to determine the quenching factor.[66] With the help of standard curves for a solvent system chosen, showing counting efficiency against absorbancy at 400 mμ, the simple determination of absorbancy alone lets one easily obtain the efficiency factor for the correction of the sample counting rate. Halvorsen[52] applied both the internal standard method and the color correction method over a comparable range of quenching, and he found the latter to result in a greater accuracy than the first. Also Ross and Yerick,[124] examining the number of quenching coefficients with regard to mixtures of colors, found a wide range of linearity of counting efficiency versus absorbancy. Similar results were reported by Iwakura and Kasida.[72] The correction for color quenching in background-counting rates can also be made by using a reference curve constructed from color intensity versus counting efficiency. This is recommenced particularly in view of the possible differences in the degree of color quenching in the background from that in the isotopic sample. Thus, with two standard curves, one for the counting efficiency in the isotopic sample, the other for the efficiency in the background sample, both dependent on color intensities, the necessary correction factors can be read off the curves without additional manipulation except determination of absorbancy at 400 mμ.[66] It is clear that the standard curves are valid only for one type of solvent system.

Chemical and color quenching can also be corrected by the discriminator or channel-ratio technique. Davidson[28] preferred this technique because of the simplicity of comparing the counting rates for each sample obtained in two pulse-height windows of different size, one 10–50 volts wide, and another 10–100 volts wide. Since the spectrum of pulse heights generated in the phototubes is altered owing to quenching in the scintillator solution, the ratio of counts in the two channels changes accordingly. If the two windows are set in such a manner that the number of counts of an isotope standard, in absence of quenchers, is in the smaller window or channel one half of that in the larger window, the recognition of quenching is particularly easy. This approach was found as useful for the correction of color quenching as was the optical method, if the counting rates were relatively high.[66,72] Also, chemical quenching altered the two-channel ratio according to the counting efficiency determined by the internal standard technique,[72] and the relationship was linear down to an efficiency of 15% relative to the unquenched sample.[145] Quenching correction with the two-channel ratio appears therefore the method of choice, unless the counting rate is low. In this case, the technique becomes increasingly inaccurate, and the internal standard method is to be preferred. Liquid scintillation counters are now commercially available that can use the two-channel readings to compute the net counting rate corrected for quenching.

Another mode of correcting for quenching is based on correlating the degree of quenching to the amount of labeled substance in the sample.[114] This approach may be principally convenient when the quenching is indeed a simple exponential function of the concentration of the quenching substance, the amount of which varies usually with the labeled sample. Thus, by extrapolating in a reference curve to 0 g of substance, the counting rate without quenching can be determined. Peng[114] used the extrapolation technique to correct for quenching caused by milligram amounts of protein per sample. For the construction of the reference curve at least two comparable samples of different weights are needed to plot the sample concentration versus the logarithm of the corresponding net count.

The extrapolation technique has, however, the disadvantage that a new reference curve must be constructed for each set of an experiment, a procedure which might become more laborious than the technique with "internal standard." Reexamining the conditions of the extrapolation technique in work with animal tissue solubilized by hyamine, Halvorsen[52] reported that, owing to the low energy of the β-particle from tritium, the logarithm of the counting rate may not adhere to a linear function in the region of low sample concentration, (e.g., below approximately 1 mg/ml of hyamine added to 19 ml of toluene with PPO and POPOP). On the other hand, Vaughan[162] found that the internal standard method corrected for quenching linearly up to 10 mg of proteins.

It should be pointed out that samples in homogeneous scintillating systems which show a pronounced degree of quenching can sometimes be counted with a higher efficiency by the gel technique,[63] as will be discussed later in this chapter.

3.4 PHOSPHORESCENCE AND CHEMILUMINESCENCE

A substance which, upon exposure to light, absorbs energy and then releases it again by emission of photons over a longer period than 1 microsecond is called a phosphorescent substance. If energy absorbed or "trapped" by a substance is released as light within less than 1 microsecond, the process is called fluorescence. Thus, scintillators are fluorescent substances. Chemiluminescence means that light is emitted during a chemical reaction, for example, when a peroxide oxidizes organic compounds. For theoretical considerations of these complex phenomena, the reader is referred to textbooks in physics. In liquid scintillation counting, phosphorescence and chemiluminescence may seriously interfere with proper counting if the processes are not recognized as such or if they cannot be eliminated. There are a few factors which may contribute to these phenomena, and it is worthwhile to consider them here so that they may not suddenly arise in an experiment as a surprise.

3.4.1. *Phosphorescence*

One of the contributing factors is the glass vial used as the container of the scintillator solution.[27] If ordinary glass or quartz counting bottles are exposed to ultraviolet light or daylight, phosphorescence occurs in which there are two components.[28] The major emission of photons occurs during 2–3 minutes after exposure, although a minor degree of photon emission continues for 1–2 hours. The emitted photons cause a high pulse rate in the phototube. It is therefore necessary to avoid exposure of the counting vials to daylight prior to counting.

The time necessary for dark adaptation after exposure to daylight may be longer when the phosphorescence arises from the scintillator solvent. Lloyd and co-workers[89] reported on the phosphorescence from various materials which are likely to be incorporated in a scintillation counting system. In addition to confirming the phosphorescence from glass containers, several solvents designated "analytical reagent grade" were also tested. Figure 3.11 gives as an example the phosphorescence of toluene after exposure to a sun lamp. Again, an initially fast and a subsequently long-lasting component of photon emission was observed. An appreciable number of counts could still be observed 1–2 hours after exposure. The phosphorescence of solvents was found to be critically dependent on impurities, and a high-purity sample of toluene did not exhibit significant phosphorescence. Addition to the toluene of scintillators, such as p-terphenyl and POPOP, increased phosphorescence by a factor of approximately 10 or more and addition of water reduced it. In another study, a period of about 7 hours was found necessary for complete dark adaptation following exposure of the scintillator solution to daylight for 10 minutes.[17] It is clear, then, that a scintillator solution prepared for counting should not be exposed to daylight or, if this cannot be avoided, sufficient time for dark adaptation must be allowed, preferably several hours, if low activity samples are to be measured.

3.4.2. *Chemiluminescence*

The sample to be counted may cause chemiluminescence in the liquid scintillating system.

Although addition of water to a phosphorescing liquid scintillating system had a considerable quenching effect,[89] addition of water to a PPO–naphthalene–dioxane system after dark adaptation caused spurious counts

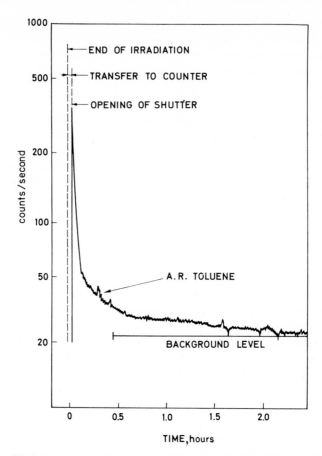

FIG. 3.11. Phosphorescence of toluene, analytical reagent, after 10 minutes of exposure to a sun lamp. Courtesy of Lloyd *et al., Symp. Intern. At. Energy Agency.*[89]

initially as high as one million per minute for 10–35 minutes, with a slow decline thereafter over a period of more than 15 hours.[15] A similar effect was observed due to friction of the dioxane on the walls of the container in the presence of air.[21] The effect was not observed when the dioxane was thoroughly purified. This again implies and urges caution in selecting purified solvent systems only.

It was found that proteins solubilized in hyamine and added to toluene–PPO exert strong chemiluminescence.[148,149,162] Also quaternary amines other than hyamine containing digests of biological material cause chemiluminescence, even without a scintillating solvent—an additional disadvantage to the yellow coloration which occurred in these samples. Herberg[64] ascribed the phenomenon to the presence of tyrosine and tryptophan. At least several days of dark adaptation were required before the counts from chemiluminescence descended to the level of normal background. Halvorsen[52] observed two components in the emission process—one fast, with a half-time of 3–4 mintes; the other slower, having a half-time of 6–7 hours. Protein dissolved in potassium hydroxide failed to show chemiluminescene.

Chemiluminescence increased obviously with increasing sample weight, and amounts of proteins below 3 mg per milliliter of hyamine caused only a negligible degree of light emission,[64] provided the hyamine was highly purified. The primary solvent system also had an effect in that the rate of photon emission diminished with increasing viscosity of the solvent added to the hyamine digest.

Herberg[64] showed that acidification of the protein solution in hyamine immediately eliminated chemiluminescence. Consequently, it is not necessary to wait several days for the light emission to fall to the level of the instrumental background. Acidification with concentrated hydrochloric acid or acetic acid of the protein hyamine in scintillator solution, however, may result in separation of the liquid phases at temperatures near 0°C, at which counts are usually taken. In case of phase separation, the addition of dioxane or alcohol will restore homogeneity. The acidification has another advantage when hydrogen peroxide is used to bleach a discolored scintillator solution containing a hyamine digest of tissue. Hydrogen peroxide is a quenching substance, and if quenching persists after hydrogen peroxide treatment, the counting rate is restored upon addition of the acid.[65]

It is perhaps the presence of "impurities" which causes chemiluminescence when simple paper, for example, of a chromatogram is added to toluene–PPO–POPOP. The phenomenon could be eliminated in a scintillator solvent with high water-holding capacity upon acidification with hydrochloric acid.[14] A similar chemiluminescence perhaps due to proteins, amino acids, or "impurities" may be observed when biological material extracted from animal tissue with acetic alcohol or dilute alcohol is introduced into a conventional scintillator solution.

In their work on the phosphorescence of various materials, Lloyd and collaborators[89] found that optical filtration of the photons emitted by phosphorescence led to a more selective registration of the photon pulses caused by the isotope of the sample. It would be interesting to see whether the application of an optical filter could also partly discriminate against photon spectra from chemiluminescence.

It is recommended that in case of doubt as to the presence of chemiluminescence or phosphorescence the samples should be counted repeatedly at intervals of several hours to check the counting stability. The same procedure in the presence of an isotopic standard checks the operating stability of the counting equipment. It should be routine to use solvents and scintillators of highest purity only. Exposure of counting solutions and vials to daylight prior to counting should be avoided, and dark adaptation should last at least several hours.

3.5. THE BACKGROUND-COUNTING RATE

The statistical variation of a sample-counting rate increases when it approaches the background-counting rate. Sample net counts per minute, which fall within the number of counts per minute expressing the statistical variation of the background, are, of course, meaningless. To be significant, sample net counts should be higher than twice the standard deviation of the background-counting rate. According to the *National Bureau of Standards, U.S. Handbook* 80: "the minimal detectable activity is defined as that activity of a radionuclide concerned, which in a given counting time, increases the reading of the instrument by an amount equal to 3 times the standard deviation of the background recorded at that time." It is clear, then, that all attempts should be made to keep the background-counting rate as low as possible.

In liquid scintillation counting background "noise" arises within the various components of the sample and the counting equipment.[15,153]

The contribution to the background from the phototubes[15] is caused by the emission of electrons also in the dark, a process which is temperature dependent. It can be greatly depressed by keeping the equipment in a freeze cabinet at the lowest possible temperature that is tolerated by the liquid scintillator solution, usually near 0°C. The residual thermionic emission can, moreover, be distinguished to a considerable extent by a coincidence arrangement of two phototubes and by the proper discriminator circuitry so that only few of the random pulses reach the scaler. Other spurious pulses in the phototubes may be caused by scintillations in the glass of the phototubes or in the "light pipers," which facilitate optical contact between sample and phototube. Other contributions to the background may come from accidental vibrations of the settings of phototubes and related equipment. In general, the contribution to the background from "machine noise" other than from the phototubes is very small and negligible.

Radioactive isotopes present as contaminants in the equipment, for example, in the glass and metal used for the housing of the phototubes and for that of the sample, account for a small contribution to the total background when external radiation and cosmic radiation have been reduced to negligible values by adequate shielding.

A major source of background counts originates in the glass vials containing the liquid scintillator. At optimal conditions of the equipment,

TABLE 3.4

EVALUATION OF THE COMPOSITION OF THE BACKGROUND COUNTING RATE[a]

| Sample[b] | H³ settings [counts/50 minutes/channel width (volts)[c]] | |
	10–50	10–∞
Dark vial[d]	125 ± 14.9	245 ± 38.8
Blank sample well	881 ± 37.4	1636 ± 51.1
Empty vial	1895 ± 61.0	2747 ± 76.9
Ethyl alcohol[e]	2066 ± 47.1	3155 ± 50.9
Ethyl acetate	2033 ± 56.9	3079 ± 72.3
Toluene	2420 ± 64.2	3622 ± 92.0
Phenyl isothiocyanate	1722 ± 43.5	2614 ± 42.3
Dioxane[f]	2140 ± 51.3	3140 ± 60.6
PPO in toluene	2382 ± 89.7	4823 ± 142.3
PPO–POPOP–toluene	2407 ± 73.8	4837 ± 94.2

[a] Reproduced by permission of Peng, *Anal. Chem.*[114]

[b] Samples dark-adapted at 0°C overnight before counting. No attempt was made to remove dissolved oxygen from the sample.

[c] Average of more than 20 individual uninterrupted counts.

$$\text{Standard deviation} = \sqrt{\frac{n\Sigma x^2 - (\Sigma x)^2}{n(n-1)}}$$

[d] Glass vial sprayed inside and outside with black paint.

[e] Ten milliliters of solution used in counting.

[f] Frozen at −8°C.

including proper shielding, the K⁴⁰ content of ordinary glass vials may be responsible for as much as 70% of the total background-counting rate.[2] Glass vials with a low K⁴⁰ content are now commercially available for liquid scintillation counting. Even better are vials made of silica.

The components of the background-counting rate expectedly differ for various equipments. The data of Peng,[114] listed in Table 3.4, give an example of a survey of background counts and their sources. The measurements were made in two different channels set for tritium, with an empty vial painted black, with an empty transparent vial, and with various solvents (10-ml volume) and scintillator solutes. All samples had been dark-adapted at 0°C overnight prior to counting. The values were obtained with the automatic Tri-Carb scintillation spectrometer (Packard Instrument Co., Inc.). The background obtained with the dark painted vial indicates chance coincidence of electron emission in the two phototubes. This amounted to about 5% of the total background-counting rate. The counting rate from the empty well indicates the chance coincidence in the phototubes plus the spurious scintillations from the glass envelope of two phototubes facing each other, amounting to about 30% of the background. The transparent empty vial gives the contribution from K^{40} in the glass vial plus chance coincidence and spurious scintillations, about 50–70%. The addition to the background from the samples of various solvents without solutes is attributed to Cherenkov radiations, which are photons produced by charged particles (here of cosmic origin) moving through a medium at high speed. This accounted for 8–9% of the entire background rate. When a scintillator was added to the solvent, the entire contribution from external radiation, mainly cosmic radiation, reached approximately 20–40%. The relative contributions to the background vary when the channel width was reduced to 10–50 volts, as illustrated in Table 3.4. The composition of the background was also checked by Kaufmann and collaborators,[79] who found approximately 2% for chance coincidence and about 50% for "internal gamma contamination," consisting of K^{40} and other radioactive isotopes in the glass vial, the quartz in the phototube face plates, and the stainless steel and lead housing. About 10% of the total background-counting rate was attributable to cosmic radiation and 25% to Cherenkov radiation.

3.6. SIMULTANEOUS ASSAY OF TRITIUM AND C^{14}

Double-tracer methods often add to experimental efficiency, for certain problems they are indispensable. Studies of enzymatic and chemical reaction mechanisms, of isotope effects, analytical yields in isolation procedures, and timing of short-lived biological phenomena, all profit from or depend on simultaneously using tritium and a second label such as C^{14}.

Tritium and C^{14} in one sample can be measured by liquid scintillation counting principally in two ways. One is the separation of the isotopes prior to counting them. Thus, the sample may be burned or combusted and the generated water and carbon dioxide may be trapped separately, and each may be counted independently. The main problem here is to introduce quantitatively the water and the carbon dioxide into the appropriate homogeneous counting system. This method will be discussed later in this chapter. The other approach is to measure tritium and C^{14} contained in one liquid scintillating system. This is possible since the energies of the two radiations differ greatly. The β-radiation from C^{14} is approximately 10 times more energetic than the β-radiation from tritium. The fluorescence in the scintillator and consequently the pulse-height spectrum in the phototubes are accordingly different for the two isotopes.

The two different radiations can be registered by a suitable counting instrument in two separate channels. These channels are selected for a given scintillating system by setting on the counter at a certain high voltage the pulse-height discriminators for optimal "window widths." An instrument with three discriminator controls allows the separation of pulse heights within the range of the spectrum from A to B and from B to C immediately adjacent to each other (see Fig. 3.8). This accounts for the fact that with this arrangement the spectra of two isotope radiations are not sufficiently separated and that at a high voltage, set for tritium to reach a maximum counting rate in the lower channel, the pulses from C^{14} are not registered maximally in the higher channel. Thus, slight fluctuations in the supplied voltage may cause significant changes in the counting rate of C^{14}.

The double-counting technique is greatly improved with newer counters that have four discriminator controls which allow two pulse-height windows, A to B and C to D, to be set not adjacent but separate from each other. An additional feature is the placement of a gain control into the amplifier circuitry by which excessive pulse heights, generated at high voltage by the higher energy regions of the low-energy radiation spectrum, can be reduced to become registered in the selected channel width. These improvements now make it possible to count at one high-voltage setting both tritium and C^{14} simultaneously at the maximum counting rate, e.g., at the balance point; therefore they eliminate almost the total contribution from tritium in the channel set for C^{14}.[75] The counting operation becomes thus more stable and less sensitive to fluctuations in the high-voltage line. Figure 3.12 illustrates the discriminator bias curves for tritium and C^{14} at one operation.

3.6.1. Screening Method, Simultaneous Equation Method, and Discriminator Ratio Method

Okita and collaborators[103] devised the three basic methods to calculate the radioactivity of tritium and C^{14} in one sample from the counting rates in the two channels. For the screening method the two isotopes are assayed successively at two different optimal high-voltage settings, while for the simultaneous equation technique and the discriminator ratio method, both measurements are taken simultaneously at one high-voltage setting. These methods were the first approach to double-isotope counting by the liquid scintillation technique and they found wide interest.[117] Kliman and Peterson[85] preferred the screening method, since inadequate stability of the instrument did not permit the simpler discriminator ratio method with an older type of counter.

The screening method is based on two measurements of the sample at two different high voltages applied to the phototubes. The counting efficiencies are determined with the proper standards of tritium and C^{14}.

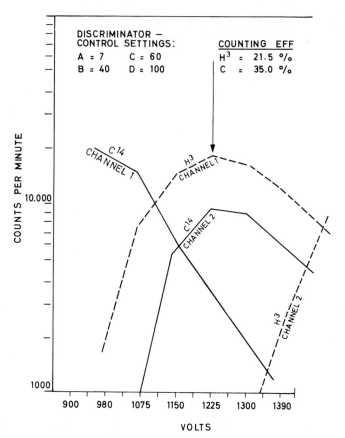

Fig. 3.12. Discriminator bias curves for tritium and C^{14}, obtained in two pulse-height windows, set with four discriminator controls A–B and C–D. Courtesy of Kabara *et al.*, *Advan. Tracer Methodol.*[75]

With the measurement at the two different phototube voltage settings, the pulse heights are discriminated for tritium and C^{14}. At high voltage tritium plus C^{14} is counted, whereas at lower voltage, C^{14} impulses alone are registered. Hence, at the low-voltage measurement the counting efficiency for tritium must be 0, and for C^{14}, above 0, whereas at the high-voltage measurement the counting efficiency for both isotopes must be greater than 0.

When C = C^{14} dpm and H = H^3 dpm and

N_1 = net counts per minute at low voltage
N_2 = net counts per minute at high voltage
h_1 = H^3 efficiency at low voltage

$$h_2 = \text{H}^3 \text{ efficiency at high voltage}$$
$$c_1 = \text{C}^{14} \text{ efficiency at low voltage}$$
$$c_2 = \text{C}^{14} \text{ efficiency at high voltage}$$

and

$$N_1 = Hh_1 + Cc_1$$

and

$$N_2 = Hh_2 + Cc_2$$

If $h_1 = 0$ and $c_1 > 0$ and h_2 and $c_2 > 0$ then

$$C = \frac{N_1}{c_1}, \qquad H = \frac{N_2 - Cc_2}{h_2}.$$

The simultaneous equation method keeps constant the high voltage applied to the phototubes. Two pulse-height windows are set to scale both tritium and C^{14} pulses.

When $C = \text{C}^{14}$ dpm and $H = \text{H}^3$ dpm and

$$N_1 = \text{net cpm in channel 1}$$
$$N_2 = \text{net cpm in channel 2}$$
$$h_1 = \text{H}^3 \text{ efficiency in channel 1}$$
$$h_2 = \text{H}^3 \text{ efficiency in channel 2}$$
$$c_1 = \text{C}^{14} \text{ efficiency in channel 1}$$
$$c_2 = \text{C}^{14} \text{ efficiency in channel 2}$$

then

$$C = \frac{N_1 h_2 - N_2 h_1}{c_1 h_2 - c_2 h_1} \qquad \text{and} \qquad H = \frac{N_1 c_2 - N_2 c_1}{h_1 c_2 - h_2 c_1}$$

The discriminator ratio method simplifies the use of the efficiency factors for tritium and C^{14}, and it gives the lowest counting error of the three methods. As in the simultaneous equation method, the measurements are taken at one high voltage applied to the phototubes with two pulse-height windows selected to discriminate optimally for tritium and C^{14}. This is particularly applicable when four discriminators can be used to choose the appropriate window widths.[75] When

$$N_1 = \text{net count per minute in channel 1}$$
$$N_2 = \text{net count per minute in channel 2}$$
$$H_1 = \text{H}^3 \text{ net count per minute in channel 1}$$
$$H_2 = \text{H}^3 \text{ net count per minute in channel 2}$$
$$C_1 = \text{C}^{14} \text{ net count per minute in channel 1}$$
$$C_2 = \text{C}^{14} \text{ net count per minute in channel 2}$$

and when

$$a = \frac{H_2}{H_1} \quad \text{and} \quad b = \frac{C_2}{C_1}$$

and since

$$N_1 = H_1 + C_1 \quad \text{and} \quad N_2 = H_2 + C_2$$

then

$$H_1 = \frac{bN_1 - N_2}{b - a}, \quad C_2 = \frac{b(N_2 - aN_1)}{b - a},$$

and

$$H^3\text{dpm} = \frac{H_1}{\text{channel 1 } H^3 \text{ efficiency factor}},$$

$$C^{14}\text{dmp} = \frac{C_2}{\text{channel 2 } C^{14} \text{ efficiency factor}}$$

Since impulses from tritium are completely or nearly completely screened out in channel 2 in the counter with four discriminator controls, $a = H_2/H_1$ becomes 0, and the calculations are further simplified. The counting efficiency factors are determined by proper standards.

3.6.2. *Experiences and Errors*

The accuracy of the double-counting technique also depends on the optimal ratio of the isotope contents in the sample. The error is smallest if the ratio, in disintegrations per minute, of tritium over C^{14} is in the range of 1:1 to 15:1 in an instrument with three discriminator controls. Below 1 and above 15 the error of the method increases rapidly. The counting error for tritium rose beyond 6% when the ratio fell below 1; it was 10.5% for a ratio of 0.5 and 19.5% for a ratio of 0.25. The total error, the sum of predictable errors for tritium and C^{14}, was 11% for a ratio of 10, 12% for a ratio of 3, and 15% for a ratio of 1.[85] The ratio may be considerably higher when the pulse-height windows are set by four discriminator controls, as shown in Table 3.5.[75] Even a ratio of 200:1 allowed the tritium counting with an error of less than 2%; it was 11% for C^{14}. A ratio lower than 1 increased the error. It is needless to say that for obtaining a low error the counting rate in each channel must be sufficiently above background, preferably not less than by a factor of 3, if the background rates are approximately 40 cpm.[75,85]

Prockop and Ebert[117] compared various solvent systems as to their capacity to allow an optimal separation of pulse heights from H^3 and C^{14} into two pulse-height windows set with three discriminator controls.

TABLE 3.5

ACCURACY OF ASSAYING DOUBLE-LABEL SAMPLES BY LIQUID
SCINTILLATION COUNTING[a]

H³(dpm)	C¹⁴(dpm)	Ratio of H³:C¹⁴	Error (%)	
			H³	C¹⁴
945	1,768	0.50:1	8.0	1.2
945	884	1.07:1	4.1	2.6
18,912	17,675	1.07:1	4.1	0.3
189,120	176,750	1.07:1	6.5	9.2
9,456	177	5.35:1	0.6	1.6
1,891	177	10.70:1	1.7	1.4
94,560	1,768	53.00:1	2.2	0.6
1,891	18	107.00:1	0.5	23.0
18,912	88	214.00:1	1.6	11.0

[a] All samples were counted for 10 minutes. Reproduced from Kabara et al., Advan. Tracer Methodol.[75]

This study appears particularly desirable since various scintillator solutions produce different pulse-height spectra[28] and different discriminator bias curves, and since solvent systems with a higher capacity for water holding quench various energy levels to a different degree.[13] The authors suggested the use of Methyl Cellosolve in a toluene–PPO–POPOP system. This system allowed not only a good separation of the pulse heights from tritium and C¹⁴ and thus a wide range of stability of counting efficiency versus H^3/C^{14} ratio, but it also had the advantage of accommodating acids and salts. With a ratio of at least 20, for C¹⁴ counts per minute over background counts per minute, up to 0.5 ml of water could be assayed for tritium and C¹⁴ with a small error. The counting error remained low even when in the sample the H^3/C^{14} ratio was as high at 49. Various scintillating systems optimal for different biological material are discussed later in this chapter.

If more than two radioactive isotopes are present in one sample, they can be counted provided the energies of their radiation are sufficiently different. Wu[182] thus assayed from one sample H³, C¹⁴, and P³². The high-energy β-particles of P³² were counted first in a single channel at a lower setting of the high voltage. Subsequently, H³ and C¹⁴ were assayed in two channels simultaneously at a higher voltage.

3.7. COUNTING STATISTICS

The principle methods of statistics in assessing counting rates[109,116] apply, of course, to any type of activity measurement. Still, the number of variables in the scintillation counting technique exceeds those encountered usually with the gas-detection methods. For this reason and to avoid duplication, this section is placed within the context of the liquid scintillation counting technique.

3.7.1. *Stable Counting*

Before attempting a statistical analysis of counting rates, it is important that one makes sure that the counting instrument operates in a stable manner. As mentioned in the previous section, scintillation counting stability is best when the high voltage is at the "balance point." Experimental samples should always be counted repeatedly so that variations in the counting rates may be recognized. For example, if 30 minutes is the desired counting time, a sample may be counted for 5 minutes six times. The minimum counting time required for optimal statistics depends, of course, on the counting rate. If the sample is relatively "hot," single 1-minute counts repeated several times may be sufficient. A counting rate is considered to be significant when it has the value of at least three standard deviations of the background-counting rate.

3.7.2. *The Simple Counting Error*

The statistical analysis of counting rates is rather simple when carried out by standard methods. The appropriate standard error and the significance between two means are usually required.

If the variations in counting rates within a group of comparable counts of one sample are very small, which is often the case with high counts, the counting error can be neglected. The error increases when a counting rate of the experimental sample approaches the value of the background-counting rate and when the counting time is reduced. An ordinary determination of the counting error for one sample includes, therefore, these variables: gross counting rate, background-counting rate, time used to count the gross count of the samples, and the time used to count the background. Thus, a conveniently applicable formula to determine the counting error for low counting rates in per cent was used by Van Slyke and Sinex:[160]

$$\% \text{ error} = \pm \frac{100}{N_s} \times \sqrt{\frac{N_G}{T_G} + \frac{N_B}{T_B}}$$

where N_s is the net count of the sample; N_G, gross count of the sample; N_B, background count; and T_G, T_B, the respective counting times in minutes.

3.7.3. *Propagation of Error in Liquid Scintillation Counting*

In liquid scintillation counting, as Whisman and collaborators[175] have pointed out and as discussed by Herberg,[67, 68] the number of variables

TABLE 3.6

EXPECTED COUNTING ERROR DEPENDING ON COUNTING TIME AND SAMPLE PER
BACKGROUND RATIO[a]

$\dfrac{\text{Net sample cpm}}{\text{Background cpm}}$	Counting time (minutes)	Approximate counting error (%)
1	1	23
	5	10
	10	7
	50	4
2	1	13
	5	6
	10	4
	50	2
5	1	7
	5	3
	10	2–3
	50	Less than 2

[a] Reproduced by permission of Herberg, *Anal. Chem.*[68]

accessible for inclusion in statistical analysis is greater than in ordinary counting procedures. Thus, the counting error may not only be required for the net counting rate of the sample and the background, but perhaps also of the sample and background after addition of an internal standard for quenching determination and of the internal standard itself, all subject to statistical variations. With these variables, the expected errors in per cent were calculated depending on counting time and the relative isotopic count versus background, as shown in Table 3.6. Similar data can be calculated with the formula in Section 3.7.2 if a background of 40 cpm is assumed.

An adequate internal standard counting rate is about 20,000 cpm, and the counting error is negligibly small. But if all variables in the counting precedure and those inherent in the sample preparation, such as pipetting, are to be considered for the estimation of the over-all error of the method, the necessary mathematical steps become quite complicated, and they should be programmed for an electronic computer. Herberg[68] gives the equations by which the per cent error in a counting rate, corrected for counting efficiency, can be determined. The mathematics are based on the propagation of error equation, by which an unspecified number of independent variables can be utilized.

3.8. THE APPLICATION OF VARIOUS SCINTILLATING SYSTEMS

The technique of liquid scintillation counting has been adapted to a large variety of substances. With all adaptations and applications, it is paramount to achieve an intimate contact of the tritium-containing compound with the scintillator system. The best efficiency is obtained when all components form a stable solution which does not show phase separation at the temperature used for counting, usually about 0°C.

The efficiency of liquid scintillation counting is lower than that of the gas-counting technique. The overall efficiency is nevertheless frequently superior in liquid scintillation counting, because relatively large amounts of a sample can be assayed. For comparing the over-all counting efficiencies of various scintillating systems, the actual counting efficiency of a scintillator solution determined with an appropriate internal standard is related to the amount or volume of dissolved substance that is assayed. Thus, the term "figure of merit" was introduced,[83] which is the product of the per cent counting efficiency and the sample amount per the total volume of the scintillating system. The higher the "figure of merit," the higher are the statistically significant counts that can be obtained from a sample. In choosing a suitable scintillator solution for counting a particular substance one must therefore not only consider the absolute counting efficiency, but also the total volume of sample substance that can be introduced into the solution. Thus, a low counting efficiency may be compensated for by a large volume of substance; on the other hand, a system with a high counting efficiency needs only a small volume of sample to yield a sufficient "figure of merit."

Several scintillating systems will be presented since they proved useful for different substances. Various systems are shown in Table 3.7. The scintillator solution should be identical for all samples of one experiment. Unless a heterogeneous system is used, homogeneity of the different liquid phases in the counting vial must be assured, usually by vigorous shaking and checking at the temperature which is chosen for the counting. Chemiluminescence and phosphorescence should be prevented and quenching should be reduced by proper precautions.

3.8.1. *Counting of Substances Soluble in Xylene or Toluene*

The most commonly used solvents and scintillators have already been listed. Accordingly, the following basic scintillator solutions were found to be most useful: 3–5 g/liter of PPO, 0.1–0.3 g/liter of POPOP or dimethyl-POPOP in toluene or xylene; or p-terphenyl in xylene or toluene dissolved to saturation at counting temperature plus 0.1 g/liter of POPOP.

These systems give a counting efficiency of about 15% for tritium and can be counted at 0°C. Because of the limited solubility of the p-terphenyl at lower temperatures, the PPO is generally preferred.

TABLE 3.7

POPULAR AND USEFUL SCINTILLATING SOLUTIONS

Solution	Comments	Reference
Basic scintillator solutions		
1. PPO, 4 g POPOP, 0.1 g Toluene or xylene, 1000 ml	—	55
2. POPOP, 0.1 g/liter *p*-Terphenyl Toluene or xylene (Saturated solution at counting temperature)	—	118, 122
3. PPO, 10 g POPOP, 0.25 g Naphthalene, 100 g Dioxane, 1000 ml	—	49, 172
Systems for counting water and aqueous solutions		
1. PPO, 5 g POPOP, 0.1 g Toluene or xylene, 1000 ml	Holds up to 0.3 ml of H_2O in 10 ml of solvent, with up to 4 ml of absolute ethanol Counting efficiency less than 10%.	56
2. POPOP, 0.1 g/liter *p*-Terphenyl Toluene or xylene (Saturated solution at counting temperature)	As above; without POPOP it is useful for those acids which react with PPO, POPOP	56, 82
3. PPO, 10 g POPOP, 0.25 g Naphthalene, 100 g Dioxane, 1000 ml	Holds 3 ml of H_2O at a counting efficiency of 8% for a 15-ml total volume	172
4. PPO, 10 g POPOP, 0.25 g Naphthalene, 200 g Dioxane, 1000 ml	Holds 1 ml of H_2O at a counting efficiency of 15% for a 15-ml total volume	172
5. PPO, 6.5 g POPOP, 0.13 g Naphthalene, 104 g Methanol, 300 ml Dioxane, 500 ml Toluene, 500 ml	Holds 10% H_2O or concentrated HCl in 10 ml solvent plus 3 ml of $0.5\ M$ ethanolic potassium hydroxide; maximum counting efficiency to 15%	65
6. PPO, 4 g POPOP, 0.2 g Naphthalene, 60 g Ethylene glycol, 20 ml Methanol, 100 ml Dioxane, 880 ml	Holds 10% H_2O at counting efficiency of 10%. For quenching in this system, see Table 3.8	16
Systems for counting in the presence of hyamine		
1. PPO, 9 g POPOP, 0.2 g Toluene, 1000 ml	Holds up to 3 ml of hyamine (wet tissue digest), may be blended into 10 ml of solvent with 2–5 ml of absolute ethanol. Counting efficiency less than 5%	127
2. PPO, 10 g POPOP, 0.25 g Naphthalene, 100 g Dioxane, 500 ml Toluene, 500 ml	Holds up to 5 ml of hyamine (wet tissue digest) may be blended into 10 ml of solvent with 1 ml of dioxane. Counting efficiency about 5% with tissue digest, 2.5% with blood digest	35

Water is essentially insoluble in toluene or xylene. The amount of substances soluble in toluene or xylene is limited by the quenching it produces. The degree of quenching rises exponentially with the amount of the quencher. If the basic scintillator solution is diluted by the addition of a secondary solvent and the substance to be counted, the concentration of the scintillator solute (PPO, POPOP, p-terphenyl, etc.) should be readjusted.

Liquids or solids which are soluble in the standard solvents for the scintillators are, of course, readily and easily prepared for counting. From biological material such substances are extractable with organic solvents, e.g., lipids. The appropriate substance may be directly dissolved in the scintillator or may be added to it in an appropriate volume. Aromatic substances soluble in toluene or xylene may be directly extracted from a water phase by ultrasonic treatment in the counting vial.[134] The method was useful with substances which showed a high partition ratio from the aqueous phase to the scintillator solution. In case of incomplete extraction, which is tested in a separation funnel, the proper correction must be made. Alcohol extracts may contain water-soluble and lipid-soluble material, and it is best to choose a scintillating system for them devised for aqueous solutions.

If a substance is not soluble in xylene or toluene, it may be converted to one that can be easily dissolved or serve as a solvent itself. This has been repeatedly useful for C^{14}-labeled compounds. It is more difficult with tritium-labeled material, since during the chemical reaction tritium may be lost. Bloom,[12] in experiments with C^{14} and tritium-labeled glucose, converted the labeled terminal group of glucose to a derivative of formaldehyde which was soluble in toluene.

If tritium is present as labeled water, it may be transferred via acetylene to benzene which then can serve as a scintillating solvent for PPO, POPOP, and naphthalene.[155] With a commerical benzene synthesizer (Packard Instrument Co.), two samples may be prepared per day. Hydrogen exchange between tritiated water and toluene (with sulfuric acid) was used by Dostrovsky and co-workers[34] to obtain tritium-labeled toluene as the primary solvent in the scintillating system. These methods are designed especially for low-level counting of tritium in natural water and are not optimal for counting tritium in biological tracer studies.

3.8.2. Counting of Water and Aqueous Solutions

Most biological substances, but many of them to a limited degree, are soluble in water, acid, or alkali. They can be assayed in a scintillator solution having the capacity to hold a certain amount of water.

Some of these systems accommodate acids better than others. Very useful are those containing the quaternary amine hyamine, whereby the application of liquid scintillation counting has been expanded to nearly any type of biological material. In the following, the scintillating systems without hyamine will be treated first, and the use of hyamine will be discussed in a separate section.

When in biological material the tritium is bound to water, it may be separated by distillation. If a larger volume of tritiated water is to be counted, for example, from wet tissue, blood, plasma, or urine, the water is obtained by simple distillation or by codistillation with dry benzene.[172] For water samples smaller than 1 ml, one of the microdistillation techniques should be adequate, such as the "cold-finger technique" in which the water is distilled from a total volume of about 1–2 ml at room temperature under vacuum into a small fingerlike container that serves as the cold trap.[161] Ussing and Wernstedt[159] described another useful technique for small water samples. One milliliter or less of the labeled liquid is put into a petri dish (bottom dish). A second petri dish of the same diameter is placed on the first one, margin to margin, so that both form a flat cylinder. The dishes are held together by tape. The bottom dish is placed on a medium hot plate, and on the top dish is placed a beaker with dry ice and alcohol. After the bottom dish has become dry, the water trapped as ice in the top dish is melted and can be transferred with a micropipette into a prepared scintillator solution. The labeled sample should be evaporated to dryness to avoid isotopic fractionation. Urine to be counted may be decolorized with charcoal,[102] if it is not distilled[143] prior to addition to an adequate scintillating system. If a sample has a high salt content, the solubility may be impaired and it may be necessary to desalt prior to adding to the scintillator solution. An ion exchange resin or other desalting devices may be used for this purpose. Rather large quantities of salt, e.g., 2% sodium chloride, may be accommodated in a dioxane–ethylene glycol–methanol system.[16] Acid solutions are usually strong quenchers and may require neutralization without precipitation prior to counting.

A small amount of water or a dilute aqueous solution may be dissolved in toluene or xylene in the presence of a mutual solvent such as absolute alcohol.[56] As more water is added, more ethanol is necessary to maintain a homogeneous phase. When the samples are prepared at room remperature, the homogeneity of the liquid phases must be checked at the temperature used for the actual counting. Two-tenths of a milliliter of water may be brought into 10 ml of toluene, plus PPO as scintillator, at 0°C, with approximately 2.5 ml of absolute ethanol. Addition of solutes to the water changes the optimal volume ratio which can be quickly found by testing with an appropriate un-labeled solution. The counting efficiency, which is optimally about 10% in this system, falls with increasing amounts of water and alcohol. Two and five-tenths of a milliliter of absolute ethanol lowers the counting efficiency to about 5–7%, the addition of 0.2 ml of water depresses it further to about 3–5%. Quenching may be further increased, depending upon the chemical nature of the solutes. The addition of naphthalene to this system, contrary to a dioxane solution, does not increase the counting efficiency[82]; it may rather decrease it[32] if the solution is acidic. Deoxygenation of the counting sample may increase the counting efficiency by a factor of approximately 1.5.[183]

Dioxane as a scintillator solvent, introduced by Farmer and Berstein,[42] accommodates larger volumes of water. However, the counting efficiency with dioxane as the only solvent is much lower than that with toluene or xylene, and dioxane freezes at 12°C. These disadvantages become negligible by the addition of naphthalene[49] and secondary solvents which increase the counting efficiency and lower the freezing point. Dioxane and naphthalene PPO and POPOP in optimal relative concentration may hold 20% water at 3°C with a counting efficiency of 8.6%,[172] yielding thus a very high "figure of merit." Various modifications of the dioxane-naphthalene system suitable for counting at low temperature (see Table 3.7) include, for example, xylene, ethanol, anisole, 1,2-dimethoxyethane, benzyl alcohol, glycerol, and Cellosolve (ethylene glycol, monomethyl ether). The "DAM-611-cocktail," [27] consisting of dioxane, anisole, and dimethoxyethane (6:1:1), can hold as much as one-fourth its volume as water with a counting efficiency of 2–3%. It has been used satisfactorily also to count diluted trichloroacetic acid and biological material dissolved in hyamine.[54] Another particularly useful system was described by Bray.[16] It consists of dioxane, methanol, naphthalene, and ethylene glycol, plus PPO and POPOP, with a high capacity for water, and it remains a homogeneous system at −8°C. It can be used for a large variety of substances including acids, bases, and salts. Table 3.8 gives the quenching effect of various substances with this system.

3.8.3. The Use of Hyamine and Alkali Digests

If a labeled substance is not soluble in water, it may be hydrolyzed in acid or alkali. Thus, animal tissue was prepared for counting after digestion in 1 N potassium hydroxide[17] or in 0.5 M alcoholic potassium hydroxide.[65] Among quaternary amines, hyamine has proved especially useful.

TABLE 3.8

SURVEY OF THE DEGREE OF QUENCHING OF VARIOUS SUBSTANCES IN BRAY'S SOLVENT[a]

Substance	Quenching(%)[b]	Without protein
Sucrose, 1 M	11.7	—
HCl, 1 N	69.5	—
H_2SO_4, 1 N	58.7	—
NaCl, 2%	21.3	—
NaOH, 0.5 N	24.3	—
Tris, 0.2 M, pH 8.2	2.8	—
Acetate, 0.15 M, pH 5.0	2.7	—
Liver homogenate in		
2.5% TCA[c]	26.5	3.6
5% TCA[c]	32.0	5.8
20% TCA[c]	—	43.3
10% Acidic $ZnSO_4$, 0.75 N NaOH	13.7	2.0
5% PCA[d]	56.8	—
Boiled	10.0	26.3
Crude	42.0	—

[a] PPO, 4 g/liter; POPOP, 0.2 g/liter; naphthalene, 60 g/liter; ethylene glycol 20 ml; methanol, 100 ml; dioxane, to 1000 ml. Reproduced by permission of Bray, *Anal. Biochem*.[16]

[b] Data given for 1 ml of solvent added to 10 ml of scintillating solvent.

[c] Trichloroacetic acid.

[e] Perchloric acid.

Hyamine-10X is a registered trademark (Rohm and Haas, Inc.) of (*p*-diisobutylcresoxyethoxyethyl)dimethylbenzylammonium chloride. It was converted to its hydroxide by Passman *et al.*[111] for liquid scintillation counting of labeled carbon dioxide. Besides its alkalinity, hyamine has the advantage of having branched methyl groups which makes it readily soluble in toluene. Hyamine is now routinely used in liquid scintillation counting. It eliminates laborious combustion methods for routine work and can be applied to practically any biological material. The popularity of liquid scintillation counting of tritium and other soft β-emitters is largely due to this quaternary amine.

Recrystallized and purified hydroxide of Hyamine-10X, as a 1.0 M methanolic solution (in short, hyamine) is commerically available. Highest purity is crucial. If the material is impure, recrystallization and treatment with silver oxide (Ag_2O) and daylight illumination are recommended.[40] Impurities may increase the chemiluminescence and the chemical and the color quenching.

Hyamine was used to solubilize tritium-labeled proteins and amino acids by Vaughan *et al.*[162] and Steinberg *et al.*[148, 149] Most amino acids, except arginine, dissolved in hyamine in amounts of approximately 20 mg/ml. Proteins such as insulin, RNase, lysozyme, ovalbumin, and serum albumin in an amount of 10 mg dissolved readily in 1 ml of hyamine at a temperature of 37°C. Mixed tissue proteins, precipitated with trichloro-acetic acid and extracted with ethanol–ether also dissolved readily in amounts of 10 mg/ml of hyaline by heating to 55°–60°C for 1–2 hours. Depending on the type and amount of protein, a yellow-brown discoloration and temporarily high spurious counts owing to chemiluminescence were observed, and correction for the considerable quenching was necessary. Also Radin[119] reported on the potential use of hyamine as a solubilizing agent for a variety of substances: weak acids, crude tissue homogenates, nucleic acids, and purines. More recently, the optimal relationship of sample weight to volume of hyamine in combination with various scintillating systems has been established with the aim of achieving the best counting efficiency with whole-animal tissue and blood.[17,35,52,64,65,127,154]

In principle, approximately 250 mg of wet tissue or about 0.4 ml of blood, added to 1 ml of hyamine, is heated in a closed vessel at a temperature of 45°–65°C until the material is completely dissolved. This may take 24 hours or more. Mechanical shaking during the incubation is helpful. The temperature of incubation should be kept below 65°C to avoid loss of solvent and to minimize the yellowish-brown discoloration, which varies from tissue to tissue, probably with its blood content. Discoloration may be reduced by pretreating the same, for example, with dilute perchloric acid or by shortening the incubation time if possible. This is facilitated by treating the sample with ultrasonics.[121,167] Wet tissue, in general, dissolves more easily than a lyophilized one. Still, lyophilization may be necessary when the moisture content to the fresh tissue leads to a phase separation in the final counting preparation.

Tissue and proteins may also be dissolved in potassium hydroxide (1 N aqueous solution or 0.5 M ethanolic solution) which can then be added to hyamine[17] or directly to an appropriate scintillator solution.[65] The pretreatment with potassium hydroxide may also reduce the discoloration in the hyamine.[17] There was no advantage gained from substituting potassium hydroxide totally for hyamine in work with tritium.[65]

If 1 ml of hyamine is to be counted, it may be added to 19 ml of toluene with PPO and POPOP, giving a counting efficiency of approximately 10–15%.[52] Addition of absolute alcohol to this system allows the relative increase of the volumes of water and hyamine, but it reduces the counting efficiency. Five milliliters of hyamine may be assayed in one counting sample with 10 ml of toluene–dioxane (1:1) with PPO, POPOP, and naphthalene[35] (see Table 3.7). This counting system allows an efficiency of 2.5–5% which varies mainly with the degree of discoloration due to the blood content of the tissue. The relative volumes of hyamine and water should be kept at the minimum, since both are quenchers, and in case of low-level counting it is recommended the optimal volume relationship be tested.[17,152]

If the discoloration of the tissue digest in hyamine is intense, it may be bleached prior to preparing the counting sample by adding to 1 ml of hyamine about three drops of a 30% hydrogen peroxide solution.[65] The complete system after addition of the scintillator solution should then be acidified by adding 0.1 ml of concentrated hydrochloric acid or glacial acetic acid per milliliter of hyamine. Acidification not only eliminates chemiluminescence, but also restores or even improves the counting efficiency after treatment with hydrogen peroxide, which is known to be a quencher. Should acidification lead to phase separation in the cold, addition of ethanol or dioxane will restore the homogeneity. Salt may precipitate upon acidification and can be cleared by centrifugation.

Formamide instead of hyamine was tried by Kinnory and co-workers[84] for preparing organic material for liquid scintillation counting. The technique of preparing the sample appears to be more laborious with formamide than with hyamine, and it has not become popular.

3.8.4. Counting of Acids

Acids are strong quenchers and should be neutralized prior to adding the scintillator solution, or the acid (hydrocholoric, acetic, or formic) may be evaporated. Main and Walwick[96] used formic acid to hydrolyze DNA to nucleotides which, after evaporation in vacuo, were placed in ethanol and counted in toluene–PPO–POPOP. The danger of some loss of tritium by labilization during evaporation, however, must be kept in mind.

Small volumes of acid may be blended into a scintillator solvent with hyamine. The scintillating solvent of Bray[16] shows about 70% quenching when 1 ml of 1 N HCl is added to 10 ml of solvent. According to Herberg,[65] 1 ml of concentrated HCl can be dissolved in 3 ml of 0.5 M ethanolic potassium hydroxide and 10 ml of "Diotol" [65] (see Table 3.7). Sulfuric acid was counted in a system containing Primene 81R, which is a primary amine and a weaker base than hyamine and has branched methyl groups, accounting for its easy solubility in toluene.[120]

If small volumes of a strong acid are to be counted, the toluene (or xylene)–PPO–POPOP (or p-terphenyl) system plus absolute ethanol may be useful. The main quencher in this system is the ethanol. Thus, 0.2 ml of 10% perchloric acid necessitates 3.5 ml of absolute ethanol as a secondary solvent to maintain phase homogeneity with 10 ml of the primary solvent (toluene–PPO–POPOP). Addition of ethanol alone to the toluene–PPO–POPOP drops the counting efficiency to approximately 6%; it falls to about 5% when the acid is introduced. The measurements were taken at a counting temperature of 3°C. The efficiency of p-terphenyl and tetramethylquarterphenyl was found to be less quenched by hydrochloric and nitrous acids than that of PPO in xylene–dioxane–ethanol (2.5:4:3.5).[41] Oxazoles such as PPO–POPOP dissolved in toluene are sensitive to acids perhaps by salt formation[82] and show at times a yellow discoloration upon addition of an acid.[117] This is not observed with p-terphenyl or when the reagents are highly purified. The disturbing yellow discoloration in a toluene–PPO–POPOP system may be reduced in the presence of 6 ml of Cellosolve (ethylene glycol, monomethyl ether) per 10 ml of primary solvent.[117] This system holds 0.5 ml of water and the quenching effect of salts is reduced. Moreover, it proved useful in the double counting of tritium and C[14].

Acids may also be counted by heterogeneous scintillator systems.

3.8.5. *Heterogeneous Counting Systems*

Substances which cannot be brought into homogeneous phase with the scintillating solvent or which are not suitable for counting in a homogeneous phase because of extreme quenching properties can be counted in a heterogeneous system. Thus, suspensions or emulsions may be prepared with a liquid scintillating solvent or absorbed on filter membranes. A liquid may be assayed with the help of solid scintillators such as crystals or plastic scintillators.

Immiscible liquids or solids to be assayed for radioactivity may be emulsified or brought into suspension in a scintillating solvent[59] and held in such state by repeated rapid shaking. When the particles or the fine droplets of the suspension or emulsion are larger in diameter than a few microns, considerable absorption of the tritium β-particles occurs. Suspension or emulsion counting of tritium may therefore not be accepted as a quantitative method unless the size of the droplets or particles in suspension can be controlled or normalized to a standard. Since this is extremely difficult or impossible, the method is not suited for quantitative work and has an expectedly low efficiency. Detergents may have a limited value in improving the counting efficiency of emulsions.[119] These techniques may prove useful in quickly checking semiquantitatively the tritium content in a sample. The results are better in work with C[14].

In order to prevent the suspended particles or droplets in the scintillating solvent from setting, gelling agents were added. It is clear that the addition of a gelling agent to the liquid scintillating system improves only the stability of the system; it does not change particle or droplet geometry and hence does not influence the factor of β-absorption. Still,

samples in gel form can be monitored with greater reliability, reproducibility, and ease, since they do not need to be shaken frequently and
hence can be fed into an automatic sample changer. Gelling agents in
liquid scintillation counting may at times be useful in counting in the
presence of strong quenchers.[63] The reduction of quenching is probably
due to dilution of the sample by the gelling substance.

In 1956, Funt[45] reported a liquid scintillating system containing
aluminum stearate, 5% by weight. After vigorous shaking, gelling was
induced in the counting sample by subsequent heating to 70°C or by
adding 1% phenol. Sixty per cent of the pulse heights of the original
solution was obtained. By using aluminum 2-ethylhexanoate in place of
aluminum stearate, immediate gelling occurred without heating.[48] Thixcin,* a modified hydroxystearate and a derivative of castor oil, has
become a convenient agent to yield "thixotropic gels" with scintillator
solutions.[176] Such gels become fluid when they are agitated and they
reverse to gel on standing. Twenty-five grams of powdered Thixcin are
usually added to 1000 ml of scintillator solution (PPO and POPOP in
toluene) and mixed in a blender for 3 minutes. Twenty-two milliliters
of this scintillator can support 1 g of solid substance in gel and is advantageous for work with C^{14}. In order to prevent the separation of an
aqueous phase from the viscous counting solution in the presence of
Thixcin (3 g/100 ml), hyamine is of benefit.[137] Thus, by supplementing
a 3% Thixcin–toluene–PPO–POPOP solution with 5% hyamine, 1 ml of an
aqueous solution could be supported by 19 ml of solvent in a stable emulsion. The prepared samples were shaken manually and then treated by
ultrasound for 15 minutes to assure a thorough mixing of the components.
When more than 1 ml of aqueous solution was added, the efficiency of the
technique fell rapidly.

Another thixotropic gel, called Cab-O-Sil,† is 99% silica, with a particle size of less than 0.02 μ. It has been used in concentrations of 3–5%
with toluene or dioxane to produce a nearly transparent gel. Cab-O-Sil
has the advantage over Thixcin in that it mixes easily with the solvent
and does not need special blending or heating.[108] Blanchard and Takahashi[11] used Cab-O-Sil for counting labeled polymeric substances which
tend to adsorb on the wall of the counting vial. The Cab-O-Sil prevented this adsorbtion and thus improved the counting efficiency. Small
pieces of thin-layer chromatography plates can be efficiently assayed
when suspended in 15 ml of toluene–PPO–POPOP with 4% Cab-O-Sil.[146]

With Aerosil, another commercial silica gel,** bone particles, finely
ground and sieved, were suspended in toluene, and the counting efficiency

* Baker Castor Oil Co., Inc., 40 Avenue A, Bayonne, New Jersey.
† G. L. Cabot, Inc., 125 High Street, Boston 10, Massachusetts.
** Bush, Beach, and Segner Bayley, Ltd., England.

for tritium was reported to be 6%.[52] The silica gel with xylene, dioxane, ethanol, naphthalene, PPO, and POPOP gave a suitable system for assaying urine.[24]

Instead of keeping small particles suspended in a gel, adsorption to a filter membrane or filter paper may be simple and may give adequate results.[47] The sensitivity of the technique depends, of course, on the reproducibility with which tritium can be counted from a disc or strip of filter membrane or paper. Indeed, the counting is reproducible when the position of the paper or membrane before the phototubes is kept constant.[166] When a paper strip with a tritiated compound adsorbed on it is suspended perpendicularly in the scintillating solvent, a counting efficiency of 1.5% was obtained with a standard deviation of 2% from the mean of four replicate samples. The counter had two phototubes in coincidence circuit. Reproducible counts were also obtained when a zonal strip from a paper chromatogram was placed into the solvent in in the vial as a small upright cylinder.[91]

Any solute may be dried on discs of filter paper, which can then be placed into the counting vial containing toluene–PPO–POPOP,[10,94] similar to the technique of Mans and Novelli.[93] The counting efficiency for tritium varies with the amount of substance adsorbed; it was about 2.5% with a trichloroacetic acid extract of tissue culture cells and the data were reproducible from each of triplicate samples. Whole bacteria (*Escherichia coli*) containing tritium were assayed from a filter membrane submerged in a liquid scintillating system,[5,80] and it was shown that, mainly for geometrical reasons, this technique was superior to the use of paper discs.[5]

Steinberg[150,151] has successfully used a different approach to count larger amounts of liquids not suitable for counting with a liquid scintillator. Small beads or crystals of a solid scintillator can be suspended in the liquid to be assayed.

Plastics with embedded scintillators such as *p*-terphenyl or PPO behave very much like liquid solvents with regard to the transfer process of excitation energy leading to the emission of photons.[169] Although these have proved useful for higher energy β-radiations, tritium radiation is too weak to obtain a reasonable counting efficiency. Scintillator crystals, especially anthracene crystals, because of their low solubility, are, however, suitable.[69,151]

Anthracene gives as high a counting efficiency as PPO crystals. The fluorescence from anthracene shows peaks at 445 and 422 mμ, a range of the spectrum which corresponds to the sensitivity range of the phototubes.

The counting efficiency with a solid scintillator suspended in a liquid to be assayed increases linearly with the volume of the liquid added until

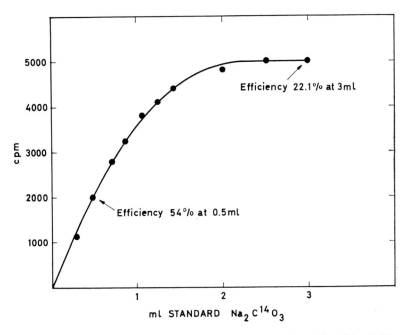

Fig. 3.13. An example of the limits of efficiency in counting with solid scintillators. Anthracene crystals, 1 g, were wet with an increasing volume of a liquid containing a C^{14} standard ($Na_2C^{14}O_3$). For tritium, the plateau is reached with a volume of 0.6 ml (see text). Courtesy of Steinberg, *Anal. Biochem.*[151]

a plateau is reached, after which the registered counts reflect solely the specific activity, a situation analogous to counting from an infinitely thick layer of labeled solids (see Fig. 3.13). The "plateau volume" is also the optimal volume for peak efficiency. It is reached when all of the crystals are coated with the liquid to be counted. The use of a detergent can prevent the floating of the crystals. Using anthracene crystals in work with tritium, Myers and Rosenblum[100] found the optimal volume to be 0.6 ml for 1 g of crystals. The counting efficiency ranged about 2%. Anthracene crystals mixed with POPOP (9:1) were used by Scharpenseel and Menke[130] to assay aqueous solutions. They obtained a counting efficiency of 1%. Grinding the anthracene crystals to a smaller size did not improve the counting efficiency, but rather decreased it nearly twofold.[100]

A particular advantage of this method is the lack of chemical quenching, since there is no energy transfer such as in the liquid solvents. Only color quenching and turbidity are of importance with this technique. Absorption measurements of colored solutions at 400 mμ are sufficient in most instances to correct for quenching with the help of an appropriate standard reference curve. The low counting efficiency of

2% or less is not a disadvantage of the method, since it is compensated for by the advantage of measuring relatively large volumes and by its usefulness in all those situations in which a scintillator solution is insufficient or inapplicable. The choice of the liquids for counting is limited only by the chemical interaction with the anthracene crystals. The technique further permits easy recovery of the substance after counting. Scintillator crystals found a particularly useful application for assaying tritium in effluents from chromatographic columns, which is discussed later in this chapter.

Plastic scintillators used as containers and mounted directly on a phototube can hold labeled liquids or solids. This was found to be unsuitable for tritium,[74] contrary to work with C^{14}. Plastic scintillators have also been applied to measuring tritium activity in effluents from chromatographic columns with little success (see Section 3.10).

3.9. COMBUSTION TECHNIQUES WITH LIQUID SCINTILLATION COUNTING

The various heterogeneous scintillation counting systems discussed thus far are often inadequate for low-level counting. The problem is overcome by burning the labeled substance. The generated water can then be counted with a relatively high over-all efficiency. Combustion techniques for liquid scintillation counting are similar to those which have been described for gas counting (discussed earlier in this chapter), and methods using sealed tubes, furnaces, or bombs are suitable for both. Combustion in flasks has been adapted especially for scintillation counting for the convenience of generating water and preparing the counting sample quickly. It is reemphasized that tritium-labeled material must be burned completely to avoid isotopic fractionation.

Conventional chemical combustion techniques are time consuming. For example, labeled organic material may be oxidized in sealed glass tubing in the presence of copper oxide.[73] After breaking the tube, the generated water is collected by vacuum distillation and is added to a liquid scintillator for tritium counting. Kelly and collaborators[81] preferred the combustion technique that was originally described by Schöniger.[131] The principle of the device is shown in Fig. 3.14. A heavy walled flask is equipped with a platinum basket which is suspended from the stopper of the flask and connected to a discharge circuit. Dried or wet organic material, approximately 200 mg wrapped in filter paper or placed into a dialysis casing, or liquids poured into gelatinous capsules can be placed into the basket so that they can be burned in a atmosphere of pure oxygen upon closing the electrical current. The generated water is cold-trapped on the bottom of the flask set on ice. After combustion, the proper scintillator solution is placed in the flask to absorb the tritiated

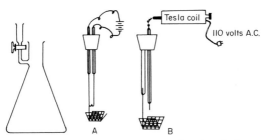

FIG. 3.14. The components of a "Schöniger" combustion flask used for generating tritiated water and/or C^{14} dioxide. Two types of ignition are given as A and B. (Courtesy of Kelly et al., Anal. Biochem.[81]

water. Water can be placed in the bottom of the flask prior to combustion to serve as a carrier of the tritiated water generated by the combustion.[38] An aliquot of the water is finally assayed by liquid scintillating counting. The induction coil ignition may be replaced by an infrared light ignition, which lacks an external electrical circuit, permitting the use of simple rubber stoppers on the flasks.[104] Dobbs[31] modified the flask so that it had three necks and a round bottom. Samples which did not burn well were mixed with cellulose powder. Liquid samples were placed in gelatinous capsules. The combustion was triggered by an electrical discharge. The liquid scintillator containing an aliquot of water was injected conveniently through a side arm into the flask prior to its opening to avoid losses of radioactivity by evaporation. Flushing the system with nitrogen improved the counting efficiency.

The above flask-combustion techniques are limited thus far to a sample size of several hundred milligrams. If gram amounts of tissue are to be employed in one step, bomb-combustion techniques are preferred. Shepperd and Rodegker[139] thus used a bomb-combustion system to analyze the tritium contained in 1–1.5 g of dry biological material. The water and carbon dioxide generated in the combustion were collected in a cool trap in a vacuum train. The tritiated water was finally transferred into ethanol for scintillation counting. An oxygen bomb-combustion technique for up to 2 g of biological material was reported also by McFarlane and Murray.[95] The arrangement of the vacuum train of traps attached to the exhaust of the bomb is shown in Fig. 3.15. After combustion under 250–300 lb of oxygen pressure, the carbon dioxide and water are trapped together in the cold spiral, from which the carbon dioxide is transferred below 0°C into the "cold finger" immersed in liquid nitrogen. After manometric measurement, the CO_2 is added to phenethylamine, which may be dissolved in a liquid scintillator for the assay of C^{14}. The tritiated water is then separately distilled into a cold trap in which it is weighed. It is

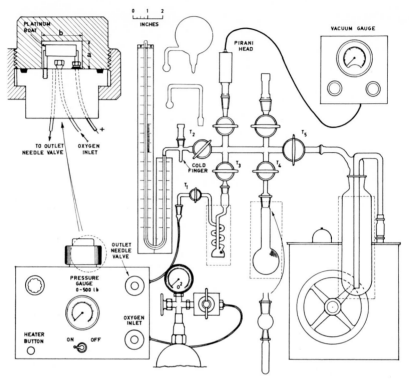

FIG. 3.15. Vacuum train and traps connected to the exhaust of a combustion bomb; to prepare tritiated water and/or C^{14} dioxide from labeled material for liquid scintillation counting (see text). Courtesy of McFarlane et al., Anal. Biochem.[95]

finally dissolved in dioxane and then added to the appropriate scintillator solution.

3.10. SCINTILLATION COUNTING OF CHROMATOGRAPHIC EFFLUENTS

Scintillation counting devices have been modified to assay effluents of chromatographic columns. Although proportional gas-flow counters and ionization-flow chambers (discussed earlier in this chapter) are highly efficient in most instances for work with gas chromatography, scintillation counting has also been used. The latter is especially suited to liquid effluents. Scintillator solutions and solid scintillators have both proved useful.

A plastic scintillator in the form of a capillary approximately 1 m long and wound in a tight spiral was tried in assaying gaseous effluents labeled with C^{14}.[46] It was of little value for tritium counting. For C^{14} the counting efficiency was 58%. Scintillator crystals, such as anthracene[130] and particularly p-terphenyl crystals coated with silicone oil,[78] were, however, efficient for low-level tritium counting. p-Terphenyl crystals coated with silicone oil were found to be superior to anthracene. They could easily be put into toluene containing PPO prior to counting and gave a higher counting efficiency. Therefore, cartridges were filled with the silicone-coated crystals and were set up as traps for the effluent gas after passage through a combustion train. They were exchanged periodically and prepared for counting. This scintillation device, according to Karmen et al.,[78] gave a better overall sensitivity and efficiency for low-level counting than the ionization chamber. A high counting efficiency with C^{14} was obtained by Love and Moore[92] who condensed the effluent hot gases directly into a scintillator solution which circulated in cooled tubing connected to a cell that was mounted directly on a phototube. Dutton[36] describes an automatic device to condense gas in a scintillator solution and fill single vials with the condensed gas. This is particularly advantageous for tritium counting since the single vials can be stored and assayed for any length of time and still yield good counting statistics.

Liquid effluents from chromatographic columns may be introduced directly into a liquid scintillator, perhaps after volume concentration. Thus, each sample fraction collected from the column may be counted separately. Various automatic devices to place the effluent directly into a scintillator solution have been described. In one method the aqueous effluent was mixed with a liquid scintillator and passed through a coiled or bent glass tubing placed between two phototubes.[130] With this arrangement, the counting efficiency for tritium was in the range of 2–4%. In case the effluent liquid does not dissolve well in a scintillator solution, scintillator crystals are useful. For example, a cell of 1-ml volume filled with anthracene crystals was constructed for an automatic amino acid analyzer; a counting efficiency of 2% for tritium was obtained.[133] In another arrangement, consisting of a bent glass tube filled with powdered anthracene and POPOP in optical contact with the phototubes, the counting efficiency was 1%.[130] The variation in counting efficiencies with anthracene may have been due to different sizes of the crystals and different relationships of crystal weight to liquid volume.

Despite the fact that plastic scintillators are practically inapplicable for tritium work, their use for assaying liquid chromatographic effluents should be mentioned here to illustrate their applicability to isotopes emitting a higher energy radiation than does tritium. In 1957, Schram and Lombaert[132] spread the liquid effluent over the surface of a plastic scintillator which was mounted on a phototube connected to a discriminator

circuit. A hollow ball of polyvinyl toluol with embedded scintillating molecules was used by Krakau and Schneider.[87] The liquid effluents were chan-
nelled through the ball, which was placed between two phototubes. For C^{14}
the counting efficiency was as high as 88%. Instead of a plastic sheet or a
plastic ball, Funt and Hetherington[46] used a capillary tubing 1 m in length,
made a scintillating plastic. The capillary was wound in a tight spiral and
put into silicone oil in front of the phototube, allowing a counting efficiency
of 58% for C^{14}. Scharpenseel and Menke[130] dimininshed the inner diameter
of the plastic tubing through which the liquid effluent passed to 0.7 mm. In
another attempt, small beads made of plastic scintillator (diameter 0.5
mm) were used. The tritium-counting efficiency with these devices was
below 1%. In a different approach exchange resins containing a scintillator can be of value to assay adsorbed material. When the resin particles were put in toluene, the counting efficiency for C^{14} was 35%.[62] The
technique appears to be of little value for tritium counting.

4. Measurement of Tritium in Paper or Thin-Layer Chromatograms

Paper or thin-layer chromatograms may be analyzed for tritium in
various ways. Long strips of the chromatogram may be scanned by gas
counters or liquid scintillation counting, or the chromatogram may be
divided into small zones for individual measurements. Likewise, chromatographic "spots" may be cut out. Eluates of such zones or spots can
be monitored by liquid scintillation counting. The separated zones or spots
may be burned to yield tritiated water for liquid scintillation counting or
may be reduced further to hydrogen–tritium gas for gas counting. Finally,
radioactivity may be localized in a chromatogram by the autoradiographic technique in which the amplification of the weak β-radiation by
a scintillator proved useful.

Because of the low energy of the tritium radiation, the counting
efficiency is lowest with direct scanning techniques. It is even less con-
trollable in paper chromatograms because of the irregular geometry
inherent in the texture of the paper. Even under optimal conditions,
tritium is counted from a dry solid paper or a gel of a thin-layer
chromatogram with an efficiency below 1%.

4.1. Assaying of Single Chromatographic Zones

The highest accuracy and efficiency is obtained when chromatographic
zones or "spots" are measured individually by the combustion or elution
technique. The latter is the simpler technique and has the advantage of
permitting spectrophotometric analysis prior to adding the eluate to a
proper scintillating solvent without the paper. Or the eluate may be
and the volumes of the eluates of a series of zones or "spots" should be

constant to ease subsequent calculations. Thus, spots or zones of paper chromatograms are cut into small pieces which are transferred to an elution vessel containing a measured volume of solvent such as water, dilute acid, or base. The elution may be carried out directly in the counting vial, to which a proper scintillating solvent is added later. Depending on the amount of paper used, it may be necessary to elute in a separate vessel and transfer by filtration the eluate or part of it to the proper scintillating solvent without the paper; or the eluate may be evaporated to dryness in the counting vial and redissolved in a small volume of a proper solvent prior to addition of the scintillator solution.

Small sections of gel of thin-layer chromatograms containing tritiated substances do not need elution, but may be directly suspended in a liquid scintillating solvent system containing a thixotropic agent such as Cab-O-Sil, in a concentration of 4%.[146] An apparatus for cutting thin-layer plates into small zones of reproducible width for liquid scintillation counting has been described.[147]

Simpler methods than the elution or combustion techniques in preparation for liquid scintillation or gas counting may be more convenient, but they fail to give a comparable efficiency. For example, a section of a paper chromatogram may be directly submerged in a scintillator solution contained in a regular counting vial. This technique has already been mentioned in the section on heterogeneous counting systems. For reproducible counting, the position of the paper submerged in the liquid scintillator is critical. When, for example, the piece of paper was formed into a small cylinder and was put upright into the counting vial filled with scintillator solution, reproducibility in counting was satisfactory,[91] however, with some sacrifice of efficiency. If the small paper strip was oriented parallel to the axis joining two phototubes, the efficiency was lower; still as little as 1.5% variation within ten repeated counting rates was observed with this arrangement.[29] Wang and Jones[166] suspended the paper strip perpendicularly in the scintillating solvent. A counting efficiency of 1.5% for tritium was thus obtained with a standard deviation of 2% from the mean of four replicate samples. It is clear that the position of a paper strip in the counting vial should be the same for each sample. Otherwise discrepancies in relative efficiency of perhaps 10% or more are to be expected. The thickness and quality of the paper also influences the counting efficiency.[91]

4.2. Assaying by Continuous Scanning

Continuous scanning of a whole strip of a chromatogram is also feasible with tritium, provided the specific activity of the substances adsorbed to the paper or thin-layer chromatogram is high enough.

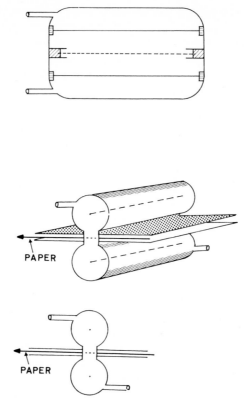

FIG. 3.16. The principal design of a double gas-flow counter for scanning paper chromatograms. The paper strip is led through a slit to be assayed by the counting chambers from both sides simultaneously. Adapted from Osinski, *Intern. J. Appl. Radiation Isotopes.*[105]

Several gas-counting devices have already been mentioned in Section 2.2.3. Particularly successful are those with a "four-π geometry." Osinski[105] thus constructed a four-π windowless gas-flow counter which consists of two separate chambers with open windows that face each other and are far enough apart so that a paper strip may be led through the slit, as schematically indicated in Fig. 3.16. In that way the paper strip is scanned simultaneously from both sides. With tritium on the paper a maximum efficiency of 1% was obtained. A similar counter was introduced by Wenzel.[170] For scanning thin-layer chromatograms, two-π gas-counting devices are applicable and may be brought into close contact with the surface. Thus, Schulze and Wenzel[135] described a proportional gas-flow counter with an open slit that may be directly applied to the surface of thin-layer chromatograms. The counting efficiency for tritium in a layer 0.25 mm thick was approximately 0.3–0.4%. This counter has been modified for scanning paper chromatograms also.[8] Another device introduces the total paper strip, which is put on a cylinder, into a container filled with argon–methane as the counting gas. Within the enclosure, the paper is passed along a windowless gas-flow counter. In this manner, 3.3×10^{-3} μc of tritium could be detected on paper.[22]

Paper chromatograms may be scanned also by scintillation techniques. In case the adsorbed substances are insoluble in organic solvents, the paper may be placed in a container holding a scintillator solution, in which it is automatically passed along a phototube with a narrow window. Or a crystalline scintillator may be sprayed on the paper; thus, anthracene dissolved in benzene led quickly to a dry layer of microcrystals of anthracene on the paper.[136] The paper thus prepared can be monitored by a phototube. The counting efficiency for tritium was reported to be 0.80%. A remarkable counting efficiency of 10% or more was reported when the paper strip was prepared by soaking in a toluene solution of a plastic scintillator or when it was placed between two sheets of tissue paper soaked with the dissolved plastic. After drying, the intimate contact of the scintillator in the plastic with the substance adsorbed by the paper assured an efficient output of photons.[26]

Paper and thin-layer chromatograms may be effectively assayed with the help of photographic film. Although this method is very efficient for isotopes with more energetic radiation, in the case of tritium additional manipulations are required. For work with thin-layer chromatograms as well as with paper chromatograms, Sheppard and Tsien[140] successfully used dry nuclear track emulsion NTB supported on glass plates (Kodak). These plates could be pressed tightly onto dry thin-layer chromatograms or onto paper on a firm support. At the end of the photographic exposure time, the photographic plates could be separated from the chromatograms and developed. After 1 week of exposure, 0.01 μc of tritium per spot was detected. Coating the nuclear track plates with a 0.05% aqueous solution of chrome alum $[CrK(SO_4)_2 \cdot 12H_2O]$[140] or spraying the chromatogram with a dissolved plastic[147] facilitated the separation prior to photographic development.

Various scintillators have been tried to amplify the weak β-radiation from tritium to produce an image in a photographic film. Wilson[177] soaked the paper chromatogram in a liquid scintillator in a flat, light-tight tank. An X-ray film was placed firmly on the paper. After a suitable exposure time, the film was removed from the paper and dried from the liquid scintillating solvent so that it could be processed photographically. The images were reasonably good. Autoradiograms may thus be obtained from paper chromatograms, as long as the substances localized in the "spots" are not soluble in the solvent of the scintillator. Substances soluble in the scintillator solution will, of course, not remain in position on the paper during the exposure time. A better way perhaps is to spray the paper with a saturated solution of anthracene in benzene, as described by Seliger and Agranoff.[136] The benzene evaporates and leaves microcrystals of anthracene on the paper, avoiding displacement of adsorbed substances prior to application of the film. For preparing thin-layer chromatograms for autoradiography a scintillator solution may be sprayed on, or the scintillator, such as PPO and POPOP, may be mixed on the layer plate beforehand.[135] A mixture of anthracene powder and silica gel had the same properties as pure silica gel for thin-layer chromatography.[168] The anthracene increased the autoradiographic efficiency about 100 times, and 0.005 μc of tritium produced a spot on an X-ray film after 1 day of exposure at $-70°$C.

Paper chromatograms may be coated or soaked with liquid photographic emulsion or "nuclear track emulsion." [115,123] Most intimate contact is thus provided between the silver halide crystals of the emulsion and the tritium-labeled substance in the paper, and the efficiency is therefore rather high. After a sufficient exposure time in the cold and in a dry atmosphere, photographic development is the same as for ordinary film. The method has, however, the serious disadvantage that it is not applicable to water-soluble substances, since they are diluted and displaced when the paper is soaked with the liquid photographic emulsion. Displacement of water-soluble compounds may be less drastic when the liquid-film emulsion is applied with a spray apparatus.[23]

An attractive technique appeared to be the substitution of the thin layer in agar gel electrophoresis by a photographic film (Kodirex) soaked with the buffer. The electrophoresis was carried out in the darkroom.[88] After the electrophoretic run, the film was dried, stored for exposure, and finally developed.

Foss[44] has suggested a novel technique of measurement for tritium in an intact paper chromatogram which combines autoradiography, radioiodine bound to the silver grains of the developed film emulsion, and an ordinary chromatographic strip scanner. The first step is to prepare a suitable autoradiogram by one of the photographic techniques. Then, after photographic development, the autoradiogram is treated further with inorganic I^{131} to bind it to the silver grains in the film. The position of the I^{131} bound in the film can be easily determined by ordinary counting devices with a relatively high sensitivity; I^{131} thus denotes the position of the tritium.

5. Measurement of Tritium in Very High Concentrations

Special modifications of counting devices have been reported to measure tritium in very high concentrations, which only rarely are of interest to biological investigators. Quick checking of very high specific activities may be needed during the preparation of tritium-labeled molecules, in certain health physics problems, and in chemistry, physics, and industry.

For this purpose a single phototube may monitor a liquid scintillation system in such a way that not electronic pulses but an integral current in μa is registered in a suitable recorder. A current of about 0.2 μa may be obtained from 1 μc of tritium, so that samples containing several microcuries may be measured.[37, 174]

Another method of counting tritium makes use of the "Bremstrahlung" (roentgen radiation) that is generated by the β-particles in matter. This "Bremstrahlung" is very weak, yielding only 1–2 cpm per 1 μc of tritium.[6,173] The "Bremstrahlung" itself is assayed by a Geiger-Müller counter without the problem of radiation absorption.

6. Conclusion

It is apparent that there is no barrier anymore to counting tritium in any biological substance. The appropriate counting equipment, discussed here in principle, is commercially available and can be handled with great ease. It is hoped that this chapter will guide the reader in the selection of the technique and equipment best suited for his purpose.

In view of the possibility of labeling with tritium any biological compound and of counting it in any form, it is not surprising that the amount of literature on the use of tritium-labeled compounds in biology and medicine is rising very rapidly. The need for caution is obvious, for it is now possible, after all, to have tritium trace an unknown compound through unknown reactions to unknown end products. One is confronted at times with this extreme situation in the study of the site of cellular metabolism by the autoradiographic technique, which is discussed in the following chapter.

REFERENCES

1. H. J. Ache, A. Thiemann, and W. Herr, Radiogaschromatographische Analyse Tritium markierter aromatischer Nitro- und Halogen-verbindungen bei höheren Temperaturen, *Z. Anal. Chem.,* **181**: 551 (1961).
2. B. W. Agranoff, Silica Vials Improve Low-Level Counting, *Nucleonics,* **15**(10): 106 (1957).
3. E. L. Alpen and H. G. Mandel, A Rapid Assay for Tritium in Bacterial Cells, *Biochim. Biophys. Acta,* **43**: 317–321 (1960).
4. J. S. Anand and D. Lal, Synthesis of Methane from Water for Tritium Measurement, *Nature,* **201**: 775–777 (1964).
5. S. Apelgot and M. Duquesne, Méthode de scintillation en milieu liquide appliquée à la mésure quantitative du tritium fixé dans les bacteries, *J. Chim. Phys.,* 1961: 774–777 (1961).

6. P. J. Ayers, W. H. Pearlman, D. T. Tait, and S. A. S. Tait, The Biosynthetic Preparation of (16-H³)-Aldosterone and (16-H³)-Corticosterone, *Biochem. J.,* **70**: 230–236 (1958).

7. A. E. Bainbridge, P. Sandoval, and H. E. Suess, Natural Tritium Measurements by Ethane Counting, *Science,* **134**: 552–553 (1961).

8. F. Berthold, Recent Methods for the Automatic Evaluation of Thin-Layer and Paper Radiochromatograms, *Symp. Radioisotope Sample Measurement Techniques Med. Biol. 1965,* Intern. At. Energy Agency, Vienna.

9. J. C. Bevington and D. F. Evans, Experiments with Tritium in Macromolecular Chemistry, *Makromol. Chem.,* **36**: 145–151 (1960).

10. D. Billen, Sedimentation of a DNA-Polymerase Component from Bacterial Extracts, Biochem. Biophys. Res. Commun., **7**: 179 (1962).

11. F. A. Blanchard and I. T. Takahashi, Use of Submicron Silica to Prevent Count Loss by Wall Adsorption in Liquid Scintillation Counting, *Anal. Chem.,* **33**: 975–976 (1961).

12. B. Bloom, The Simultaneous Determination of C^{14} and H^3 in the Terminal Groups of Glucose, *Anal. Biochem.,* **3**: 85–87 (1962).

13. B. Bloom, Use of Internal Scintillation Standards in Heterogeneous Counting Systems, *Anal. Biochem.,* **6**: 359–361 (1963).

14. W. F. Bousquet and J. E. Christian, Quantitative Radioassay of Paper Chromatograms by Liquid Scintillation Counting, *Anal. Chem.,* **32**: 722–723 (1960).

15. I. S. Boyce and J. F. Cameron, A Low Background Liquid Scintillation Counter for Assay of Low Specific Activity Tritiated Water, in *Tritium in the Physical and Biological Sciences, Symp. Intern. At. Energy Agency,* **1**: 231–247 (1961).

16. G. A. Bray, A Simple Liquid Scintillator for Counting Aqueous Solutions in a Liquid Scintillation Counter, *Anal. Biochem.,* **1**: 279–285 (1960).

17. W. O. Brown and H. G. Badman, Liquid Scintillation Counting of C^{14}-Labelled Animal Tissues at High Efficiency, *Biochem. J.,* **78**: 571–578 (1961).

18. G. L. Brownell and H. S. Lockhart, CO_2 Ion Chamber Techniques for Radiocarbon Measurement, *Nucleonics,* **10** (2): 26 (1952).

19. E. T. Busch and D. L. Hansen, Improvement of Liquid Scintillation Counting Efficiencies by Optimization of Scintillator Composition. Relative Efficiencies for Three New Fluors, *Symp. Radioisotope Sample Measurement Techniques Med. Biol. 1965,* Intern. At. Energy Agency, Vienna.

20. F. Cacace and I. Ul Haq, Radiometric Analysis of Tritiated Organic Compounds by Means of Vapor Phase Chromatography, *Science,* **131**: 732–733 (1960).

21. A. Caillot, G. Courtois, R. M. Hours, Y. Filipecki, and I. C. Tanguy, Some Aspects of the Measurement of Low Levels of Tritium by Liquid Scintillation Counting, *Symp. Radioisotope Sample Measurement Techniques Med. Biol., 1965,* Intern. At. Energy Agency, Vienna.

22. F. J. Carleton and H. R. Roberts, Determination of the Specific Activity of Tritiated Compounds on Paper Chromatograms Using an Automatic Scanning Device, *Intern. J. Appl. Radiation Isotopes,* **10**: 79–85 (1961).

23. J. Chamberlain, A. Hughes, A. W. Rogers, and G. H. Thomas, An Evaluation of the Available Techniques for the Autoradiography of Tritium on Chromatograms, *Nature,* **201**: 774–775 (1964).

24. L. Chanarin, E. H. Belcher, and V. Berry, The Utilization of Tritium Labelled Folic Acid in Megaloblastic Anemia, *Brit. J. Haematol.,* **9**: 456–463 (1963).

25. D. R. Christman, Counting Soft Betas, *Nucleonics,* **19** (5): 51–64 (1961).

26. E. A. Davidson, Techniques for Paper Strip Counting in a Scintillation Spec-

trometer, *Packard Technical Bulletin No. 4* (1962), Packard Instrument Company, Inc., Box 428, La Grange, Illinois.

27. J. D. Davidson and P. Feigelson, Practical Aspects of Internal-Sample Liquid-Scintillation Counting, *Intern. J. Appl. Radiation Isotopes,* **2**: 1–18 (1957).

28. J. D. Davidson, Homogeneous Counting Systems, in *Liquid Scintillation Counting* (C. G. Bell, Jr. and F. N. Hayes, eds.), p. 88, Pergamon Press, London, 1958.

29. J. D. Davidson (1961), Cited by E. A. Davidson, Personal Communication, 1962.

30. H. E. Dobbs, The Detection of Tritium Labeled Compounds in Vapour Phase Chromatography, *J. Chromatog.,* **5**: 32–37 (1961).

31. H. E. Dobbs, Oxygen Flask Method for the Assay of Tritium–Carbon-14–Sulfur-35-Labeled Compounds, *Anal. Chem.,* **35**: 783–786 (1963).

32. H. E. Dobbs, Effect of Naphthalene on the Quenching of Liquid Scintillation Solutions, *Nature,* **197**: 788 (1963).

33. H. E. Dobbs, Measurement of Liquid Scintillation Counting Efficiencies, *Nature,* **200**: 1283–1284 (1963).

34. I. Dostrovsky, P. Avinur, and A. Nir, Liquid Scintillation Counting Method of Natural Tritium and Its Applications to Hydrology and Meteorology, in *Liquid Scintillation Counting* (C. J. Bell, Jr. and F. N. Hayes, eds.), p. 283–287, Pergamon Press, London, 1958.

35. J. Dulcino, R. Bosco, W. G. Verly, and J. R. Maisin, Assay of Tritium and Carbon^{14} in Animal Tissues by Liquid Scintillation, *Clin. Chim. Acta,* **8**: 58–65 (1963).

36. H. J. Dutton, Monitoring Gas Chromatography for H^3- and C^{14}-Labeled Compounds by Liquid Scintillation Counting, *Advan. Tracer Methodol.,* **1**, 147 (1963).

37. C. Eaborn, E. Matsukawa, and R. Taylor, Measurement of Tritium, *Rev. Sci. Instr.,* **28**: 725–726 (1957).

38. J. F. Eastham, H. L. Westbrook, and D. Gonzales, Liquid Scintillation Detection of Tritium and Other Radioisotopes in Insoluble or Quenching Organic Samples, in *Tritium in the Physical and Biological Sciences, Symp. Intern. At. Energy Agency,* **1**: 203–208 (1961).

39. M. L. Eidinoff, The Quantitative Measurement of Tritium: Hydrogen-Alcohol-Argon Mixtures, *J. Am. Chem. Soc.,* **69**: 2504–2507 (1947).

40. F. Eisenberg, Jr., Preparation of the Alkaline Absorbent for Radioactive CO_2 in Liquid Scintillation Counting, in *Liquid Scintillation Counting* (C. G. Bell, Jr. and F. N. Hayes, eds.), pp. 123–125, Pergamon Press, London, 1958.

41. G. Erdtmann and G. Herrmann, Tritiumzählung in flüssigen Szintillatoren mit *p*-oligo-phenylen, *Radiochim. Acta,* **1**: 103–107 (1963).

42. E. C. Farmer and I. A. Berstein, Determination of Specific Activities of C^{14} Labeled Organic Compounds with a Water-Soluble Liquid Scintillator, *Science,* **115**: 460 (1952).

43. L. E. Feinendegen, V. P. Bond, W. W. Shreeve, and R. B. Painter, RNA and DNA Metabolism in Human Tissue Culture Cells Studied with Tritiated Cytidine, *Exptl. Cell Res.,* **19**: 443–459 (1960).

44. O. P. Foss, personal communication, 1961.

45. B. L. Funt, Scintillating Gels, *Nucleonics,* **14** (8): 83–84 (1956).

46. B. L. Funt and A. Hetherington, Spiral Capillary Plastic Scintillation Flow Counter for Beta Assay, *Science,* **129**: 1429–1430 (1959).

47. B. L. Funt and A. Hetherington, Scintillation Counting of Beta Activity on Filter Paper, *Science,* **131**: 1608–1609 (1960).

156   TRITIUM-LABELED MOLECULES IN BIOLOGY AND MEDICINE

48. B. L. Funt, Scintillation Counting with Organic Phosphors, *Can. J. Chem.,* **39:** 711–716 (1961).
49. M. Furst, H. Kallmann, and F. H. Brown, Increasing Fluorescence Efficiency of Liquid-Scintillation Solutions, *Nucleonics,* **13** (4): 58–60 (1955).
50. M. Furst and H. Kallmann, Concentration Quenching of Liquid Scintillators, in *Liquid Scintillation Counting* (C. G. Bell, Jr. and N. F. Hayes, eds.), pp. 237–245, Pergamon Press, London, 1958.
51. R. F. Glascock, *Isotopic Gas Analysis for Biochemists,* Academic Press, New York, 1954.
52. K. Halvorsen, Direct Measurement of Tritium in Biological Materials with the Liquid Scintillation Counter, in *Tritium in the Physical and Biological Sciences, Symp. Intern. At. Energy Agency,* **1:** 313–323 (1961).
53. J. Hasan, A Zinc Fusion Method for the Determination of Tritium in Biological Material by Gas Counting, in *Tritium in the Physical and Biological Sciences, Symp. Intern. At. Energy Agency,* **1:** 361–368 (1961).
54. J. H. Hash, Determination of Tritium in Whole Cells and Cellular Fractions of *Bacillus megaterium* Using Liquid Scintillation Techniques, *Anal. Biochem.,* **4:** 257–267 (1962).
55. F. N. Hayes, R. D. Hiebert, and R. L. Schuch, Low Energy Counting with a New Liquid Scintillation Solute, *Science,* **116:** 140 (1952).
56. F. N. Hayes and R. G. Gould, Liquid Scintillation Counting of Tritium Labaled Water and Organic Compounds, *Science,* **117:** 480 (1953).
57. F. N. Hayes, D. G. Ott, V. N. Kerr, and B. S. Rogers, Pulse Height Comparison of Primary Solutes, *Nucleonics,* **13** (12): 38 (1955).
58. F. N. Hayes, D. G. Ott, and V. N. Kerr, Pulse Height Comparison of Secondary Solutes, *Nucleonics,* **14** (1): 42 (1956).
59. F. N. Hayes, B. S. Rogers, and W. H. Langham, Counting Suspensions in Liquid Scintillators, *Nucleonics,* **14** (3): 48–51 (1956).
60. F. N. Hayes, Chemistry of the Counting Sample, in *Liquid Scintillation Counting* (C. G. Bell, Jr. and F. N. Hayes, eds.), pp. 83–87, Pergamon Press, London, 1958.
61. F. N. Hayes, Solutes and Solvents for Liquid Scintillation Counting, *Packard Technical Bulletin No. 1,* revised, 1962, Packard Instrument Co., Inc., La Grange, Illinois.
62. A. H. Heimbuch, H. Y. Gee, A. De Haan, and L. Leventhal, The Assay of Alpha and Beta Emitters Using Scintillating Ion Exchange Resin, *Symp. Radioisotope Sample Measurement Technique Med. Biol., 1965,* Intern. At. Energy Agency, Vienna.
63. S. Helf, C. G. White, and R. N. Shelley, Radioassay of Finely Divided Solids by Suspension in a Gel Scintillator, *Anal. Chem.,* **32:** 238–241 (1960).
64. R. J. Herberg, Phosphorescence in Liquid Scintillation Counting of Proteins, *Science,* **128:** 199–200 (1958).
65. R. J. Herberg, Determination of C^{14} and Tritium in Blood and Other Whole Tissues, *Anal. Chem.,* **32:** 42–46 (1960).
66. R. J. Herberg, Backgrounds for Liquid Scintillation Counting of Colored Solutions, *Anal. Chem.,* **32:** 1468–1471 (1960).
67. R. J. Herberg, Counting Statistics for Liquid Scintillation Counting, *Anal. Chem.,* **33:** 1308–1311 (1961).
68. R. J. Herberg, Statistical Aspects of Liquid Scintillation Counting by Internal Standard Technique, *Anal. Chem.,* **35:** 786–791 (1963).

69. R. Hofstadter, S. H. Liebson, and J. O. Elliot, Terphenyl and Dibenzyl Scintillation Counters, *Phys. Rev.*, **78**: 81 (1950).

70. H. S. Isbell, H. L. Frush, and R. J. Peterson, Tritium Labeled Compounds. I. Radioassay of Tritium Labeled Compounds in "Infinitely Thick" Films with a Window Gas Flow Proportional Counter, *J. Res. Natl. Bur. Std.*, **A63**: 171–175 (1959).

71. H. S. Isbell, H. L. Frush, and N. B. Holt, Tritium Labeled Compounds, V. Radioassay of Both Carbon[14] and Tritium in Films with a Proportional Counter, *J. Res. Natl. Bur. Std.*, **A64**: 363 (1960).

72. T. Iwakura and Y. Kasida, C[14] and H[3] Measurement by the Use of a Liquid Scintillation Spectrometer: Color Quenching, *Symp. Radioisotope Sample Measurement Techniques Med. Biol., 1965*, Intern. At. Energy Agency, Vienna,

73. H. I. Jacobson, G. N. Gupta, C. Fernandez, S. Hennix, and E. V. Jensen, Determination of Tritium in Biological Material, *Arch. Biochem. Biophys.*, **86**: 89–93 (1960).

74. J. S. Jenkinson, Scintillation Counting of Carbon-14, *Nature*, **186**: 613–614 (1960).

75. J. J. Kabara, N. Spafford, M. A. McKendry, and N. L. Freeman, Recent Developments in Simultaneous C[14] and Tritium Counting, *Advan. Tracer Methodol.*, **1**: 76–85 (1963).

76. H. Kallmann and M. Furst, The Basic Process Occurring in the Liquid Scintillator, in *Liquid Scintillation Counting* (C. G. Bell, Jr. and F. H. Hayes, eds.), p. 3, Pergamon Press, London, 1958.

77. M. D. Kamen, *Radioactive Tracers in Biology, An Introduction to Tracer Methodology*, 3rd ed., Academic Press, Inc., New York, 1957.

78. A. Karmen, I. McCaffrey, J. W. Winkelman, and R. L. Bowman, Measurement of Tritium in the Effluent of a Gas Chromatography Column, *Anal. Chem.*, **35**: 536–542 (1963).

79. W. J. Kaufmann, A. Nir, G. Parks, and R. M. Hours, Recent Advances in Low Level Scintillation Counting of Tritium, in *Tritium in the Physical and Biological Sciences, Symp. Intern. At. Energy Agency*, **1**: 250–260 (1961).

80. E. Kellenberger, K. G. Lark, and A. Bolle, Amino Acid Dependent Control of DNA Synthesis in Bacteria and Vegetative Phage, *Proc. Natl. Acad. Sci. U.S.* **48**: 1860–1868 (1962).

81. R. G. Kelly, E. A. Peets, S. Gordon, and D. A. Buyske, Determination of C[14] and Tritium in Biological Samples by Schöniger Combustion and Liquid Scintillation Techniques, *Anal. Biochem.*, **2**: 267–273 (1961).

82. V. N. Kerr, F. N. Hayes, and D. G. Ott, Liquid Scintillators, III. The Quenching of Liquid Scintillator Solutions by Organic Compounds, *Intern. J. Appl. Radiation Isotopes*, **1**: 284–288 (1957).

83. F. E. Kinard, Liquid Scintillator for the Analysis of Tritium in Water, *Rev. Sci. Instr.*, **28**: 293–294 (1957).

84. D. S. Kinnory, E. L. Kanabrocki, J. Greco, R. L. Veatch, E. Kaplan, and Y. T. Oester, A Liquid Scintillation Method for Measurement of Radioactivity in Animal Tissue and Tissue Fractions, in *Liquid Scintillation Counting* (C. G. Bell, Jr. and F. N. Hayes, eds.), pp. 223–229, Pergamon Press, London, 1958.

85. B. Kliman and R. E. Peterson, Double Isotope Derivative Assay of Aldosterone in Biological Extracts, *J. Biol. Chem.*, **235**: 1639–1648 (1960).

86. E. König and S. O. Brattgard, A Quantitative Micromethod for Determination of Specific Radioactivity of H[3]-purines and H[3]-pyrimidines, *Anal Biochem.*, **6**: 424–434 (1963).

87. G. Krakau and H. Schneider, Empfindliche Messmethoden für Radiokohlenstoff, *Atomkernenergie*, **3**: 515–522 (1958).
88. M. Lambiotte, Un nouveau procédé de séparation et de détection des substances tritiées: l'électrophorèse autoradiographique en couche mince de gélatine photographique, *Compt. Rend.*, **260**: 1799–1802 (1965).
89. R. A. Lloyd, S. C. Ellis, and M. H. Hallowes, Phosphorescence in Liquid Scintillation Counting, in *Tritium in the Physical and Biological Sciences, Symp. Intern. At. Energy Agency*, **1**: 263–278 (1961).
90. W. Lobunez and F. Karush, The Assay of Tritium in the Form of Ammonia and the Measurements of Exchangeable Hydrogen, *J. Am. Chem. Soc.*, **81**: 795–798 (1959).
91. R. B. Loftfield, Scintillation Counting of C^{14}-labeled Paper Chromatograms, *Advan. Tracer Methodol.* **1**, 121–126 (1963).
92. A. E. Love and D. Moore, Scintillation Counter for Measuring Radioactivity of Vapours, *Nature*, **182**: 133–134 (1958).
93. R. J. Mans and G. D. Novelli, Measurement of the Incorporation of Radioactive Amino Acids into Protein by a Filter Paper Disc Method, *Arch. Biochem. Biophys.*, **94**: 48–53 (1961).
94. G. Marin and M. A. Bender, A Comparison of Mammalian Cell Killing by Incorporated H^3-Thymidine and H^3-Uridine, *Intern. J. Radiation Biol.*, **7**: 235–244 (1963).
95. A. S. McFarlane and K. Murray, C^{14} and H^3 Specific Activities by Bomb Combustion and Scintillation Counting, *Anal. Biochem.*, **6**: 284–287 (1963).
96. R. K. Main and E. R. Walwick, A Simplified Quantitative Assay for Tritiated Thymidine Incorporated into DNA, *Biochem. Biophys. Res. Commun.*, **4**: 52–55 (1961).
97. L. H. Mason, H. J. Dutton, and L. R. Bair, Ionization Chamber for High Temperature Gas Chromatography, *J. Chromatog.*, **2**: 322–323 (1959).
98. W. F. Merrit, System for Counting Tritium as Water Vapour, *Anal. Chem.*, **30**: 1745–1746 (1958).
99. M. Muramatsu and T. Sasaki, Solid Counting of Octadecane-1-H^3, *Science*, **131**: 302–303 (1960).
100. L. S. Myers, Jr. and C. Rosenblum, A Rapid Method for Determining Tritium Water in Urine Following Acute Exposure, *Health Phys.*, **9**: 345–347 (1963).
101. B. J. O'Brien, The Measurement of Natural Tritium Levels in Geiger Counters, in *Tritium in the Physical and Biological Sciences, Symp. Intern. At. Energy Agency*, **1**: 344–350 (1961).
102. G. T. Okita, J. L. Spratt, and G. V. Leroy, Liquid Scintillation Counting for Assay of Tritium in Urine, *Nucleonics*, **14** (3): 76–79 (1956).
103. G. T. Okita, J. J. Kabara, F. Richardson, and G. V. Leroy, Assaying Compounds Containing H^3 and C^{14}, *Nucleonics*, **15** (6): 111–114 (1957).
104. V. T. Oliverio, C. Denham, and J. D. Davidson, Oxygen Flask Combustion in Determination of C^{14} and H^3 in Biological Materials, *Anal. Biochem.*, **4**: 188–189 (1962).
105. P. A. Osinski, Detection and Determination of Tritium Labeled Compounds on Paper Chromatograms, *Intern. J. Appl. Radiation Isotopes*, **7**: 306 (1960).
106. G. Östlund, A Hydrogen Gas Counting System for Natural Tritium Measurement, in *Tritium in the Physical and Biological Sciences, Symp. Intern. At. Energy Agency*, **1**: 333–339 (1961).
107. D. G. Ott, Chemistry of the Counting Sample, in *Liquid Scintillation Counting*

(C. G. Bell and F. N. Hayes, eds.), pp. 101–107, Pergamon Press, London, 1958.

108. D. G. Ott, C. R. Richmond, T. T. Trujillo, and H. Foreman, Cab-O-Sil Suspensions for Liquid Scintillation Counting, *Nucleonics*, **17** (9): 106–108 (1959).

109. R. T. Overman and H. M. Clarke, *Radioisotope Techniques,* McGraw-Hill Book Company, Inc., New York, 1960.

110. L. E. Packard, Instrumentation for Internal Sample Liquid Scintillation Counting, in *Liquid Scintillation Counting,* (C. G. Bell, Jr. and F. N. Hayes, eds.), pp. 50–66, Pergamon Press, London, 1958.

111. J. M. Passmann, N. S. Radin, and J. A. D. Cooper, Liquid Scintillation Technique for Measuring Carbon^{14}-dioxide Activity, *Anal. Chem.,* **28**: 484 (1956).

112. P. R. Payne and J. Done, Assay of Tritium Labeled Substances: A Combustion Bomb Method of Preparation of Gas for Counting, *Nature,* **174**: 27–28 (1954).

113. E. A. Peets, J. R. Florini, and D. A. Buyske, Tritium Radioactivity Determination of Biological Materials by a Rapid Dry Combustion Technique, *Anal. Chem.,* **32**: 1465–1468 (1960).

114. C. T. Peng, Quenching of Fluorescence in Liquid Scintillation Counting of Labeled Organic Compounds, *Anal. Chem.,* **32**: 1292–1296 (1960).

115. F. Polvani, G. D. Roversi, and R. Silvestrini, Employment of the H^3-Progesterone in the Examination of the Synthesis of 17-OH-Cortico-Steroids by Human Placental Tissue, in *Tritium in the Physical and Biological Sciences, Symp. Intern. At. Energy Agency,* **2**: 121–130 (1961).

116. W. J. Price, *Nuclear Radiation Detection,* McGraw-Hill Book Company, Inc., New York, 1958.

117. J. J. Prockop and P. S. Ebert, A Simple Method for Differential Assay of Tritium and Carbon^{14} in Water-Soluble Biological Materials, *Anal. Biochem.,* **6**: 263–271 (1963).

118. M. S. Raben and N. Bloembergen, Determination of Radioactivity by Solution in a Liquid Scintillator, *Science,* **114**: 363–364 (1951).

119. N. S. Radin, Methods of Counting Acids and Other Substances by Liquid Scintillation, in *Liquid Scintillation Counting* (C. G. Bell, Jr. and F. N. Hayes, eds.), pp. 108–114, Pergamon Press, London, 1958.

120. N. S. Radin and R. Fried, Liquid Scintillation Counting of Radioactive Sulfuric Acid and Other Substances, *Anal. Chem.,* **30**: 1926–1928 (1958).

121. F. Rapkin, Hydroxide of Hyamine 10-X, *Packard Technical Bulletin No. 3,* 1961, Packard Instr. Co., Inc., Box 428, La Grange, Illinois.

122. G. T. Reynolds, F. B. Harrison, and G. Salvini, Liquid Scintillation Counters, *Phys. Rev.,* **78**: 488 (1950).

123. A. W. Rogers, Autoradiography of Tritium-Labelled Compounds on Paper Chromatograms, *Nature,* **184**: 721 (1959).

124. H. H. Ross and R. E. Yerick, Quantitative Interpretation of Color Quenching in Liquid Scintillator Systems, *Anal. Chem.,* **35**: 794–77 (1963).

125. H. H. Ross, Theoretical and Experimental Aspects of Quenching Variables from Biomedical Samples in Liquid Scintillator Systems, *Symp. Radioisotope Sample Measurement Techniques Med. Biol., 1965,* Intern. At. Energy Agency, Vienna.

126. J. Rydberg, Determination of the Absolute Activity of Solid Tritium Samples, *Acta Chem. Scand.,* **12**: 399–407 (1958).

127. B. Scales, Liquid Scintillation Counting. The Determination of Background Counts of Samples Containing Quenching Substances, *Anal. Biochem.,* **5**: 489–496 (1963).

128. H. W. Scharpenseel, Tritium und C^{14} Direktmarkierung und Flüssigkeits-Szintillations-Spektrometrie, *Angew. Chem.*, **71**: 640–646 (1959).

129. H. W. Scharpenseel, Die kombinierte Gaschromatographie und Aktivitätsmessung C^{14} und H^3 markierter Substanzen, *Angew Chem.*, **73**: 615–619 (1961).

130. H. W. Scharpenseel and K. H. Menke, Radio Column Chromatographic Assay of H^3-labeled Substances, in *Tritium in the Physical and Biological Sciences, Symp. Intern. At. Energy Agency*, **1**: 281–301 (1961).

131. W. Schöniger, Eine mikroanalytische Schnellbestimmung von Halogen in organischen Substanzen, *Mikrochim. Acta*, **1**: 123–129 (1955).

132. E. Schram and R. Lombaert, Continuous Determination of C^{14} and S^{35} in Aqueous Medium by a Scintillation Device. Application to Chromatographic Effluents, *Anal. Chim. Acta*, **17**: 417–422 (1957).

133. E. Schram and R. Lombaert, Dosage continu du Carbone^{14} dans les effluents chromatographiques au moyen de poudres d'anthracène, *Arch. Intern. Physiol. Biochim.*, **68**: 845 (1960).

134. J. Schulze and F. A. Long, A Method of Liquid Scintillation Counting Utilizing Ultrasonic Extraction, *Anal. Biochem.*, **4**: 99–102 (1962).

135. P. E. Schulze and M. Wenzel, Automatische Aktivitätsmessung bei der Trennung radioaktiver Verbindungen auf Dünnschicht Chromatogrammen, *Angew. Chem.*, **74**: 777–779 (1962).

136. H. H. Seliger and B. W. Agranoff, Solid Scintillation Counting of Hydrogen-3 and Carbon-14 in Paper Chromatograms, *Anal. Chem.*, **31**: 1607–1608 (1959).

137. J. Shapira and W. H. Perkins, Liquid Scintillation Counting of Aqueous Solutions of C^{14} and Tritium, *Science*, **131**: 414–415 (1960).

138. J. Sharpe, *Nuclear Radiation Detectors*, Methuen and Company, Ltd., London: John Wiley & Sons, Inc., New York, 1955.

139. H. Sheppard and W. Rodegker, Determination of H^3 and C^{14} in Biological Materials Using Oxygen Bomb Combustion, *Anal. Biochem.*, **4**: 246–251 (1962).

140. H. Sheppard and W. H. Tsien, Autoradiography of Tritium Containing Thin Layer Chromatograms, *Anal. Chem.*, **35**: 1992 (1963).

141. H. Simon, H. Daniel, and J. F. Klebe, Die Messung von C^{14} und H^3 in der Gasphase, *Angew. Chem.*, **71**: 303–308 (1959).

142. H. Simon, G. Müllhofer, and R. Medina, A Universal Method for Radio-Gas-Chromatography and for the Fast Determination of Carbon^{14} and/or Tritium Labelled Substances Independent of Other Elements Present, *Symp. Radioisotope Sample Measurement Techniques Med. Biol., 1965*, Intern. At. Energy Agency, Vienna.

143. J. D. Simpson and J. R. Greening, Preparation of Tritiated Water Samples by Distillation, *Nature*, **186**: 467–468 (1960).

144. W. F. Siri, The Gross Composition of the Body, in *Adv. Biol. Med. Phys.*, **4**: 252–254 (1956).

145. A. H. Smith and G. W. Reed, The Standardization of a Liquid Scintillation System, *Symp. Radioisotope Sample Measurement Techniques Med. Biol., 1965*, Intern. At. Energy Agency, Vienna.

146. F. Snyder and N. Stephens, Quantitative C^{14} and Tritium Assay of Thin Layer Chromatography Plates, *Anal. Biochem.*, **4**: 128–131 (1962).

147. F. Snyder, Quantitative Radioassay Methods for Thin-Layer Chromatography, *Symp. Radioisotope Sample Measurement Techniques Med. Biol., 1965*, Intern. At. Energy Agency, Vienna.

148. D. Steinberg, M. Vaughan, C. B. Anfinsen, and J. D. Gorry, Preparation of H³-proteins by the Wilzbach Method, *Science*, **126**: 448 (1957).
149. D. Steinberg, M. Vaughan, C. B. Anfinsen, J. D. Gorry, and J. Logan, The Preparation of H³-proteins by the Wilzbach Method and a Simple Method for Liquid Scintillation Counting of Radioactive Proteins, in *Liquid Scintillation Counting* (C. G. Bell, Jr., and F. N. Haynes, eds.), pp. 230–236, Pergamon Press, London, 1958.
150. D. Steinberg, Radioassay of C¹⁴ in Aqueous Solutions Using a Liquid Scintillation Spectrometer, *Nature*, **182**: 740–741 (1958).
151. D. Steinberg, A New Approach to Radioassay of Aqueous Solutions in the Liquid Scintillation Spectrometer, *Anal. Biochem.*, **1**: 23–39 (1960).
152. S. R. Stitch, Liquid Scintillation Counting for C¹⁴-steroids, *Biochem. J.*, **73**: 287–292 (1959).
153. R. K. Swank, Limits of Sensitivity of Liquid Scintillation Counters, in *Liquid Scintillation Counting* (C. G. Bell, Jr. and F. N. Hayes, eds.), p. 23, Pergamon Press, London, 1958.
154. H. Takahashi, T. Hattori, and B. Marno, Liquid Scintillation Counting of Biological Compounds in Aqueous Solution, *Anal. Chem.*, **35**: 1982–1983 (1963).
155. M. Tamers, R. Bibron, and G. Delibrias, A New Method for Measuring Low Level Tritium Using a Benzene Liquid Scintillator, in *Tritium in the Physical and Biological Sciences, Symp. Intern. At. Energy Agency*, **1**: 303–311 (1961).
156. B. M. Tolbert, Tritium Measurements Using Ionization Chambers, *Adv. Tracer Methodol.*, **1**: 167–177 (1963).
157. R. Tykva and D. Grünberger, Rapid Assay of Tritium Labeled Substances in Geiger-Müller Gas Counting Tubes, in *Tritium in the Physical and Biological Sciences, Symp. Intern. At. Energy Agency*, **1**: 353–359 (1961).
158. R. Tykva, The Simultaneous Determination of H³ and C¹⁴ Radioactivity in Biological Material by Means of an Internal Proportional Gas Counter, *Symp. Radioisotope Sample Measurement Techniques Med. Biol., 1965*, Intern. At. Energy Agency, Vienna.
159. H. Ussing and A. Wernstedt, A Distillation Device for Small Water Samples, *Skand. Arch. Physiol.*, **83**: 169 (1940).
160. D. D. Van Slyke and F. M. Sinex, The Course of Hydroxylation of Lysine to Form Hydroxylysine in Collagen, *J. Biol. Chem.*, **232**: 797 (1958).
161. B. E. Vaughan and E. A. Bohling, Rapid Assay Procedures for Tritium-labeled Water in Body Fluids, *J. Lab. Clin. Med.*, **57**: 159 (1961).
162. M. Vaughan, D. Steinberg, and J. Logan, Liquid Scintillation Counting of C¹⁴ and H³-labeled Acids and Proteins, *Science*, **126**: 446 (1957).
163. W. G. Verly, J. R. Rachele, V. du Vigneaud, M. L. Eidinoff, and J. E. Knoll, A Test of Tritium as a Labeling Device in a Biological Study, *J. Am. Chem. Soc.*, **74**: 5941–5943 (1952).
164. H. Von Buttlar and W. Stahl, A Low Level Geiger Counter for Tritium, in *Tritium in the Physical and Biological Sciences, Symp. Intern. At. Energy Agency*, **1**: 325–330 (1961).
165. H. Von Buttlar and B. Wiik, Enrichment of Tritium by Thermal Diffusion and Measurement of Dated Antarctic Snow Samples, *Science*, **149**: 1371–1373 (1965).
166. C. H. Wang and D. E. Jones, Liquid Scintillation Counting of Paper-Chromatograms, *Biochem. Biophys. Res. Commun.*, **1**: 203 (1959).
167. C. H. Wang, cited by E. Rapkin, personal Communication, 1961.

168. P. G. Waser and U. Lüthi, Low Temperature Autoradiography of H³ Compounds on Anthracene/Silica Gel Thin Layers, *Advan. Tracer Methodol.*, in press.

169. A. Weinreb and P. Avivi, Comparison between Energy Transfer in Liquid and Plastic Solutions, in *Liquid Scintillation Counting* (C. G. Bell, Jr. and F. N. Hayes, eds.), pp. 270–273, Pergamon Press, London, 1958.

170. M. Wenzel, Messung Tritium-markierter Substanzen auf dem Papierchromatogramm, *Atompraxis*, **7**: 86–88 (1961).

171. M. Wenzel and P. E. Schulze, Tritium-Markierung; Darstellung, Messung und Anwendung nach Wilzbach ³H-markierter Verbindungen, Walter De Gruyter & Company, Berlin, 1962.

172. H. Werbin, I. L. Chaikoff, and M. R. Imada, Rapid Sensitive Method for Determining THO in Body Fluids by Liquid Scintillation Spectrometry, *Proc. Soc. Exptl. Biol. Med.*, **102**: 8–12 (1959).

173. T. Westermark, L. Devell, and N. A. Ghanem, On the Use of Bremsstrahlung for the Determination of Tritium in Aqueous and Organic Systems, *Nucl. Instr. Methods*, **9**: 141–144 (1960).

174. T. Westermark, B. Grapengiesser, H. Lindroth, and N. A. Ghanem, Note on the Determination of Tritium by Means of Liquid Scintillators and DC Measurements of Photomultiplier Currents, *Nucl. Instr. Methods*, **9**: 357–359 (1960).

175. M. L. Whisman, B. H. Eccleston, and F. E. Armstrong, Liquid Scintillation Counting of Initiated Organic Compounds, *Anal. Chem.*, **32**: 484–486 (1960).

176. C. G. White and S. Helf, Suspension Counting in Scintillation Gels, *Nucleonics*, **14**(10): 46–48 (1956).

177. A. T. Wilson, A Liquid Scintillation Autoradiographic Technique for the Use of Tritium as an *in vivo* Tracer, *Proc. 2nd Intern. Conf. Peaceful Use At. Energy, Geneva*, **25**: 213 (1958).

178. K. E. Wilzbach, L. Kaplan, and W. G. Brown, The Preparation of Gas for Assay of H³ in Organic Compounds, *Science*, **118**: 522–523 (1953).

179. K. E. Wilzbach and P. Riesz, Isotope Effects in Gas-Liquid Chromatography, *Science*, **126**: 748–749 (1957).

180. R. Wolfgang and C. F. Mackay, New Proportional Counters for Gases and Vapours, *Nucleonics*, **16**(10): 69–73 (1958).

181. R. Wolfgang and F. S. Rowland, Radioassay by Gas Chromatography of H³ and C¹⁴ Labeled Compounds, *Anal. Chem.*, **30**: 903–906 (1958).

182. R. Wu, Simultaneous Studies of Phosphate Transport and Glycolysis by a Simple Scintillation Counting Procedure with P³², C¹⁴, and H³ compounds, *Anal. Biochem.*, **7**: 207–214 (1964).

183. C. A. Zeigler, D. J. Chleck, and J. Brinkerhoff, Radioassay of Low Specific Activity THO by Improved Liquid Scintillation Techniques, in *Liquid Scintillation Counting* (C. G. Bell, Jr., and F. N. Hayes, eds.), pp. 185–190, Pergamon Press, London, 1958.

CHAPTER 4

Autoradiography

1. Introduction

This chapter will discuss the principal methods of autoradiography or radioautography. The term "autoradiography" is used here to describe the method by which an "autoradiogram" is obtained. In an autoradiogram, a radiation source within a structure, such as a tissue section or a single cell, is localized by a photographic film with optimally fine grains in close contact to the structure. The term "radioautography" is used in the *Index Medicus* of the National Library of Medicine. But the term "autoradiography" has been also used for years, and no misunderstanding has arisen in its exact meaning. Kopriwa and Leblond[108] suggested, however, that the term "autoradiography" be restricted to the method by which an image is produced in a photographic film by an object interposed between the radiation source and the film. With this definition "historadiography" would be synonymous with "autoradiography." For example, tritium uniformly distributed in gelatin placed on a glass slide has been used to determine density differences in a specimen section placed on the slide and covered with nuclear track emulsion.[5] In the following, the term "autoradiography" will be used synonymously with "radioautography" (see Fig. 4.1).

Ionizing radiation produces an image on a photographic plate just like ordinary light, and a photographic plate was the tool by which radioactivity was detected.[12] The photographic emulsion, owing to its tremendous amplification, still remains a most sensitive device for the detection of radioactivity. A single charged particle of sufficient energy interacting with a silver halide crystal renders millions of silver ions susceptible to reducing agents, leading to a permanent record of the particle's interaction in the form of a photographic picture or image. In 1924, Lacassagne and Lattès[110] had already employed a photographic film to study the distribution of polonium in various tissues of the rabbit.

The demands of modern nuclear physics led to the development of photographic emulsions with silver halide grains which have a diameter of about 0.1–0.4 μ, whereas normal photographic emulsions have grains with a diameter of 0.5–3.0 μ. These fine grain emulsions are also called "nuclear track emulsions." When radioactive isotopes became available commercially on a large scale subsequent to the development of nuclear reactors, the nuclear track emulsions became immensely suitable for high-resolution autoradiography. In 1946, Belanger and Leblond[13] used nuclear track emulsion in liquid form, and Pelc[144] applied it as stripping film 5 μ thick with a gelatinous support 10 μ thick. Phosphorus-32 was mostly used at that time and a high resolution to the level of single cells was not yet obtainable. A statement in 1947[11] on theoretical grounds and on the basis of limited success with P[32] warned that "autoradiography of single cells having activities equal to those obtained by previous authors in experiments on bulk tissue is clearly impossible," and "there is little point in discussing the biological implications of an experiment which on physical grounds is possible, but scarcely practical at the present time." Fitzgerald et al. in 1951[64] chose tritium with its low energy β-radiation as a label and brought autoradiographic resolution to the level of single cells. By carefully analyzing and demonstrating the usefulness of tritium-labeled com-

A:

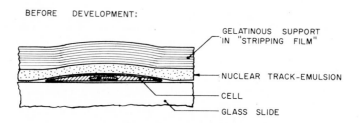

BEFORE DEVELOPMENT:

GELATINOUS SUPPORT IN "STRIPPING FILM"

NUCLEAR TRACK-EMULSION

CELL

GLASS SLIDE

AFTER DEVELOPEMENT:

GELATINOUS SUPPORT IN "STRIPPING FILM"

DEVELOPED EMULSION WITH SILVER GRAINS

CELL
GLASS SLIDE

Fig. 4.1A–D. Schematic cross section (A) and photographs (B–D) of autoradiograms, prepared with stripping film (AR-10, Kodak). HeLa cells showing position of labeled RNA in interphase (B), and in late prophase (C), after short-term labeling with H[3]-cytidine. (D) Chromosome of *E. coli*, labeled with H[3]-thymidine. Courtesy of Cairns, *Cold Spring Harbor Symp. Quart. Biol.*[33]

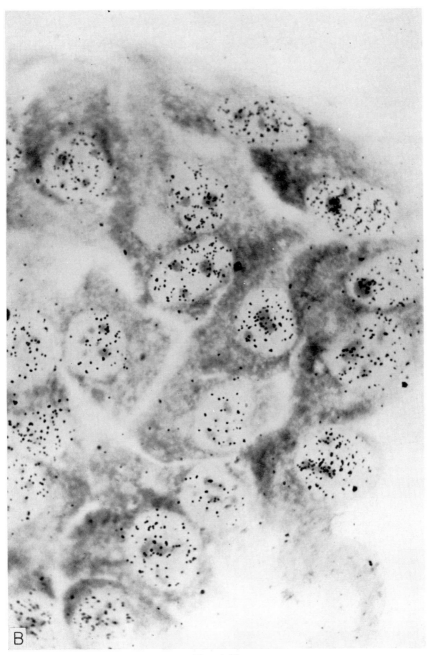

FIG. 4.1B

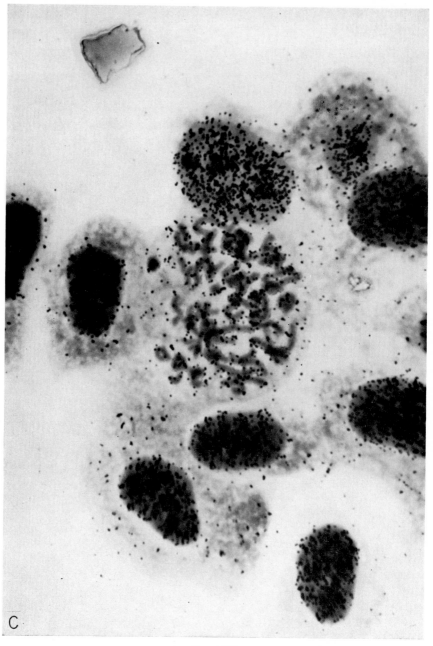

FIG. 4.1C

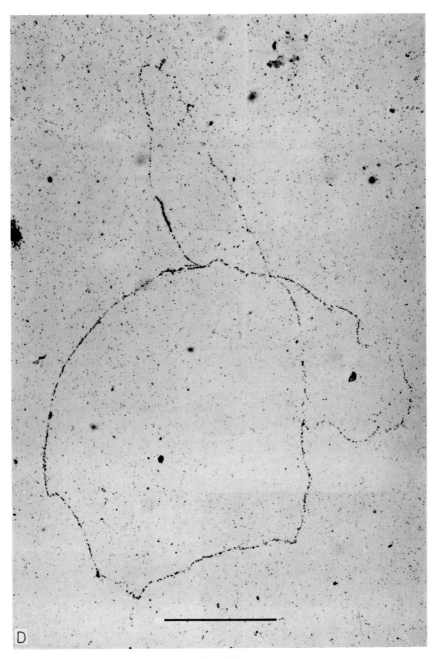

Fig. 4.1D

pounds for autoradiography, these authors stimulated a most useful development of this technique applied to single cells. More recently, nuclear track emulsions have also been adapted to the electron microscope, and the first attempts by Liquier-Milward in 1956[118] were followed by encouraging progress toward maximum possible resolution on the subcellular level.

Various reviews on autoradiography have been written in the past, and the reader is referred to them for more information on the steps of development leading to the present day knowledge of this valuable tool.[26,62,65,156,188,189] It is the aim of this chapter to review the more recent advances and to discuss possibilities and limitations of the autoradiographic technique for quantitative and qualitative detection of tritium in biological material.

2. The Photographic Image

2.1 THE LATENT IMAGE

The process by which an autoradiographic image is obtained is nearly identical to the process by which an ordinary photographic picture is produced. Instead of photons, ionizing radiation interacts with the photographic emulsion.

A photographic emulsion consists of gelatin into which are embedded silver halide crystals, usually silver bromide. The size of the crystals and their proportion to the gelatin varies for different emulsion types. In ordinary optical emulsions there are fewer crystals per unit volume of gelatin, and they are larger (diameter of more than 0.5 μ) than in nuclear track emulsions. The latter emulsions, with a high proportion of fine crystals, are used in nuclear physics to trace the tracks of charged particles. Table 4.1 shows the principal differences between ordinary optimal emulsions and nuclear track emulsions. For autoradiography only nuclear track emulsions are suitable, the most popular ones are listed in Table 4.2.

If charged particles, such as electrons, pass through an emulsion,

TABLE 4.1

GENERAL COMPARISON OF OPTICAL AND NUCLEAR TRACK EMULSIONS[a]

Composition	Optical emulsion	Nuclear track emulsion
AgBr:gelatin (weight)	47:53	80:20
AgBr:gelatin (volume)	15:85	45–55
Grain diameter (μ)	0.5–3.0	0.1–0.4

[a] Modified with permission from Fitzgerald, *Analytical Cytology*.[65]

TABLE 4.2

CHARACTERISTICS OF SOME POPULAR NUCLEAR TRACK EMULSIONS[a]

Emulsion	Manu-facturer	Grain diameter (μ)	Relative sensitivity (grain count/unit area/ isotope content of specimen)[c]
L-4 (gel)	Ilford	0.12[b]	0.9–1.2 (D-178, 5 minutes)
K-5 (gel)	Ilford	0.18[b]	0.7–0.9 (D-178, 3 minutes)
G-5 (gel)	Ilford	0.32[b]	1.8–2.2 (D-72, 2 minutes)
NTB (gel)	Kodak	0.27[b]	0.4–0.5 (D-72, 2 minutes) (D-170, 6 minutes)
NTB-2 (gel)	Kodak	0.27	1.0 (D-72, 2 minutes) (D-170, 6 minutes)
NTB-3 (gel)	Kodak	0.23[b]	1.1–1.4 (D-72, 2 minutes)
V-1055 (gel)	Kodak	0.17[b]	—
AR-10 (stripping film, 5 μ emulsion, 10 μ gelatin support)	Kodak	0.20	—
NTE (gel)	Kodak	0.03–0.05	
NUC-307 (gel)	Gevaert	0.07	1.6 (D-170, 20 minutes)
NUC-715 (gel)	Gevaert	0.15	1.9 (D-170, 10 minutes)

[a] Modified with permission from Kopriwa and Leblond, *J. Histochem. Cytochem.*,[108] Caro and van Tubergen, *J. Cell Biol.*,[38] and Young and Kopriwa, *J. Histochem. Cytochem.*[207]

[b] With permission from Caro and van Tubergen,[38] measured in the electron microscope. All emulsions were developed with D-19 (Kodak) for 2 minutes at 20°C, except for L-4 (Ilford) which was developed 4 minutes.

[c] With permission from Kopriwa and Leblond[108] and Young and Kopriwa,[207] the type of developer and the developing time in minutes are listed in parentheses; the sensitivity of the emulsion is partially a function of grain size, compensating for the lower inherent sensitivity of the smaller grains.

they are liable to interact with silver bromide crystals or molecules of the gelatin. By ionization, electrons are set free and a negative charge is trapped in the crystal and held first at the sensitivity specks of ionized silver.[198] These "sensitivity specks" consist mainly of silver sulfide deposits on the surface of the silver bromide crystals. A "latent image" is thus produced, i.e., a silver bromide crystal has acquired additional electrons and some of the silver ions have become elementary silver atoms. The crystals, thus, become easily susceptible to reducing agents (developers) which convert more silver ions to metallic silver. Small nuclei of metallic silver constitute the final image.

The minimum energy required to produce a latent image is approximately 35 ev. The efficiency of a photographic emulsion depends, hence, on the amount of energy lost from the trajecting particle per single crystal, which has a density 6.47 times that of water. In general, an electron with lower energy has a greater chance to activate a silver halide crystal than one with higher energy. It was thus estimated that an electron with the energy of 10 kev would lose approximately 150 ev per crystal grain of a diameter of 0.01 μ, whereas an electron with the energy of 100 kev loses only 17 ev per grain.[146]

If the number of silver atoms in the grain reduced by the incident particle is relatively small, the atoms are probably located more on the surface of the crystal. There is also evidence that a direct relationship between the position of this latent image in the crystal and the path of the particle does not exist.[126] Moreover, a single hit of an electron from tritium was reported to produce, at times, three distinct latent images in one crystal.[38]

Small silver halide crystals are less sensitive than larger crystals. But photographic emulsions with small grains yield a "denser" image than those with larger grains. One β-particle may activate not only one but a succession of crystals to carry a latent image leading to the formation of grain tracks. With the low-energy electron from tritium, however, a few rare tracks only are produced in any type of nuclear track emulsion, owing to the high density of the silver halide crystals. Thus, Caro and Schnös[41] showed for the emulsion L-4 (Ilford) that the β-particles from tritium produced 78% single grains, 16.5% double grains, and 5% gave 3 grains, so that the mean grain count per incident particle was 1.28. Formation of grain tracks was practically absent in monolayers of crystals. In the fine-grain stripping film AR-10 (Kodak), a rare and single track does not consist of more than two grains only per incident electron.[89] Two crystals may be activated by one hit when they are too close and touch each other.[126]

2.2 THE FINAL IMAGE

The latent image is converted to the final image by the action of a reducing agent or developer, and a grain of metallic silver is the product. Such reducing agents are, for example, hydroquinone, amino-phenols, triphenols, or ferro-oxalate, in solution of various pH. The popular metol is p-methylaminophenol sulfate and amidol is 2,4-di-aminophenol hydrochloride. Used mostly are metol–hydroquinone developers, such as Kodak's D-72 and D-19, or Ilford's ID-19. Kodak's D-170 is an amidol developer.

The crystals which carry a latent image are the most sensitive to the action of a developer, and their silver is reduced first. But the silver halide crystals without latent image are also acted upon in time, and an "overdeveloped" photograph is totally black, as any amateur photographer knows. If two crystals touch each other but only one carries a latent image, the developer acts on both. In order to obtain a visible picture from the latent image only, the developing process must be sufficiently long for the production of a small grain of metallic silver in those crystals carrying a latent image, but the process must also be short enough to prevent the reduction of the silver of those crystals not activated. The latter would contribute to "background" in the final image.

With the length of the developing process, the single nucleus of metallic silver grows larger to reach a maximum according to the size of the silver halide crystal. But this is not necessarily desirable as long as the developed silver grains are just big enough for proper recognition. A smaller silver grain, moreover, has the advantage of improving the resolution.

The difference in sensitivity of activated and nonactivated crystals to the action of the developer is characterized by the gap or delay in the time it takes for the silver of the nonactivated crystals to become reduced after all latent images have been developed.[50] The duration of this delay varies with different emulsion types and is rather crucial for obtaining good autoradiograms. Figure 4.2 shows an example, the action of the developer D-19 (Kodak) on two different nuclear track emulsions after exposure to tritium β-radiation.[38] The two emulsions are K-5 and L-4 (Ilford) that have grains less than 0.2 μ in diameter. With the emulsion L-4, there is a definite plateau lasting perhaps 5 minutes after full development of the latent image until the "background" rises steeply. But with the emulsion K-5, the background rises even prior to full development of the latent image. The sensitivity of development of background grains could be reduced when Kodak Antifog No. 1 (benzotriazole) was added to the D-19 developer and a plateau similar to that in L-4 was the result. The development of background grains can also be slowed down by potassium bromide.[62] Another method of gaining more leeway in the crucial timing of development is to dilute the developer or to decrease the temperature at which development is carried out. If the emulsion is very thick, more time is needed to develop all latent images, and increasing background may be troublesome. For the stripping film, a developing time of 6 minutes (at 18°C) is usually adequate. For autoradiograms prepared with liquid emulsions 3 minutes are usually sufficient.

The temperature at which development is carried out must be observed carefully. It is obvious that with increasing temperature the reaction proceeds faster and timing becomes more difficult. The efficiency of development decreases below 20°C, and background grains appear in increasing numbers above 18°C.[108] Artifacts or lifting of stripping film

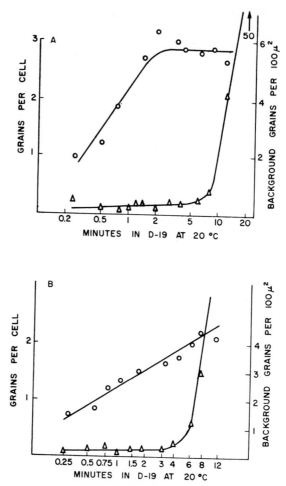

Fig. 4.2. The efficiency of the developer D-19 (Kodak) on two different nuclear track emulsions; (A) L-4, (B) K-5 (both Ilford). The developing conditions were identical. Nonactivated silver halide crystals are developed to background grains sooner in K-5 than in L-4. Courtesy of Caro and van Tubergen, *J. Cell Biol.*[38]

from the autoradiographic preparation are likewise temperature dependent. Belanger,[15] for example, developed even at 4°C to avoid these effects. For most purposes a temperature between 16° and 20°C should suffice. Most important is the constancy of the procedures to obtain reproducible results.

Different developers have advantages for various photographic emulsions. Developers such as Mikrodol-X (Kodak) or Promicrol (May and Baker, England) produce fine grains and are, therefore, recommended for fine-grain emulsions such as L-4 (Ilford). Often they do not reproduce, but are judged useful for electron microscopic work that requires the highest possible resolution. Other developers for fine-grain emulsions were also tested, such as Ansco 110, Ansco-Finex-L, and Unibath.[38] When using fine-grain developers, the low sensitivity of very small silver halide crystals may be increased by pretreating the emulsion prior to development with a dilute solution of gold chloride (gold latensification), beneficial for autoradiography with the electron microscope.[165] Dektol (D-72, Kodak) is suitable for obtaining fine silver grains, but since it may overdevelop rapidly with the result of increasing background,[108] the development must be carried out under strict conditions of optimal timing and temperature. To allow a very small silver halide crystal to develop to its maximum, the D-19 developer is good. This developer is also widely used and recommended for nuclear track emulsions with medium-size grains such as NTB, NTB-2, NTB-3, AR-10 (all Kodak), and G-5 and K-5 (Ilford). Also excellent are the developers D-178 and D-170 (both Kodak). Metol–hydroquinone developers can be stored in the dark for several days. A batch of 300 ml of D-19 (Kodak or Ilford) lasts for about 50–60 auto-radiograms.[111]

Autoradiography may benefit from developing colored grains instead of black grains. The technique of color development of autoradiograms was discussed in detail by Sims and Graham.[171] Table 4.3 shows the steps for developing silver grains colored red or blue. The method is useful for autoradiography with the light microscope, since it may help to improve the contrast of the autoradiographic image against the stained section underneath.

Another type of developing latent images exists. This is called the physical type of development,[94] in contrast to the chemical development described above. It produces fine grains and has been used for autoradiographic work in conjunction with the electron microscope.[38] By physical development, the silver halide crystals which do not carry a latent image are dissolved and are removed; metallic silver is attached to those crystals which carry a latent image. The silver is donated, for example, from silver nitrate in the solution. This method of development is, however, not recommended for quantitative work because of lack of reproducibility and instability of the developed grains.

Following the ordinary method of chemical development, the emulsion is rinsed with water or 1–3% acetic acid for a few seconds. The nonde-veloped crystals are made water-soluble and are removed from the emul-sion by the process of fixation. The emulsion becomes translucent during the procedure. Fixation proceeds by complex formation of the silver halide with sodium or ammonium thiosulfate in aqueous solution of 15% at a pH

TABLE 4.3

PHOTOGRAPHIC DEVELOPMENT OF COLORED GRAINS IN AUTORADIOGRAMS[a]

The autoradiograms are processed in freshly prepared solutions.

Step A. Development for 3 minutes at 24°C in:

Sodium carbonate	40 g
Sodium sulfite	2 g
Potassium bromide	1 g
"Genochrome" [b]	2.5 g
Ethylene glycol	40 ml
Acetone containing 2 g of α-naphthol	100 ml
Distilled water to	1000 ml

This solution develops blue grains; for red grains substitute p-nitrophenylacetonitride for α-naphthol.

Step B. For 2 minutes, wash in tap water
For 2 minutes, treat with:

Potassium ferricyanide	30 g
Potassium bromide	15 g
Distilled water	1000 ml

Step C. For 2 minutes, wash in tap water
For 2 minutes, treat with:

Sodium sulfite	40 g
Sodium thiosulfate	240 g
Formalin	100 ml
Distilled water to	1000 ml

Step D. For 2 minutes, wash in tap water
For 5 minutes, treat with neutral red, 0.02%

Step E. For 1 minute, wash in tap water
Dip into solution of:

Gelatin	10 g
Chrome alum (heated)	1 g
Distilled water	1000 ml

Dry in air

---

[a] Slides may not be treated with alcohol, since blue stain is alcohol-soluble. Reproduced with permission of Sims and Graham, *Quart. J. Microscop. Sci.*[171]

[b] May and Baker, Ltd., Dagenham, Essex, England.

---

of approximately 6. Concentrations of 5–25% thiosulfate have been tried also, but too low a concentration of the fixative will usually leave silver halide undissolved in the emulsion. Kodak Fixer or Kodak Acid Fixer with a pH of 4.4 is widely used. The temperature should be the same as that recommended for development, 18°–20°C. The length of the fixation is less crucial than the timing of development, and it depends on the emulsion thickness and the grain size. For nuclear track emulsions with medium-sized crystals, at least 3 minutes are usually required, and at least 6 minutes should be used for stripping film emulsions which have a 10-μ thick support of gelatin. Fixation may continue twice as long as the time used for development without affecting the final image, which remains stable over a wide range of time. Certain salts, such as sodium chloride in low concentration, accelerate the process of fixation, but this is not required in autoradiographic work.

A film hardener, such as 2% potassium alum, is at times added to the fixer in order to prevent swelling and displacement of the emulsion on the object it covers. Four to 5% Formalin after fixation serves the same purpose. Many other hardeners may be used.[127] The commercial Kodak Acid Fixer already contains a hardener.

Following fixation, the film is washed in distilled or deionized water. It is important that all chemicals be removed from the film, and at least 30 minutes are required for that purpose in the case of stripping film. Even traces of thiosulfate may cause a disturbing yellowish granulation on microscopic examination of the processed film, and fading of the developed silver grains may also occur. The time of washing also depends, of course, on the thickness of the film. Sometimes a special "hypo-remover" may be of benefit, such as a bath of hydrogen peroxide–ammonia,[188] but it is usually not necessary.

Finally, the preparation is dried simply in an air stream or through increasing alcohol concentrations. Alcohol treatment of the film at times improves the permeability of the gelatin for stains (see below). After completion of the photographic processing, the thickness of the film layer is reduced to approximately one-half that of the undeveloped dry emulsion. In the light microscope, the dry film shows discrete black silver grains, which, in proper position over a biological structure, show the approximate site of the radiation source in that structure. In the electron microscope, the grains impress as threads and loops of bizarre shape.

3. Factors That Influence the Quality of Autoradiograms

The quality of an autoradiogram depends largely on the limit of resolution of two distinct images produced by two point sources of radiation. It is already self-suggesting that the resolution in an autoradiogram depends principally on the size of the silver halide crystals in the nuclear track emulsion, on the emulsion thickness, on the range of the particles, and on the angle at which the particle collides with the crystal. The length of the particle track is a function of its energy and the density of matter the particle has to traverse prior to interacting with a crystal. There are other factors which determine the quality of an autoradiogram, such as the fading of the latent image before it is developed, further various artifacts, and the degree of background.

3.1. RESOLUTION AND EFFICIENCY

The limits of autoradiographic resolution with tritium may be estimated from the energy spectrum of the tritium β-particles. The problem has been investigated extensively, and a definition of the term resolution was requested. According to Doniach and Pelc,[51] the "resolving power for a source of zero diameter is defined by the distance between the point of maximum exposure and the point at which the number of developed grains is halved." The doubling of this distance provides another definition, saying that "resolution gives the value of approximately twice the distance at which the image density decreases to 50% of its maximum value." [39] A different approach defines resolution of two points being obtained if the film density between them falls to one-half the density on each point.[75] According to Lamerton and Harriss:[113] "the resolution of a given autoradiographic technique shall be defined as the distance d, if the images of 2 uniformly active cylindrical sources of diameter d can just be resolved when the centers are separated by a distance $2d$." Odeblad[134] approached the problem of resolution by the matrix theory, which emphasized the geometric relationships between histological section and photographic emulsion with crossover radiation, and he explored the mode of exposure, practical performance of quantitative autoradiography, and selection of autoradiographic technique. In the following discussion, resolution is the value of approximately twice the distance at which the image density decreases to one-half of its maximum value over the source.

3.1.1. Resolution for Light and Electron Microscope

The range of the β-particles is determined by their energy and the density of matter they traverse. That the tritium β-particles, due to electronic interactions and collisions, follow a tortuous and curved path in matter was discussed in Chapter 1. This must be taken into account when calculations of the resolution to be expected for certain experimental conditions are to be meaningful. If the trajectory of all β-particles is assumed to be straight, the calculated resolution gives maximum values. Thus, an image spread of several microns around a point source in autoradiograms of tissue sections 2 μ thick, as was calculated by Doniach and Pelc[51] on the basis of a straight linear path of the tritium electrons, is a maximum value. The range limits of the low-energy β-particles due to absorption in biological material were considered in the calculation of autoradiographic resolution by Robertson and co-workers[162] and by Caro,[39] and it was shown that the resolution improves with thinner sections. At 4–5 μ above a point source, the radiation dose rate falls to one-half the axial dose rate at a distance of about 2 μ away from the axis of the point source. This distance is reduced to about 1.3 μ at a tier 2–3 μ above the point source. Below 1 μ above the point source the dose rate falls to one-half already at a distance of about 0.2 μ from the zero axis.[162] In other words, those labeled biological structures which are closest to the emulsion give not only the highest grain density but also the best resolution, where as those labeled structures further away cause an increasing image spread to a maximum at an intermediate depth below "infinite thickness." When it is recalled that in biological material 80% of the tritium electrons have a range below 1 μ and 99% do not reach beyond 3 μ and only 2% reach a distance of 2.5 μ,[39] it follows that the maximum range of image spread is rare and that in theory the resolution obtainable with tritium in a histological section should be lower than 1 μ. Since the density of the silver halide crystals is about six times that of water, and the maximum range of the tritium β-particles in the emulsion hence is below 1 μ, the contribution to image spread from tracks in the emulsion is neglible.

The resolving power of tritium was directly tested by Hill,[90] who used tritium embedded in an Araldite section, 0.75 μ thick, covered with stripping film AR-10 (Kodak). In the AR-10 emulsion the silver grains, fully developed, are approximately 0.2–0.3 μ in diameter. It was concluded that the frequency distribution of grain densities descends to one-half its peak value at 0.21–0.30 μ from the source. This corresponds to a resolution of about 0.6 μ. This degree of resolution was also obtained by Steffensen[178] in his work with *Drosophila* salivary chromosomes containing H³-thymidine. For ordinary light microscopy, a resolution of 0.6 to about 1 μ is satisfactory.

It must be remembered, however, that the optimal resolution is less meaningful if two adjacent sources, such as two cellular compartments, contain a grossly different amount of label. In order to quantitate the labeling intensities of two adjacent structures unequally labeled in a section 3 μ thick, the near maximum image spread must be taken into account, as Perry *et al.*[150] have emphasized in their work on RNA-labeling in nucleoli.

For work on subcellular structures with the electron microscope, a better resolution is wanted than that obtained in light microscopy. To achieve this, Caro and van Tubergen[38] applied to an ultrathin section a nearly single layer of silver halide crystals of the emulsion L-4 (Ilford) with a grain size of about 0.12 μ in diameter. Under optimal conditions the maximum resolution of approximately 0.1 μ was obtained and agreed with the theoretical prediction.[39] The resolution from tritium in ultrathin sections is obviously limited by the grain size of the nuclear track emulsions. Emulsions with a grain size of 0.3–0.05 μ are now available for autoradiography combined with electron microscopy[165] and the problem of decreased sensitivity of the small grains can be overcome. The introduction of emulsions that have still smaller grains with a metal heavier than silver, and thus have a higher sensitivity, could perhaps be useful.[147] Working with ultrathin sections for electron microscopic autoradiography poses the additional problem of maintaining an equal section thickness in order to obtain quantitative data. Furthermore, the isotope content required for a reasonable image density may be prohibitive because of biological toxicity.

3.1.2. *Absorption in Biological Specimen*

A histological section uniformly labeled with tritium will register autoradiographically increasing amounts of radiation with increasing section thickness until a plateau is reached at "infinite thickness". For tissue sections of unit density infinite thickness is reached practically at about 3 μ. Approaching infinite thickness, the attenuation of the β-particles becomes increasingly effective. Hence, grain counts in autoradiograms over structures of different thicknesses or densities need correction in order to be comparable.

Perry *et al.*[150] have tried to quantitate their autoradiographic data from tissue culture cells grown on glass surface by applying correction factors for the various thicknesses of the structures. Setting the cytoplasm equal to 1, they found a correction factor of 1.6 for the cell nucleus, and 2.3 for the nucleolus. A similar correction factor of 1.5 for the nuclear labeling versus cytoplasmic labeling in cultured fibroblasts was obtained by Marin and Bender,[122] on the basis of activity measurements by liquid scintillation counting compared with grain counts in autoradiograms.

Since the "infinite thickness" of various biological structures is a function of their density, Maurer and Primbsch[123] determined the factor of β-absorption in sections on the basis of their density in milligrams dry mass per square centimeter. Tissue densities can be measured by interference microscopy.[81] Thus, in sections of liver embedded in methacrylate a limit of registrable tritium radiation was found at a thickness of 1–2 μ for the cytoplasm, at 2–3 μ for the nucleus, and at less than 1 μ for the nucleolus. It follows that autoradiographic data from tritium need corrections for β-absorption in order to become quantitative. As the "infinite thickness" may vary by factor of 2–3 within a single dry cell, it is to be expected that the degree of β-absorption varies also with different cell types and different methods of fixation and embedding prior to sectioning. Even greater difficulties are encountered when smears of cells are examined, since sizes and thicknesses vary between cell types as well as within a single cell.

3.1.3. Efficiency in Terms of Disintegrations per Silver Grain

The number of tritium disintegrations in a biological structure which leads to the activation of one silver halide crystal in the emulsion overlaying the structure has been measured or estimated by various authors. Hughes[93] held 20 disintegrations to be necessary to activate one silver halide crystal in AR-10 stripping film. Lajtha and Oliver,[112] also working with AR-10 emulsion, estimated for cell smears 20 disintegrations; for sections, 50 disintegrations; and for microorganisms, 5 disintegrations to yield one grain. Maurer and Primbsch[123] found with AR-10 film that 16 disintegrations were necessary to yield one grain in sections of liver cells 3 μ thick, labeled with H[3]-tyrosine. On the other hand, Kisieleski et al.[106] reported that from 3-μ sections of tissue with nuclear labeling and AR-10 film 100–200 disintegrations of tritium were represented by one silver grain. Wimber and collaborators[200] held that 10–11 disintegrations produced one silver grain in AR-10 film over thin squash preparations, and 19 disintegrations produced one grain in NTB emulsion. Marin and Bender[122] measured 10 disintegrations to yield one grain for tissue culture cells labeled in the cytoplasm plus nucleus. For bone marrow cell smears labeled with H[3]-thymidine, 14–17 disintegrations were found per grain at average.[24] All these data were obtained under various conditions, and differences in the technique of development, in latent image fading, or in chemical effects on the emulsion by the staining procedure may have influenced the results. It is worthwhile to keep in mind that autoradiograms which are not obtained by absolute identical techniques may not be compared with each other. As an approximation, the autoradiographic method can be held to have an efficiency of about 5% when the thickness of the tritium-containing material is about 3 μ. The determination of the autoradiographic efficiency at average per preparation is very helpful for estimating the radiation dose delivered to a biological structure even if the value for single cells may vary considerably.

3.2. FADING OF THE LATENT IMAGE

If the exposure time of an emulsion prior to its development is relatively long, i.e., more than a few days, fading of the latent image may be observed and may lead to a false interpretation of the finally developed image. Fading of the latent image means that in the course of time an activated silver halide crystal carrying a latent image falls back to the state of inactivation and loses its predisposition to be easily developed. The result is a nonlinear increase of the intensity

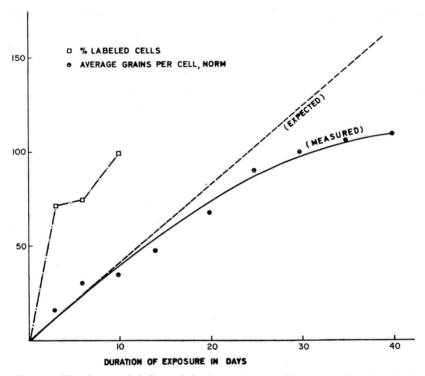

Fɪɢ. 4.3. The degree of fading of the latent image with various duration of the exposure of AR-10 (Kodak) to tritium. Modified, courtesy of Baserga and Nemeroff, *Stain Technol.*[7]

of the image with the exposure time of the film to the radiation (see Fig. 4.3). The fading is held to be due mainly to oxidation of the silver atoms carrying the latent image. The degree of fading is greater if fewer silver atoms are involved in the latent image. This also means that fading of the latent image is more frequently observed with incident particles of low ionizing power.[89]

Some of the means to avoid the fading of the latent image have been listed.[89] Thus, the fading is eliminated when the autoradiographic preparations during the time of exposure are kept in an oxygen-free environment, such as in dry nitrogen or helium. Exposures made at low temperature and humidity (about 4°C and with a desiccant) may be equally effective in avoiding latent-image fading. Under these conditions Kopriwa and Leblond[108] reported in NTB-2 emulsion (Kodak) a direct linear relationship between the number of developed silver grains and the exposure time up to 1 year. Absence of Drierite alone finally caused a total fading of the latent image. Also, repeated short exposures of the film to humidity may lead to a reduction in the number of developable silver grains.[117] Yet Wimber and collaborators[200] reported avoidance of fading at times by simply keeping the temperature at 4°C without additional control of humidity. The beneficial effect of low temperature on preserving the latent image is often more desirable than an increased sensitivity of the film at room temperature. In general, it is recommended that autoradiograms be exposed at a low temperature and in a dry atmosphere.

There may also be an influence on the latent image by the underlying tissue. Thus, oxidizing agents such as perchloric acid, often used for histochemical extractions, and various fixatives such as Zenker's, Helly's, and Schaudinn's may, if not carefully removed or protected against by coating the specimen, lead to a desensitization of the emulsion to the developer.[65] Osmium tetroxide[165] and potassium permanganate[107] were found to affect the sensitivity of fine-grain emulsions. Residual moisture in the tissue underlying the film or in the film in consequence of insufficient drying may, of course, also be responsible for the phenomenon.[174]

3.3. BACKGROUND

The quality of an autoradiogram varies with the degree of background. Some of the possible causes for the production of images by means other than the isotope of the experiment have been mentioned already in the section on development of the image (Section 2.2). Thus, the timing of development at a certain temperature for a given developer is crucial for obtaining a true image with little background. Increased background from backscattering of radiation is usually not a problem with the low-energy β-particles from tritium, but may come into play if the histological section is ultrathin.

Film emulsions may already carry latent images before they are used for autoradiography. This happens when emulsions are exposed too long to cosmic radiation owing to improper storage shielding or when they are heated excessively. Also, an accidental exposure to radiation could have occurred without being noticed. The safe light in the darkroom may have been too bright, an electrical switch close to the work bench may have not been insulated properly, and the darkroom may leak light from the outside. It is obvious that proper handling of the film will reduce the number of background grains to a minimum. All film should be stored at low temperature but not in a frozen state, with avoidance of excessive relative humidities, and shielded if indicated.

Increased background may be induced by electrostatic sparkings when stripping film is handled in too dry an atmosphere. By heating liquid emulsions beyond the temperature recommended, background may be produced. Repeated dipping of slides carrying tissue into liquid emulsions may lead to a contamination of the emulsion with labeled soluble substances leaching out of the tissue.

Chemographic images may contribute to background. Silver halide grains in the emulsion may thus be activated by sulfhydryl groups, for example, in cysteine and glutathione.[22] But since small molecules are removed during the process of fixation and since sulfhydryl groups are ordinarily not stable during protein denaturation in the cell,[132] they do not contribute to background in autoradiograms from tissue fixed in a conventional manner. Other substances may be responsible for chemographic images, especially in the liver[191]; but most fixed tissues exhibit few chemographic effects under ordinary circumstances.[191] Still, treatment of viable cells with substances containing SH-groups may cause increased background, as it was observed in autoradiograms of acetic alcohol-fixed cells which had been exposed *in vivo* to β-mercaptoethanol.[175] In unfixed or freeze-dried preparations, chemographic images must always be expected to contribute heavily to background. They can be prevented by a protective coating, for example, with celloidin.[108] Keeping the preparations during exposure at a temperature below 0°C was also said to reduce the chemographic effects.[148] In addition to sulfhydryl groups in unfixed tissue, luminescent material also may cause false images.[149] The luminescence appeared to be induced at low temperature by the β-particles from tritium. Since the luminescent material was distributed among various tissues to different degrees, autoradiograms from unfixed tissue sections did not reflect the true distribution of the tracer.

Because of the danger of contaminating the preparation with photochemically active substances, it is clear that all containers and solutions which are brought into contact with the film must be meticulously clean. Thus, the glass slides may be pretreated with chromic sulfuric acid for 24 hours, then washed in water for 24 hours, and stored in 96% ethanol until use.[135]

Background that has been caused prior to application of the film may be detected on test slides from the film batch used. It can be removed to a considerable extent by exposing the film after being mounted on a specimen for 3–6 hours to vapors of 3% hydrogen peroxide in a staining dish whose bottom is covered with several layers of thick filter paper.[38,206] The slides should not touch the filter paper which is soaked with the hydrogen peroxide. Of course, the procedure must be carried out in the dark. After thorough washing and drying, the autoradiographic preparations are then stored in the cold for regular exposure. The method, however, should not be used when labeled lipids fixed with osmium are examined, since they may become solubilized by hydrogen peroxide.

An attempt has also been made to oxidize background selectively after exposure of the film. Brenner[30] used a solution of 0.1 ml of a 20% stock solution of potassium ferricyanate in 20 ml of 15% sodium thiosulfate. Submersion of the autoradiogram prior to development for 45–60 seconds at 23°–26°C was recommended. It is very difficult, however, to bleach background grains exclusively without also affecting at least to some extent the latent image caused by the isotope in the experiment. Usually the background is not so high as to require a controlled oxidation, and lower background density can be corrected for by appropriate evaluation of the finished autoradiogram.

3.4. ARTIFACTS

Artifacts may arise during the preparation of autoradiograms or during the photographic processing, and they may affect the efficiency of the method to a great extent. The tissue preparation may be distorted, may be ruptured, may contain vacuoles, or may show displacements of tissue elements. The overlaying film may slip and thus superimpose on the tissue an image that does not fit or make sense. Irregularities in the film, especially after application of liquid emulsion, may impress as holes, cracks, or streaks without image. The film layer may be grossly uneven. In the case of stripping film, air locks between section and film may be so small that they may be mistaken for grain accumulations. Some of these artifacts may be accompanied by a localized fading of the latent image. This is usually quickly recognized, as it follows some pattern in the film connected with the artifacts. Bacterial contamination in the emulsion, stain particles, and small cracks and scratches are usually easily recognized as such and are not mistaken for silver grains belonging to the true image or the background.

3.5. FADING OF THE FINAL IMAGE

The autoradiogram finally developed and fixed may still alter the quality of its image during storage and further processing such as staining. The fixative (thiosulfate) improperly removed by washing may cause, in time, a fading of the developed silver grains. If autoradiograms are stained for work with the light microscope through the gelatin after photographic processing, the image may be affected by certain stains used at an excessive pH,[179] as will be discussed below. Likewise, attempts to remove the gelatin in autoradiograms, for example, for electron microscopic evaluation, are apt to remove at least some of the silver grains too.

Processed autoradiograms should be stored properly protected against excessive temperatures and humidity and against chemical fumes. It is well known that old photographs tend to bleach.

3.6. CONCLUSION

Later in this chapter various autoradiographic methods will be reviewed with emphasis on proper control of the techniques. Patience and experience will prevent misinterpretations. Preparing the specimen carefully and adhering to routine standards in the application and processing of the autoradiographic film will give confidence with which to judge the final result. Baserga and Nemeroff[9] have recommended the simultaneous processing of known standard slides along with the batches of unknown preparations in order to trace with greater ease potentially misleading images caused by the technique.

4. The Darkroom

An ordinary, clean darkroom can be used for autoradiographic work, and the special equipment necessary is inexpensive. A refrigerator provides for the storage of the nuclear track plates or emulsions. A proper safe light, with Wratten filter No. 2 (Kodak), or a light of the OA series (Kodak), or Ilford S safe light No. 902 should be installed not closer than 3–4 feet above the work bench. Tap water as well as distilled or deionized water must be available in the darkroom. For the work with stripping film, a simple open water bath with a round edge is to be used. The liquid emulsion technique requires an adjustable water bath with a thermometer to keep constant temperature. Razor blades are necessary, if not a special cutting device, for cutting stripping film; and a thumb forceps is needed to strip the film from the supporting glass plate. Coplin jars and beakers to hold the liquid emulsions are also standard equipment. Glass dishes usually used for staining (volume approximately 300 ml) and slide racks, made of glass or plastic, with a metal wire holder are conveniently used for photographic processing. Other slide racks, perhaps of wood, serve for drying of the applied film emulsion. The preparations are dried conveniently with adjustable hair dryers. For easier handling of the dryers, two or three of them can be mounted on a wooden board which is movable.[1] Light-proof boxes (Bakelite) that can be sealed with insulating tape should be large enough to hold about 20 slides plus a desiccant for storage and exposure in the refrigerator. Less convenient are larger light-proof boxes with several trays, each with about 20 slide preparations.[95] In any case, a small or larger container with a desiccant, such as Drierite, must be enclosed for humidity control. These containers are conveniently made from small plastic centrifuge tubes which have many small perforations and can be stoppered easily.[1] A small bag of fine mesh gauze may be sufficient as well.

For work with stripping film, the darkroom temperature should be controlled at 18°–20°C, and the relative humidity should be about 60%. If possible, the proper installations should be made to maintain these conditions; at least a thermostat should be in the room. Strict controls are not necessary when stripping film is applied according to the method of Mazia and Bucher,[125] as will be discussed below. Handling of liquid emulsions requires slightly different conditions, which may be secured in a humid climate simply by a warm air flow from the hair dryers.[1] Slides covered with liquid emulsions should be dried at approximately 28°C and at an optimal humidity of 60–80%. Kopriwa and Leblond[108] reinvestigated the best conditions for work with liquid emulsions and they suggested the use of a special drying oven set at 28°C, with controlled humidity of 70–80% to assure a uniform emulsion coat and low background.

Various applications and techniques of autoradiography may need additional equipment which shall be specified in the appropriate sections below.

5. The Autoradiographic Preparation

Autoradiographic film may be applied in a single or double layer to normally fixed tissue sections or cell smears for examination by light microscopy (regular single-layer and double-layer technique of autoradiography); a single layer of film may cover ultrathin sections prepared for the electron microscope (electron microscopic autoradiography); or finally, film may be mounted on frozen, freeze-dried, or simply dried tissue to study labeled small molecular substances soluble in water, dilute acid, or a chemical fixing agent (dry-mounting technique of autoradiography).

Since the autoradiographic technique is chosen according to the type of specimen, it is best to discuss the preparation of the specimen and the appropriate autoradiographic technique together. Whatever technique is chosen, the preparation of the specimen must conform to the type of labeled compound in the experiment.

5.1 REGULAR SINGLE-LAYER AUTORADIOGRAPHY

In the first attempts at autoradiography a single layer of nuclear track emulsion was applied to biological specimens (section or cell smear) which were fixed by conventional methods for light microscopy. Intimate contact of film and specimen was achieved by coating the specimen with a liquid film emulsion[13] or by covering it with stripping film[144] which has a 5-μ thick nuclear track emulsion supported by a gelatin layer 10 μ thick on a glass plate. Both techniques have remained essentially unchanged, yet considerable refinements were introduced with the advent of tritium-labeled precursors.

5.1.1. *Specimen Fixation*

Conventional autoradiograms register only such label that is bound to molecules which are not removed from the specimen by the process of fixation. Because of varying sensitivity of compound classes to fixing agents, the method of fixation depends on the compound and the cellular structure to be examined. In case of doubt, pilot experiments with various reagents will decide the proper choice of fixation. Moreover, fixation does not necessarily always prevent diffusion of a labeled compound or even its movement into the emulsion, as Levi[115] has emphasized.

Small molecular compounds such as those soluble in water, in dilute acid, or in organic solvents are nearly totally or totally lost with most of the common fixatives.[74] Blanck and co-workers reported as early as 1951[21] a 40% loss of P^{32} from tissue fixed in formalin and Bouin's solution or just exposed to physiological saline.

The different degree of solubility of certain small molecular components in various solutions may be of advantage for their assessment by autoradiography. Thus, an optimal fixing solvent can be chosen according to the compound class.[63] Within the group of nucleic acid precursors, in HeLa cells in culture, acetic alcohol extracts thymidine and thymidine monophosphate and a major portion of thymidine diphosphate, while 2% perchloric acid subsequently extracts the thymidine triphosphate and the rest of the thymidine diphosphate[59]; small nucleotide chains with less than 10 nucleotide units are also considered to be acid-soluble. It is thus possible to separate by careful extraction various groups of acid-soluble nucleotides, which indeed also show different metabolic behavior as seen in HeLa-S_3 cells by competitive inhibition of pyrimidine interconversion.[56,57] Depending on the type of tissue, some of the heterogeneous nucleic acids may also be extracted by various fixing agents. Vincent[194] mentioned the likely loss of some RNA in the acid-soluble fraction of sea urchin eggs. Table 4.4A gives a survey of the losses of nucleotide material observed in various tissues with different fixing solutions. Kopriwa and Leblond[108] thus checked autoradiographically the degree of labeling from H^3-cytidine (RNA precursor) remaining in mouse liver cells after five different fixations. It is seen that Zenker's fixation left the least amount of label (Table 4.4A). Table 4.4B lists the data of Schneider and Maurer.[167] From

TABLE 4.4A

INFLUENCE OF VARIOUS FIXING AGENTS ON THE RETENTION OF LABEL IN MOUSE LIVER AFTER INJECTION OF H^3-CYTIDINE[a]

Fixative	Number of grains/1000 μ^{2b}
Carnoy	124.4 ± 3.8
Bouin	116.6 ± 5.1
Formalin	105.5 ± 1.9
Zenker	3.1 ± 0.2
Zenker plus iodine and cysteine[c]	75.1 ± 2.1

[a] With permission of Kopriwa and Leblond, *J. Histochem. Cytochem.*[108]

[b] Unstained sections.

[c] To remove mercury salts after Zenker fixation, liver sections were placed in Lugol's solution ($I_2:KI:H_2O = 1:2:100$) for 5 minutes; 5% thiosulfate, 5 minutes; running water, 10 minutes; 0.2 M cysteine, 2 hours; running water, 20 minutes; and distilled water before drying.

TABLE 4.4B

INFLUENCE OF VARIOUS FIXING AGENTS ON THE RETENTION OF LABEL IN MOUSE TISSUES AFTER INJECTION OF H^3-CYTIDINE[a]

Fixative	pH	Number of grains/1000 μ^2 in absolute numbers and normalized to the value after Formalin fixation															
		Liver epithelium		Renal tubule epithelium		Adrenal cortex		Adrenal marrow		Colon epithelium		Colon ganglion cells		Small intestine muscle		Small intestine ganglion cells	
		g	%	g	%	g	%	g	%	g	%	g	%	g	%	g	%
n-Formalin	7.0	230	100	190	100	570	100	180	100	220	100	700	100	110	100	360	100
Carnoy–chloroform	3.4	90	39	170	80	450	79	130	72	160	73	100	14	40	36	170	47
0.5% TCA–5% Formalin	~1.3	160	70	130	69	290	51	140	78	170	77	140	20	100	91	500	140
5% TCA–6% Formalin	~0.9	50	22	—	—	—	—	—	—	—	—	—	—	—	—	—	—
20% Glacial acetic acid–concentrated ethanol	2.8	160	70	—	—	—	—	—	—	—	—	—	—	—	—	—	—
Methanol		50	22	—	—	—	—	—	—	—	—	—	—	—	—	—	—

[a] Data taken 20 minutes after injection. With permission of Schneider and Maurer, *Acta Histochem.*[167]

the modes of fixation tested with the various tissue specimens neutral formaldehyde (6%) appeared to preserve most activity in the tissue. The different degree of label extraction in the various tissues is striking. No loss of RNA was observed when plant cells were fixed in 2% formaldehyde.[121]

Differential extraction techniques combined with autoradiography for water-soluble substances (see Section 5.5 of this chapter) are promising indeed. Thus, Woods and Zubay[204] extracted from freeze-dried seedlings of *Vicia faba* selectively transfer RNA. The seedlings, after freeze-substitution, were embedded in paraffin and sectioned. The sections were then placed on dry nuclear track emulsion and deparaffinized with toluene. They were subsequently treated with 67% ethanol containing 0.67% potassium acetate and then exposed to the extraction mixture consisting of cold (2°C) 0.01 M $MgCl_2$, 0.3 M NaCl, and 0.001 M Tris buffer at pH 7.4. The selective removal of transfer RNA from the chromatin portion of the nucleus was confirmed by parallel biochemical analysis.

The loss of protein or its subunits in a buffered solution of osmium tetroxide, during subsequent treatment with alcohols and embedding in methacrylate, was shown to involve mainly material of small molecular weight. Still 10% of the losses were precipitable with trichloracetic acid.[40] Extraction of proteins (up to 15%) in osmium tetroxide solutions varied with different types of buffer systems.[119] The extraction of hemoglobin during the fixation of amphibian erythrocytes with osmium tetroxide solutions could be prevented at pH of 6.2 by addition of calcium ions to a total concentration of 0.01 M.[192]

Small molecular material may leach from fixed cells by partial hydrolysis. Thus, 53% of leucine that was bound to transfer RNA was released in a water bath over a period of 30 minutes at 37°C,[173] but no protein was observed to be lost in 5% trichloroacetic acid and 45% acetic acid in the presence of 1.37% lanthanum triacetate for 3–5 minutes.

Following fixation, soluble substances may still be released from tissue during embedding in paraffin or methacrylate or during contact with other processing solutions. Loss of nucleic acid derivatives was observed during flattening of paraffin sections of pancreas on water.[97] Some labeled thymidine not yet polymerized into DNA was shown to be extractable from ascites tumor cells upon cell fractionation after fixation with acetic acid–alcohol.[45] Loss of labeled amino acids during embedding of pancreatic tissue in methacrylate was observed to fall with time after injection of the precursor. At 7.5 minutes, the loss was about 25% of the label incorporated; 15 minutes later the loss involved only 9%.[40]

It must also be considered that various modes of fixation alter cell geometry to different degrees. Thus, swelling or shrinkage of a cell changes with its thickness, the density per unit area. A considerable effect on the absorption of the tritium β-particle is to be expected. Autoradiograms of monolayers of tissue culture cells (HeLa) labeled with H^3-cytidine and fixed with absolute methyl alcohol showed at times a lower labeling intensity than when the cells were fixed with acetic alcohol (1 vol glacial acetic acid: 3 vol 95% ethanol). The differences were maximally about 10% when the acetic alcohol was freshly prepared. In this case, the cells were flatter and larger, and the β-absorption was consequently reduced.[59] An example is shown in Table 4.5. The geometry of cells may also change with alterations of the composition and pH of osmium tetroxide solutions.[192]

Maurer and Primbsch[123] found a shrinkage 10% higher for the cell nuclei in liver sections embedded in paraffin and 30% higher for the cytoplasm than that observed with sections embedded in methacrylate.

TABLE 4.5

INFLUENCE OF VARIOUS FIXING AGENTS ON THE RETENTION OF LABELED RNA AND
DNA IN HeLa CELLS AT VARIOUS TIMES AFTER SHORT-TERM LABELING

Labeling with H³-cytidine	Fixation	Mean grain count per cell (with AR-10)		
		Nucleus	Cytoplasm	Total
A. For 5 minutes	Methanol (absolute)	42.8	—	42.8
	Acetic acid–ethanol (1:3)	43.8	—	43.8
	Methanol (absolute) followed by 2% perchloric acid (4°C)	51.9	—	51.9
B. For 30 minutes followed by regular culture condition for 72 hours	Methanol (absolute)	69.5	114.0	183.5
		63.5	129.6	193.1
	Acetic acid–ethanol	73.0	131.7	204.7
		63.3	144.4	207.7
	Methanol (absolute) followed by 2% perchloric acid (4°C)	64.5	122.6	187.1
		61.3	114.1	175.4

Labeling with H³-thymidine	Fixation	Mean grain count, nucleus	H³ counts/ minute of fixing agents (±ctg error)
A. For 30 minutes	Methanol (absolute)	55.2	257 ± 5
	Acetic acid–ethanol, followed by 2% perchloric acid (4°C)	60.6	614 ± 11
B. As in (A) followed by regular culture condition plus carrier thymidine for 30 minutes	Methanol (absolute)	57.8	40 ± 2
	Acetic acid–ethanol, followed by 2% perchloric acid (4°C)	56.5	79 ± 3
C. As in (A) and (B) but culture continued for 90 minutes	Methanol (absolute)	56.1	22 ± 2
	Acetic acid–ethanol, followed by 2% perchloric acid (4°C)	60.2	13 ± 2

It is clear, then, that a fixative should be chosen carefully, with the understanding that various modes of fixation are not interchangeable. Small molecular material and substances soluble in the solutions used for processing the preparations can be examined autoradiographically by techniques discussed below. The experimental conditions must be kept strictly constant at all times to obtain comparable data.

For the study of labeled proteins and nucleic acids it is suggested, in general, to fix small tissue pieces for sectioning in Carnoy's fixative, in Bouin's solution, in 4–6% neutral buffered Formalin, or in a combination of these, such as Carnoy's fixative for 2 hours followed by Formalin saline for 24 hours. In the case of bony structures, decalcification may follow the fixation. Thus, the bones may be treated with a 10% solution of disodium versenate or with 10% Formalin containing 0.2 M ethylenediaminetetraaceteic acid (EDTA) at pH 7.5 for 12 hours.[185] The treatment with the detergent may cause translocation of the labeling and this should be watched. After fixation the tissue is thoroughly washed, dehydrated, and embedded in paraffin or another medium such as methacrylate, prior to sectioning in the usual manner. Undecalcified bones may be processed by embedding in a hard plastic and by special sectioning techniques.[142]

Cell suspensions can be prepared in smears according to known histological techniques, for example, by drawing out a film of the cell suspension on a microscopic glass slide, by using a small paint brush to paint the cells in concentrated suspension on the slide in several gentle strokes, or by squashing thin tissue pieces such as those from bone marrow or concentrated cell suspensions between two slides. Such preparations should be dried rapidly after they have been made to allow for optimal morphological preservation. They are fixed best in absolute methyl alcohol for 10 minutes. Cellular morphology is often less well preserved by fixation in acetic alcohol (glacial acetic acid: 95% ethanol; 1:3), but this may be required at times prior to further histochemical treatment. Following fixation, it is recommended that the preparations be treated with 2% perchloric acid at 4°C for 30–45 minutes and washed thoroughly prior to dehydration with alcohol. That way acid-soluble substances are completely or nearly completely removed, and the labeled macromolecules alone can be investigated. In addition, subsequent staining often gives a better contrast after the perchloric acid treatment. Tissue sections or smears should be washed free of any reducing or oxidizing chemicals before they are covered with film to avoid chemographic effects or fading of the latent image (see Sections 3.2 and 3.3 in this chapter).

Cells which have grown on a Millipore filter—for example, in a diffusion chamber—may be fixed first in the usual manner, after which the membrane must be cleared and softened by alcohol treatment so that it can be transferred to a clean glass slide for autoradiography.[18] While the membrane is hardening on the slide, gentle pressure may be applied. The membrane is then secured on the slide with a ring of Scotch tape, which can be removed again before mounting the autoradiographic film. The dry Millipore membrane usually sticks tightly to the glass slide. Cairns[32,33] applied the Millipore filter on the slide with a cement.

5.1.2. Staining Techniques Prior to Mounting the Emulsion

The biological specimen may be treated by any histochemical technique[48,142] prior to autoradiography, as long as the specimen can be thoroughly freed from oxidizing or reducing chemicals before application of the film. It is, indeed, the combination with specific histochemical methods that makes autoradiography potent. Before an established routine procedure of cytohistochemistry is chosen for tissue specimen containing tritium as a tracer, it is strongly advisable to consider the possible exchange and loss of the label during the procedure in question. This is particularly paramount in those reactions employing acids at high temperatures.

Most staining procedures can be preferentially postponed until completion of the photographic processing of the autoradiograms. Stains which tend to leach can still be used prior to application of the photographic emulsion if the stained specimen is protected by a thin collodion coating.[108,128] In working with tritium, however, the loss of efficiency and resolution caused by absorption of the tritium electrons in even a thin layer must be weighed against the possible advantage of using a stain prior to autoradiographic processing. As discussed later in this chapter, various stains still do not leach nor cause chemographic effects—e.g., hematoxylin–eosin,[108] the peroxidase staining,[154] or acetic orcein or the group of aldehyde stains in the Feulgen technique or periodic acid Schiff reaction. The latter two staining techniques involving hydrolysis with hydrochloric acid or periodic acid must be carried out, of course, prior to mounting the nuclear track emulsion.

The eminent usefulness of the Feulgen technique[60] for selectively staining DNA and of the periodic acid Schiff method[100,101] for polysaccharides, collagen fibers, basement membranes, etc., must be questioned for work with autoradiography as long as the techniques are not strictly controlled with regard to loss of labeled substances. In the case of the Feulgen technique, not only RNA but also the purine bases of DNA are liberated by hydrolysis in hydrochloric acid or perchloric acid[42,203]; thus a label bound to the purine bases is concomitantly lost. Also, the pyrimidine bases of DNA are partially lost if the hydrolysis time exceeds an optimal limit, which is, however, not identical with the optimal hydrolysis time needed to achieve maximum binding of the dye.[114,166,203] Lang and Maurer[114] have recently re-examined the various steps of the Feulgen technique on tissue sections labeled with H^3-thymidine. Various cell types of the mouse showed the same pattern, i.e., after a hydrolysis time for maximum stainability, 50% of the tritium was lost. Also, rinsing with water subsequent to hydrolysis greatly influenced the amount of label retained on the DNA. In order to use the Feulgen technique with confidence it is therefore necessary to keep strict time limits for the steps of hydrolysis and subsequent rinses. Even mild acid hydrolysis removes cytoplasmic DNA, as was shown by Brachet and Ficq,[28] who therefore modified the technique by substituting 1 N HCl in absolute alcohol for the aqueous acid solution. Still, the cytoplasmic DNA could not be totally preserved.

Feulgen-stained squash preparations are often used for studying the labeling of chromosomal DNA. The method of freezing and thawing of squashed cell preparations[43] to preserve the squashed material during transfer of the coverslip to another slide for eventual autoradiography has recently been improved. Jona[96] described a squash technique using Scotch tape No. 665 to manually squash the cells after they were fixed, Feulgen-stained, and soaked for 2–5 minutes in 45% acetic acid. The adhesive side of the tape was covered with a plastic transparent sheet and the cells did not stick to the nonadhesive side. When the clean side on which the specimen was squashed had been soaked in a gelatin–chrome alum solution (gelatin, 10 g; chrome alum, 1 g; water, 1000 ml), the material remained in place on the slide and no loss occurred during the removal of the Scotch tape after the squashing. After removal of the Scotch tape and washing for 5–10 minutes in tap water, the specimen was ready for autoradiography.

Chromosomal preparations may be made easily from cell suspensions by treating the cells with a hypotonic solution such as 0.5–1% sodium citrate in water or with diluted Hanks balanced salt solution prior to fixation with acetic alcohol, after which the chromosomes are spread on the slide by rapid drying. The chromosomes can be stained prior to autoradiography with acetic orcein. Vaious modifications of this technique have been described.[53,70,158] To spread the chromosomes of metaphase free of cytoplasm, Prescott and Bender[155] recommended disrupting the cells by repeatedly changing the acetic acid prior to drying the sample on the slide.

5.1.3. Enzymatic and Acid Hydrolysis of the Specimen

Differential extraction of cellular components other than small molecular material[48,142] before autoradiographic film is applied may remove a certain fraction of the tracer from a cell, leaving other tracer behind for identification. Differential extraction methods are most useful in work with nucleic acids and proteins, and enzymes and acids are both employed.

Enzymatic hydrolysis of nucleic acids of fixed tissues, using RNase or DNase in a 0.1% buffered solution (in 0.005 M Mg^{2+} in the case of DNase) according to the classic papers by Brachet[27] and Kaufmann et al.[102] have been used extensively in combination with autoradiography. Care should be taken that no extraction occurs in the control preparation when a buffer is used as the blank reagent. Depending on the type of fixation, not all of the RNA of DNA may be digested by the appropriate enzymes. RNA hybridized with DNA is usually resistant to RNase.[25] After acid fixation, however, as in acetic alcohol (1 vol glacial acetic acid:3 vol 95% ethanol), all RNA has been shown to be susceptible to the enzyme action, indicative of the separation of the hybrid strands. Indeed, after fixation in acetic alcohol, the DNA was sufficiently accessible so that it could serve as a primer and be cytochemically localized with a polymerase system and nucleotides labeled with tritium.[195] Moreover, it must be kept in mind that not all enzymes within a cell may be necessarily inactivated by fixation. Cellular DNase, for example, retains some of its activity after mild fixation to become active when the RNA is removed by RNase.[120]

The use of acids to extract nucleic acids poses difficulties, some of which have already been mentioned in Section 5.1.2. The specificity of acid extractions is not sharply limited. Thus, perchloric acid extraction of RNA[136] invariably results in a partial or total removal of the purines from DNA.[42] Hence, if the label is attached to the purine bases, this method is very impractical for separating RNA label from DNA label. Another difficulty is the optimal hydrolysis time, which varies with different tissue or cell types and which needs to be established in pilot experiments. Prolonged RNA extraction with perchloric acid results also in partial removal of proteins[99] and DNA pyrimidines.[114,203] Still, 10% perchloric acid containing 10% acrolein removed 85% of the RNA within 18–24 hours at a temperature of 0°–5°C without labilizing DNA phosphate.[197] RNA is usually extracted with 10% perchloric acid in the cold[136] or at room temperature for 2–5 hours, after which the DNA is extracted by 10% perchloric acid at 65°–90°C for 20 minutes to 2 hours, depending on the type of tissue. Acid-extraction methods can be used for autoradiography without adaptations, provided the acid is totally removed before the film is applied. Possible tritium–hydrogen exchange during acid treatment must be kept in mind and can be easily tested.

Proteins also may be selectively removed from the cells by enzymatic hydrolysis, e.g., with a 0.5% aqueous solution of pepsin prior to au-toradiography.[77,78] Histones are soluble in 10% sulfuric acid and can thus be differentially removed prior to autoradiography.[28] Proteins may also be attacked by their characteristic solubilities in solutions of various ionic strength, a principle that has not been utilized to its full possibilities as yet in conjunction with autoradiography.

5.1.4. *Use of Tritiated Dyes, Coupling Agents, and Enzymatic Inhibitors*

Another useful technique in combination with autoradiography is the histochemical coupling of a labeled substance or reagent specifically to a cellular constituent analogous to the binding of a dye within a fixed cell. This approach will undoubtedly contribute greatly to the future development of cytology and cytochemistry. The preparation of the specimen for this type of work depends, of course, on the coupling reactions desired. For localizing enzymes with labeled substrate, for example, freeze-drying of the tissue may be the choice. Belanger[14] examined the uptake of P^{32}, S^{35}, and Ca^{45} by bone, cartilage, arteries, and neoplastic tissue, after formaldehyde–ethanol fixation, to gain in-formation on the effects of nutrition and aging in the different tissues. Barnard and Ostrowski[3] reported on the application of tritium-labeled reagents to measure amino groups in proteins (after fixation) or tritium-labeled antibody to locate, autoradiographically, antigens bound to cells. Furthermore, with tritium-labeled inhibitors, enzymes were located within single cells after fixation. Thus, with tritiated malonate, succinic dehydrogenase was localized in the mitochondria,[139] and tritiated DFP (diisopropylphosphorofluoridate) was used to demonstrate acetylcho-linesterase in neural end plates.[139,140] The latter technique has been extended to the quantitative interpretation[4] and also to other tissues in addition to neural end plates.[141] Hempel[88] measured sulfhydryl groups in fixed tissue sections by coupling them with tritiated N-phenyl-maleimide and found a sharp localization of the label over sections of skin according to expectation from other histochemical methods. The localization of cytoplasmic DNA in oocytes by labeled actinomycin was preferred by Brachet and Ficq[28] before the Feulgen technique, because this DNA fraction was found to be very labile in acid. The specific coupling of diazotized 2-amino-p-benzenedisulfonic acid to guanylic acid was advantageous to Mondrianakis and Beer[131] in attempting a base-sequence determination in nucleic acids with the electron micro-scope.

5.2. SINGLE LAYER APPLICATION OF EMULSION

The available nuclear track emulsions for autoradiography differ in their grain size and sensitivity (see Table 4.2). Generally, the smaller the size of the silver halide crystal is, the lower the sensitivity of the emulsion, but the higher the possible resolution and grain density attainable. There is a concomitant greater susceptibility for fading of the latent image. For autoradiography with the light microscope, a developed silver grain of 0.2–0.3 μ is quite sufficient. Emulsions having grains of that size are Ilford's G-5 and K-5, Kodak's NTB-2 and NTB-3 in liquid or gel form, and the stripping film from Kodak (AR-10).

Whether to use a liquid emulsion or the stripping film often depends largely on the darkroom facilities. Until recently, stripping film was superior in giving reproducible data with a low background and was therefore preferred when the temperature and humidity of the darkroom could easily be controlled. But the liquid emulsions have now been improved greatly and vary less from one shipment to another, and the background is usually considerably lower than previously. Because of the greater ease of application, liquid emulsions are more popular now than stripping film. Moreover, by using tritium, an uneven thickness of the emulsion layer is little cause for error in quantitation as long as the layer is at least about 1 μ thick. A regular and even emulsion thickness is the advantage of the stripping film for work with higher energy radiation, e.g., from C^{14}. The ease of handling liquid emulsions is complemented by the stability of the film mounted on a specimen; on the other hand, stripping film easily shifts on the specimen or even becomes lost during photographic processing and subsequent straining. Also, small air locks occur frequently when the film is used on sections. The advantages and disadvantages of the two types of emulsions need to be tested before a choice is made. It is, however, suggested that with tritium a medium-sized grain emulsion in liquid form should be tried first for ordinary light microscopic work.

5.2.1. *Liquid Emulsion Mounting*

Liquid emulsion may be mounted on a tissue section and smear for work in the light microscope by various manipulations—for example, with the help of a dropper or a brush, or with an applicator to assure uniform thickness. Dipping the slide into the liquid emulsion is efficient and simple; then the superfluous emulsion should be drained off and the preparation dried and stored for photographic exposure. The conditions under which slides should be covered in such a manner were carefully reexamined by Kopriwa and Leblond,[108] and the reader should also consult this paper if he wishes to use the liquid emulsion technique.

Emulsions which gel at room temperature must be liquified prior to use. This is done by placing the container, such as a coplin jar, with sufficient gel into a water bath covered with a lid and set at a constant

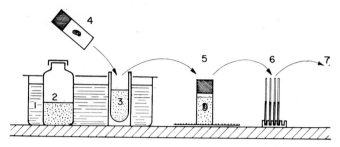

FIG. 4.4. The application of liquid emulsion: (1) constant temperature water bath 45°C; (2) stock emulsion; (3) Coplin jar with liquid emulsion; (4) slide dipped into the liquid emulsion; (5) placed briefly on filter paper; (6) put on slide holder for drying; (7) and transferred into storage box for exposure.

temperature of 40°–45°C (see Fig. 4.4). When the emulsion is sufficiently warmed, it may be stirred gently with a glass rod or porcelain spoon without causing air bubbles. Liquid emulsion may also be poured from the stock container into the coplin jar. If indicated, the emulsion may be diluted with distilled water. The effect of the degree of dilution on the thickness of the dry emulsion mounted on the slide by simple dipping was examined by Falk and King.[54] A threefold dilution of NTB-2 (Kodak) results in a dry layer about 0.85 μ thick. A fourfold dilution yields 0.76 μ and a tenfold dilution gives a layer about 0.37 μ thick, and about 0.145 μ is reached with a dilution 1:20. A slide carrying the deparaffinized tissue section or the cell smear properly fixed is then dipped into the emulsion in the coplin jar until it is sufficiently covered. The slide is withdrawn carefully and drained quickly of superfluous emulsion before it is placed vertically on filter paper for 10–15 seconds. The preparation, still in the vertical position with ground glass label up, is then put on a slide rack. In case a very liquid (diluted) emulsion is used, it may be better to place the slides horizontally for drying. The emulsion should not dry too quickly. Otherwise, very uneven coating and an increased background may result. The optimal temperature for drying is about 25°–30°C, and the relative humidity should be about 70–80%. If a special drying oven is not at hand, an air blow from a hair drier 2–3 feet away suffices. The slides dry within about 1 hour.

The dry slides are then stored in a 20-slot black slide box (Bakelite), and a drying agent such as Drierite, retained in small bags or perforated plastic capsules, is placed in the box. The box is closed and sealed with tape; it is put into a refrigerator for exposure at 4°C. If it is indicated that the slides be protected against chemical and physical damage, they may be coated with a solution of 10 g of gelatin and 5 ml of glycerol in 1000 ml of water.[174] At the end of the proper exposure time, which usually should be checked for a new set of experiments with test slides, the slide box is removed from the refrigerator and allowed to equilibrate with room temperature before the slides are transferred to slide carriers (made of glass or plastic) with a wire holder to be processed photographically.

5.2.2. *Stripping Film Mounting*

The application of stripping film such as Kodak's AR-10 is more difficult and needs some exercise and experience, and the user should not be discouraged at the first trial. Important for easy use is a controlled temperature and humidity in the darkroom, as Pelc[145] pointed out earlier. If the air is too dry, the film gives sparks when stripped off the supporting glass plate, and it curls immediately after its detachment from the glass. If the atmosphere is too humid, the film sticks and tears. The optimal humidity is 60% and the temperature should be 18°–20°C.

The film plates in the package should be removed from the refrigerator and put on the workbench about 30 minutes prior to use. One plate at a time is taken out of the dark wrapping and placed on a clean towel with the film side up. A small razor blade is used to cut first a 5-mm margin along the edges and then the pieces are cut to the size desired. It is easy to do this freehand, but an appropriate apparatus can be used as well. After the film has been cut on the glass plate, the single pieces are stripped off the plate by gently pulling, with a small thumb forceps, one end into the direction of the other still on the glass. Should the film curl up, gentle breathing on it usually leads to an immediate straightening. Each film piece, emulsion side down, is then quickly placed on the surface of distilled water, using the round and clean edge of the water bath as a guide (see Fig. 4.5). After about a minute, the film pieces are stretched and soaked sufficiently to be mounted. The side with the tissue section or smear is submerged in the water and brought slowly under the floating film piece. Then one edge of the slide is lifted out of the water so that it carries one end of the film which then wraps around the turning slide. The film should lock at the back side. The preparation is subsequently placed into a slide rack, in vertical position, before a hair drier (room temperature). The dry preparations are then transferred into a Bakelite box containing Drierite for exposure in the refrigerator.

If the darkroom conditions do not prove to be optimal for handling stripping film, the film pieces removed from the glass support may curl so much that they cannot be placed properly on the water. Moreover, electrostatic flashing is observed when the film is stripped off the plate, which results in streaks of background grains in the developed emulsion. Mazia and Bucher[125] have described a method by which these difficulties can be overcome. The whole film plate to be used is submerged

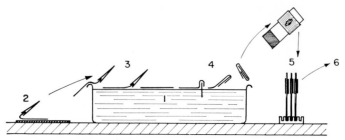

Fig. 4.5. The application of stripping film: (1) water bath with round edge; (2) the film piece is stripped off the supporting glass plate with the help of a thumb forceps; (3) film is floated, emulsion side down, on the water surface for 2–3 minutes; (4) microscopic slide is positioned underneath the floating film, and the film is wrapped around the slide; (5) the preparation is put on slide holder for drying; (6) and transferred into storage box for exposure.

in absolute ethyl alcohol for 15–30 seconds, then it is put into 90% ethyl alcohol in a flat bottom dish for cutting. The film pieces are peeled off— while the glass plate is still submerged—and then floated on to the water, emulsion side down. If a large number of autoradiograms are to be prepared, the water on which the film strips float should be changed at intervals to avoid too high a concentration of ethyl alcohol being carried over with the strips.

Displacement on the slide or floating away of the stripping film during later processing can be avoided in several ways: (1) by coating the back side of the glass slide with a sticky solution (1% gelatin, albumin, serum, etc.); (2) by seeing to it that the film, when mounted over the section or smear, comes to an overlap on the back side of the slide; (3) by keeping the water bath on which the film pieces float, prior to being mounted, at a temperature a few centigrades higher than that of the solutions for photographic processing, such as 23° versus 20°C; and (4) by avoiding any abrupt handling of the slides while they are submerged in processing solutions.

Should stripping film be placed on a biological specimen coated with a layer of celloidin, "Formvar," or "Vinalak," as Bishop and Bishop[20] and Stubblefield[183] have done in their studies of chromosomal labeling, the film may be held in place over the cells during photographic processing, if necessary, by a glass frame secured with rubber bands.

5.3. THE APPLICATION OF EMULSION IN DOUBLE LAYER

The double-layer autoradiographic technique aims at registering two different isotopes contained in the same specimen, such as tritium and C^{14}. It takes advantage of the fact that the mean β-energies of the two are different by a factor of about 10. Although the tritium β-particles do not traverse more than 1 μ in the undeveloped emulsion, C^{14} electrons range beyond 10 μ. Only about 40% of the β-particles from C^{14} are absorbed in a layer consisting of processed NTB emulsion 7 μ thick and of a protective celloidin coat 5 μ thick. Although the double-layer autoradiography allows a sharp distinction of the two different β-radiations, it is not essential for that purpose. Thus, Pilgrim and Maurer[152] and Wimber and Quastler[201] differentiated tritium and C^{14} by the characteristic tracks of grains of the latter in a heavy emulsion layer, approximately 20–40 μ thick.

The double-layer method places a second layer of film emulsion on a completely processed regular autoradiogram (see Fig. 4.6). A celloidin coat protects the first autoradiogram. Tritium registers then only in the first emulsion, while the image in the second emulsion is derived from C^{14} only. Attention must be given to the relative specific activities of the two isotopes in the specimen in order to obtain comparable images in the two emulsions. Depending on the type of the experiment, the dose of C^{14} must be sufficiently lower than that of tritium in order to allow the optimal autoradiographic exposure time for C^{14} to be long enough and not to obscure the image from tritium in the first emulsion. It is clear that this method is useful only if the double-labeled macromolecules are not only preserved in the cell during chemical fixation but if they are also inert toward the photographic processing and possibly staining before the second layer of emulsion is applied.

The double-layer autoradiogram may consist of equal or different types of emulsions. Thus, a liquid emulsion may be placed on a stripping film, or two layers of liquid emulsion or two layers of stripping film may be combined. The stripping film gives the advantage of rather even emulsion thickness, but as AR-10 it has the disadvantage of a 10-μ thick gelatin support which may, however, be selectively removed to improve the resolution of the second emulsion. The dipping film has the advantage of easy handling and relative thinness, but it is more difficult to control its thickness.

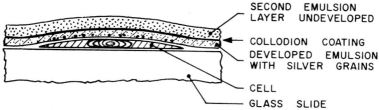

SECOND   EMULSION
LAYER   UNDEVELOPED

COLLODION   COATING
DEVELOPED   EMULSION
WITH   SILVER   GRAINS

CELL
GLASS   SLIDE

Fig. 4.6. Schematic cross section of double-layer autoradiogram, with two layers of liquid emulsion.

Two layers of stripping film were used by Krause and Plaut[109] to check the relative rate of incorporation of H³-thymidine and C¹⁴-thymidine. A liquid emulsion as the first layer, if sufficiently thin, allows a better resolution in the second layer. Thus, Baserga and Nemeroff[8] applied a liquid emulsion (NTB-Kodak) as the first layer which was 7μ thick after photographic processing. After staining with Mayers hematoxylin and eosin, the dry autoradiograms were then coated by dipping them into embedding solution A-4700* diluted with alcohol–ether (1:2) and neutralized with concentrated ammonia to avoid destaining. This resulted in a protective coat $5\ \mu$ thick and impermeable to water. For the second layer, the same liquid emulsion was chosen. In a subsequent improvement, Baserga and Lisco[10] diluted the emulsion for the first layer with water 1:1. A fine-grain emulsion (Ilford L-4) was preferred as the first layer and one with relatively coarse grains (Ilford G-5), as the second layer by Olszewska.[137] A coating with 1% celloidin separated the two. Kesse and collaborators[103] carefully examined the double-layer technique and preferred as the first layer the emulsion NUC-715 (Gevaert) as a thin coating in order to improve the resolution and to facilitate the staining through the developed thin film. This was then coated by dipping into 7% celloidin in amylacetate. Alcohol–ether as a solvent removed the stain from the specimen. NTB-2 (Kodak) was the second emulsion layer. For achieving optimal geometry of the first emulsion layer and hence a reproducible image in the second, Dawson and co-workers[49] recommended the use of stripping film without gelatin support.

The silver grains in the two layers of emulsion may be distinguished with greater ease when they are colored. Thus, Dawson and co-workers[49] redeveloped the first emulsion with a color developer, added a protective coating of celloidin 0.1 μ thick, and the second emulsion was mounted. The techniques of color development of autoradiograms were discussed in Section 2.2 of this chapter.

It should be emphasized that the double-layer technique does not allow a quantitative evaluation of grain tracks from C¹⁴ electrons in the second emulsion unless the thickness of the first layer emulsion is entirely uniform. Considerable alterations in the absorption of the C¹⁴ β-particles may occur with slight variations in the geometry of the first emulsion. Even thickness of the first layer is difficult to achieve with liquid emulsions; perhaps a calibrated applicator should be used for this purpose. Stripping film without gelatin support provides nearly uniform thickness, but it is difficult to mount. Selective digestion of the gelatin

* Randolph Products Co., Carlstadt, New Jersey.

support (10 μ) of the stripping film AR-10 with a trypsin solution[8] again introduces the uncertainty of nonuniform thickness.

5.4. ELECTRON MICROSCOPIC AUTORADIOGRAPHY

The usefulness of autoradiography with electron microscopy depends on the optimal resolution of a reproducible autoradiographic image and on the sharpness of structural contrast of the specimen under the emulsion layer. Considerable progress has been made recently to satisfy the principal demands for both. The main difficulties are in keeping the ultrathin section and the emulsion layer over it as thin and uniform as possible—the emulsion preferably as a monolayer of silver halide crystals—and in keeping the developed silver grains within a minimum size (see Fig. 4.7). The effort with regard to the latter is, of course, limited by the size of the silver halide crystals in the emulsion. A satisfactory contrast of the specimen may be obtained by using an appropriate stain prior to mounting of the emulsion or by removing the gelatin of the emulsion after photographic processing.

Assuming that the technical difficulties are solved adequately, there still remains the serious drawback of isotope content necessary in an ultrathin section to yield a reasonable image density. Two factors are mainly responsible for this problem. One is the low sensitivity of very small silver halide crystals arranged in a monolayer over the specimen. Thus, for the fine-grain emulsions L-4 (Ilford) and NTE (Kodak) 12 electrons having an energy of 5–10 kev or five tritium electrons at average were necessary to hit a monolayer of crystals to produce one latent image.[41,165] Moreover, latent images produced on very fine grains, which have a low sensitivity, tend to fade relatively easily. The other factor is the toxic biological effect of the tritium radiation, which may exceed the limits of tolerance if the isotope is administered in a sufficient amount so that the ultrathin tissue section can give an acceptable image density. Theoretical and practical aspects of electron microscopic autoradiography have been discussed particularly by Caro,[39] Caro and van Tubergen,[38] Granboulan,[76,77] Pelc,[147] and Meek and Moses.[126]

5.4.1. Specimen Preparation

The electron microscopic examination requires ultrathin sections, 100 mμ and less, and an adequate contrast to the electron beam. Accordingly, the technique of fixation, embedding, and cutting differs from that commonly used for the light microscope.[74,143]

The preparation of a specimen for autoradiography combined with the electron microscope is identical to that of ordinary ultrathin sections. Attention must be given, however, to the possible effects of the fixing

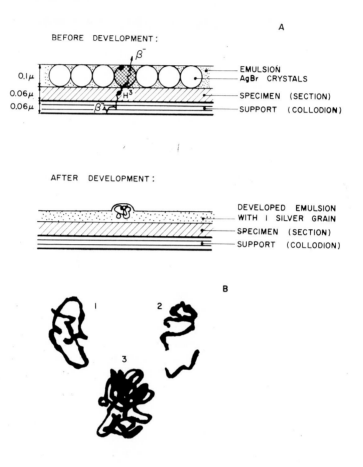

BEFORE DEVELOPMENT:

0.1μ — EMULSION / AgBr CRYSTALS

0.06μ — SPECIMEN (SECTION)

0.06μ — SUPPORT (COLLODION)

AFTER DEVELOPMENT:

DEVELOPED EMULSION WITH I SILVER GRAIN

SPECIMEN (SECTION)

SUPPORT (COLLODION)

B

1 + 2 AFTER FINE GRAIN DEVELOPMENT (MICRODOL-X)
3 AFTER REGULAR DEVELOPMENT (D-19)

FIG. 4.7. (A) Schematic cross section of an autoradiogram for electron microscopy, with a single layer of silver halide crystals, before and after development. (B) Appearance of silver grains in the electron microscope: L-4 (Ilford) after development in (1, 2) Microdol-X; (3) D-19, undiluted. Courtesy of Caro and van Tubergen, *J. Cell Biol.*[38]

agents on the integrity and composition of the specimen with regard to tracer labilization. This was discussed earlier in this chapter. Also the latent image may be partially or totally bleached, for example, by potassium permanganate[107] and osmium tetroxide in the case of NTE (Kodak),[165] unless a protective coating is placed between section and emulsion. Increased background may result from staining the section with lead stain prior to mounting the emulsion.[159] However, uranyl-acetate instead of the lead stain does not cause such an effect.[40]

Usually the tissue is fixed in a buffered solution of osmium tetroxide (1–2%, pH 7.4–7.8), in vapor of 2% osmium tetroxide, or in formal-dehyde. The latter was preferred by the Granboulans[77,78] who used it as 10% formaldehyde diluted with an equal volume of a buffered 10% acro-lein solution. After proper dehydration in graded alcohols, the tissue is embedded in a suitable medium hard enough to allow thin sectioning of the ultramicrotome. Popular embedding material is a methacrylate or an epoxy resin. A water-soluble epoxy resin (Durcupan) can be used as dehydrating agent prior to embedding in Araldite, which is water-in-soluble.[177] Histochemical extractions on ultrathin sections are carried out more easily when the embedding medium is water-soluble. The sections are then mounted flat on a small grid, perhaps coated with a collodion film and a layer of carbon. The specimen may be covered with nuclear track emulsion prior to or after its placement on the grid. Przy-bylsky[157] recommended the use of grids made of titanium instead of copper, since titanium grids were not only thicker but also more inert with the emulsion and photographic processing solutions. Nickel or stain-less steel grids appeared to be suitable also.[107]

5.4.2. Emulsion Mounting

The first attempts to apply autoradiographic techniques to electron microscopy date back only a few years. Liquier-Milward in 1956,[118] work-ing with Co[60], applied a relatively thick layer of liquid emulsion to ultrathin sections, and O'Brien and George[133] used an α-track-sensitive emulsion to demonstrate the site of absorption of polonium-210 on the wall of yeast cells. But the methods gave essentially no better resolution than could be obtained with the light microscope.

A considerable improvement was introduced in 1961 by Przybyl-ski,[157] who studied H[3]-thymidine incorporation by Tetrahymena pyri-formis. He applied the liquid emulsion G-5 (Ilford), diluted 1:5 with distilled water, liberally on to 100-mμ thick sections with the help of a brush or a fine bore pipet. After exposure and development, he re-moved the gelatinous matrix of the emulsion with 0.2% trypsin for 1 hour at 38°C. But some of the silver grains may have been removed concomitantly with the gelatin. The size of the developed silver grains was kept small by diluting the developer D-19 with water 1:50 and by shortening the developing time to 3 minutes. At a developing time of 1 minute the silver grains appeared as small spheres instead of as silver coils. A similar application technique was used early by Caro.[36] The emulsion (Ilford K-5) diluted 1:8 with an aqueous solution of potassium bromide (0.01%) was blown from a Pasteur pipet into a small bubble which was then gently placed over the section.

In 1961, Revel and Hay,[159] in their work with tritiated thymidine, applied the fine grain liquid emulsion L-4 (Ilford) diluted with water 1:7 to the sections on the grid with a platinum loop (3 cm in diameter), in which the emulsion formed a thin layer of gel and promised to yield uniform thickness. The authors subsequently preferred the simple dipping of the slide to which were attached the grids carrying sections.[160] After exposure and development in Dektol (Kodak), diluted with water 1:2, for 2 minutes and fixation in the regular manner, the preparations were stained with Karnowsky's lead stain[98] in 0.02 N NaOH, or the preparations still wet were immersed without staining in 0.05 N NaOH for 20 minutes to remove the gelatinous matrix of the emulsion. Both operations, the lead staining and the removal of the gelatinous matrix with NaOH, improved greatly the morphological contrast of the structure in the electron microscope. However, some of the silver grains were also removed by the NaOH treatment. This could be avoided by using 0.02 N NaOH for not more than 10 minutes.[160] Lead staining prior to application of the film resulted in dense background. Hampton and Quastler[83] also used a wire loop to cover sections with NTA or NTB-3 (Kodak) emulsion, diluted with water 1:2, and after exposure and photographic processing in the usual manner (D-19, 5 minutes; Kodak acid fixer, 10 minutes), a solution of pepsin was used to remove the gelatinous matrix of the emulsion before examination in the electron microscope. L. A. George[72] also used a wire loop to transfer liquid NTA (Kodak) emulsion. In order to improve even thickness of the film, a drop of 0.05% sodium lauryl sulfate as a detergent was added to 2 ml of emulsion, which was diluted with water 1:1. The emulsion was just gelled in the wire loop prior to application to the specimen. To keep the silver grains small the autoradiograms were developed at 4°C.

At about the same time van Tubergen[193] obtained a better autoradiographic resolution by using the fine grain liquid emulsion V-1055 (Kodak), which was also allowed to gel in a wire loop before being mounted on the section. The resolution was sufficient to localize the site of DNA synthesis in *Escherichia coli* and to observe a semiconservative manner of DNA replication in this organism.

Pelc *et al.*[146] diluted the emulsion G-5 (Ilford) 1:10 with water. To achieve optimally controlled thickness and continuity of the film the section was placed on a Formvar membrane suspended in a small hole of a plastic slide. By pouring the warm diluted emulsion on and off the slide quickly and by drying the emulsion on the membrane, a remarkable continuity in film thickness was obtained. The sections were transferred to the grids after complete photographic processing while they were still wet.

In order to improve the resolution with the liquid emulsion NTB-3 (diluted 1:2) over ultrathin sections on grids, Harford and Hamlin[84] applied a magnetic field of 10,000 gauss to the preparations while they were stored for exposure at 4°C. The number of grains per area increased by this treatment. It was, however, pointed out by Caro[37] that a considerably higher strength of a magnetic field, near 3.4×10^7 gauss, would be required to bend the curved pathways of electrons of an energy of 10 kev.

A careful study as to the optimal conditions to be used for autoradiography in conjunction with electron microscopy was reported by Caro and Van Tubergen[38] and by Caro.[39] The liquid emulsion L-4 (Ilford) was preferred because of its fine grain size (0.1 μ in diameter) and sufficient sensitivity. The 0.1-μ thick sections placed on grids coated with collodion and carbon were mounted on regular microscopic glass slides to be covered with emulsion. To get the thinnest continuous layer the emulsion, diluted with water 1:2, was heated to 45°C for 15 minutes, stirred, then chilled for 2–3 minutes in an ice bath, then finally returned to room temperature for 30 minutes. A loop made of platinum, silver, or copper wire 4 cm in diameter, when dipped into the viscous emulsion, held a thin film that could be placed intact on the sections. A further improvement of the film quality was obtained by a more laborious method, which consisted of bringing a more liquid, less viscous emulsion on to a small agar bloc coated with collodion. When the film had dried on the collodion membrane, it was floated off the agar bloc, emulsion side up, and was then mounted on the section placed on the grid. With techniques executed carefully, a resolution of 0.1 μ was obtained. Only 1.8% of the developed silver grains were double. The technique of mounting the emulsion with a wire loop has been employed in various laboratories[86,126,184] despite the fact that it may not yield reproducible results.

A further improvement toward a uniform thinness of the emulsion layer was reported by Koehler and co-workers.[107] A drop of the liquid emulsion diluted with water was spread with a centrifuge evenly over the section on the grid mounted on a glass slide. The thickness of the layer could be varied by changing the dilution of the emulsion and by altering the speed of the centrifuge. The layer could be kept thin enough so that the electron microscopic picture showed adequate contrast without the gelatin of the film being removed. Mitochondrial and protoplast DNA were examined by this technique.[16]

New types of emulsions yielding silver grains below 0.1 μ in diameter have been reported, and the autoradiographic technique was further improved. Thus Granboulan[76] introduced the emulsion NUC-307 (Gevaert) whose silver halide grains have a diameter of about 0.07 μ. It melts at 45°C, and the sections were dipped into it undiluted[19,76,207] or diluted to one-fourth with water.[77,78] Principally, the grid with the section attached may be dipped into the emulsion.[160,207,208] A more uniform layer of single crystals appeared, however, to be obtainable when the section was placed not on the grid but directly on a glass slide coated with collodion so that it could then be covered with emulsion by dipping. Thus, the edges of the grid did not interfere with an equal layer thickness. After complete photographic processing, the collodion membrane carrying the autoradiogram was floated off the slide on distilled water, and then the grid was put in place.[77,78,165] For subsequent removal of the gelatin by acetic acid the collodion membrane was covered with a carbon layer prior to placing the section on it.[77,78] The emulsion was developed with D-19[77] or with D-170 (Kodak).[207]

Salpeter and Bachmann[164,165] used the emulsion NTE (Kodak), which has a grain size of about 0.05 μ. The emulsion was concentrated by centrifugation and redilution and then applied with a pipet dropper or by dipping the section secured on a collodion membrane on a glass slide similar to Granboulan's technique. In order to avoid desensitization of the emulsion by the underlying specimen, a carbon layer was placed between the section and the emulsion. The thickness of the emulsion layer was controlled visually with interference colors. Sensitization with gold prior to development resulted in grains 0.05 μ in diameter. If the preparations were developed for 1 minute at 24°C with regular Dektol (Kodak), diluted 1:2 with water, the grain size increased to 0.08–0.14 μ in diameter. The developed autoradiograms were finally floated off the glass slide on to water and put on the grid for electron microscopic examination.

Quite a different approach was used by Silk and collaborators.[168] The ultrathin sections mounted on grids were covered in a vacuum with a layer of evaporated silver metal 150–450 A thick from a silver-coating device. After subsequent exposure to bromine vapor, the dry sections were then coated with a solution of 1% gelatin in water, using a wire loop. After autoradiographic exposure and development in Promicol (May and Baker, England), the gelatin layer was removed with water at 37°C for 16 hours, leaving the silver grains firmly attached to the sections. The method was used to localize tritium in monkey kidney cells in culture after feeding of H^3-thymidine. The autoradiograms showed a localization of grains mainly over the cytoplasm. This result is unusual, since H³-thymidine as a specific DNA precursor in the mammalian cell shows a definitely predominate localization of the label in the cell nucleus in conventional autoradiograms. Little label, if any is present in the cytoplasm. The reason for this discrepancy is unexplained.

5.4.3. *Photographic Processing*

The photographic processing of autoradiograms for the electron microscope is principally identical to the one used for ordinary autoradiograms for light microscopy. But in order to keep the size of the silver grains small or to develop a small grain emulsion fully, the various conditions of the developing process need to be controlled carefully.

The developer first reduces the silver halide of the crystal at the place where the latent image resides, which, however, is not necessarily identical to the site of impact of the charged particle. From this starting point metallic silver "grows" throughout the crystal, forming threads curled and coiled into bizarre loops (see Fig. 4.7b). The developing process may be interrupted at any stage. Too small a grain of metallic silver from a larger silver halide crystal is of no advantage since it does not indicate the exact site in the crystal where the particle hit. Furthermore, too small a silver grain may be difficult to recognize at lower magnification. There may be, moreover, the danger of disintegration when it is hit by the electron beam of the microscope.

Developing can be timed better when its speed is reduced. Thus, the temperature may be kept low, and the developer may be diluted severalfold, or addition of potassium bromide to the developer may be helpful. D-19, diluted 1:1, for 1 minute, and Dektol (Kodak), diluted 1:1, for 2 minutes generally proved useful for small to fine grain emulsions such as Ilford L-4. Some types of developers are faster than others, some are more suitable for fine grain emulsions. For the latter Microdol-X (Kodak) proved an adequate developer since it can produce a single strand of silver as a "grain" rather than as a bizarre coil, as maybe seen, for example, after development in undiluted D-19. Extremely fine grains are less reproducible and at times undesirable. D-19 and D-170 (Kodak) undiluted are both adequate developers for the very fine-grain emulsion NUC-307 (Gevaert),[77,207] while Dektol (Kodak), diluted 1:2, for 1 minute at 24°C was suitable for NTE (Kodak).[165] Following the development, the preparations are washed quickly and fixed, for example, in Kodak rapid fixer for 5 minutes. They are then washed in running water and dried. Kodak acid fixer is less suitable for very thin emulsion layers because it contains a gelatin hardener which may cause uneven patterns in the emulsion gelatin, obscuring the image.

5.4.4. *Improvement of Contrast and Staining*

The contrast of the specimen in the beam of the electron microscope may suffer if the layer of emulsion gelatin over the section is not adequately thin. To achieve a satisfactory contrast the section may be stained before mounting of the emulsion or after photographic processing, or the gelatin of the emulsion may be selectively removed from the processed autoradiogram prior to electron microscopic examination.

Uranyl acetate (1%) in a 30% ethanol solution for 2–5 minutes was found acceptable for staining the specimen prior to autoradiography since it does not interfere with the latent image.[40] However, lead staining[161] caused increased background.[159]

After photographic processing when the preparations were still wet, Karnovsky's lead stain[98] in 0.02 N NaOH for 30 minutes was reported to give excellent contrast since it also digests the gelatin of the emulsion.[159] The gelatin may also be removed by 0.02 N NaOH for 10 minutes[160] prior to use of a suitable stain such as hot toluidine blue (1%) in an aqueous solution of borax (1%).[160] All treatment by alkaline solutions tends to remove not only the gelatin but some silver grains as well; furthermore, dirt may easily precipitate on the section. Treatment of the autoradiograms with solutions of enzymes such as trypsin[157] or pepsin[83] also removed silver grains occasionally. Consequently, other means were tried to free the section of gelatin. For example, 0.1–0.2 N acetic acid was used for 5–15 minutes at 37°C.[76] In another recent attempt, the section was exposed for a moment to a high-electron beam with little effect on the structure of the preparations,[126] while the gelatin was selectively removed. Evaluating the various techniques, it appears that the fewest errors are introduced by staining the section prior to autoradiography[40] and by keeping the emulsion layer as uniformly thin as possible, preferably as a packed monolayer of silver halide crystals. In case a section is stained prior to autoradiography the emulsion can be protected by a carbon layer 30–60 A thick. The resolution was reported to be affected little by this layer.[165]

The preparations are finally examined in the electron microscope with optimal voltage and microampere to overcome chromic aberrations due to the thickness of the preparation. Increasing the voltage and microampere causes disintegration of the section, a disadvantage despite the increase of the contrast.[83]

Electron microscopic autoradiography is a new technique which is in the process of further improvement. The results achieved thus far are truly encouraging.

5.5. The Dry Mounting Technique of Autoradiography

The loss of material soluble in fixing agents from the cells prior to the application of nuclear track emulsion poses an undesirable limitation of the autoradiographic method to cytochemistry. The technical difficulties in overcoming this limitation still are considerable despite continuous efforts at improving methods. In order to obtain a satisfactory autoradiogram of labeled components soluble in fixing agents, the mode of fixation has to be properly chosen, and with small molecular material any chemical fixation is often totally inadequate. In the latter case, the specimen must be frozen, freeze-dried, or simply dried before it is brought in contact with the nuclear track emulsion. A considerable difficulty here is to keep the frozen or dry specimen attached to the emulsion layer. Whatever the attempt in this regard, an optimal resolution of the image requires a direct contact between specimen and emulsion with no layer interposed. Since moisture may cause leaching or diffusion of the small molecular material in the specimen, the emulsion should be dry or nearly dry when affixed to the specimen. Various techniques have been used to achieve good "dry autoradiograms"; they will be discussed subsequently according to the single steps of the procedures.

5.5.1. Specimen Preparation

The necessity of preventing denaturation or extraction of compounds in a cell has been known for many years to histochemists working with enzymes. Freezing the tissue and drying it in the frozen state has thus become an established procedure for more than three decades.[73] The quality of morphology of a specimen prepared by freezing and drying depends on: (1) the size of the sample to be frozen; (2) the relation of tissue volume and its surface area; (3) the water content of the tissue; (4) the rate of freezing; (5) the temperature of dehydration; (6) the effect of changes in rate of dehydration as influenced by the degree of vacuum employed; and (7) miscellaneous factors involved in handling of the dried material.

After examining these various factors, it is recommended[67,170] that the size of a tissue block should be small, about 1 mm thick and several millimeters square. The freezing should be rapid, i.e., by plunging the tissue sample on an aluminum foil into isopentane cooled in a bath of liquid nitrogen at −170° to −180°C (see Fig. 4.8). The best cytological details are then preserved in a surface layer of the tissue block. A thermoelectric freeze apparatus has been suggested which allows subsequent dehydration without tissue transfer.[69] If the specimen is a single layer

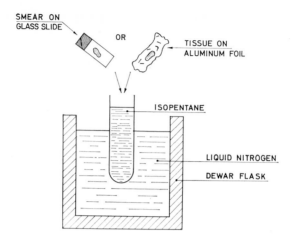

FIG. 4.8. For rapid freezing the piece of tissue on an aluminum foil may be plunged into isopentane cooled to the temperature of liquid nitrogen. Courtesy of Fitzgerald, Lab. Invest.[67]

of cells on a slide, such as a cell smear, freezing prior to drying is not necessary if rapid drying can be accomplished.

A frozen tissue block may be sectioned or it may be dehydrated slowly, then embedded, and sectioned for transfer to the film.

The frozen tissue block may be cut on a freezing microtome with carbon dioxide, preferably in a cold room to avoid precipitation of moisture on the section.[138] Transferring the section to the nuclear track emulsion is more convenient when the cryostat is used,[186] in which tissue block and section are handled near the microtome enclosed in a deep freezer with large enough windows and arm holes. The sectioning of tissue in the frozen state eliminates a source of error by not allowing diffusion or loss of lipid or water-soluble substances, which may occur during freeze substitution and embedding.

Dehydration of the frozen tissue may be accomplished in a freeze-drying apparatus under vacuum[69,73,91] or slowly by chemical means in the cold,[21,170] such as by immersion in absolute ethyl alcohol, tertiary butyl alcohol, or propylene glycol, at $-20°$ to $-60°C$ for several hours to a week (see Fig. 4.9). The freezing agent and the dehydrating agent may be identical, which eliminates the transfer of the specimen. Certain compounds in the cell may be specifically precipitated during this step. Thus, addition of basic lead acetate, lead phosphate, and potassium bichromate causes precipitation of phosphorus in situ.[188] Osmium tetroxide, mercuric chloride, or picric acid may likewise be added,[55] but attention must be given to possible photochemical effects of such compounds.

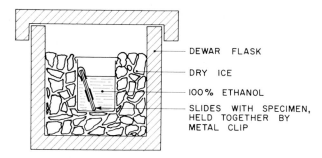

- DEWAR FLASK
- DRY ICE
- 100% ETHANOL
- SLIDES WITH SPECIMEN, HELD TOGETHER BY METAL CLIP

FIG. 4.9. The frozen specimen may be dehydrated in the cold by immersion into absolute ethanol or another suitable solvent (freeze substitution). Courtesy of Fitzgerald, *Lab. Invest.*[67]

The freeze-drying technique by chemical means is, of course, applicable only if the labeled compounds in the tissue remain insoluble during the procedure. Labeled phosphorus was shown not to leach out.[21]

Following dehydration *in vacuo* or by freeze substitution, the tissue may be fixed by exposure to osmium tetroxide vapor[199] before it is embedded for sectioning in a suitable material such as paraffin (melting point, 56°–58°C). Epoxy resin[199] has been used also, but it is a water-soluble embedding medium and calls for reservation in work with water-soluble substances. One should watch for diffusion or loss of soluble compounds with any embedding procedure.

5.5.2. *Emulsion Mounting*

The dry transfer of an embedded section from the microtome to the film is less difficult when the section is flat and straightened. A thin layer of paraffin on the microtome knife serves that purpose.[91] The transferred section may be attached to a dry emulsion plate by applying some pressure, for example, with a rubber stopper[71] or a piece of Teflon.[29] Branton and Jacobson[29] subsequently warmed the preparation to 45°C for 3–5 minutes to make the attachment firmer. In a modified approach the dry emulsion on the slide was first coated by immersing it in 5–10% glycerin in absolute alcohol with subsequent drying. Then the dry section attached to a cellophane adhesive tape was placed on the emulsion and held in place by aluminum plates under pressure. After sufficient exposure, the adhesive tape was removed with xylene prior to photographic development.[82] In a more difficult approach, the dry section was first floated on a bath of warm mercury (50°C) and a dry nuclear track plate was then pressed against the floating section.[85] In another attempt, as a result of first floating stripping film on water, then passing it through dry chloroform prior to mounting it on the slide carrying the dry section, moisture was put to use. The preparation was then passed through a fresh bath of dry chloroform and dried rapidly in absolute ethanol and cool air.[34] For extracting differentially transfer RNA in seedlings of *Vicia faba*, Woods and Zubay[204] freeze-dried the specimen in alcohol, then dried it, and embedded it in paraffin. The section was attached to dry film and then deparaffinized with toluene. It was then fixed with 67% ethanol containing 0.67% potassium acetate prior to differential extraction. The dried slides finally were exposed and developed as usual.

In case a specimen sticks well to a slide, dry emulsion can be attached more efficiently. Fitzgerald[67] put the frozen section on a glass slide, then dehydrated it in the frozen state in a vacuum apparatus or freeze substitution fluids such as cold alcohol, acetone, or butanol. When slide preparations were then transferred from the cold to room temperature, enough moisture was precipitated to allow dry stripping film to be firmly attached to the section on the slide using a small rubber roller. Exposure of the preparation to 90% relative humidity for 1–2 hours or immersing it in 10% formaldehyde for 5–10 minutes helped to keep the film in place during subsequent photographic processing.

Fitzgerald *et al.*[66] also mounted dry stripping film on dry cell smears by pressure of the thumb. The film adhered to the cells because of a small amount of moisture that condensed on the slide when it was brought from the cold to room temperature. The preparations withstood photographic processing and staining procedures. Liquid emulsion gelled in a wire loop could be placed on dry cells on a glass slide, and when a trace of moisture was added, for example, by breathing on the specimen, a good and firm apposition was achieved.[129,130,182] In another attempt, cells from a suspension were placed directly on slides precoated with emulsion with a fine hair brush for quick drying.[58] After autoradiographic exposure, the cells on the emulsion were fixed in absolute methyl alcohol for 10 minutes and dried again. Only a few cells were lost from the emulsion during subsequent photographic processing and staining. The emulsion was inert to the methyl alcohol. No moisture was used by Cummins and Mitchison,[47] who pressed yeast cells freeze-dried from a filter on to a dry emulsion. The attachment was firm enough for many cells to withstand subsequent photographic processing.

A frozen section may be placed directly from the knife on a dry emulsion plate perhaps with a fine hair brush electrostatically loaded on hard rubber,[186] and it may be flattened in a drop of cold hexane if the compound labeled is not a lipid. A solution of 0.005% acrylic resin in anhydrous ether was found useful as a flattening agent. It assured, in addition, a firm attachment also throughout subsequent thawing after sufficient exposure in the cold prior to photographic processing.[105] When the mounted specimen is transferred to room temperature after exposure in the cold and at low humidity, thawing of the residual moisture in the section also causes a firm adherence of emulsion and section.[2,202] Another possibility is to warm the cold emulsion with the section attached by placing a finger tip on the slide opposite the frozen section. Drying and coating the section is not necessary since fixation in alcohol or acetic alcohol prior to photographic processing causes a firm attachment, as Appleton[2] has done. Frozen sections must, of course, be stored for exposure at a sufficiently low temperature to avoid thawing. A low humidity is necessary.

Which of the various techniques gives the best results is difficult to state in general; the least moisture permitted, the better the chance of preventing displacement of water-soluble material in the specimen. A combination of the methods described by Fitzgerald[67] and Branton and Jacobson[29] gives the best prospects for work with dry sections. For frozen sections, Appleton's technique[2] appears best. For single cells, the technique of Miller[129] and of Cummins and Mitchison[47] is the most promising. In differential extraction of small molecular material, the technique of Woods and Zubay[204] proved its applicability.

If a section separates from the emulsion during subsequent handling (deparaffinization or photographic processing), depending on the type of tissue, it may perhaps be replaced on the emulsion after processing by another section that was cut from the block adjacent to the one lost.[187] This may be facilitated with the help of radioactive glass ink.[92] But for high-resolution autoradiography, these techniques are to be avoided. Slipping or loss of a dry section from the emulsion during photographic processing is prevented by coating the preparation with cellulose acetate (cellulose acetate, 0.5 ml; 2-butanone, 100 ml; acetone, 10 ml). This was found to be the best coating among various ones tested for the purpose.[29]

Fixation of a frozen or dry tissue section on the film emulsion at the end of the exposure time prior to photographic processing may lead to a firmer attachment. But it must be remembered that the specimen during fixation changes its geometry, i.e., it may shrink—thus altering its optimal position with regard to the autoradiographic image. Furthermore, some chemical fixatives damage the photographic emulsion. Thus, sublimate and acetic acid may destroy the emulsion, which is, however, inert toward alcohol and acetone.[58,65,67,187] Acetic acid in alcohol[2] and 10% formaldehyde[67] have also been used, but formaldehyde may cause some fading of the latent image.[187]

Whole small laboratory animals may be frozen, sectioned in the frozen state, and placed on the emulsion[31] for certain studies on labeled small molecular material. Thus, the distribution of labeled water in the total animal may be checked. The resolution with such large sections is good enough for the purpose of a survey.

5.5.3. Concluding Remarks

The staining of autoradiograms will be discussed below, but it may be said here that the staining time needs to be adjusted according to whether the specimen is stained through the gelatin of the emulsion after photographic processing or whether the specimen placed on top of the emulsion is easily accessible. In the latter case, the staining time is shorter, but great care must be taken that the preparations are not touched except by liquid in order to avoid destruction. If the specimen lies underneath the film, the staining procedure is identical to the methods outlined below.

When evaluating autoradiograms of soluble material, it is important to consider chemographic effects to avoid erroneous conclusions. Tissue-bound agents such as SH-groups[22] or luminescing material[149] may activate silver halide crystals and thus contribute to background. One may prevent or reduce chemographic effects by interspacing a protective layer of collodion. For protection of specimen, see Section 6.1. Low chemographic effects were observed when the autoradiographic preparations were kept at a temperature below 0°C during the period of exposure.[148] It is paramount with this type of autoradiographic technique to carry out exactly parallel experiments with unlabeled tissue in order to check the validity of images obtained from the labeled material. By comparing the two sets of autoradiograms meaningful conclusions can be drawn.

The attempts at autoradiography of small molecular material have certainly been rewarding. But the variability of the success shows the need for further improvement, "for the smaller, soluble, shuttling messengers, activators, and repressors, may have as much significance in cellular metabolism, as far as operation is concerned, as the relatively insoluble, controlling macromolecules." [67]

6. Staining of Autoradiograms

Autoradiograms may be evaluated by phase-contrast microscopy without the use of staining. But for most work with biological material, staining adds contrast and brilliance that identifies subcellular structures and various tissue components.

6.1. Staining Prior to Mounting the Emulsion

The specimen in an autoradiogram can be stained before application of the nuclear track emulsion, if labeled material is not displaced or extracted by the staining procedure and if the stain does not fade or leach out during photographic processing or cause chemographic effects or latent image fading. Staining of processed autoradiograms avoids these disadvantages and yields, in many instances, satisfactory preparations. A thin coating of collodion between stained specimen and film may protect and may also allow one to remove the emulsion layer safely for indentification of the specimen or to repeat autoradiography. The disadvantage of a protective coating is the lowering of autoradiographic efficiency and resolution. Thus, a coating from a dip into 0.25% celloidin decreases the grain count to 83% of that in control slides.[108] A synthetic resin immiscible with water, (Vinalak), or Formvar has also been used. A very thin coating was obtained by spreading a drop of the Vinalak on the surface of distilled water prior to being mounted on the specimen,[20] or the slide can be dipped into a 0.5% Formvar solution in ethylene dichloride.[183] A negligible effect on resolution was claimed.

Various staining techniques, if properly controlled, proved useful without the need for a protective coating prior to application of the nuclear track emulsion. Thus, hematoxylin–eosin stained sections retain their quality throughout autoradiographic processing if the staining is sufficiently intense.[108] The Feulgen-staining technique or other aldehyde-staining methods, such as the periodic acid Schiff reaction (PAS),[100] must be carried out at least until completion of the hydrolysis step before the specimen is covered with emulsion. A partial loss of labeled material must be expected (see Section 5.1 in this chapter). Strict control of the duration of hydrolysis and subsequent rinsing is essential for reproducible data.[114,166] Acetic orcein staining of chromosomes prior to spreading them by squashing proved useful also with autoradiography.[53,104,176] In their work on the synthesis of complex carbohydrates in the Golgi region, Peterson and Leblond[151] used a modified Hale's collodial iron technique besides the periodic acid Schiff reaction and Maillat's technique prior to autoradiography. The peroxidase-staining technique was modified by Popp and collaborators[154] for use in combination with autoradiography. The stain was applied to the bare cell smears and again after autoradiographic processing. Reticulocytes may be stained by first treating the unfixed cells with brilliant cresyl blue. After fixation in methanol, the reticulum remained without stain. Restaining the cells with Giemsa after autoradiographic processing yielded the reticulum of the cells in good color contrast.[153]

6.2. STAINING OF PROCESSED AUTORADIOGRAMS

The staining of the specimen through the gelatin of the processed emulsion results, if done with care, in quite satisfactory preparations.

Nevertheless, finer details of cellular structure may often become obscured, perhaps partly due to the effect of the photographic processing solutions on the binding capacity of certain cellular compounds for stains, or certain compounds may be extracted altogether. A serious problem is the barrier and stainability of the gelatin.

Some stains diffuse more readily when the gelatin has been pretreated. Ficq[61] recommended a simple bath of the autoradiograms in 70% ethanol. Likewise, a treatment in 50% methanol in citric acid–phosphate buffer (pH 6), followed by absolute methanol, proved effective.[1]

The contrast of the stained specimen suffers from concomitant staining of the superimposed gelatin. This may be avoided by choosing the proper pH of the staining solution below or above the isoelectric point of the gelatin, which is 4.9.[17,172] Thus, basic dyes stain the gelatin little at a pH below 4.9,[17] while at a higher pH acid dyes react little. Stained gelatin may be selectively cleared without destaining the specimen by a short treatment with a plain buffer,[111] or 70% ethanol.[61] Increasing alcohol concentrations[65] and absolute alcohol for 30 seconds[15] was likewise efficient. A weak acid is also useful[145] as long as it does not affect the image. An aqueous solution of trypsin (0.01%), buffered at pH 7.6, was also suggested as an effective destaining procedure by digesting the gelatin at 37°C for 6–8 minutes[6]; however, displacement of silver grains may limit the usefulness of this method.

6.2.1. Sensitivity to pH of the Developed Image

The silver grains of the film are sensitive to certain stains and pH. For example, gallocyanin–chrome alum-staining at a low pH of 1.7–2.4 caused a total or partial loss of the silver grains when the stain was used for longer than 1 hour. But grains remained well visible after 3 hours of staining at pH 3.4.[179] Hematoxylin at pH 2.5 for 1 hour did not change the quality of the image. It has been also observed that Giemsa staining at accidentally excessive pH led to a complete fading of silver grains, which were, however, retrievable when the autoradiograms were washed in a buffer of pH 5–6.[59]

6.2.2. Application of the Staining Solution

Autoradiograms may be stained just like ordinary histological preparations in slide racks which, on a wire holder, are submerged into the staining solutions in a conventional glass dish. Although this is technically easy and adequate for autoradiograms prepared with liquid emulsion, it frequently causes the detachment of stripping film from the specimen. To prevent the displacement of stripping film the stain is better applied to the slides which are placed horizontally on two parallel glass rods that bridge over a larger dish. By keeping the staining solution confined just to the part of the slides that carries the specimen, the film remains in position even if some bulging and lifting occurs. For the washings a plastic squeeze bottle is convenient, and the individual slide should then be kept slightly tilted so that the undersurface stays dry. All manipulations should be smooth. The staining can be carried out at room temperature, preferably not higher than 20°C. Belanger[15] stained at 4°C to prevent artifacts. After destaining the gelatin, if indicated, the autoradiograms are finally dried in an air stream at room temperature.

6.2.3. *Processing of the Stained Autoradiogram*

The stained and dry autoradiograms made with liquid emulsion should be mounted with a cover slip for protection. This is not necessary with stripping film preparations. The gelatinous cover of this film protects the autoradiographic image well, and after years of proper storage no change in the quality of the autoradiograms has been observed. A cover slip may be mounted only after the autoradiogram has been dried thoroughly and, if necessary, cleaned with a soft cloth or lens tissue, perhaps with xylene. As a mounting medium, Canada balsam or a synthetic medium such as Parmount or "HSR" properly diluted may be used equally well. Belanger[15] treated the autoradiograms with cedar oil–absolute ethanol (1:1) for 5–15 minutes, followed by pure cedar wood oil for 1.5–2 hours, followed by xylene and Canada balsam (1:1) for 2–3 hours before the cover slip was put on.

6.2.4. *Useful Staining Solutions*

The intensity and coloration of the stains can be varied by changing the staining time, the degree of dilution, and the pH. Various types of tissue differ in their tolerance to certain stains, as is well known. For example, to stain HeLa tissue culture cells satisfactorily with Giemsa solution 20 minutes are sufficient, but for bone-marrow cell smears 40 minutes are usually required with the same stain. Before staining a large number of autoradiograms, one should check the desired staining quality and intensity and note the staining time of the best preparations on test slides under the microscope.

The pH of the staining solution is critical for color contrast. Basophile material stains more intensely at higher pH, whereas acidophilic substances are more brilliant at lower pH. For example, a Giemsa solution with a pH of 5.5 stains the cytoplasm and nucleoli a less intense blue than at pH 7.5. For the red nuclei, this situation is reversed. Various cellular components can be selectively stained with a succession of basic and acid dyes. In order to minimize concomitant staining of the gelatin, Siperstein[172] suggested that the basic stains be applied at a pH below the isoelectric point of the gelatin (pH 4.9), and an acid dye above that value. He thus stained with methanil yellow (0.025%) at pH 9.1, and subsequently with toluidine blue (0.025%) at pH 3.6 to get an optimal color contrast in the cells of rat hypophysis.

For most tissue sections, hematoxylin eosin[145,169] proved satisfactory, and Giemsa[46,79,174] and May Grunwald[174] give adequate results with most cells in smear preparations and monolayers, such as tissue culture cells grown on a glass surface. Methyl green pyronine[27,44] is simple to use and distinguishes between RNA and DNA. Azure B,[205] methylene blue,[15] and toluidine blue[145] are convenient for surveys, simple contrast, and quick checks.

7. Evaluation of Autoradiograms

7.1. VISUAL EVALUATION

Only those autoradiograms should be evaluated which are technically adequate. They should be neither overexposed nor underexposed, and the background should be low. There should be no difficulty in correlating the specimen with the appropriate image in the emulsion. It may be advantageous for identifying the specimen to have the autoradiogram prepared on a cover slip and mount it after complete processing on a regular glass slide, emulsion side down so that the grains lay under the specimen instead of above it.[2,53] If the grain density is higher than 3–4 per μ^2, for an average grain size of 0.2-μ diameter, grain counting becomes increasingly inaccurate and the specimen underneath the silver grains becomes obscured. Moreover, a coincidence error must be expected with increasing grain density, causing a decrease of autoradiographic efficiency, because a silver halide crystal once activated to carry a latent image is insensitive as a detector of subsequent particle interactions.

It is usually not difficult to distinguish in the light microscope a silver grain from artifacts, small air locks, stain particles, or dirt in the emulsion. If the specimen is overstained or contains pigment densely packed, an optical filter in the microscope may be helpful. Grains colored by an adequate developing procedure may contrast with the specimen better than black grains.[171] Grains are unmistakable in the electron microscope by their bizarre and curly form.

Although electron microscopic autoradiography aims at the precise localization of a tracer within subcellular structures, quantitation of the amount of tracer present is prohibited unless the geometry of section and emulsion layer is strictly reproducible. Conventional autoradiograms likewise do not allow correlation of the number of silver grains over a structure to the amount of tritium contained therein unless the geometry of the structure and the degree of absorption of the β-particles is taken into account. With these considerations, however, grain counts are meaningful, and even specific activities may be approximately determined in conjunction with cytospectrophotometric data.

Grain counting is facilitated by a calibrated grid or a micrometer device mounted in the ocular of the microscope or superimposed on photographs. Thus, sizes of objects can be measured also. The microscopic field showing specimen with superimposed grains may be reproduced on paper or a translucent sheet for planimetry.[87,163,196] Frequently a photograph is desirable for permanent record. Photographs of repeated autoradiograms of one specimen and separate evaluation of each record can be used for the construction of composite pictures giving a lower degree of statistical variation than a single autoradiogram. This technique proved helpful for determining quantitatively the labeling intensity of chromosomes.[183] For highest accuracy with regard to the position of the grains it is essential to differentiate grains fully over a structure from those touching the structural border and from those crossing it to various extent. An accurate grain count with precise localization may then be compared with theoretical expectations based on various assumptions of label distribution.[35,178]

It is often sufficient to determine whether a structure in the specimen is labeled or not without counting individual grains over the labeled structure. This mode of evaluation is particularly suitable for studying kinetics of cellular proliferation, for example, with H^3-thymidine incorporated specifically into DNA, some aspects of which shall be discussed in Chapter 5. Differentiating labeled cells from those unlabeled is easy when the grain counts are well above background. It is also reliable at that level since geometric factors influencing the degree of β-absorption in individual cells do not interfere with data on labeling indices. Also the requirement for resolution is less rigid.

7.2. COUNTING MACHINES

Grain counting machines have not become popular despite the fact that visual grain counting is tedious and quite time-consuming. They are not easy to handle and thus far compare unfavorably in sensitivity, efficiency, and judgment with visual counting. Various principles of counting machines have been proposed. The device reported by Dudley and Pelc[52] let a flying spot, produced on a television projection tube at the site of the ocular of the microscope, scan the preparation under oil immersion in closely parallel lines. A phototube at the condenser of the microscope registers the density of the transmitted light. When the scanning spot passes a silver grain, about 30–50% of the light is absorbed. In another approach, Mazia and co-workers[124] converted a two-dimensional photographic record of an autoradiogram into a pattern of lines, with the help of a cylindrical lens placed with its long axis parallel to the long axis of the strip to be scanned. The width of the strip to be scanned could be adjusted to the diameter of a cell nucleus. The density of lines recorded at any level is proportional to the number of grains. A single-plane scanner (cyto-analyzer) that was developed to read automatically Papanicolaou smears from an illuminated image by measuring optical density and area of every cell densitometrically valid was proposed by Tolles[190] to be adaptable for evaluating autoradiograms. Other recording equipment utilizing dark-field illumination has been discussed by Gullberg[80] and Tolles.[190] The difficulty in dark-field microscopy to differentiate artifacts properly from single grains was emphasized. Further development of automatic recording equipment for grain counting is certainly needed.

7.3. Correction for Background

Background correction requires a sample size sufficiently large for statistical analysis. There may be considerable variations in the density of background grains in one autoradiogram and between various preparations processed simultaneously. Showers of grains as background may cover areas with or without tissue underneath. In other preparations fewer background grains are localized over the specimen than over blank areas.[191] It is important to select only those areas of the autoradiogram for evaluation that show the least variations in background density.

The number of background grains per unit area is at times so far below the density of the true image that a correction for the net grain count is of no benefit to data interpretation. If the true image density, on the other hand, is too low for accurate assessment, the autoradiograms should be exposed longer before they are processed.

7.3.1. Correction in a Single Autoradiogram

Background is corrected by deducing from the grain count over a defined structure, such as a cell, the value of background grains per corresponding area. It is hence necessary to determine the area of emulsion overlaying the structure and to measure the average number of background grains per unit area of emulsion. The latter may be obtained by simply finding in the same autoradiogram the mean number of grains overlaying another structure comparable in size but known to be unlabeled. If this is impractical, the areas for background determination should be chosen in the neighborhood of the labeled structures.

In case labeling indices within a representative group of objects such as cells are to be compared in a set of autoradiograms, an arbitrary background may be assigned to each value. Thus, the number of cells within a representative group with more than 1, 2, and 3 grains may be observed to follow a similar pattern[23] in a series of autoradiograms (see Fig. 4.10). Errors due to variations in background between different autoradiograms, of course, are best assessed by simultaneously comparing in each autoradiogram the grain counts over a comparable structure known to be unlabeled.

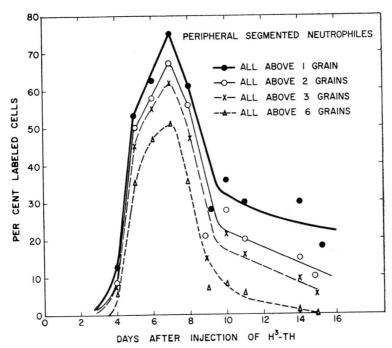

FIG. 4.10. The slopes of the labeling indices of peripheral segmented neutrophiles after assignment of an arbitrary background remain parallel, with the peak value at day 7 after a single injection of H³-thymidine. Courtesy of Bond et al., The Kinetics of Cellular Proliferation.[23]

7.3.2. Correction with the Help of Control Autoradiograms

Whether background grains are distributed at random over cells and cell-free areas or whether this is not so is at times difficult to ascertain, particularly if a majority of cells is labeled. To overcome this uncertainty, data from two separate autoradiograms may be compared, one from a labeled specimen, another from a representative sample but unlabeled. To be comparable both specimens must be prepared histochemically and autoradiographically in a strictly identical manner. In the unlabeled control autoradiogram all silver grains are background. The mean number of grains overlying cells of a selected population may then be used to correct the mean grain count of the representative labeled sample. Stillström[180,181] has extended this approach to determine for a given cell population not only labeling index and mean grain count corrected for background but also the distribution of the corrected grain counts. The calculations are relatively simple but tedious, and the solutions should be provided by an electronic computer. This mode of background correction assumes that two preparations processed under exactly the same conditions have the same geometry and the same background density and distribution. Since this is rarely the case, mean data from several autoradiograms, also from several specimens in parallel, should be used for the computations to guard against erroneous conclusions.[68]

7.4. The Quantitative Meaning of Grain Counts

The net grain count after background deduction is not a measure of the isotope content unless the β-absorption has been corrected for in the specimen. The correction factor depends on the density, in milligram per square centimeter, of the dry biological preparation. This was discussed in Chapter 1 and earlier in this chapter. The density of a specimen can be determined, for example, by interference microscopy.[81] Figure

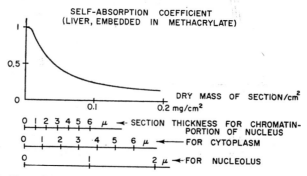

Fig. 4.11. The tritium β-absorption (fraction of tritium β-particles leaving the section to produce latent images in the nuclear track emulsion) varies with the type of tissue and with the subcellular structure owing to the different density of the dry mass, in mg/cm². The figure indicates the various absorptions found for nucleus, nucleolus, and cytoplasm in sections of liver embedded in methacrylate. Courtesy of Maurer and Primbsch, *Exptl. Cell Res.*[123]

4.11 illustrates the change of the tritium β-absorption with varying thickness of liver cell sections.[123] Owing to the higher density of the nucleolus small changes in structure thickness result in a greater alteration of the β-absorption than would be observable with equal changes in the thickness, for example, of the chromatin portion of the nucleus. Various cell types which have unequal morphology are often also unequally thick in a smear preparation, and the degree of β-absorption may vary consequently by a factor of 2.[123] Within a cell smear, the β-absorption in the nucleus is higher than in the thin cytoplasm surrounding it, and corresponding correction factors of 1.6[150] and 1.5[122] have been determined for tissue culture cells.

The autoradiographic image over two or more labeled structures superimposing each other is, of course, a composite one if the layers of the structures together are less than infinitely thick. Thus, Perry *et al.*[150] estimated that, in autoradiograms of monolayers of HeLa cells uniformly labeled with tritium, 11% of the cytoplasmic grain count is routinely counted as nuclear, and 1.3% of the nuclear count and 0.6% of the cytoplasmic grain count are included in the grains overlying the nucleoli. A layer of cytoplasm unlabeled and 0.5 μ thick when superimposed on a labeled nucleus may decrease the grain count to one-half of the value obtained from the nucleus in direct contact with the emulsion.[123]

It is self-evident that an indiscriminate application of grain count data to describe metabolic functions in the specimen is apt to mislead considerably. It is, however, permissible to compare from related autoradiograms the relative labeling intensities of structures which have a very similar size, thickness, and density, for example, of cells with similar morphological criteria. The number of such cells evaluated should be large enough for the mean value to have a tolerable statistical variation.

It is useful to determine the average autoradiographic efficiency for an autoradiogram by relating the mean grain count produced during a given exposure time to the number of isotopic disintegrations which occurred during the same period of time in a sample identical to that used for the autoradiogram. This value is helpful for assessing isotope content in single cells and is a prerequisite also for the dosimetry of absorbed radiation emitted from the incorporated isotope. As a guide line, it may be assumed that the autoradiographic efficiency is about 5% for tritium uniformly distributed in a biological specimen 3 μ thick (see Section 3.1 in this chapter), yet this value may be higher or considerably lower.

It is reemphasized again, as Levi and Rogers[116] also have pointed out, that relatively quantitative meaning of grain counts requires a strict control of the technique throughout histochemical and autoradiographic processing; it requires accuracy in grain counting and corrections for the different geometries of cells or cell structures in relation to the film emulsion. "Unless these factors have been recognized and corrected for" quantitative correlation of grain counts to isotopic content "becomes an illusion." [116]

8. A Summarizing Survey of Autoradiographic Difficulties and Their Causes

(1) *The number of background grains is relatively high, randomly distributed over the entire slide.*

Possible causes: (*a*) The film emulsion was exposed to light (dark room leaks light, safe light too close to workbench, electrical switches improperly insulated); it was exposed to radiation (contaminating γ-source in or in neighborhood of dark room); the liquid film emulsion contained radioactivity which leaked out from specimen dipped into the emulsion; or the film emulsion was too old, contained bacterial growth, or was exposed to excessive heat or to reducing agents (or fumes) (exposure box improperly sealed). (*b*) The film was overdeveloped (the temperature of the processing solutions too high, excessive developing time). (*c*) The microscopic glass slide was improperly cleaned before application of the film.

(2) *The number of background grains is relatively high and distributed unevenly over the slide.*

Possible causes: (*a*) Check as for 1. (*b*) In case of stripping film, there was electrostatical flashing when the film was removed from the glass plate (the humidity in the dark room was too low or the film was peeled off its supporting plate too abruptly). (*c*) Various thickness of liquid emulsion and rapid uneven drying of the applied emulsion produced latent images in areas of pressure—around edges of structures or of the specimen or of the cover slip. (*d*) Water-soluble labeled compounds improperly removed or improperly preserved in the tissue diffused out of the cells, or reducing agents or luminescing material were not removed from the specimen by histological fixation.

(3) *The autoradiogram shows little or no image.*

Possible causes: (*a*) The autoradiogram was not exposed long enough prior to development, or the isotope content of the structure was too low. (*b*) the latent image faded prior to development owing to exposure to excessive humidity, temperature, oxidizing agents, or certain histological fixing agents improperly removed from the specimen prior to mounting of the film. (c) The autoradiogram was exposed excessively long to the photographic fixative or to excessive pH after photographic processing, for example, during the staining.

(4) *The density of the autoradiographic image is distributed grossly unevenly.*

Possible causes: (a) Check as for 3. (b) Greatly uneven and insufficient coating of the slide with liquid emulsion. (c) Around air pockets trapped between film and specimen the latent image faded, or the preparation, dried unevenly after application of emulsion, contained residual moisture.

(5) *The image in the autoradiogram completely processed fades during storage.*

Possible causes: (a) In case of liquid emulsion, the processed autoradiogram was not protected by a cover slip (the gelatinous support of stripping film provides adequate protection). (b) The photographic fixative was not completely washed out of the emulsion. (c) Trace amounts of oxidizing agents or certain histological fixing agents remained in the specimen.

(6) *The emulsion has artifacts not related to the photographic image (reticulation, displacement, or slipping of the emulsion).*

Possible causes: (a) The content of "hardener" in the photographic fixative or subsequent wash was too high (emulsion is reticulated). (b) Displacement of stripping film occurred due to lack of proper provisions —locking of the film at the under surface of the slide; "subbing" of the under surface of the slide to secure firm attachment; the temperature of the processing solutions and staining solutions was higher than the temperature of the water bath used to float the film on the slide; the wet autoradiogram was handled too abruptly while being transferred from one solution to another.

REFERENCES

1. E. Adamik, personal communication, 1958.
2. T. C. Appleton, Autoradiography of Soluble Labelled Compounds, *J. Roy. Microscop. Soc.*, **83**: 277–281 (1964).
3. E. A. Barnard and K. Ostrowski, Applications of Radioautography to Cytochemistry Using Direct-Labeling Methods, *Biochem. J.*, **85**: 27 (1962).
4. E. A. Barnard and K. Ostrowski, Autoradiographic Methods in Enzyme Cytochemistry II. Studies on Some Properties of Acetylcholinesterase in its Sites at the Motor End-Plate, *Exptl. Cell Res.*, **36**: 28–43 (1964).
5. F. Barreira, A. B. Carvalho, and J. M. V. Sobral, Beta Historadiography with Tritium, *Intern. J. Appl. Radiation Isotopes*, **14**: 428–429 (1963).
6. R. Baserga and D. Banks, A Simple Procedure for the Destaining of Stripping Film Autoradiograph, *J. Pathol. Bacteriol.*, **84**: 239–241 (1962).

7. R. Baserga and K. Nemeroff, Factors Which Affect Efficiency of Autoradiography with H³-thymidine, *Stain Technol.*, **37**: 21–26 (1962).

8. R. Baserga and K. Nemeroff, Two Emulsion—Autoradiography, *J. Histochem. Cytochem.*, **10**: 628–635 (1962).

9. R. Baserga and K. Nemeroff, The Use of Standard Slides in Semiquantitative Radioautography with Tritiated Compounds, *Stain Technol.*, **38**: 111–116 (1963).

10. R. Baserga and E. Lisco, Duration of DNA Synthesis in Ehrlich Ascites Cells as Estimated by Double Labeling with C^{14}- and H³-thymidine and Autoradiography. *J. Natl. Cancer Inst.*, **31**: 1559–1571 (1963).

11. S. I. Bayley, Autoradiography of Single Cells, *Nature*, **160**: 193–194 (1947).

12. H. Becquerel, Sur les radiations émises par phosphorescence, *Compt. Rend.*, **122**: 420–421 (1896).

13. L. F. Belanger and C. P. Leblond, A Method for Locating Radioactive Elements in Tissues by Covering Histological Sections with Photographic Emulsion, *Endocrinology*, **39**: 8–13 (1946).

14. L. F. Belanger, Autoradiography of *in vitro* Activated Sections of Tissue as a Tool in Histochemistry, in Relation to Metabolic Disorder and Cancer, *Lab. Invest.*, **8**: 139–146 (1959).

15. L. F. Belanger, Staining Processed Autoradiographs, *Stain Technol.*, **36**: 313–317 (1961).

16. P. R. Bell and K. Mühlethaler, Evidence for the Presence of Deoxyribonucleic Acid in the Organelles of the Egg Cells of *Pteridium aquilinum*, *J. Mol. Biol.*, **8**: 853–862 (1964).

17. J. A. Bergeron, Controlled Staining of Autoradiographs, *Stain Technol.*, **33**: 221 (1958).

18. I. Berman and E. J. Newby, Autoradiography and Staining of Hematopoietic Cells Grown on Millipore Membranes *in vivo*, *Stain Technol.*, **38**: 62–65 (1963).

19. W. Bernhard and N. Granboulan, The Fine Structure of the Cancer Cell Nucleus, *Exptl. Cell Res.*, *Suppl.* **9**: 19–53 (1963).

20. A. Bishop and O. N. Bishop, Analysis of Tritium Labeled Human Chromosomes and Sex Chromatin, *Nature*, **199**: 930–932 (1963).

21. H. Blanck, P. L. McCarthy, and E. D. De Lamater, A Non-vacuum Freezing-Dehydrating Technique for Histology, Autoradiography and Microbial Cytology, *Stain Technol.*, **26**: 193 (1951).

22. F. A. Board, Sulfhydryl Detection by Histochemography, *J. Cell. Comp. Physiol.*, **38**: 377–387 (1951).

23. V. P. Bond, T. M. Fliedner, E. P. Cronkite, J. R. Rubini, and J. S. Robertson, Cell Turnover in Blood and Blood Forming Tissues Studied with Tritiated Thymidine, in *The Kinetics of Cellular Proliferation* (F. Stohlman, Jr., ed.), pp. 188–200, Grune and Stratton, New York, London, 1959.

24. V. P. Bond and L. E. Feinendegen, Intranuclear ³H-thymidine: Dosimetric, Radiobiological and Radiation Protection Aspects, *Health Phys.*, **12**: 1007–1020, 1966.

25. J. Bonner, R. C. Huang, and N. Maheshwri, The Physical State of Newly Synthesized RNA, *Proc. Natl. Acad. Sci. U. S.*, **47**: 1548–1554 (1961).

26. G. A. Boyd, *Autoradiography in Biology and Medicine*, Academic Press Inc., New York, 1955.

27. J. Brachet, La détection histochimique des acides pentoses nucléiques, *Compt. Rend.*, **133**: 88–90 (1940).

28. J. Brachet and A. Ficq, Détection cytochimique au moyen d'actinomycin radioactive de l'acide désoxyribonucléique (DNA) cytoplasmique des oefs de Batraciens, *Compt. Rend.*, **258**: 6258–6260 (1964).

29. D. Branton and L. Jacobson, Dry, High Resolution Autoradiography, *Stain Technol.*, **37**: 239–242 (1962).

30. R. M. Brenner, Controlled Oxidation of Background Grains in Radioautographs, *J. Histochem. Cytochem.*, **10**: 678 (1962).

31. H. C. Bubel and P. F. Bonventre, Apparatus for Preparation of Whole Animal Sections for Autoradiography, *J. Lab. Clin. Med.*, **61**: 324–328 (1963).

32. J. Cairns, A Minimum Estimate for the Length of the DNA of *E. coli* Obtained by Autoradiography, *J. Mol. Biol.*, **4**: 407–409 (1962).

33. J. Cairns, The Chromosome of *Escherichia coli*, in *Synthesis and Structure of Macromolecules, Cold Spring Harbor Symp. Quant. Biol.*, **28**: 43–46 (1963).

34. M. J. Canny, High Resolution Autoradiography of Water-Soluble Substance, *Nature*, **175**: 857 (1955).

35. L. G. Caro, Localization of Macromolecules in *E. coli* I. DNA and Protein, *J. Biophys. Biochem. Cytol.*, **9**: 539–553 (1961).

36. L. G. Caro, Electron Microscopic Radioautography of Thin Sections: The Golgi Zone as a Site of Protein Concentration in Pancreatic Acinar Cells, *J. Biophys. Biochem. Cytol.*, **10**: 37 (1961).

37. L. G. Caro, Proposed Use of Magnetic Fields in Electron Microscopic Radioautography, *Nature*, **191**: 1188 (1961).

38. L. G. Caro and R. P. van Tubergen, High Resolution Autoradiography. I. Methods, *J. Cell. Biol.*, **15**: 173–183 (1962).

39. L. G. Caro, High Resolution Autoradiography. II. The Problem of Resolution, *J. Cell. Biol.*, **15**: 189–199 (1962).

40. L. G. Caro and G. E. Palade, Protein Synthesis, Storage and Discharge in the Pancreatic Exocrine Cell. An Autoradiographic Study, *J. Cell. Biol.*, **20**: 473 (1964).

41. L. G. Caro and M. Schnös, Tritium and Phosphorus-32 in High Resolution Autoradiography, *Science*, **149**: 60–62 (1965).

42. E. Chargaff and J. N. Davidson, *The Nucleic Acids,* Academic Press Inc., New York, 1955.

43. A. D. Conger and L. M. Fairchield, A Quick Freeze Method for Making Smear Slides Permanent, *Stain Technol.*, **28**: 281–283 (1953).

44. H. J. Conn, *Biological Stains, A Handbook of the Nature and Uses of the Dyes Employed in the Biological Laboratory,* The Willims & Wilkins Company, Baltimore, Maryland, 1961.

45. A. R. Crathorn and K. V. Shooter, Uptake of Thymidine and Synthesis of Deoxyribonucleic Acid in Mouse Ascites Cells, *Nature,* **187**: 614–615 (1960).

46. E. P. Cronkite, V. P. Bond, T. M. Fliedner, and J. R. Rubini, The Use of Tritiated Thymidine in the Study of DNA Synthesis and Cell Turnover in Hemopoietic Tissue, *Lab. Invest.*, **8**: 263–277 (1959).

47. J. E. Cummins and J. M. Mitchison, A Method for Making Autoradiographs of Yeast Cells Which Retain Pool-Components, *Exptl. Cell Res.*, **34**: 406–409 (1964).

48. J. F. Danielli, Ed., *General Cytochemical Methods*, Academic Press, Inc., New York, 1958.

49. K. B. Dawson, E. O. Field, and G. W. W. Stevens, Differential Autoradiography of Tritium and Another Beta-emitter by a Double Stripping Film Technique, *Nature*, **195**: 510–511 (1962).

50. D. Demers, *Ionographie, Les emulsions nucleaires, Principes et applications,* Les Presses Universitaires de Montreal, Montreal, 1958.
51. I. Doniach and S. R. Pelc, Autoradiograph Technique, *Brit. J. Radiol.,* **23:** 184–192 (1950).
52. R. A. Dudley and S. R. Pelc, Automatic Grain Counter for Assessing Quantitatively High Resolution Autoradiographs, *Nature,* **172:** 992–993 (1953).
53. H. J. Evans, A Simple Microtechnique for Obtaining Human Chromosome Preparations with Some Comments on DNA Replication in Sex Chromosomes of the Goat, Cow, and Pig, *Exptl. Cell Res.,* **38:** 511–516 (1965).
54. G. J. Falk and R. C. King, Radioautographic Efficiency for Tritium as a Function of Section Thickness, *Radiation Res.,* **20:** 466–470 (1963).
55. N. Feder and R. L. Sidman, Methods and Principles of Fixation by Freeze Substitution, *J. Biophys. Biochem. Cytol.,* **4:** 593 (1958).
56. L. E. Feinendegen, V. P. Bond, and R. B. Painter, Studies on the Interrelationship of RNA Synthesis, DNA Synthesis and Precursor Pool in Human Tissue Culture Cells Studied with Tritiated Pyrimidine Nucleosides, *Exptl. Cell Res.,* **22:** 381–405 (1961).
57. L. E. Feinendegen, V. P. Bond, and W. L. Hughes, RNA Mediation in DNA Synthesis in HeLa Cells Studied with Tritium Labeled Cytidine and Thymidine, *Exptl. Cell Res.,* **25:** 627–647 (1961).
58. L. E. Feinendegen and V. P. Bond, Differential Uptake of H^3-thymidine into the Soluble Fraction of Single Bone Marrow Cells, Determined by Autoradiography, *Exptl. Cell Res.,* **27:** 474–484 (1962).
59. L. E. Feinendegen, unpublished data, 1965.
60. R. Feulgen and H. Rossenbeck, Mikroskopisch-chemischer Nachweis einer Nucleinsäure vom Typus der Thymonucleinsäure und die darauf beruhende elektive Färbung von Zelkernen in mikroskopischen Präparaten, *Z. Physiol. Chem.,* **135:** 203–248 (1924).
61. A. Ficq, Autoradiographic Study of the Relation between Nucleic Acids and Protein Synthesis, *Lab. Invest.,* **8:** 237–242 (1959).
62. A. Ficq, Autoradiography, in *The Cell* (J. Brachet and A. E. Misky, eds.), Vol. I, pp. 67–90, Academic Press Inc., New York, 1959.
63. D. A. Fishman and M. D. Gershon, A Method for Studying Intracellular Movement of Water-Soluble Isotopes Prior to Radioautography, *J. Cell Biol.,* **21:** 139–143 (1964).
64. P. J. Fitzgerald, M. L. Eidinoff, J. E. Knoll, and E. B. Simmel, Tritium in Radioautography, *Science,* **114:** 494–498 (1951).
65. P. J. Fitzgerald, Radioautography, Its Use in Cytology, in *Analytical Cytology,* (R. C. Mellors, ed.), 2nd ed., McGraw-Hill Book Company, New York, 1959.
66. P. J. Fitzgerald, M. G. Ord, and L. A. Stocken, A Dry Mounting Autoradiographic Technique for the Localization of Water Soluble Compounds, *Nature,* **189:** 55–56 (1961).
67. P. J. Fitzgerald, "Dry" Mounting Autoradiographic Technique for Intracellular Localization of Water Soluble Compounds in Tissue Sections, *Lab. Invest.,* **10:** 846 (1961).
68. T. M. Fliedner, personal communication, 1964.
69. R. H. Frist and M. D. Maser, Freeze-Drying of Biological Specimen for Electron Microscopy Using Thermo-Electric Cooling, *J. Cell Biol.,* **22:** 293 (1964).
70. J. L. J. Gaillard and A. Schaberg, A New Spreading Procedure for Human Chromosomes, *Exptl. Cell Res.,* **36:** 415–417 (1964).

71. J. C. Gallimore, E. C. Bauer, and G. A. Boyd, A Non-leaching Technique for Autoradiography, *Stain Technol.*, **29**: 95 (1954).
72. L. A. George II, Electron Microscopy and Autoradiography, *Science*, **133**: 1423 (1961).
73. I. Gersh, The Altmann Technique for Fixation by Drying While Freezing, *Anat. Record*, **53**: 309-337 (1932).
74. I. Gersh, Fixation and Staining, in *The Cell* (J. Brachet and A. E. Mirsky, eds.), Vol. I, pp. 21-66, Academic Press, Inc., New York, 1959.
75. H. J. Gomberg and M. J. Schlesinger, Jr., High Resolution Radiation Detectors in Research, *Intern. Conf. Peaceful Uses At. Energy, Geneva, 1955,*
76. P. Granboulan, Resolving Power and Sensitivity of a New Emulsion in Electron Microscope Autoradiography, *J. Royal Microscop. Sci.*, **81**: 165-171 (1963).
77. P. Granboulan, The Comparison of Emulsions and Techniques in Electron Microscope Radioautography, in *The Use of Radioautography in Investigating Protein Synthesis, Symp. Intern. Soc. Cell Biol., Montreal, 1964,* (C. P. Leblond and K. B. Warren, eds.), pp. 43-63. Academic Press, Inc., New York, 1965.
78. N. Granboulan and P. Granboulan, Cytochimie ultrastructurale du nucléole, II. Etude des sites de synthéses du RNA dans le nucléole et le noyau, *Exptl. Cell Res.*, **38**: 604-619 (1965).
79. W. D. Gude, A. C. Upton, and T. T. Odell, Giemsa Staining of Autoradiograms Prepared with Stripping Film, *Stain Technol.*, **30**: 161-162 (1955).
80. J. E. Gullberg, Grain Counting Instrumentation, *Lab. Invest.*, **8**: 94-98 (1959).
81. A. J. Hale, *The Interference Microscope in Biological Research*, E. & S. Livingston, Edinburgh, 1958.
82. L. Hammarström, L. E. Appelgreen, and S. Ullberg, Improved Method for Light Microscopy Autoradiography with Isotopes in Water Soluble Form, *Exptl. Cell Res.*, **37**: 608-613 (1965).
83. J. C. Hampton and H. Quastler, The Combined Use of Autoradiographic and Electron Microscopic Techniques for Studies in Ultrathin Sections of Tritium Labeled Cells of the Intestinal Epithelium, in *Tritium in the Physical and Biological Sciences, Symp. Intern. At. Energy Agency,* **2**: 103 (1961).
84. C. G. Harford and A. Hamlin, A Method of Electron Microscopic Autoradiography with Tritium Labeled Cells in a Magnetic Field, *Lab. Invest.*, **10**: 627-635 (1961).
85. J. E. Harris, J. F. Sloane, and D. T. King, New Techniques in Autoradiography, *Nature*, **166**: 25 (1950).
86. E. D. Hay and J. P. Revel, The Fine Structure of the DNP Component of the Nucleus, *J. Cell. Biol.*, **16**: 29-51 (1963).
87. K. Hempel and W. Erb, Eiweiss und Melanin Stoffwechsel im Melanom der Maus, *Z. Zellforsch. Mikroskop. Anat., Abt. Histochem.*, **58**: 125-140 (1962).
88. K. Hempel, Uber eine neue autoradiographische Methode zum histochemischen Nachweis Protein gebundener Sulphydryl Gruppen mit tritiiertem N-Phenyl-maleinimid, *Exptl. Cell Res.*, **31**: 594-596 (1963).
89. R. H. Herz, Methods to Improve the Performance of Stripping Emulsions, *Lab. Invest.*, **8**: 71-75 (1959).
90. D. K. Hill, Resolving Power with Tritium-autoradiographs, *Nature*, **194**: 831-832 (1962).
91. M. W. Holt, R. F. Cowing, and S. Warren, Preparation of Radioautographs of Tissues without Loss of Water-Soluble P^{32}, *Science*, **110**: 328 (1949).

92. T. Huang, Histological Autoradiogram of Soluble Compounds, *Intern. J. Appl. Radiation Isotopes*, **8**: 234 (1960).

93. W. L. Hughes, Autoradiography with Tritium, *Proc. Symp. on Tritium in Tracer Applications*, pp. 38–40, New Engl. Nuclear Corp., New York, 1957.

94. I. H. James, The Mechanism of Development, in *The Theory of the Photographic Process*, (C. E. K. Mees, ed.), The Macmillan Company, New York, 1964.

95. D. L. Joftes, Liquid Emulsion Autoradiography with Tritium, *Lab. Invest.*, **8**: 131–136 (1959).

96. R. Jona, Squashing under Scotch Tape No. 665 for Autoradiographic and Permanent Histologic Preparations, *Stain Technol.*, **38**: 91–95 (1963).

97. M. Jonsson and S. Lagerstedt, Losses of Nucleic Acid Derivatives from Fixed Tissues during Flattening of Paraffin Sections on Water, *Experientia*, **14**: 157–159 (1958).

98. M. J. Karnovsky, Simple Methods for "Staining with Lead" at High pH in Electron Microscopy, *J. Biophys. Biochem. Cytol.*, **11**: 729 (1961).

99. F. H. Kasten, Loss of RNA and Protein and Change in DNA During a 30 Hour Cold Perchloric Acid Extraction of Cultured Cells, *Stain Technol.*, **40**: 127–135 (1965).

100. F. H. Kasten, The Chemistry of Schiff's Reagent, *Intern. Rev. Cytol.*, **10**: 1–100 (1960).

101. F. H. Kasten, Recent Studies of the Feulgen Reaction for Deoxyribonucleic Acid, *Biochem. Pharmacol.*, **4**: 86–98 (1960).

102. B. P. Kaufmann, M. R. McDonald, and H. Gay, The Distribution and Interrelation of Nucleic Acids in Fixed Cells as Shown by Enzymatic Hydrolysis, *J. Cell Comp. Physiol.*, **38** (Suppl. I): 71–94 (1951).

103. M. Kesse, E. B. Harriss, and E. Gyftaki, Autoradiography of H³-Thymidine and C¹⁴-Thymidine in Bone Marrow Using a Double Emulsion Technique, in *Radioisotope Sampling Measurement Techniques in Medicine and Biology, Symp. Intern. At. Energy Agency, Vienna, 1965*, pp. 537–546.

104. Y. Kikuchi and A. A. Sandberg, Chronology and Pattern of Human Chromosome Replication, I. Blood Leukocytes of Normal Subjects, *J. Natl. Cancer Inst.*, **32**: 1109–1143 (1964).

105. W. B. Kinter and T. H. Wilson, Autoradiographic Study of Sugar and Amino Acid Absorption by Everted Sacs of Hamster Intestine, *J. Cell Biol.*, **25**: 19–39 (1965).

106. W. E. Kisieleski, R. Baserga, and J. Vaupotic, The Correlation of Autoradiographic Grain Counts and Tritium Concentration in Tissue Sections, Containing H³-Thymidine, *Radiation Res.*, **15**: 341–348 (1961).

107. J. K. Koehler, K. Mühlethaler, and A. Freywyssling, Electron Microscopic Autoradiography. An Improved Technique for Producing Thin Films and Its Application to H³-thymidine Labeled Maize Nuclei, *J. Cell Biol.*, **16**: 73–80 (1963).

108. B. M. Kopriwa and C. P. Leblond, Improvements in the Coating Technique of Radioautography, *J. Histochem. Cytochem.*, **10**: 269–284 (1962).

109. M. Krause and W. S. Plaut, An Effect of Tritiated Thymidine on the Incorporation Thymidine into Chromosomal Deoxyribonucleic Acid, *Nature*, **188**: 511–512 (1960).

110. A. Lacassagne and J.-S. Lattès, Méthode auto-histo-radiographique pour la détection dans les organes du polonium injecté, *Compt. Rend.*, **178**: 488–490 (1924).

111. L. G. Lajtha, High Resolution Autoradiography: Isotope Uptake of Individual Cells, *J. Phot. Sci.*, **2**: 130–134 (1954).
112. L. G. Lajtha and R. Oliver, The Application of Autoradiography in the Study of Nucleic Acid Metabolism, *Lab. Invest.*, **8**: 214–221 (1959).
113. L. F. Lamerton and E. B. Harriss, Resolution and Sensitivity Considerations in Autoradiography, *J. Phot. Sci.*, **2**: 135–144 (1954).
114. W. Lang and M. Maurer, Zur Verwendbarkeit von Feulgen-gefärbten Schnitten für quantitative Autoradiographie mit markiertem Thymidin, *Exptl. Cell Res.*, **39**: 1–9 (1965).
115. H. Levi, A Discussion of Recent Advances Towards Quantitative Autoradiography, *Exptl. Cell. Res.*, **4** (Suppl.): 207 (1957).
116. H. Levi and A. W. Rogers, On the Quantitative Evaluation of Autoradiograms, *Mat. Fys. Medd. Dan. Vid. Selsk.*, **33**(No. 11) (1963).
117. C. Levinthal and C. A. Thomas, Jr., Molecular Autoradiography. The Beta-ray Counting from Single Virus Particles and DNA Molecules in Nuclear Emulsion, *Biochim. Biophys. Acta*, **23**: 453–465 (1957).
118. J. Liquier-Milward, Electron Microscopy and Radioautography as Coupled Techniques in Tracer Experiments, *Nature*, **177**: 619 (1956).
119. J. H. Luft and R. L. Wood, The Extraction of Tissue Protein During and after Fixation with Osmium Tetroxide in Various Buffer Systems, *J. Cell Biol.*, **19**: 46A (1963).
120. M. R. McDonald and B. P. Kaufmann, The Degradation by RNase of Substrates Other than Ribonucleic Acid, *J. Histochem. Cytochem.*, **2**: 387 (1954).
121. J. McLeish, Quantitative Relationships between Deoxyribonucleic and Ribonucleic Acid in Isolated Plant Nuclei, *Proc. Royal Soc. (London)*, **B158**: 261–278 (1963).
122. G. Marin and M. A. Bender, A Comparison of Mammalian Cell Killing by Incorporated H^3-thymidine and H^3-uridine, *Intern. J. Radiation Biol.*, **7**: 235–244 (1963).
123. W. Maurer and E. Primbsch, Grösse der beta-Selbstabsorption bei der ^{3}H-Autoradiographie, *Exptl. Cell Res.*, **33**: 8–18 (1964).
124. D. Mazia, W. S. Plaut, and G. W. Ellis, A Method for the Quantitative Assessment of Autoradiography, *Exptl. Cell Res.*, **9**: 305–312 (1955).
125. D. Mazia and N. L. R. Bucher, A Method for Avoidance of Electrostatic Flashing in Preparing Autoradiographs with Stripping Film, *Experientia*, **16**: 215–216 (1960).
126. G. A. Meek and M. J. Moses, Localization of Tritiated Thymidine in HeLa Cells by Electron Autoradiography, *J. Roy. Microscop. Soc.*, **81**: 187–197 (1963).
127. C. E. K. Mees, Ed., *The Theory of the Photographic Process*, The Macmillan Company, New York, 1964.
28. B. Messier and C. P. Leblond, Preparation of Coated Radioautographs by Dipping Sections in Fluid Emulsion, *Proc. Soc. Exptl. Biol. Med.*, **96**: 7–10 (1957).
129. O. L. Miller, Jr., Autoradiographic Study of Soluble H^3-thymidine Derivatives in Single Cells, *J. Cell Biol.*, **19**: 50A (1963).
130. O. L. Miller, Jr., G. E. Stone, and D. M. Prescott, Autoradiography of Soluble Materials, *J. Cell Biol.*, **23**: 654–658 (1964).
131. E. N. Mondrianakis and M. Beer, Base Sequence Determination in Nucleic Acids with the Electron Microscope, III. Chemistry and Microscopy of Guanine-Labeled DNA, *Proc. Natl. Acad. Sci. U.S.*, **53**: 564–571 (1965).

132. B. Mundkur, Electron Microscopical Studies of Frozen Dried Yeast. V. Localization of Protein Bound Sulphhydryl, *Exptl. Cell Res.*, **34**: 155–181 (1964).

133. R. T. O'Brien and L. A. George, Preparation of Autoradiograms for Electron Microscopy, *Nature*, **183**: 1461–1462 (1959).

134. E. Odeblad, Matrix Theory for Quantitative Evaluation of Autoradiographs, *Lab. Invest.*, **8**: 113–123 (1959).

135. W. Oehlert, P. Nettesheim, and R. Machemer, Die Anwendung flüssiger Emulsionen bei autoradiographischen Untersuchungen mit H³-markierten Substanzen, *Histochem.*, **3**: 98–106 (1962).

136. M. Ogur and G. Rosen, The Nucleic Acids of Plant Tissues. I. The Extraction and Estimation of Desoxypentose Nucleic Acid and Pentose Nucleic Acid, *Arch. Biochem.*, **25**: 262–276 (1950).

137. M. J. Olszewska, Double autoradiographie des noyaux en interphase, *Exptl. Cell Res.*, **33**: 571–574 (1964).

138. H. Oster, H. W. Kundt, and R. Taugner, Methodische Untersuchungen zur autoradiographischen Darstellung wasserlöslicher Stoffe in der Niere, *Arch. Exptl. Pathol. Pharmakol.*, **224**: 476 (1955).

139. K. Ostrowski and E. A. Barnard, Application of Isotopically-labeled Specific Inhibitors as a Method in Enzyme Cytochemistry, *Exptl. Cell Res.*, **25**: 465–468 (1961).

140. K. Ostrowski, E. A. Barnard, Z. Stocka, and Z. Darzynkiewicz, Autoradiographic Methods in Enzyme Cytochemistry, *Exptl. Cell Res.*, **31**: 89–99 (1963).

141. K. Ostrowski, E. A. Barnard, Z. Darzynkiewicz, and D. Rymaszewska, Autoradiographic Methods in Enzyme Cytochemistry. III. Measurements on Esterase in Cells of Mouse Kidney, *Exptl. Cell Res.*, **36**: 43–52 (1964).

142. A. G. E. Pearse, *Histochemistry, Theoretical and Applied*, 2nd ed., Little, Brown & Company, Boston, Massachusetts, 1960.

143. D. C. Pease, *Histological Techniques for Electron Microscopy*, Academic Press Inc., New York, 1960.

144. S. R. Pelc, Autoradiograph Technique, *Nature*, **160**: 749–750 (1947).

145. S. R. Pelc, The Stripping Film Technique of Autoradiography, *Intern. J. Appl. Radiation Isotopes*, **1**: 172–177 (1956).

146. S. R. Pelc, J. D. Coombes, and G. C. Budd, On the Adaptation of Autoradiographic Techniques for Use with the Electron Microscope, *Exptl. Cell Res.*, **24**: 192 (1961).

147. S. R. Pelc, Theory of Electron Microscope Autoradiography, *J. Roy. Microscop. Soc.*, **81**: 131–139 (1963).

148. S. R. Pelc, personal communication, 1965.

149. P. Pellerin, P. Fallot, M. Laine-Boszormenyi, and F. Serrel, Low-temperature Autoradiography for the Detection of Tritium in Tissue, with Removal of Luminescence Induced by Tritium, *Nature*, **184**: 1385–1386 (1959).

150. R. P. Perry, R. Errera, E. A. Hell, and H. Durwald, Kinetics of Nucleoside Incorporation into Nuclear and Cytoplasmic RNA, *J. Biophys. Biochem. Cytol.*, **11**: 1–13 (1961).

151. M. R. Peterson and C. P. Leblond, Synthesis of Complex Carbohydrates in the Golgi Region, as Shown by Radioautography after Injection of Labeled Glucose, *J. Cell Biol.*, **21**: 143–148 (1964).

152. C. Pilgrim and W. Maurer, Autoradiographische Bestimmung der DNS-Verdopplungszeit verschiedener Zellarten von Maus und Ratte bei Doppelmarkierung mit ³H- und ¹⁴C-Thymidin, *Naturwissenschaften*, **49**: 544–545 (1962).

153. P. Pinheiro, C. P. Leblond, and B. Droz, Synthetic Capacity of Reticulocytes as Shown by Radioautography after Incubation with Labeled Precursors of Protein or RNA, *Exptl. Cell Res.*, **31**: 517–537 (1963).
154. R. A. Popp, W. D. Gude, and P. M. Popp, Peroxidase Staining Combined with Autoradiography for Study of Eosinophilic Granules, *Stain Technol.*, **37**: 243–247 (1962).
155. D. M. Prescott and M. A. Bender, Preparation of Mammalian Metaphase Chromosomes Free of Cytoplasm, *Exptl. Cell Res.*, **25**: 222–223 (1961).
156. D. M. Prescott, Autoradiography with Liquid Emulsion, in *Methods in Cell Physiology*, (D. M. Prescott, ed.), Academic Press, Inc., New York, 1965.
157. R. D. Przybylski, Electron Microscope Autoradiography, *Exptl. Cell Research*, **24**: 181–184 (1961).
158. L. Razavi, An Inexpensive and Simple Method for Preparing Chromosome Spreads, *Proc. Soc. Exptl. Biol. Med.*, **188**: 717–719 (1965).
159. J. P. Revel and E. D. Hay, Autoradiographic Localization of DNA Synthesis in a Specific Ultrastructural Component of the Interphase Nucleus, *Exptl. Cell Res.*, **25**: 474 (1961).
160. J. P. Revel and E. D. Hay, An Autoradiographic and Electron Microscopic Study of Collagen Synthesis in Differentiating Cartilage, *Z. Zellforsch. Mikroskop. Anat., Abt. Histochem.*, **61**: 110 (1963).
161. E. S. Reynolds, The Use of Lead Citrate at High pH as Electron Opaque Stain in Electron Microscopy, *J. Cell Biol.*, **17**: 209 (1963).
162. J. S. Robertson, V. P. Bond, and E. P. Cronkite, Resolution and Image Spread in Autoradiographs of Tritium Labeled Cells, *Intern. J. Appl. Radiation Isotopes*, **7**: 33–37 (1959).
163. R. Ross and E. P. Benditt, Wound Healing and Collagen Formation. A Quantitative Radioautographic Study of the Utilization of Proline-H³ in Wounds from Normal and Scorbute Guinea Pigs, *J. Cell Biol.*, **15**: 99–108 (1962).
164. M. M. Salpeter and L. Bachmann, Enhanced Contrast in High Resolution Autoradiography, *J. Cell Biol.*, **19**: 63A (1963).
165. M. M. Salpeter and L. Bachmann, Autoradiography with the Electron Microscope, a Procedure for Improving Resolution, Sensitivity and Contrast, *J. Cell Biol.*, **22**: 469–477 (1964).
166. R. E. Savage and W. S. Plaut, The Effect of HCl Hydrolysis on the Retention of Thymidine in DNA, *J. Biophys. Biochem. Cytol.*, **4**: 701 (1958).
167. G. Schneider and W. Maurer, Autoradiographische Untersuchung über den Einbau von ³H-Cytidin in die Kerne einiger Zellarten der Maus und über den Einfluss des Fixationsmittels auf die ³H-Aktivität, *Acta Histochem.*, **15**: 171–181 (1963).
168. M. H. Silk, A. O. Hawtrey, I. M. Spence, and J. H. S. Gear, A Method for Intracellular Autoradiography in the Electron Microscope, *J. Biophys. Biochem. Cytol.*, **10**: 577–587 (1961).
169. E. B. Simmel, The Use of Fast, Coarse Grain Stripping Film for Radioautography, *Stain Technol.*, **32**: 299–300 (1957).
170. W. L. Simpson, An Experimental Analysis of the Altmann Technic of Freezing-Drying, *Anat. Record*, **80**: 173 (1941).
171. R. T. Sims and C. A. Graham, The Photographic Development of Colored Grains in Radioautographs, *Quart. J. Microscop. Sci.*, **105**: 107–112 (1964).
172. E. R. Siperstein, Identification of the Adrenocorticotrophin-producing Cells in Rat Hypohysis, *J. Cell Biol.*, **17**: 521 (1963).

173. J. L. Sirlin, J. Jakob, and C. J. Tandler, Transfer of the Methyl Group of Methionine to Nucleolar Ribonucleic Acid., *Biochem. J.*, **98**: 447–452 (1963).
174. R. S. Speirs, V. Jansen, E. E. Speirs, S. Osada, and L. Dienes, Use of Tritiated Thymidine to Study the Origin and Fate of Inflammatory Cells, in *Tritium in the Physical and Biological Sciences, Symp. Intern. At. Energy Agency*, **2**: 301 (1961).
175. P. R. Srinivasan, M. Brunfaut, and M. Errera, The Role of Sulphhydryl Groups in RNA Metabolism, *Exptl. Cell Res.*, **34**: 61–70 (1964).
176. B. D. Srinivasan and C. V. Harding, Chromosome Spreads from Rabbit Lens Epithelium for Cytologic and Autoradiographic Studies, *Stain Technol.*, **38**: 283–285 (1963).
177. W. Stäubli, A New Embedding Technique for Electron Microscopy, Combining Water Soluble Epoxy Resin (Durcupan) with Water Insoluble Araldite, *J. Cell Biol.*, **16**: 197 (1963).
178. D. M. Steffensen, Evidence for the Apparent Absence of DNA in the Interbands of *Drosophila* Salivary Chromosomes, *Genetics*, **48**: 1289–1301 (1963).
179. U. Stenram, Loss of Silver Grains from Radioautographs Stained by Gallocyanin-chrome Alum, *Stain Technol.*, **37**: 231–234 (1962).
180. J. Stillström, Grain Count Corrections in Autoradiography, *Intern. J. Appl. Radiation Isotopes*, **14**: 113–118 (1963).
181. J. Stillström, Grain Count Corrections in Autoradiography. II., *Intern. J. Appl. Radiation Isotopes*, **16**: 357–363 (1965).
182. G. E. Stone, O. L. Miller, Jr., and D. M. Prescott, H³-Thymidine Derivative Pools in Relation to Macronuclear DNA Synthesis in *Tetrahymena pyriformis*, *J. Cell Biol.*, **25**: 171–177 (1965).
183. E. Stubblefield, Quantitative Tritium Autoradiography of Mammalian Chromosomes. I. The Basic Method, *J. Cell Biol.*, **25**: 109–119 (1965).
184. D. C. Swartzendruber and M. G. Hanna, Electron Microscopic Autoradiography of Germinal Center Cells in Mouse Spleen, *J. Cell Biol.*, **25**: 109–119 (1965).
185. M. L. Tanzer and R. D. Hunt, Experimental Lathyrism. An Autoradiographic Study, *J. Cell Biol.*, **22**: 623 (1964).
186. R. Taugner, H. Hole, G. Grigoleit, and U. Wagenmann, Herstellung geeigneter Gefrierschnitte zur Autoradiographie der Niere in einer Kühlkammer mit eingebautem Mikrotom, *Arch. Exptl. Pathol. Pharmakol.*, **234**: 330 (1958).
187. R. Taugner and U. Wagenmann, Serienmässige Herstellung von Gefrierschnitt-Autoradiogrammen mit optimalen Kontakt, *Arch. Exptl. Pathol. Pharmakol.*, **234**: 336 (1958).
188. J. H. Taylor, Autoradiography at the Cellular Level, in *Physical Techniques in Biological Research* (G. Oster and A. W. Pollister, eds.), Vol. III, pp. 545–574, Academic Press Inc., New York, 1956.
189. J. H. Taylor, Autoradiography with Tritium Labeled Substances, *Advan. Biol. Med. Phys.*, **7**: 107–129 (1960).
190. W. E. Tolles, Methods of Automatic Quantitation of Micro-autoradiographs, *Lab. Invest.*, **8**: 99–108 (1959).
191. E. A. Tonna and E. P. Cronkite, Factors which Influence the Latent Image in Autoradiography, *Stain Technol.*, **33**: 255–260 (1958).
192. J. Tooze, Measurements of Some Cellular Changes During the Fixation of Amphibian Erythrocytes with Osmium Tetroxide Solutions, *J. Cell Biol.*, **22**: 551–563 (1964).
193. R. P. van Tubergen, The Use of Radioautography and Electron Microscopy for

the Localization of Tritium Label in Bacteria, *J. Biophys. Biochem. Cytol.*, **9**: 219–222 (1961).

194. W. S. Vincent, P^{32} Incorporation into Starfish Oocyte Nucleoli, *Biol. Bull.*, **107**: 326 (1954).

195. R. C. Von Borstel, D. M. Prescott, and F. J. Bollum, Cytochemical Localization of Primer DNA Using DNA Polymerase, *J. Cell Biol.*, **19**: 72A (1963).

196. H. Washawsky, C. P. Leblond, and B. Droz, Synthesis and Migration of Proteins in Cells of the Exocrine Pancreas as Revealed by Specific Activity Determination from Radioautography, *J. Cell Biol.*, **16**: 1–23 (1963).

197. M. L. Watson and W. G. Aldridge, Selective Electron Staining of Nucleic Acids, *J. Histochem. Cytochem.*, **12**: 96–103 (1964).

198. J. H. Webb, The Action of Charged Particles on the Photographic Emulsion, in *The Theory of the Photographic Process* (C. E. K. Mees, ed.), The Macmillan Company, New York, 1964.

199. K. R. Wilske and R. Ross, The Autoradiographic Localization of Lipid- and Water-Soluble Compounds, *J. Cell Biol.*, **19**: 75A (1963).

200. D. E. Wimber, H. Quastler, O. L. Stein, and D. R. Wimber, Analysis of Tritium Incorporation into Individual Cells by Autoradiography of Squash-preparations, *J. Biophys. Biochem. Cytol.*, **8**: 327–331 (1960).

201. D. E. Wimber and H. Quastler, A C^{14}- and H^{3}-thymidine Double Labeling Technique in the Study of Cell Proliferation in *Tradescantia Root* Tips, *Exptl. Cell Res.*, **30**: 8–22 (1963).

202. V. H. Witten and V. Holstrom, New Histologic Technics for Autoradiography, *J. Lab. Invest.*, **2**: 368 (1953).

203. P. S. Woods, A Chromatographic Study of Hydrolysis in the Feulgen Nucleal Reaction, *J. Biophys. Biochem. Cytol.*, **3**: 71 (1957).

204. P. S. Woods and G. Zubay, Biochemical and Autoradiographic Studies of Different RNA's: Evidence that Transfer RNA is Chromosomal in Origin, *Proc. Natl. Acad. Sci. U.S.*, **54**: 1705–1712 (1965).

205. J. W. Woodard, E. Rasch, and H. H. Swift, Nucleic Acid and Protein Metabolism during the Mitotic Cycle in *Vicia faba, J. Biophys. Biochem. Cytol.*, **9**: 445–462 (1961).

206. H. Yagoda, *Radioactive Measurements with Nuclear Emulsions*, John Wiley & Sons, Inc., New York, 1949.

207. B. A. Young and B. M. Kopriwa, The Use of the Gevaert NUC-307 Nuclear Emulsion for Radioautography at the Electron Microscope Level, *J. Histochem. Cytochem.*, **12**: 438–441 (1964).

208. A. S. Zelickson, H. M. Hirsch, and J. F. Hartmann, Melanogenesis: An Autoradiographic Study at the Ultrastructural Level, *J. Invest. Dermatol.*, **43**: 327–332 (1964).

CHAPTER 5

General Factors Influencing the Incorporation of Exogenous Precursors in Intact Organisms, Exemplified Mainly for the Case of Nucleic Acids

1. Introduction

One may classify labeled organic molecules into two groups with regard to the role they play in living matter. One group comprises all those molecules which are true reactants in one or more places in the chain of metabolic reactions. The other group contains those molecules which are strangers in a given metabolic environment, but which, because of structural similarities to native molecules, compete with them in their normal metabolism. These molecules may also be called anttimetabolites. In this chapter, some true metabolites will be discussed with the aim at drawing the attention of the investigator to possible pitfalls in the interpretation of data obtained with them. Because of the abundant material available, data on nucleic acids and their precursors were preferentially selected to exemplify among the general factors influencing the incorporation of labeled precursors: (1) the effects of the route of administration and of the efficiency of circulation or vascularization with regard to the target tissue to be reached by the precursor; (2) enzymatic reaction pathways and their adaptations to changes in the equilibrium of substrates and reaction products comprising the "soluble pool" of a cell or cell system; (3) the degree of metabolic renewal ("turnover") of cellular constituents and the problem of reutilization; (4) likewise the turnover of cell systems and the simplification of the steady state, where cell production equals cell death; and finally (5) influences on cell metabolism and proliferation by stimulating and inhibiting factors such as hormones, diurnal rhythms, age, and temperature. The topics in this chapter emphasize true tracer conditions which require that neither the label bound to a molecule nor the carrier compound may initiate metabolic abnormalities in the organism studied.[155] It will be shown that the prerequisite of noninterference of the carrier molecules can be violated easily if the amount of tracer administered surpasses the level of enzyme saturation. Changes of metabolic reaction rates of labeled precursors due to kinetic isotope effects, which in certain instances may become of considerable magnitude, were discussed in Chapter 2 and will not be considered here. Biological effects due to tritium decay are reviewed in Chapter 6.

2. Routes of Administration of the Labeled Precursor

A labeled molecule, selected as a tracer, may be administered in various ways, depending on the type of living organism that is used in the experiment and depending on the physical state of the tracer molecule, whether gaseous, liquid, or solid.

2.1. Culture or Nutrient Medium

Any living organism may ingest a tracer compound, which in gas form may also be a component of the atmospheric environment. Bacteria, single cells, small multicellular organisms, plants, or part of them are usually labeled by exposure for a certain period of time to a proper nutrient medium containing the tracer. The transport and the intercellular distribution of small labeled molecules in plants occur so rapidly that, for example, H^3-thymidine is incorporated within 5 minutes from the nutrient solution into cells of root tips, and after a 30-minute exposure it needs only 10 minutes to wash out completely the tracer not taken up by the cells.[98] Efficient labeling of parasites may be facilitated by appropriate arrangement, as in the case of cestodes living in the bile duct. Thus, tritiated nucleosides were injected into bile ducts dilated *in vivo* by distal ligation and were readily available for the parasites.[92]

2.2. Ingestion

In more highly developed animals, ingestion of a tracer with nourishment may be adequate or even desirable for particular studies on the absorption mechanism in the gastrointestinal (G.I.) tract. If the tracer is to be distributed throughout the animal, this route of administration is most uncertain. Besides metabolic alterations of the labeled molecule, the absorption efficiency in the gastrointestinal tract is difficult to predict accurately. Still, Rubini *et al.*[281] showed that oral administration of H^3-thymidine (500 μc in guinea pigs and 100 μc in rats) resulted in the labeling of DNA throughout the body. Tritiated water after oral administration absorbs readily in the G.I. tract within about 40 minutes.[253]

2.3. SUBCUTANEOUS OR INTRAMUSCULAR INJECTION

In order to become completely distributed in an animal organism within a short period of time, the labeled compound must quantitatively enter the blood circulation. This is obviously achieved most easily by injection of the tracer solution into a suitable vein, artery, or a cardiac ventricle. Care must be taken that the tracer solution is not deposited accidentally into the tissue outside the vascular system, or the substance may diffuse out of the circulation at the injection site so that reabsorption into the circulation may perhaps crucially delay the availability of the precursor. This may happen, for example, in rodents by too rapid injection into the tail vein. Because of the delay in absorption and the potential localized metabolism of the tracer molecule, subcutaneous or intramuscular injection is the inferior mode of administering a tracer when a uniform and rapid distribution in the entire organism is desired.

2.4. INTRAVASCULAR INJECTION

The importance of prompt distribution of a tracer in the vascular system is readily seen in the case of thymidine, since injected H^3-thymidine is removed from the circulating blood within minutes to be incorporated by proliferating cells or to be catabolized.[260,279,309] All H^3-thymidine is removed from the circulation within 40–60 minutes after injection,[308] and data obtained with the thymidine analog I^{131}-deoxyuridine in mice indicated that the half-time for its incorporation into DNA is only 5 minutes.[148] Indeed, H^3-thymidine passed through the bloodstream, the vascular barrier, the cell wall, and the steps of phosphorylation to become incorporated into DNA so rapidly that when mice were killed 15 seconds after intravenous injection of H^3-thymidine, labeled cells could already be demonstrated in the bone marrow (it required 90 additional seconds to isolate the marrow from the killed animals and to prepare the cytological preparations for autoradiography).[104] Under *in vitro* conditions, H^3-thymidine was incorporated into DNA also within 30 seconds.[237]

A similar rapid clearance from the circulation after intravenous injection was observed for RNA precursors[109] and labeled amino acids.[58,325] Only 3% of labeled amino acids remained in the blood 10 minutes after injection.[30]

2.5. Intraperitoneal Injection

Intraperitoneal injection requires the diffusion of the labeled precursor through the peritoneum into the circulation. This route of administration has been found useful particularly in small animals, and it may at times be as adequate as intravascular injection. Thus, 85% H³-thymidine was removed from the peritoneal cavity within 15 minutes, 90% was absorbed in 30 minutes, 96% was absorbed within 1 hour.[258] Similar results were seen with H³-cytidine,[339] but the precursor is likely to enter metabolism of local tissue, whereby a fraction only of the precursor may be made available for total distribution. This was demonstrated to a varying degree for H³-thymidine and H³-cytidine in the mouse by Peterson and Baserga,[245] who compared the influence of various routes of injection on the efficiency of cellular incorporation (see Table 5.1). Intraperitoneal injection of the precursors resulted in a greater labeling intensity of cells in the gastrointestinal tract, spleen, and peritoneal tumor cells than after intravenous or subcutaneous injection; at the same time, cells away from the peritoneal cavity, like those in the heart or aorta, were labeled only one-third to one-fourth as intense as after intravenous administration. Pelc and Appleton[243] observed the diffusion of H³-thymidine from the peritoneal cavity into the sourrounding tissue to proceed at a speed of 2 μ per second, and the neighboring cells were labeled predominantly.

2.6. Injection into the Cerebrospinal Fluid

Administration of labeled molecules into the cerebrospinal fluid has also been used. From their work with various labeled nucleosides Altman and Chorover[3] concluded that this mode of tracer administration is indeed ill suited for supplying the brain with metabolites. Labeling was

TABLE 5.1

GRAIN COUNTS IN MICE AFTER INJECTION OF H³-CYTIDINE INTRAPERITONEALLY (ip) OR INTRAVENOUSLY (iv)[a]

Tissue	Males		Females	
	ip	iv	ip	iv
Small intestine (muscle)	249	143	333	84
Urinary bladder	367	146	517	82
Aorta	86	223	105	132
Heart	70	286	125	178

[a] Per 100 cells in tissue sections. Reproduced with permission from Peterson and Baserga, *Arch. Pathol.*[245]

observed close to the wall of the cerebral ventricle only, in a region not more than about 3.6 mm deep. A diffuse labeling pattern of the brain is obtainable by injecting precursors into the circulating blood, as long as the blood-brain barrier may be passed, as it is in the case for nucleosides,[342] amino acids,[295] or norepinedrine,[287] for example. Wulff et al.[339] showed that after H^3-cytidine injection into mice and rats the brain cells incorporated only about 10% of the tracer taken up by the liver or kidney cells.

2.7. INHALATION OR ABSORPTION THROUGH THE SKIN

Tritium-labeled compounds may enter the body through the skin or the lungs, often unnoticed during accidental exposure. Tritium gas and tritiated water are examples of compounds commonly encountered by the investigator. Tritiated water is absorbed through the inert barrier of the outer skin within a few minutes.[253] Administration and metabolism of tritiated water will be discussed at the end of this chapter.

3. Vascular Distribution of the Labeled Precursor

The distribution of a labeled precursor in an organism is seldom truly uniform and depends, in addition to the mode of administration, on the efficiency of a circulatory system to transport the precursor equally well to all parts of an organism. Whereas single cells or bacteria in culture can be uniformly exposed to a tracer in their environment, in multicellular organisms the distribution of a precursor to the individual cells depends on the efficiency of circulation, diffusion, or both. In their early studies with the autoradiographic technique, Lacassagne and Lattes[177] already noticed lack of uniform distribution of injected polonium in tumor tissue in the animal. There was more tracer observed in the vascularized part of the tumor than in the center, where there were also signs of necrosis. Kligerman and co-workers[172] showed this effect for H^3-thymidine also and demonstrated autoradiographically the label localized mainly in the immediate perivascular tissue of a tumor. The inefficient diffusion and probably metabolic alterations in solid, nonvascularized tissue are illustrated also by the observation that when minced tissue pieces of mammary tumors were exposed in vitro to medium containing H^3-thymidine, only those cells became labeled which were within several cell diameters away from the surface of the tissue piece,[154] and the labeling intensity diminished with increasing distance from the surface.

In the normal animal, varying degrees of vascularization undoubtedly influence the labeling pattern of single cells with regard to their position relative to the vascular bed. Some cells are close to a capillary and hence have a first chance to incorporate a labeled molecule that was transported via the circulating blood. Other cells are more remote and can incorporate only those tracers which were not utilized by the first cells. However, when the size of intracellular pools is adequate, labeled precursors may redistribute from cell to cell and thus balance unequal blood supply and provide a more uniform distribution. A nonuniform tracer distribution is particularly obvious in organs with dense cellularity and relatively poor vascularization as in lymphoreticular tissue[72] (see Fig. 5.1).

The diffusion of a tracer in a dense cellular mass is obviously also influenced by the metabolic activity and requirement of the cells. For example, in the brain, various nucleosides diffused from the cerebral ventricle into the surrounding tissue to a depth depending on the nucleoside.[3] The grain density in autoradiograms fell to near zero at 1.5 mm away from the ventricular wall for H^3-adenine, whereas H^3-thymidine was distributed to a distance of about 3.6 mm away from the ventricle. The difference in the two results may indicate the greater demand of the cells for adenine than for thymidine. In areas where nearly all cells proliferate and are all metabolically very active, such as in the bone marrow, the diffusion of precursors probably ranges over a considerably shorter distance. Whether this distance still extends at least one-half the distance from one blood vessel to the next, e.g., in the bone marrow from one sinusoidal border to the next one, is not clear. In bone-marrow sections prepared soon after a single injection of H^3-thymidine, one occasionally has the impression of nonuniform label distribution. Exact data are not known. Still, if the labeled precursor is allowed to be absorbed over a prolonged period of time, the chance of reaching all cells is expected to increase. This may be due to providing the tracer in excess of the needs of those cells closest to the bloodstream, but also may result from a change of cellular position by ameboid migration *in situ*.

4. The Acid-Soluble "Pool"

In discussing macromolecular biosynthesis, it is customary to refer to the acid-soluble fraction (i.e., small molecular fraction in a cell) as the "soluble pool." The various small molecular components are present in this fraction in varying amounts, which may be constant relative to each other. The constituents of the pool are continuously interchanged, catabolized, or anabolized to serve as building blocks for larger molecules, and the majority of the energy needed for these reactions is also delivered by the "soluble pool." Some constituents of the pool are renewed rapidly; others turn over more slowly.

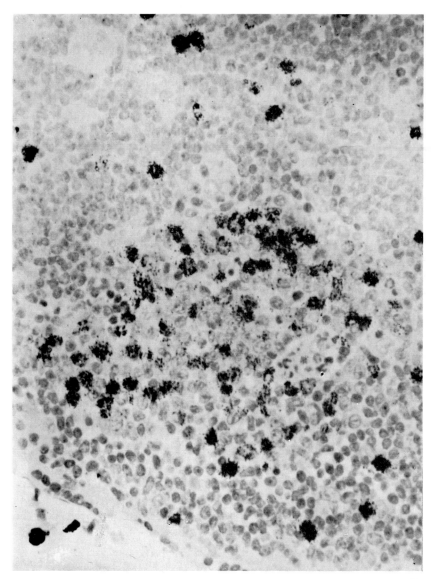

Fig. 5.1. Autoradiogram of a lymph node section showing a germinal center. The unequal label distribution after injection of H³-thymidine indicates probably also unequal availability of the tracer within the densely packed cells. Courtesy of Dr. H. Cottier, Institute of Pathology, University of Bern, Switzerland.

Synthesis and breakdown of molecules, interchanges, and energy-providing reactions are all balanced by the delicate interplay of enzymes. While, in principle, the types of enzymatic reactions are the same or very similar in the various cell types, the quantity of enzymes and their substrates varies greatly among cells. While some reactions are commonly found throughout nature, other reactions are typical for a given cell—for example, photosynthetic reactions are typical for green plants and algae. A cell maintains its integrity against the extracellular environment not only through a cell membrane but through the balanced and controlled enzymatic reactions in the soluble pool.

Metabolic control mechanisms responsible for adaptation to a changing environment are a most fascinating subject of modern biological research.[9,48,153,211,212,219,328] Problems range from the control of cell proliferation to the genetic control of enzyme synthesis. Regulation by feedback is common. The latter implies that in a chain of metabolic reactions a product formed will be an inhibitor of its own synthesis in the reactions. Changes in the concentration and distribution of small molecular substrates may also lead to direct competition for enzymes, or it may result in a repression or induction of enzymatic activity, either via synthesis of enzymes or via activation or inactivation of existing enzymes. In general, one may say that any change in the environment of a cell quickly alters the steady state of reactants in the soluble pool.

Enzymatic control mechanisms governing the synthesis of large molecules, such as proteins or nucleic acids, are being studied satisfactorily in single cells, particularly in bacteria or mammalian cells in culture, where the experimental conditions can be controlled more rigorously than is possible in complex multicellular organisms. Genetic and biochemical analyses both complement each other in this type of research.[153] Some enzymatic reaction chains will be cited here in the field of nucleic acid metabolism simply to exemplify the importance of metabolic adaptations in tracer studies and their interpretation. Thus, the degree of incorporation by a cell of H^3-cytidine into RNA over a certain period of time does not reflect per se the rate of RNA synthesis.[102] The same is true for the incorporation of H^3-thymidine into DNA.[103,223]

4.1. ENTRANCE THROUGH THE CELL MEMBRANE

A tracer enters the cell through the cellular membrane, which discriminates against large or charged molecules or both.[257] Large molecules are taken up by the cell usually by pinocytosis, a process by which the large molecule or small particle is engulfed by cytoplasmic protrusions covered by the membrane. Affinity of the cell membrane for the large particle or molecule prior to pinocytosis is a prerequisite. For example, in a tissue culture cell, uptake by pinocytosis of wheat germ lipase was quite active whereas chymotrypsin was discriminated against owing to a lack of affinity.[69] Affinities of cell membranes are influenced by surface adsorption due to immunological processes.

Small, uncharged molecules such as nucleosides or amino acids pass the cell membrane readily by diffusion or facilitated transport, but charged nucleotides (phosphorylated nucleosides) do not pass freely. Hence, the concentration of nucleosides and free amino acids in the extracellular space tends to equilibrate through the cell membrane with the soluble fraction in the cell. As already mentioned above, the entrance of thymidine into the cell and its subsequent phosphorylation and incorporation into DNA may occur within seconds.[104,237] In other words, a cell communicates with its adjacent environment most freely via small molecules; or alterations in the concentration of small molecules in the extracellular space readily influence the balance of intracellular reactions. It is obvious that a labeled molecule is a true tracer only if it does not cause a shift in the balance of the reactions. On the other hand, disturbances of the physiological equilibrium in the enzymatic reactions provide a powerful tool in studying enzymatic control mechanisms. At any rate, cells which are taken out of their physiological environment are apt to react differently toward a labeled metabolite than they do under "normal conditions." Data from *in vivo* and *in vitro* experiments will be discussed later in this chapter to illustrate this further.

4.2. Entrance into the Chain of Enzymatic Reactions

The suitability of a labeled molecule as a tracer in living cells depends on the enzymes with which the particular cell is equipped. For example, thymine is one of the four bases in the DNA molecule in all cells. However, not all cells accept its deoxyriboside, thymidine, as a precursor from the extracellular environment. Thus, *Neurospora crassa* takes up thymidine and converts it to uridine, which consequently is partly remethylated to thymidine,[110] but this organism lacks the enzyme necessary for direct utilization of thymidine for DNA synthesis. It is known that various rodents such as the woodchuck, the ground squirrel, and the chipmunk do not utilize injected H^3-thymidine at all, whereas other rodents such as the red squirrel and the chipmunk utilize H^3-thymidine for DNA synthesis in the cells in the ileum but not in the tongue. Again, other rodents such as the mouse, hamster, and gray squirrel incorporate H^3-thymidine readily.[2] These various groups of rodents are phylogenetically related. The failure to utilize H^3-thymidine, of course, does not indicate that these animals do not synthesize DNA but that the necessary precursors are synthesized by the cells without a thymidine pathway. This inability to utilize thymidine has been found, for example, in a strain of Novikoff hepatoma[216] or has been experimentally produced in tissue culture cells (mouse fibroblast or L cells) by a prolonged exposure of 90 weeks to the thymidine analog, 5-bromodeoxyuridine.[168] The cells, however, continued to use uridine and deoxycytidine as a source for their DNA-thymine. The cells had lost the capacity to produce the enzyme thymidine kinase, which phosphorylates thymidine, as a prerequisite for entrance into the metabolic reaction chain. This specific deficiency or, reversely, a specific induction by virus infection in deficient cells is a valuable tool for studies on enzymatic control mechanisms,[91,99,167,214,216] similar to the use of mutant bacteria which are genetically selected for specific requirements or deficiencies.[183] Cells can be made temporarily deficient in thymidine kinase by specific inhibitors such as amethopterin and 5-fluorodeoxyuridine and thus allow the distinction between pyrimidine interconversions and the study of their effect on nucleic acid and protein synthesis.[118,216,283]

4.3. The Size of the Acid-Soluble "Pool"

Thymidine can be traced more easily than other nucleosides, since in most higher organisms it is incorporated only into DNA.[115,271] Yet thymidine has also been found in RNA of bacterial strains such as *E. coli* and *Aerobacter aerogenes*.[189] Perhaps it is the specific precursor relationship which explains why the "pool" of thymidine is very small in most cells, for instance, about 2 μg per gram of spleen,[263] and why its renewal is so rapid during the time the precursor is utilized for DNA synthesis.[263] The less specific precursor relationship of other nucleosides, their easy interconversion and multiple functions within the cell, cause the renewal time within the soluble fraction to be much slower, concomitantly the pool size is larger than that for thymidine.[102,119]

In the HeLa cells in culture, the pool for thymidine is so small that at the tracer dose level normally added it is the specific activity of the labeled precursor and not the concentration that determines the degree of label incorporation by the cell, as was pointed out by Painter *et al.*[236] Indeed, an increase of thymidine in the medium by a factor of 10 (0.0003–0.003 μmole for 3×10^5 cells) led to only a slight increase of its incorporation into DNA despite an increase of the pool size. An increase of the amount of thymidine by a factor of 100 was followed by an increased incorporation into DNA by a factor of approximately 3 only, indicating "flooding" of a rate-limiting reaction in the precursor pool (see Fig. 5.2). Similar observations were reported by Crathorn and Shooter[75] in ascites tumor cells. In 1 hour 10^8 cells took up 0.001 μmole of thy-

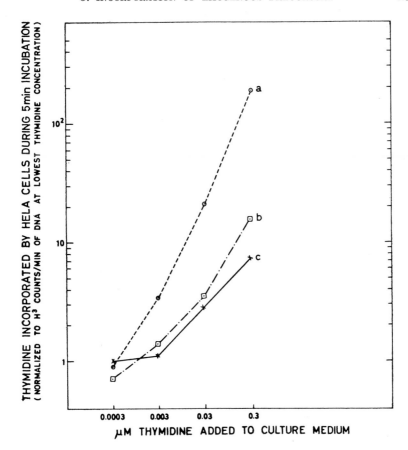

Fig. 5.2. Incorporation of H³-thymidine in HeLa-S₃ cells, after 5 minutes' exposure, as a function of increasing amounts of the tracer in the culture medium; (a) fraction soluble in acid alcohol (glacial acetic acid, 1 vol: 95% ethanol, 3 vol); (b) fraction soluble in 2% perchloric acid at 4°C; (c) DNA (approximately 3×10^5 cells per milliliter per culture, average data from four parallel cultures per point).

midine. A tenfold rise in the concentration led only to a slight increase in the amount incorporated by the cells. Corresponding data for bone-marrow cells *in vitro* were published by Rubini *et al.*[280] Cleaver and Holford[63] examined carefully the size of the thymidine pool in L cells and found that the ratio of precursor uptake was proportional to the square root of its concentration in the extracellular medium up to a concentration of 10^{-6} M. It was also indicated that with increasing concentrations of thymidine in the medium the pool size increased too. This was also observed in Novikoff hepatoma cells[119] and in root tip cells of *Vicia faba*.[98] A small thymidine pool was also seen in *Tetrahymena pyri-*

formis.[152,315] However, in *Tetrahymena pyriformis* increased concentrations of unlabeled thymidine subsequent to exposure to labeled thymidine did not affect the pool renewal.[152] Experiments with H^3-cytidine in mice showed that the rate of incorporation of this precursor increased with rising concentrations over a wide range up to 1 mg per mouse, indicative of a relatively large pool for this precursor, which was, however, somewhat larger in young mice than in old mice.[339] On the other hand, as little as 12 μg of thymidine per mouse led already to a saturation of the thymidine-incorporation mechanism.[148]

The size of the thymidine pool must be expected to vary with different cell systems, as was demonstrated for cells of the intestine, spleen, and thymus in the rat.[227,263] The pools in spleen cells and intestinal cells could be saturated more easily with thymidine than the pool in thymus cells. In mice, the amount of thymidine incorporated by testis, kidney, and liver was, however, nearly equal over a wide range of dose, and when the amount of thymidine injected exceeded 300 μg, the uptake did not increase further.[289] Also in tissue culture cells, the size of the thymidine pool may vary, even with some uncontrolled alteration in the cellular environment, as was shown by Marin and Bender[197] in "parallel experiments" with Chinese hamster fibroblasts in culture.

The size of the pool of small molecular nucleotides may be expected to vary with the stage of the cell cycle between two mitoses, as was demonstrated by Mitchison[208] in a fission yeast (*Schizosaccharomyces pombe*), where the maximum size was reached in the middle of the cycle.[209] The pool size appeared to vary also with the growth rate.[170]

Although RNA precursors were reported to be incorporated into cells throughout the cell cycle except for mitosis,[82,83,100,106,164,174,264,319] thymidine is utilized normally only during the phase of DNA synthesis. Indeed, thymidine incorporation into the soluble fraction is also limited to this time period. Thus, in *Tetrahymena pyriformis* the thymidine pool renewed only during the time the cells synthesized DNA.[314,315] Similar conclusions were drawn from studies in mouse bone-marrow cells, where H^3-thymidine incorporation into the soluble fraction was limited to those cells able to synthesize DNA.[104] Also Bianchi[17] found that the activity of the thymidine-phosphorylating enzymes and that of the DNA-synthesizing enzyme behaved in a parallel manner in a variety of normal and malignant cells (but not in all instances), similar to the results of Bollum and Potter[23] from regenerating liver. In the lily (*Lilium longiflorum*)[143] and in wheat seedlings,[144] thymidine-phosphorylating enzyme was seen to be synthesized *de novo* just prior to the commencement of DNA synthesis, whereas in the nongrowing mouse liver, thymidylate kinase remained inactive by being bound to cellular particles.[158]

Whether the rate of renewal of the intracellular thymidine pool during DNA synthesis alters in various cell types is not known. In mammalian cells *in vivo*, the effective pool appears to renew within less than 1 hour, as shown, for example, in rat spleen and thymus[263] for the total mouse,[109] and in the mouse intestinal cells.[148] But in L cells in culture, phosphorylated thymidine could be observed in the soluble fraction for as long as 3 hours.[63] No evidence has been found that incorporated thymidine remains bound within the soluble fraction over a period of one cell cycle from one DNA synthesis phase to the next after cell division. A thymidine pool, however, may persist between two DNA synthesis phases.[315] The renewal of RNA nucleotides in the pool may extend throughout the period of the entire cell cycle including mitosis,[106] and various components with rapid and delayed turnover exist.[100-102,268]

4.4. Enzymatic Reaction Pathways (Physiological Control Mechanisms, Induced Disturbances of Reaction Equilibrium)

To understand better the reasons for and consequences of changes in size and renewal of the pool of thymidine and other nucleosides, the metabolic pathways of these precursors must be considered.

Most cells are not dependent on preformed nucleosides or corresponding bases, but synthesize these *de novo* and utilize them for nucleic acid synthesis as needed. Most cells, however, can incorporate these precursors also from the extracellular space, and among them the purine bases such as adenine and guanine without ribose or deoxyribose attached are preferred over the corresponding nucleosides. On the other hand, pyrimidine nucleosides such as uridine, cytidine, and thymidine are preferred over the respective bases, and they are incorporated without cleavage of the base–sugar linkage. In *E. coli*, however, contrary to cells of higher organisms, the pyrimidine bases are well utilized.[64]

Upon entering the cell, the free bases are linked to the ribose or deoxyribose phosphate by phosphorylases, and the nucleosides are phosphorylated by kinases. Incorporation into RNA or DNA by the respective polymerases requires the appropriate nucleoside monophosphates to be phosphorylated further to di- or triphosphates. Reduction of the ribose moiety to deoxyribose for DNA occurs probably at the diphosphate level,[15] and deoxyribonucleotides are synthesized probably for the major part via the corresponding ribonucleotides. While the nucleic acid precursors of both the purine and the pyrimidine group interconvert, thymidine and its phosphates make an exception in cells of higher organisms.[115] Thymidine generally is thus phosphorylated to mono-, di-, and triphosphate[16,263] to become incorporated into DNA, or it is catabolized. Many of the enzymes catalyzing the various interconversion reactions, synthesis, and breakdown in various cell systems have been isolated and studied. Space does not allow discussion of all these reactions and the reader is referred to the appropriate textbooks, especially to the monograph by Potter[261] and the careful reviews by Schmidt[293] and Moyed and Umbarger.[218] Reactions involving thymidine, however, will be considered here in some detail.

Not all cells possess thymidine-degrading enzymes. Relatively large amounts of one of these degrading enzymes, phosphorylase, are found in the liver, but not in a variety of other tissues or in Novikoff hepatoma cells.[87] Indeed, the liver is the main site of thymidine catabolism.[120,148,261] When injected into a mammalian organism, about one half of the H³-thymidine may be degraded to tritiated water and tritiated β-aminoisobutyric acid.[279] In a tissue culture of HeLa-S3, however, the catabolism of H³-thymidine did not lead to the production of tritiated water. Tritiated water was one of the catabolites from these cells when they were exposed to tritiated cytidine or uridine.[101] In ascites tumor cells, thymidine and also cytidine and uridine may be cleaved at the deoxyribosidic N-linkage.[347] If the respective phosphorylase was blocked by large amounts of nonradioactive thymine, H³-thymidine was incorporated into DNA to a greater extent than in the control experiment.[347] Furthermore, the ribose made available by the cleavage of pyrimidine nucleosides was observed to be transferable to the purine bases.[137] In the lily, the breakdown products of H³-thymidine were found to be mainly H³-thymine, H³-dihydrothymine, H³-dihydrouracil, H³-β-ureidoisobutyric acid, and H³-β-aminoisobutyric acid.[317] It appeared that H³-dihydrothymine could be bound to some degree nonspecifically in the cells.

Phosphorylated thymidine is probably endogenously synthesized in the cell mainly from pyrimidine ribose phosphates,[56,65,102,107,134,272] whereas the exogenous thymidine supply, and hence thymidine kinase also, must be considered mainly from the viewpoint of a salvage pathway.[233] The methylation of uracil to thymine requires tetrahydrofolate.[335] At various stages of the conversion reactions of uracil or cytosine ribonucleotides to thymine deoxyribonucleotide control mechanisms have been observed. It is thus to be expected, as will be shown below, that endogenous synthesis and exogenous supply may inhibit each other, depending on the relative amounts of substrates present; furthermore, one might rightly predict that alterations in the metabolism of RNA will lead to changes in nucleotide interconversions and hence to an effect on the endogenous supply of thymidine phosphate. Large amounts of exogenous thymidine should alter the equilibrium of RNA precursors and their interconversions equally well.

Potter and his co-workers[118,119,216,262] studied these reactions *in vitro* and *in vivo* and listed various sites in the pathways of pyrimidine interconversions where thymidine triphosphate inhibits by feedback. Figure 5.3 illustrates these sites. Thymidine triphosphate is thus observed to inhibit: (1) the conversion of cytidine diphosphate to deoxycytidine diphosphate [negative feedback site (nfb. 1), see Fig. 5.3]; (2) the phosphorylation by thymidine kinase of thymidine to thymidine monophosphate (nfb. 2); it was, however, observed that deoxycytidine triphosphate, deoxyguanosine triphosphate, and deoxyadenosine triphosphate did not inhibit the thymidine kinase; (3) the phosphorylation of deoxyuridine to deoxyuridine monophosphates (nfb. 3); (4) the conversion of deoxycytidine monophosphate by deaminase to deoxyuridine monophosphate (nfb. 5), however, the deamination of deoxycytidine was not inhibited by thymidine triphosphate; and (5) furthermore, deoxycytidine triphosphate inhibited the phosphorylation by deoxycytidine kinase of deoxycytidine to deoxycytidine monophosphate (nfb. 4).

When the concentration of thymidine triphosphate was equal to that of thymidine, the thymidine kinase reaction was completely inhibited. A maximal inhibition was obtained when the concentration of ATP was low. The inhibition of the reduction of cytidine phosphate to deoxycytidine phosphate was attributed specifically to thymidine (probably thymidine phosphate), as tested *in vivo* in a mast cell neoplasma in culture.[214,215] No other pyrimidine or purine ribo- or deoxyribonucleoside

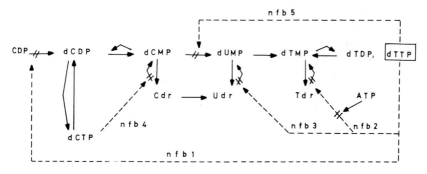

NEGATIVE FEEDBACK (n f b)
IN BIOSYNTHESIS OF d T T P

FIG. 5.3. Scheme of negative feedback (nfb) in the interconversion reactions of pyrimidine nucleotides by thymidine triphosphate (see text). Courtesy of Potter, *Exptl. Cell Res.*[262]

could duplicate the effect. Indeed, the overall rate of DNA synthesis could be modified by limiting the intracellular concentration of thymidine triphosphate, the optimal concentration of which was found to be about $5–10 \times 10^{-5}\ M$ in hepatoma cells.[118] The mechanism of the feedback control exerted by thymidine triphosphate on thymidine kinase was analyzed by Okazaki and Kornberg.[232,233] The enzyme was described to have three binding sites for the phosphate donor (nucleoside triphosphates such as ATP and dATP)—the phosphate acceptor (thymidine), for an activator (certain deoxynucleoside diphosphates), or for an inhibitor, where thymidine triphosphate was most potent.

These specific inhibitions explain the observations that in the presence of nonlabeled thymidine HeLa-S$_3$ tissue culture cells incorporated less H^3-cytidine into RNA than did the control group.[102] That the rate of RNA synthesis was not diminished to that extent was shown by the experiment in which H^3-cytidine was first added to the cells for a short period of time, after which the cultures were continued in medium containing nonlabeled thymidine. While the continued incorporation of pyrimidine nucleotides from the pool into DNA was blocked in the presence of thymidine, the acid-soluble nucleotide pool enlarged, and continued incorporation from the pool into RNA exceeded that in the control cells. Hence, the initial depression of H^3-cytidine incorporation was due to a "dilution" in the respective pool.[102] These studies were confirmed and extended in a series of reports on work with hepatoma cells,[118,119] and it was found also that, in the presence of excess thymidine, the rate of H^3-deoxycytidine incorporation into DNA was increased, probably because of a requirement for exogenous deoxycytidine induced by feedback inhibition by thymidine triphosphate of the production of deoxycytidine nucleotides. Deoxycytidine also exerted a marked effect on the incorporation of cytidine, however, without affecting the net synthesis of RNA and DNA.

The toxicity of low concentrations of thymidine on cellular reproduction was shown by Painter et al.[239] The colony-forming ability of HeLa-S$_3$ cells was depressed by as little as 0.04 μmole of thymidine ($=10$ μg) per milliliter of medium. Similar data were obtained with hepatoma cells[119] and in L cells in culture.[63] Potter[262] reported that growth inhibition of culture cells caused by excess thymidine could be relieved by deoxycytidine. The toxic effect of thymidine even in low concentrations argues in favor of using labeled thymidine with high specific activity.[238] Yet, thymidine in large amounts proved suitable for inducing synchrony in the proliferation of tissue culture cells[28,341] and caused presumably mitotic stimulation in intact mice.[131] On the other hand, depriving cells of pyrimidines, which is particularly rapid and effective in microorganisms, also leads to alterations of nucleic acid and protein synthesis, yielding information on the interrelationships and sequence of these reactions.[20,56,183,195] In *E. coli*, the incorporation of H^3-thymidine could be greatly increased by providing deoxyribose in the form of various deoxyribonucleosides.[31]

The examples cited so far make it obvious that refined controls operate in the pyrimidine pathways, affecting both *de novo* synthesis and extracellular supply. It is clear that it is not permissible to conclude *a priori* and simply from a decreased or increased cellular incorporation of labeled nucleic acid precursors that the rate of nucleic acid synthesis was concomitantly altered.

Injury and disease affect metabolic equilibrium profoundly, often beyond the range of the restitution potential of the cell. This needs to be considered also for data interpretation in tracer studies. Thus, examining the effects of radiation on DNA synthesis one must take into account changes in pool size, and tracer data must describe not only the specific activity of the DNA but also that of the acid-soluble pool.[302] Thus, Nygaard and Potter[227] could indeed ascribe the depression of incorporation of labeled thymidine into the DNA of rat tissue to a depression of DNA synthesis after total-body irradiation. A dilution effect of the pool on the incorporation of H^3-thymidine (specific activity, 36–360 mc/mmole) after X-irradiation was observed in ascites tumor cells, but not in bone-marrow cells *in vitro* or in thymus cells *in vivo*.[138] Apparently some DNA catabolism subsequent to irradiation caused the pool to enlarge in ascites cells and led to a dilution of the tracer. Zajicek and Gross[348] clearly showed the effect of the β-radiation from large doses of H^3-thymidine in DNA in ascites tumor cells to result not only in a depression of continued DNA synthesis but also in a considerable release of acid-soluble nucleotides from the labeled DNA. Also in *E. coli*, the size of the "soluble pool" increased and leaked out of the cells after irradiation upon degradation of DNA, which could be enhanced when chloramphenicol was added immediately after irradiation.[204] The degradation of DNA after irradiation was correlated to a labilization of DNA-protein bonds and to an increased activity of deoxyribonuclease.[129]

A difference in the alteration of the equilibrium in the soluble pools in pig and monkey kidney cells in culture following X-irradiation is probably important as an explanation for the different responses in these cells. In pig cells, H^3-thymidine incorporation into DNA was depressed after irradiation, but it was stimulated in monkey cells.[316] The two cells, however, differed in their ploidy. The pig cells were diploid and more radiosensitive than the monkey cells, which were subtetraploid.

The per cent distribution of thymidine and its nucleotides in the acid-soluble fraction of ascites cells was found unaltered after X-irradiation with 10,000 r.[76] Also, the activity of the isolated kinases was not changed. Hence, the decreased uptake of H[3]-thymidine into DNA of the irradiated cells was held to be caused by inhibition of the incorporation of thymidine triphosphate into DNA. The same conclusion was reached by analyzing data on the soluble pool constituents of irradiated mouse cells with the help of Quastler's four factor model.[311]

Infection may likewise significantly alter pool sizes, as Newton and co-workers observed.[223] Concomitantly with the increase of the amount of acid-soluble nucleotides in HeLa cells after infection with vaccinia virus, H[3]-thymidine incorporation into DNA fell significantly. A measurement of the DNA content of the cells, however, showed that the depressed incorporation of H[3]-thymidine did not reflect an inhibition of DNA synthesis. On the other hand, cells of infectious mononucleosis incorporated more H[3]-thymidine into DNA[116] than did normal monocytic elements circulating in the peripheral blood.[24]

It should be considered that certain viruses may induce thymidine kinase and deoxythymidylate synthetase (transmethylation) in animal cells, as was shown for vaccinia virus, herpes simplex virus, and polyomavirus in a variety of cell lines in culture.[99] Various unusual ribonucleotide distributions were found in cells of acute myoblastic and chronic myelocytic leukemia; especially uridine diphosphoglucose and uridine diphosphoacetylglucosamine levels were elevated.[220]

Differences in the rate of incorporation into DNA of H[3]-thymidine and H[3]-deoxyuridine in red cell precursors in patients with megaloblastic anemia gave supporting evidence that the methylation of deoxyuridine phosphate to thymidine phosphate was inhibited or blocked in the diseased cells.[162] Indeed, it could be demonstrated by Killmann[163] that continuous infusion of thymidine caused a marked proliferative response in the red cell precursors. It was suggested that thymidine deficiency in man may result from a deficiency of vitamin B_{12}.

Alterations in RNA metabolism with concomitant shifts in the equilibrium of the small precursors are at least partly the explanation of the effect of sulfhydryl groups on the cellular incorporation of various nucleosides and on morphogenesis.[33-35,255] An amount of 20–30 μg/ml of medium of β-mercaptoethanol and α-lipoic acid caused an increased incorporation of H[3]-thymidine into DNA and of H[3]-cytidine and H[3]-uridine into RNA in chick embryos. However, the latter two nucleosides were less well incorporated into DNA in the presence of lipoic acid, while mercaptoethanol enhanced the incorporation. Indeed, blockage of sulfhydryl groups in intact rats and various separate cell systems led to an inhibition of the reduction of uridine to deoxyuridine.[77] Moreover, *in vitro* studies indicated that reduced lipoic acid was a requirement in the reduction of uridine diphosphate to deoxyuridine diphosphate and of cytidine diphosphate to deoxycytidine diphosphate.[15,184] Furthermore, the effect of lipoic acid on morphogenesis was enhanced in the presence of lithium.[284]

A great number of antibiotics affect nucleic acid and protein synthesis, and the interaction is not always specific. A concomitant array of interrelated metabolic alterations should be expected as a result. Actinomycin, for instance, is widely used. Its action is explained not only by a depression of RNA synthesis on DNA by blocking DNA-guanine[125] but also it appears to have a degrading effect on cellular RNA[1] and to inhibit independently the synthesis of nuclear and cytoplasmic proteins.[141,275]

4.5. PRECURSOR INCORPORATION *in Vitro* VERSUS *in Vivo*

The chance of altering the delicate net of enzymatic reactions in the soluble pool must be considered in tracer studies when cells are moved from one environment to another, as from their physiological environment in an intact organism to an artificial culture medium. The question must be asked: To what degree is the equilibrium in the soluble pool of precursors affected under these conditions, i.e., *in vitro*? Cell lines established in culture conditions and which have resumed a steady and reproducible growth pattern will not be considered here. For such cell lines, the culture condition has become an acquired physiological environment, controlled changes of which allow, however, precise correlation to specific metabolic responses in these cells.

When somatic cells immediately after removal from their physiological environment are incubated in the testtube in a suitable medium with labeled nucleosides or amino acids, they appear to function for a limited period of time as well as they can be observed to do *in vivo*. For example, cells from a mammary tumor still incorporated H[3]-thymidine into DNA *in vitro* even after storage in saline at 5°C for 18 hours.[154] The *in vitro* tracer technique has thus become very helpful and convenient for the study of cellular metabolism. Tissue slices, likewise, are commonly used for an array of enzymatic investigations, some of which may serve to label biosynthetically organic compounds (see Chapter 2). One particular advantage of the *in vitro* tracer technique is the possibility of using high concentrations of labeled substances which could not be administered to an intact organism without running the risk of causing toxic effects.

Figure 5.4 illustrates the incorporation *in vitro* of H[3]-cytidine by cells of canine bone marrow for various lengths of time immediately after

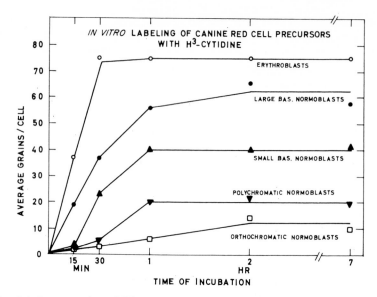

F IG. 5.4. Incorporation of H³-cytidine in the red cell precursors of dog bone marrow, with increasing exposure times under *in vitro* conditions, at 37°C; EDTA was
added to prevent clotting.

aspiration into saline containing EDTA to prevent clotting. The autoradiographic data show a lower grain count with progressing maturity
of the cells. The incorporation of the tracer continued linearly with
time up to about 40 minutes; then further incorporation stopped. The
distribution of label observed autoradiographically is practically identical to the one seen after injection of the precursor in the intact animal. The situation is similar for H³-thymidine *in vivo* and *in vitro*.

Also with H³-thymidine, incorporation ceases after about 40 minutes
of incubation, as demonstrated in ascites tumor cells[75] and normal and
leukemic hemopoietic tissue.[280,346] Addition of more labeled thymidine
led to renewed uptake in leukemic cells.[346] The cessation of precursor
incorporation is probably not only the result of exhaustion of tracer in
the medium, but is also likely caused by alterations in the soluble pool.
This is inferred from Table 5.2. Rat bone marrow was analyzed for
total RNA, DNA, and acid-soluble nucleotides immediately or after
various treatments following collection from the animal. The results are
expressed in ratios of the various fractions. Invariably the relative
amount of RNA and acid-soluble nucleotides per total cell population
fell below the value obtained when the marrow was collected directly
in ice-cold perchloric acid, indicative of increased RNA catabolism. The
relative amount of acid-soluble nucleotides after 1-hour incubation was

TABLE 5.2

RELATIVE CONTENT OF RNA, DNA, AND ACID–SOLUBLE NUCLEOTIDES (sRNA) IN
BONE-MARROW CELLS *in Vitro* WITH VARIOUS TREATMENTS INDICATIVE
OF RNA CATABOLISM[a]

Experimental conditions	RNA-P/ DNA-P	sRNA-P/ DNA-P	(sRNA-P + RNA-P)/DNA-P	sRNA-P/ RNA-P
Control cells, collected in ice cold 2%	0.409	0.159	0.569	0.388
perchloric acid	0.472	0.204	0.678	0.432
Cells collected and washed in:				
(a) Buffered saline at room tempera-	0.231	0.105	0.337	0.457
ture	0.252	0.101	0.354	0.399
(b) Buffered saline in ice bath	0.197	0.086	0.284	0.438
	0.191	0.073	0.264	0.383
(c) Serum at room temperature	0.188	0.077	0.266	0.412
	0.168	0.080	0.244	0.495
Cells collected and incubated in serum- buffered saline (1:1) for 1 hour at 37°C	0.139	0.116	0.256	0.837

[a] Expressed in terms of nucleotide phosphorus. Bone marrow of female rats.

greatly increased. In a detailed investigation of the thymidine metabolism
in vitro, Rubini and collaborators,[280] however, indicated that the thymidine pool—for example, in leukemic cells—may remain small. The labeling intensity of the cells failed to rise when the amount of thymidine
added exceeded about 0.5×10^{-3} μmole, perhaps also due to some dilution
effect. In a subsequent study, Rubini et al.[282] held the alkaline phosphatase to be at least partly responsible for the cessation of thymidine
incorporation by the cells *in vitro* after the first hour of incubation.
Since this enzyme is active optimally at an alkaline pH dephosphorylat-
ing thymidine monophosphate, it was proposed that it served a regulatory function in controlling DNA synthesis, depending on intracellular
pH changes. Another enzyme in the reaction chain of thymidine catabolism, phosphorylase, which splits the N-deoxyribosidic linkage to yield
the free thymine base and deoxyribose, was indicated as playing an
important role in regulating thymidine incorporation by cells. Normal
leukocytes rich in phosphorylase were demonstrated to release this
enzyme into the incubation medium under *in vitro* condition. Leukemic
cells low in this enzyme incorporated H^3-thymidine less readily when
normal leukocytes or cell-free medium of normal leukocytes was
added.[199,244] It was also shown in these studies that leukocytes from
patients with myelocytic leukemia in remission appeared to release a
factor which stimulated H^3-thymidine incorporation *in vitro* by leukemic
cells from patients in relapse of the disease. It is speculative to argue

whether an inhibitor was neutralized here. Various mechanisms appear, therefore, to operate in different cells under *in vitro* conditions, which perhaps are less effective in the physiological environment.

Bullough[47] has shown, also *in vitro*, the presence in skin cells of a mitotic inhibitor, which he termed chalone and which is activated by adrenaline. This important finding may well explain a variety of homeostatic adaptations operating *in vivo* basically in all cell systems, each having its specific type of chalone. This system would easily respond to changes in stress which is known to be accompanied by changes in the adrenaline output.

The presence of similar or other inhibiting factors or lack of stimulating factors in the extracellular environment, in addition to changes in the intracellular enzyme system, may be considered as an explanation for the failure of explanted guinea pig epidermis in culture to show an increase in the number of DNA-synthesizing cells upon injury, as observed in the intact skin *in vivo*.[139] Differentiating tissue, such as the embryonic lens, depends on specific factors for allowing growth and development to proceed *in vitro* as it does normally *in vivo*. At least a small amount of protein seemed necessary for some growth of the lens and its fiber formation, which could, however, also not be supported by transplantation into the coelomic cavity.[247]

The exact appraisal of which mechanism or compound is decisive in altering metabolic functions *in vitro* may perhaps best be approached by determining the substrates and the activity of isolated enzymes of the appropriate tissue after its exposure to the *in vitro* condition of the experiment. This approach proved useful, for example, in radiobiology. Thus none of the agents established to depress DNA synthesis in intact *E. coli*, such as chloramphenicol, amino acid deficiency, or X-irradiation, caused a loss of the activity of the isolated enzymes participating in DNA synthesis in these cells,[19] similar to findings in irradiated ascites tumor cells.[76] Obviously, the various treatments did not act directly on the intracellular level of these enzymes, but specific inhibitors in the cells were not excluded. Moreover, isolated DNA from regenerating rat liver after whole-body irradiation retained its function as template unaltered, but the isolated nuclei and the organ *in situ* incorporated less H^3-thymidine than the nonirradiated controls.[186] The importance of the cellular environment is also shown by the fact that cells may be less radiosensitive *in vitro* than *in vivo* with regard to H^3-thymidine incorporation into DNA, as exemplified for mouse spleen cells by Huntley and Lajtha.[149] In this context the reader is also referred to the critical review by Kelly.[156]

It must also be mentioned that in tracer studies *in vitro* the labeled molecule itself may trigger secondary alterations in the extracellular environment. For example, Rubini and co-workers[280] observed that H^3-thymidine added to normal bone-marrow cells *in vitro* generated a factor in the supernatant medium which depressed incorporation of still available tracer in a new cell batch. This inhibitory factor was not observed in identical experiments in which, however, the H^3-thymidine was omitted from the first cell batch, but was added to the second sample together with the used medium. It seems unlikely that an effect from tritium (2–5 $\mu c/ml$) on the cells or the constituents of the medium was responsible for the inhibition to become active. Still, irradiation of culture medium with 500-r X-rays at a rate of 100 r per minute was claimed to cause a depression of H^3-thymidine incorporation by embryonic calf liver cells upon subsequent incubation for as long as 4 hours.[175] A dose of 12,000 r to culture medium for *E. coli* depressed the incorporation of labeled uracil, thymidine, proline, and valine, likely caused by toxic levels of peroxides.[256]

4.6. Conclusions

Interdependent control mechanisms have become known for many other enzymatic reaction chains and cannot be discussed here. The problem of biochemical control of cellular function is in the center of wide interest, and the knowledge of these fundamental mechanisms is growing rapidly. With respect to precursor incorporation into macromolecules under various experimental conditions, it is re-emphasized that interconversions and metabolic fate of a tracer in living cells may vary greatly in a sensitive response to practically any treatment. This must be therefore always controlled rigidly.

5. Renewal of Macromolecules

The morphological and functional characteristics of a cell are determined by macromolecular constituents, including proteins, carbohydrates, lipids, and their various conjugates, all of which are ultimately controlled by the nucleic acids, which are themselves macromolecules. The rate of metabolic renewal, interconversion, or rearrangement of the various macromolecules governed by respective enzyme systems is often the primary information desired in tracer studies. For cytochemical experiments, precursors labeled with tritium are preferred since they allow best a rather precise localization of the tracer within subcellular structures by the autoradiographic technique.

Single cell studies are in many instances necessary to interpret properly biochemical data on entire cell populations. Thus, the rate of renewal of RNA fractions in a large cell population, as measured by biochemical techniques, is not necessarily identical to the renewal rate in any single cell in that population.[107] Furthermore, erroneous conclusions may be drawn if the birth and death rate of the cells in a population is not considered. Thus, RNA may be entirely preserved in the single cells, but when in a population cells divide rapidly, leave, or die, and are steadily replaced by new cell generations, biochemical tracer analyses on the whole population in the absence of reutilization could result in turnover curves which do not reflect true RNA turnover but the rate of cell renewal. DNA is generally considered to be stable, as will be discussed further below, and is not synthesized in the cells continuously, but only during a fraction of the cell-generation cycle. Hence, only a portion of cells in a population becomes labeled with an appropriate precursor such as H^3-thymidine at any given time. Biochemical analysis can thus measure the renewal rate of cells if reutilization from dead cells is excluded, but only of those cells which incorporated the precursor. No statement would be permissible with regard to renewal of all cells in the population examined.[291] Finally, it is to be considered that renewal of macromolecular constituents may change during various phases of the cell cycle and in response to alterations of the extracellular environment influencing the cell's proliferative activity, as demonstrated, for example, in fission yeast messenger RNA.[210] As a general rule, those cells proliferating most rapidly conserve macromolecules best.[96,100,101,159,165] Cell renewal in populations will be considered again in a later section of this chapter.

It does not fall within the scope of this monograph to discuss in detail the renewal rates within single cells of the various macromolecular constituents, but the reader is referred to the appropriate reviews and some references listed at the end of the book. It should be emphasized, however, that various cell types differ greatly. A few general observations will be pointed out here, not at least in order to appraise properly the possible toxicity of the radiation from tritium incorporated with various precursors (see Chapter 6). Since the physical half-life of tritium is about 12 years, it is usually the turnover rate of the carrier molecule at a certain intracellular site which determines the accumulated radiation dose from the isotope.

Owing to the short range of the β-radiation from tritium, it is further important to consider that a tritiated compound may change its position within a given cell from a region of high radiosensitivity to one less radiosensitive or vice versa. Thus, tritium bound to RNA nucleotides in a cell may deliver radiation first to the sensitive nucleus where RNA is most rapidly synthesized, and subsequently it may irradiate the less sensitive cytoplasm to which the RNA migrates after its synthesis in the nucleus. Other tritium bound to RNA nucleotides may be incorporated after precursor conversion into DNA where it becomes fixed "permanently." Differences in radiosensitivity of nucleus and cytoplasm have been evaluated by using tritiated RNA precursors.[198] It must also be considered that labeled breakdown products from macromolecules may re-enter the metabolic cycle by reutilization. If a labeled compound turns over rapidly in a cell or part of a cell and if a sizable portion of the catabolites are reutilized, the net dilution of the isotope at a given site in the cell is not determined by the rapid turnover and new synthesis but by the degree of reutilization. Problems of reutilization are discussed in Section 6.

5.1. H³-THYMIDINE BOUND TO DNA

The foregoing remarks are of particular importance with regard to tritiated nucleic acid precursors since they are not only widely used but also have unusually high specific activities and accumulate especially in the radiosensitive nucleus of the cell. In this context it is appropriate to discuss briefly the case of DNA labeled with H³-thymidine.

The site of H³-thymidine incorporation into DNA can be localized by autoradiography in the chromosomes of cells in mitosis,[318] even in single DNA molecules.[49-51] Cytoplasmic DNA synthesis has also been recognized and will be considered later in this section.

The localization of H³-thymidine in the DNA of chromosomes allowed a study of chromosome duplication. The mode of chromosomal duplication in plants and animal cells, as proposed by Taylor et al.[318] has now been confirmed for various cell types, and it proceeds in a "semiconservative" manner. This is schematically shown in Fig. 5.5. Semiconservative replication means that one newly synthesized chromatid strand together with an old one (the "template" for the new) make up a new chromosome after DNA synthesis. In contrast, conservative replication would mean that the old parts of a chromosome remain together as the newly formed chromatid strands join to become the duplicated chromosome. Semiconservative appears to be the pattern also in bacterial chromosome segregation.[203,235] In the single chromosome of *E. coli*, autoradiography further demonstrated that DNA replication begins from one growing point, as illustrated in Fig. 5.6. It was possible in chaser experiments to estimate the amount of DNA produced per minute in *E. coli* by this technique.[50]

Examination of the label distribution in the mitotic chromosomes of many different cell types at various times after a short exposure to tritiated thymidine revealed considerable asynchrony of incorporation

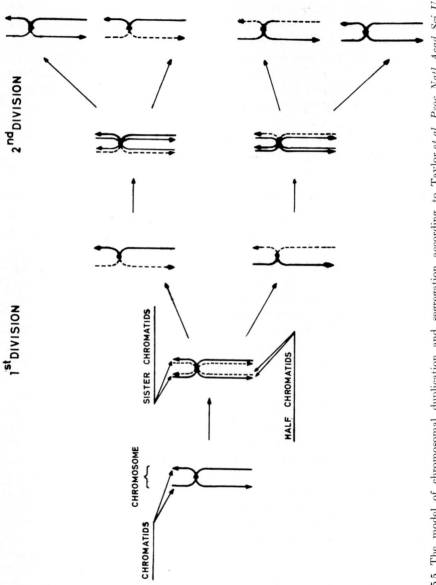

Fig. 5.5. The model of chromosomal duplication and segregation according to Taylor *et al.*, *Proc. Natl. Acad. Sci. U.S.*[318]

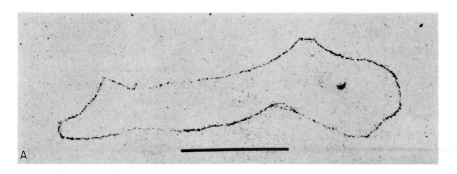

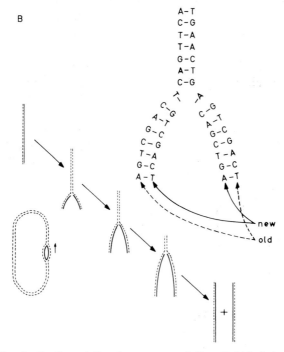

FIG. 5.6. The duplication of the chromosome of *E. coli*. (A) Autoradiogram of a single chromosome during duplication, in ring form; (B) Schematic interpretation. Courtesy of Cairns, *Endeavour*.[51]

during the phase of DNA synthesis. While at a given time of the DNA synthesis phase some chromosomes densely incorporated the tracer in limited areas, other chromosomes or part of them were entirely devoid of label. The changing patterns of chromosomal labeling at various stages of the DNA synthesis period in normal and malignant cells is just beginning to be understood in terms of nonuniformity of DNA replication with genetic implications (for references see supplementary list at the end of the volume). Some caution is necessary in interpreting these results since the concentration of tritium in chromosomes necessary for autoradiographic observations may have caused considerable radiation effects. With low dose levels of the H[3]-thymidine, however, these effects do not become manifest at the time of observation (see Chapter 6). Colchicine is often used to increase the number of cells in mitosis for scoring and could perhaps affect the labeling. Peacock[240] indicated, however, that colchicine treatment did not influence DNA replication, segregation, or the prospect of sister chromatid exchanges. The asynchrony of chromosomal replication has been confirmed also by biochemical analysis during sequential DNA synthesis. The sequences remained the same in consecutive phases of the DNA synthesis of subsequent cell cycles.[37]

Once incorporated, the tracer appears to remain bound to the DNA practically throughout the lifespan of a proliferating cell and its progeny, among which it is distributed with every cell division. This would indicate that the DNA is metabolically stable. This was also demonstrated in mice which had received *in utero* a thymidine analog, 5-iododeoxyuridine labeled with I[125]. After the age of 2 months and throughout adulthood, the animals lost little label.[67] These data confirm those of Leblond *et al.*[185] who classified three groups of cells according to the constancy of their labeling indices after a single injection of H[3]-thymidine in young and adult rodents, as presented in Table 5.3. Thus, stable cell populations could be grouped separately from growing and renewing cell populations.

5.2. METABOLIC RENEWAL OF DNA

There is evidence, however, that in certain cells or tissue a part of the DNA turns over. Thus, in cultures of *Aerobacter aerogenes* in steady-state population, regression curves of labeled DNA indicated some turnover, perhaps due to nutrient influences from the culture medium.[68] Two forms of DNA with different molecular weights were examined in wheat plants[288]; the DNA was obtained by the detergent method and chromatographed on a methylated albumin column. The low molecular weight DNA was characterized by a relatively rapid rate of turnover, and it was said to constitute as much as 20% of the total DNA of the growing regions, whereas it was negligible in resting tissue. Dormant embryos in the wheat seed had about 10% of their DNA in the low molecular weight form, and this amount rose upon induction of germination.[288] In germinating seeds of the peanut, where cells do not divide,

TABLE 5.3

STABLE CELL POPULATIONS, GROWING CELL POPULATIONS, AND RENEWING CELL POPULATIONS DETERMINED IN FORMATION AND RETENTION TESTS[a]

Cells evaluated	Labeled nuclei (%)	
	Cell formation test[c]	Cell retention test[b]
Group I. Stable cell populations		
Muscle		
Striped	0	2.2
Smooth	0	5.3
Cardiac	0.2	2.6
Cerebrum, middle-sized neurons	0	4.4
Group II. Growing cell populations		
Kidney, proximal convoluted tubule cells	0.4	0.4
Liver, parenchymal cells	0.2	3.1
Pancreas		
Acinar cells	0.5	0.4
Islet cells	0.1	3.1
Thyroid, epithelial cells	0.6	2.9
Adrenal		
Cortical cells	0.8	0.5
Medullary cells	0.2	4.3
Group III. Renewing cell populations		
Lower surface of tongue, Malpighian cells of epithelium	1.6	0
Ventral skin, Malpighian cells of epidermis	2.0	0
Thymus, cortical cells	6.7	0
Colon, epithelial cells	5.2	0
Ventral skin, connective tissue cells of derma	1.4	0.6

[a] Reproduced with permission of Leblond et al., Lab. Invest.[185]

[b] Rats receiving H^3-thymidine when 3 days old and sacrificed 6 months later.

[c] Adult mice given H^3-thymidine injection and sacrificed 8 hours later.

a labile DNA portion was observed to be associated with RNA.[61] In yeast, labilization of DNA occurred with the onset of stationary growth.[292]

Comparing the specific activities of DNA and the acid-soluble fraction and the corresponding labeling indices in autoradiograms in livers of normal mice and after hepatectomy, over a period of about 3 months after a single injection of H^3-thymidine, Devik and Halvorsen[89] concluded that the DNA in normal liver may not all be stable. In nondividing tissue of mammals evidence of metabolic renewal of a part of DNA was also presented with the finding of H^3-thymidine incorporation by those groups of cells in which mitosis is absent or a rare event.[241,242] Similar findings were reported specifically for osteoblasts.[234]

Still, a comparison of mitotic indices and labeling indices in various tissues of the rat and mouse[294] and, for example, in the bone marrow of dogs and humans[180] showed insufficient deviation to warrant a generalization of metabolic renewal of DNA in higher developed cells. It should be mentioned that DNA turnover could be induced in nematodes by cold treatment.[226]

The mechanism by which DNA may partially renew is obscure. It may perhaps involve also cytoplasmic DNA (see below). But it should be recalled that DNA repair certainly exists in microorganisms. Thus, ultraviolet light irradiation of bacteria causes the formation of thymine dimers,[298] and various other pyrimidine dimers are also principally possible.[299] These can be repaired by excision and replacement.[32,246] Thymine dimer formation was also observed in Chinese hamster cells,[326] but no excision occurred here. DNA-repair processes appear to be responsible also for the finding in the grasshopper neuroblast, where after X-irradiation H³-thymidine was incorporated at a stage of the cell cycle outside the phase of normal DNA synthesis.[192,193] In *tetrahymena*, ultraviolet irradiation caused the synthesis of excess DNA, which was eliminated during subsequent cell cycles until normal level was reached.[301]

5.3. CYTOPLASMIC LABELING FROM H³-THYMIDINE

Cytoplasmic labeling of cells has been observed repeatedly after H³-thymidine incorporation, but was not always consistent in autoradiograms partially because the degree of the observed cytoplasmic labeling was small compared to the labeling intensity in the nucleus. The reason for this cytoplasmic labeling in various cell types[86] was held by some investigators to be due to incorporation of radiochemical[123] or metabolic decomposition products of H³-thymidine.[317] X-Irradiation caused an increase of cytoplasmic labeling in cells of the bean root[146] which were exposed to H³-thymidine while being irradiated. This cytoplasmic tritium was resistant to acid hydrolysis (1 N TCA, 60°C). There was no detection of a concomitant increase in the rate of DNA synthesis. Delayed cytoplasmic labeling from H³-thymidine was found in *Tetrahymena pyriformis* when the cells were deprived of essential amino acids after DNA synthesis had started.[314]

It has now been firmly established that in a variety of cells the cytoplasm contains DNA. Thus, in eggs of *Drosophila*,[224] *Asellus aquaticus*,[176] and amphibia[36] H³-thymidine incorporation or specific binding of actinomycin[36] indicated the presence of DNA. Chloroplasts in algae are known to contain DNA which may replicate as indicated by H³-thymidine incorporation.[150,312,337] Chloroplast DNA could be isolated, and its base ratio[95,166] and its molecular weight[95,270] were determined to be distinct from mitochondrial DNA. Mitochondrial DNA has been detected in a large number of cells[10,45,62,217,221,310,344] and was described as being distinct in molecular weight and base ratio from nuclear DNA in animal cells.[267] Moreover, chloroplast and mitochondrial DNA likely have genetic functions.[122,285] In *Amoeba proteus*, DNA-synthesizing particles were demonstrated to operate also in the absence of the cell nucleus[254] and to be correlated with age, size, and nutrition of the cells.[266]

6. Reutilization of Catabolites of DNA

The question of what happens to the DNA of those cells that die has received increasing attention during recent years. From a number of laboratories there is now evidence that at least one of the DNA catabolites, namely, thymidine or its nucleotide, is released from the cells for recirculation and reincorporation into DNA[90,277] (for further references see supplementary list at the end of the volume). Since the liver is the main site of thymidine catabolism,[261] the thymidine or its nucleotides which are reutilized escapes catabolism in the liver. Thymidine re-enters cells probably close to the site of DNA breakdown. It was also shown that thymidine may be transported from the site of DNA breakdown in rapidly dividing tissue or necrotizing liver to distant organs for reutilization.[40,41] From the work of various laboratories[41,42,108,200,278] it is suggested that the thymidine as a nucleoside and not in a phosphorylated form is the major catabolite. Other pathways of thymidine reutilization are, however, not excluded. At any rate, it was demonstrated by double-labeling with C^{14}-thymidine that no kinetic isotope effect influenced the reutilization pathway of the tritium-labeled precursor.[108,121] Working with 5-iododeoxyuridine labeled with I^{131} or I^{125} as an analog of thymidine, Hughes *et al.*[148] identified iododeoxyuridine to be the main circulating radioactive catabolite during DNA turnover in mice labeled with the precursor. This was done by feeding the mice thymidine for 36 hours after injection of I^{131}-deoxyuridine. Subsequently, over half of the I^{131} appearing in the urine could be identified as being bound to deoxyuridine by cocrystallization with added carrier iododeoxyuridine.

The magnitude of thymidine reutilization can be estimated from data of parallel experiments with 5-iododeoxyuridine, which is less readily incorporated into DNA *in vivo* than thymidine[148] and which is therefore expectedly also less readily reutilized.[107] It was thus estimated that in rat bone-marrow cells, for example, about 40% of the tritium involved in DNA catabolism, or leaving the marrow with time after injection of H^3-thymidine, is replaced by labeled thymidine via reutilization as observed over a period of 11 days.[107,108] In the bone marrow, DNA becomes available when the red cell precursors lose their nuclei to become reticulocytes; at least some of the extruded nuclei from red cell precursors are phagocytized in the marrow.[70] If one compares the percentage reutilization with the relative number of most mature red cell precursors in the proliferating marrow cell population, it is suggested that by far most, if not all, thymidine for reutilization in the marrow stems from DNA breakdown in the marrow.

It appeared from studies with cells in culture (L strain fibroblasts) that phagocytized nuclei or DNA particles were completely digested and hydrolyzed to small nucleotides[12,126] before being reutilized for DNA synthesis.[142] Similar conclusions were drawn from experiments in mice which were injected with heterologous DNA.[331] Regardless of whether the injection was intravenous or intraperitoneal, the DNA was apparently also degraded already before it could reach cells.[127] DNA in ring form, such as that of polyoma virus, appeared to be digested after injection less readily than linear DNA, such as pneumococcal transforming DNA.[11]

Little is known as to whether nucleotide chains may exchange as such between cells *in vivo*. Evidence that this can happen *in vitro* has been put forward repeatedly, and it is of particular interest in the question of transfer of genetic information. For instance, when RNA from liver was added to mouse ascites tumor cells, glucose-6-phosphatase in the latter increased nearly twofold.[225] The difficulty of observing such an effect *in vivo* is probably due also to the great dilution a genetically active nucleotide is subjected to in the intact animal.[343]

Since cells catabolizing DNA usually do not utilize it for new synthesis, it is clear that *in vivo* a circulating thymidine pool serves as a physiological precursor for DNA as a major salvage pathway. Since the intracellular thymidine pool is small and since labeled thymidine as an injected tracer is readily incorporated by the cells and concentrated in the DNA, the amount of circulating precursor in equilibrium with the soluble pool of cells must be correspondingly small. It has been estimated to contain only about 0.05 μmole of thymidine in the mouse,[148] e.g., 0.6 μg per gram of body weight at average. However, the total amount of acid-soluble thymidine derivatives, for instance, in spleen cells was about 2.4 μg per gram of tissue.[263]

Other nucleosides besides thymidine and nucleotides from RNA may be transported with blood cells to distant tissue or may be released from cells and may be reincorporated and also partially converted to precursors for DNA, as exemplified in rat bone marrow.[107] The rate of RNA renewal and subsequently the degree of reutilization of RNA label exceeded that observed for DNA, partly due to an increased loss of

RNA from progressively maturing cells, as was also observed in rabbit bone marrow.[130]

Reutilization of amino acids and consequently a delayed availability after single injection is a well-known phenomenon also.[300] The degree of reutilization could be measured in autoradiograms because of a trailing of radioactivity during apposition of metabolically stable labeled collagen in the bone matrix[325] or likewise during keratin formation of the growing hair.[304]

Reutilization of the tracer should be expected to occur particularly in rapidly proliferating tissue, and it seriously affects the calculation of turnover rates, unless it is properly corrected. This is true for chemical analyses of whole cell populations and for single cell studies by autoradiography. Thus, in the bone marrow, the number of DNA-labeled cells within a morphological group of the dividing cell population is known to rise to a certain extent following a single injection of H³-thymidine.[79] This is illustrated in Fig. 5.7 which shows the labeling indices of megakaryocytes in rat bone marrow increasing with time to about 100% following a single injection of H³-thymidine.[105] Similar data were obtained by Ebbe and Stohlman.[93] The rise in labeled cells may reflect a long DNA-synthesis phase of the immature precursor cells, which are morphologically not recognized but feed into the maturing cell population; or it may also be due to a prolonged availability of labeled precursors via the reutilization pathway. The latter was shown to be the proper explanation.[93,108] It is clear that owing to reutilization over an extended period of observation the turnover rate of labeled DNA in the maturing cell population may appear unduly prolonged. It must also be considered that the magnitude of the reutilization pathway may change with any alteration of birth and death rate of the cells. As Hughes *et al.*[148] have pointed out, a precursor poorly utilized (such as 5-iododeoxyuridine) will be poorly reutilized and thus is preferable in studies on DNA renewal, whether by chemical or autoradiographic techniques.[107,108]

7. Cellular Proliferation

The labeled DNA located in the chromosomes is distributed equally with every cell division between the two daughter cells, according to the model of chromosomal replication by Taylor and collaborators,[318] as schematically shown in Fig. 5.5. This also means that the radiation dose from the β-particles of tritium diminishes by one-half per cell with each cell division. Theoretical aspects of the labeling intensities to be expected following repeated cell divisions were discussed by Cronkite and collaborators.[80] When, for the sake of discussion, re-

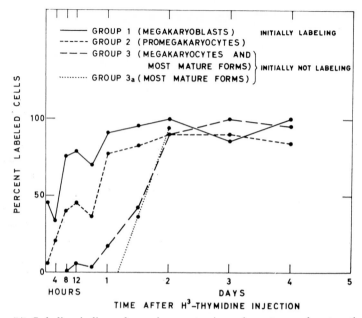

Fig. 5.7. Labeling indices of megakaryocytes in various stages of maturation, as a function of time after a single injection of H³-thymidine in rats. Only the most immature megakaryocytes incorporate the tracer at the time of injection. The rising labeling indices indicate the arrival of labeled precursor cells morphologically not recognized at the subsequent maturing stages of megakaryocytic development. Courtesy of Feinendegen et al., Proc. Soc. Exptl. Biol. Med.[105]

utilization and crossing-over of chromatids were not considered, the reduction of the labeling intensity through cell division would be exponential as long as the progeny of a cell did not exceed the number of chromosomes, since eventually cells would contain one labeled chromosome or none.

The existence of a finite DNA-synthesis time within a cell-generation cycle between two mitoses was first recognized by Howard and Pelc[145] and Lajtha et al.,[179] and the following intervals were designated: S = period or phase of DNA synthesis; R_1 or G_1 = postmitotic "rest" period (with regard to the period of DNA synthesis); R_2 or G_2 = premitotic "rest" period; M = mitosis. This is schematically indicated in Fig. 5.8. In order to allow for the accumulated knowledge in cell function, Bullough[46, 48] has extended the number of recognizable phases to 6—consisting of mitosis, followed by the apophase, during which the cell reconstitutes following division, followed by the dichophase, during which a cell is susceptible to regulating factors such as inhibitors and inducers which determine specific cell function or cell division. After this, pro-

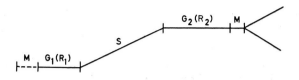

M   = MITOSIS
$G_1(R_1)$ = POSTMITOTIC REST PERIOD
S   = PERIOD OF DNA SYNTHESIS
$G_2(R_2)$ = PREMITOTIC RESTPERIOD

FIG. 5.8. Scheme of the cell cycle (generation cycle).

phase follows in preparation for cell division. The prophase again was divided into early prophase, during which the enzymes necessary for cell division are first synthesized, then into the DNA synthesis phase, and finally the antephase immediately prior to mitosis. Thus, antephase is synonymous with the G_2 phase, but apophase, dichophase, and early prophase together are equivalent to G_1. In order to avoid misunderstandings it is perhaps desirable to substitute the term early prophase by another expression such as pre-S phase. The duration of these various stages, in particular that of the S period, has been extensively investigated by the autoradiographic technique in many different cell types, and a new understanding of the kinetics of proliferating cell populations has emerged.

In an intact organism different groups of cells have different rates of division. There are several ways to identify such groups. One is to check for the occurrence and frequency of mitosis in a population. A more versatile technique has been introduced with H^3-thymidine, which, as discussed above, is specifically incorporated into DNA of cells prior to division.[147] Thus, with the help of H^3-thymidine, Leblond et al.[185] identified three groups of cells in rodents (see Table 5.3): (1) stable cell populations, (2) growing cell populations, and 3) renewing cell populations.

7.1. PRINCIPLE METHODS OF MEASURING THE KINETICS OF CELLULAR PROLIFERATION

In most instances, cells in a tissue do not mature or divide synchronously. In case of the steady state under physiological conditions, the number of cells leaving the tissue or those which die is equal to the number of cells entering by migration or cell division. Furthermore, if single cells of a specific generation are randomly spaced in time through the cell cycle, that fraction of the cells found at any part of the cycle (for example, mitosis) will be constant and equal to the fraction of time the particular cells spend in that part of the cycle.

Since labeled thymidine is incorporated into dividing cells only during the period of DNA synthesis, the labeling index within a group of comparable cells in autoradiograms can be used to calculate the DNA-synthesis time if the generation time of the cells in the particular group is known; or if the DNA-synthesis time is known, the generation time of the appropriate cells can be determined from the labeling index.

Similarly, the number of mitoses in a comparable cell population (mitotic index) depends both on the duration of the generation cycle and the mitotic event. The mitotic index can be adequate for calculating the generation time only if the duration of the mitotic event is known. The latter can be found also with the help of H^3-thymidine.

Ascertaining properly labeling indices and mitotic indices in a mixed cell population depends on precisely recognizing and correlating on a morphological basis the series or class to which a labeled cell or a mitosis belongs. Such classification in a cytological preparation is usually very difficult or even impossible to do with certainty in a diverse cell population such as the bone marrow, for example. Thus, cells prior to and after mitosis may look so much alike that on morphological grounds a difference in the generation of these cells is not recognizable.[160,161] Moreover, it is not always certain that all cells morphologically alike within a group proliferate with common time parameters.

To minimize the number of assumptions necessary to interpret kinetic data on cell proliferation it is best to evaluate only those cells which can be clearly identified by morphological and functional characteristics.

One approach is to select a particular type of cell in mitosis and to observe, following a short exposure to H^3-thymidine, the arrival and passage through the stages of mitosis of those cells which incorporated the tracer during the preceding period of DNA synthesis.[26,38, 52,53,78,81,84,111,112,173,188,201,228,265,273] Frequent sampling of the specimen is necessary to determine the time interval after H^3-thymidine labeling until the first labeled cells enter division, until all cells in mitosis show label, until nonlabeled cells again begin to arrive at mitosis, and so forth. To use an analogy, the mitotic event is a narrow window through which the passage of the cohorts of maturing cells labeled or unlabeled is observed, much as one may observe the various formations in a moving parade through a narrow gate. Since the mitotic event is much briefer (about 30–60 minutes) than the time required for DNA synthesis, and since the cells spend at an average nearly the same amount of time in the premitotic "rest" period, the duration of DNA synthesis can be determined from the time it takes for the cohort of labeled cells to pass through the stage of mitosis. Still, variations in the kinetic time parameters of the individual cells already lead to a considerable degree of straggling within the group of labeled cells within the duration of one cell cycle, so that after several cycles the fraction of labeled cells in mitosis becomes equal to the fraction of labeled cells in interphase.[202,265] The interpretation of the curve of the per cent labeled mitoses versus time after labeling with H^3-thymidine has been aided by the use of planimetric integration.[38,265]

The duration of the mitotic event from prophase to telophase may be measured likewise by establishing the time it takes for the cohort of labeled cells to enter into the consecutive mitotic stages, as exemplified by the work of Odartchenko et al.[229] in dog bone marrow in vivo.

Another method of establishing the DNA-synthesis time uses the double-marker technique. Thus, thymidine labeled with tritium or C^{14} is administered sequentially at a given time interval.[7,39,181,249,336] Since the two isotopes can be distinguished autoradiographically, the differences in the labeling indices obtained with H^3-thymidine alone and with H^3-thymidine plus C^{14}-thymidine allows the calculation of the rate of entrance of cells into the DNA-synthesis period, the rate of exit for any appropriate cell type, and subsequently the rate at which the cells arrive at mitosis.[29]

In another approach, colchicine or its derivatives are administered after injection of the tracer to prevent cells from leaving mitosis (metaphase), so that over a period of several hours the number of mitoses in a given population rises. The influx of cells into the stage of mitosis can then be used to calculate the corresponding proliferation rates.[14]

If the metaphase block caused by a low dose of colchicine is overcome, the mitosis one generation time later may show polyploidy. The appearance of polyploid mitotic figures thus may serve another parameter in parallel to the labeling indices from H^3-thymidine to define sequences in the cell cycle.[330]

These various modes of measurement have shown that the duration of the DNA-synthesis period is similar for many types of cells in a given species. In mammalian cells, this time parameter ranges most often around 6–9 hours. A mean value of 7.5 hours was found for 27 cell types of the mouse.[251] Only exceptionally have drastically different values been reported—for example, for cells of epidermis with about 30 hours,[251,303] for hepatoma cells with 17 hours,[259] and for alveolar cells of the mammary gland in mice with 20 hours.[39] An exceptionally short DNA-synthesis time of about 4–5 hours was found for the cells of germinal centers in rats[112] and for lymphocytes in the thoracic duct of calves.[73] Variations in the total cycle time appear to be due mainly to variations of the postmitotic rest period, as will be discussed further below. A relationship of the minimum generation time to the DNA content of a cell and its nuclear volume was described by Van't Hof and Sparrow.[329] Yet, a relation between DNA content of a cell and the respective DNA synthesis time was not observed in different strains of *Tetrahymena pyriformis*.[55]

Since in the steady state the number of cells leaving a population must equal the replacement by division or influx, important information may be gathered by simply measuring the rate of loss of labeled cells from the given population. This approach to cellular kinetics may not always be applicable, but in cases of blood cell formation the technique is indeed informative. Thus, to begin the analysis, cell types must be defined which do or can potentially incorporate labeled thymidine. These cells must be clearly distinguishable by morphological characteristics from those cells which do not incorporate the label because of their maturity, such as the orthochromatic normoblasts in the red cell series, the segmented neutrophilic granulocytes in the myelocytic cell series, the mature plasma cells, and the maturing forms of megakaryocytes. The influx of labeled cells into these groups of most mature and initially unlabeled cells, following a single or repeated administration of the tracer, reflects the exit rate of cells from the dividing cell population.[25,26,78,105,196,228] The proper evaluation of such exit rates of cells permits the recognition of pathologically altered cell renewal, for instance, after irradiation.[230]

For further information the reader should consult appropriate reviews and books dealing with cell proliferation in more detail.[8,13,27,48,182,313] In addition, there are a number of references on cell proliferation in the supplementary list at the end of this monograph.

8. Physiological Factors Controlling Cell Function and Proliferation

Cellular adaptations to environmental influences have been mentioned repeatedly in the preceding sections, and it was emphasized that metabolic functions within the range of a cell's capacity may alter with the phase of the cell cycle, with the rate of growth, and in response to changes in the physiological balance of enzyme substrate ratio. Extracellular factors which alter cell growth and cell function may act on cellular metabolism directly by enhancing or reducing reaction rates in an unspecific or specific manner. Other effects are elicited by stimulating, inducing, or inhibiting certain genetic characteristics. Various hypotheses have been offered to explain these reactions in a unifying view. The review by Bullough[48] tries to relate the many different observations on the control of cell proliferation and cell function to the theory that cells of any group contain a specific substance which inhibits the process of cell division in favor of letting the cell synthesize its specific functional protein in response to appropriate stimuli. The intracellular level of this substance, called a chalone, would thus act as a feedback inhibitor. Such a specific chalone has been demonstrated in the epidermis.[47] The mitotic inhibition was greatest in the presence of adrenaline acting as activator of the chalone. Even if the chalone in tissue other than the epidermis is hypothetical, the theory of its action is attractive for explaining homeostatic control in response to a variety of primarily unrelated events or agents, some of which will be mentioned briefly in this section.

8.1. DIURNAL FLUCTUATION

Diurnal rhythms (24-hour rhythms) in living systems are well known[4,140] and are particularly obvious in the case of photosynthetic activities in plants and algae containing chlorophyll. Fluctuations of cell proliferation occur in animals in a day-night rhythm and are apparently related to periodic stress situations.[46,48] The periodical variations in the number of mitoses in a cell population were complemented by the finding of a similar periodicity of H^3-thymidine incorporation, e.g., of DNA synthesis.[114] Pilgrim and co-workers[250,252] reported that the number of cells in DNA synthesis in various tissues of the mouse altered periodically as did the respective mitotic index. Some of the data are shown in Table 5.4. Cells with a low or very high proliferative rate, such as kidney cells or intestinal epithelial cells, respectively, did not show periodic fluctuations of the labeling index. This was also found for cells of the liver, the adrenal cortex, and for various cells of the rat fetus. Also various strains of ascites tumor cells failed to exhibit a 24-hour rhythm in DNA synthesis or mitotic activity. With regard to amino acid incorporation, there appeared to be a rhythm observed in isolated rat liver nuclei which were incubated *in vitro* with the precursor immediately after the animals were killed.[297]

It is obvious, therefore, that labeling indices in cell populations may lead to different interpretations of cellular function and kinetics depending on which time of day the tracer is administered or the sample collected for study.

8.2. VARIATIONS IN THE DURATION OF CELL-CYCLE PHASES

Fluctuations in the number of DNA-labeled cells in a population may indicate a partial synchrony in cell proliferation and not a true

TABLE 5.4

Diurnal Fluctuation of the Labeling Index (40 Minutes After H³-Thymidine Injection) and of the Mitotic Index in Various Tissues of Mice[a]

Tissue	Hour of day	Tritium index (%)	Mitotic index (%)	Grains per nucleus
Esophagus, bas. epith.	5.30	1.5	0.83	9.2
	11.30	1.0	0.14	9.5
	17.30	6.4	0.19	9.7
	23.30	3.7	0.14	9.5
Forestomach, bas. epith.	5.30	3.9	1.18	9.9
	11.30	3.0	0.38	9.5
	17.30	5.5	0.35	9.6
	23.30	3.8	0.42	9.6
Abdominal skin, epidermis	5.30	1.7	0.47	9.1
	11.30	1.0	0.18	9.5
	17.30	4.5	0.21	8.9
	23.30	2.7	0.19	10.2
Tongue, bas. epith.	5.30	4.9	1.01	9.7
	11.30	4.3	0.17	9.9
	17.30	20.7	0.25	9.6
	23.30	9.9	0.59	9.6
Jejunum, crypt. epith.	5.30	43	4.8	9.6
	11.30	42	4.7	9.2
	17.30	44	3.8	9.6
	23.30	41	4.7	9.8
Kidney, convoluted tubule	5.30	1.2	—	9.8
	11.30	1.2	—	9.9
	17.30	1.2	—	9.2
	23.30	1.1	—	9.1

[a] Reproduced with permission of Pilgrim et al., Nature.[250]

random distribution of cells in various phases of the cell cycle. Alternatively, diurnal variations may indicate a shift in the length of various phases in the cell cycle. Thus, prolongation of the DNA-synthesis period without concomitant prolongation of other phases of the cell cycle would lead to an increase in the number of DNA-labeled cells; similarly, alterations in the duration of the premitotic or postmitotic rest period without concomitant changes in the DNA-synthesis time would alter the labeling index. Which of the various possible mechanisms are responsible for the phenomenon of diurnal fluctuations in mammalian cell proliferation is not known. It appears likely, however, that the duration of the DNA-synthesis period is one of the more stable phases of the cell cycle, as was emphasized above. For example, in the mouse a nearly uniform DNA-synthesis time of approximately 7–8 hours was found despite alterations in the cycle times of the appropriate cells of internal organs from 9 hours to 80 days.[251,345] Similarly, the DNA-synthesis time of cells of induced carcinoma varied little from that of the cells of the normal tissue from which the tumor originated, but the cell cycle times differed greatly.[273,274] The twofold prolongation of the DNA-synthesis phase in rat hepatoma cells compared with normal liver cells attests that this is not always the case.[259] Confirming this too, the DNA-synthesis time was reduced in uterine epithelium of mice in response to estrone,[97] and the total cell-cycle time shortened proportionally so that the labeling index from H^3-thymidine was not altered. Also, in the mammary gland in mice, a shortening of the DNA-synthesis time from about 20 hours to 10 hours was observed after treatment with estradiol and progesterone.[39]

The premitotic rest period (G_2) is usually more constant than the G_1 phase, as observed in vivo in various cell types.[59,201,251,259,274,303,345] The findings were similar in a number of cell lines in culture and in ascites tumor cells.[84] Changing the pH of the culture medium of human amnion cells and kitten lung cells caused an alteration solely of the duration of the postmitotic rest period.[306] Also, Terasima and Tolmach[320] observed in synchronized HeLa cells that asynchrony arose in the G_1 phase. Yet in some cells of the mouse epidermis, the premitotic rest period appeared greatly prolonged, which may be regarded as a property of cells immediately ready to divide upon demand, such as in response to injury.[117]

Starvation may cause an alteration in the kinetics of cell renewal, as exemplified in newly hatched chickens where starvation led to a depression of cellular proliferation. Refeeding the chickens stimulated the various cells and they resumed their proliferative pattern. It was thus seen that some cells had stopped or slowed down in the postmitotic rest period, others were held in the premitotic rest period, and the DNA-synthesis time appeared slightly prolonged in the starved animals.[54]

Sisken and Morasca[307] analyzed the distribution of the lengths of the various phases in the cycle of human amnion cells in culture and also found G_1 to be more variable than G_2. In addition, compensating mechanisms appeared to help in regulating the lengths of successive phases in single cells. Thus, while the generation time showed a distribution skewed to the right, the length of the DNA-synthesis phase varied somewhat inversely to the length of the G_1 and G_2 phase plus mitosis.

8.3. GROWTH-STIMULATING FACTORS

The effects of hormones are again considered in Section 8.4. Injury stimulates cell proliferation by a mechanism that is still controversial. A well-known example is the regenerating liver, where the number of cells synthesizing DNA reaches a peak at about 20 hours after partial hepatectomy. Yet the degree of synchrony varies with the age of the animal, as discussed below. Synchrony of induced DNA synthesis around a wound was impressively demonstrated in the lens epithelium.[135] The wave of DNA-synthesizing cells around the wound progressed into the peripheral tissue at a rate of 17 μ per hour.[136] Also after bone fracture, a quiescent cell population in the periosteum was demonstrated to revert to proliferative activity and to enter the phase of DNA synthesis.[322] A similar effect, although smaller, was seen after extraperiosteal injection of saline, serum, or whole blood. Thus, neither bone fracture nor disruption of the periosteum was necessary to induce cell proliferation.[323] In liver, poisoning the cells with ethionine resulted in severe cytoplasmic alterations and nucleoprotein loss, which was held responsible for the great increase in the number of DNA-synthesizing cells that followed the injury.[231] This would suggest that a cytoplasmic factor was operative in initiating DNA synthesis. A regulating effect of the cytoplasm on nuclear RNA synthesis has been demonstrated indeed.[132] Work with microwounds in skin under *in vivo* as well as *in vitro* conditions led to the hypothesis that other factors besides those released directly by injured cells are of importance for the stimulation.[139] Still, the reported failure of the tissue explanted *in vitro* to react to the injury may be due to the environmental changes brought about by the culture condition. Only when the epidermis *in vitro* was combined with the mesenchymal portion of the dermis was labeled thymidine incorporated into the epidermis.[334] Interesting was the fact that preincubating the epidermis with unlabeled thymidine led to a subsequent increased uptake of H^3-thymidine. Skin incision first induced DNA synthesis some 200–300 cells away from the injury and subsequently at a closer distance, whereas superficial cauterization initiated DNA synthesis immediately underneath the wound.[21]

The propagation of cell proliferation after injury begins with a delay and usually involves DNA synthesis prior to an increase in the number of dividing cells. This appears to indicate that cells are responsive usually at a stage of the cell cycle prior to the DNA-synthesis phase, and it agrees with the relative constancy of the G_2 phase in comparison with the postmitotic rest period.

A better defined factor stimulating the proliferation of certain cells in mammals is erythropoietin.[151] It is probably released exclusively from the kidney into the circulation and it propagates specifically the immature erythrocytic precursors in the bone marrow. It also initiates RNA synthesis prior to the synthesis of hemoglobin.[248] Similar specific factors are the granulocytopoiesis-stimulating leukopoietins[18,85] and the mitotic inhibitor in the epidermis, termed a chalone.[47]

A few other situations illustrating homeostatic control mechanisms should also be considered here to emphasize the need for including them in the list of variables in animal experimentation. Thus, partial resection of the ileum in rats led to an increased uptake of H³-thymidine in the shortened intestine, with a slight decrease in the generation time of the intestinal epithelial cells leading consequently to an increased rate of DNA renewal in this cell population.[191] The question was raised whether there is a specific intestinal epithelial growth hormone. In mice, injection of autolytic liver tissue after partial hepatectomy stimulated the uptake of H³-thymidine into DNA of the liver parenchymal cells specifically. No such effect was seen in mesenchymal cells of the liver, in cells of renal tubules, of gastric mucosa, or of epidermis.[178] Starvation, hypophysectomy and injection of growth hormone or cortisone altered the rate of RNA-precursor incorporation in normal and regenerating liver cells of the rat, but not so in the livers of tumor-bearing animals.[57] The influence of a tumor on the number of those cells in the liver which incorporate H³-thymidine was shown in sarcoma-bearing mice, where the labeling index was increased over that found in normal controls.[222] Moreover, there was a linear relationship of increasing body weight to an increasing DNA content per liver. This seems to indicate that the size of cell populations proliferating within the body influences directly the multiplication or polyploidization of hepatic parenchymal cells. Also, the thymus appears to contain a specific factor which stimulated proliferation and increased thymidine incorporation in peripheral lymph nodes.[171]

Cells interact also *in vitro* under culture conditions. Thus, rates of DNA, RNA, and protein-precursor incorporation per cell are progressively depressed as the cultures become confluent, as was reported for human diploid fibroblasts.[187] Also, in cultures of peripheral blood lymphocytes, cell density exerted mitotic inhibition which was also dependent on the number of granulocytes present.[333] Phytohemagglutinin is usually a necessary factor for stimulating proliferation in lymphocyte cultures, but it is not required for the growth of cells of chronic myelogenous leukemia.[290] For the transformation of lymphocytes in culture to macrophages, polymorphonuclear granulocytes were required, and they needed be living and not dead cells.[128] The chemical nature of the particular substances mediating these cellular interactions is not known, but it appears to be cell-specific and perhaps is principally not different from those capable of specific enzyme inductions. Changes of cellular response *in vitro* versus *in vivo* were discussed in Section 4.5.

Stimulation of cellular metabolism and proliferation in consequence of immunological processes need to be considered when working with lymphoreticular systems.[6] Much evidence of such interactions has become available. For instance, a secondary antigenic stimulus in mice led to an increase of the incorporation of H^3-thymidine[5] and also of H^3-cytidine and H^3-leucine in lymphoid and plasmocytoid cells concomitantly with changes in the cellular composition of lymph nodes and appearance of germinal centers.[71] The increases in the size and number of the germinal centers starting during the second day paralleled the rise in the labeling index from H^3-thymidine, but this was preceded by a rise in the labeling intensity from H^3-cytidine and H^3-leucine of reticuloendothelial and histiocytic elements. These effects are obviously related to antibody synthesis, and specific changes in cellular composition with different kinetics occur.[5,71,74] RNA precursors and amino acids are obviously incorporated independently of each other, and in the mature plasma cells amino acid incorporation was predominant, whereas in blast cells the rate of incorporation of RNA precursors was much higher than that of amino acids.[206,207]

8.4. HORMONAL INFLUENCES

Stimulation or retardation of growth and cellular metabolism are among the well-known parameters for determining the effects of hormones.[48] These will not be discussed further here; but it may be pointed out that some hormones are likely to influence through stimulation of RNA and protein synthesis.

Growth hormone, cortisone, and insulin can increase the incorporation of amino acids into protein. Yet it is decreased in fasted animals and restored upon refeeding; however, no such starvation effect was seen after hypophysectomy.[332] Glucocorticoid (prednisone) stimulated leucine incorporation into glutamic-alanine transaminase.[296]

Aldosterone labeled with tritium was observed to be preferentially localized in the cell nucleus of the toad bladder *in vitro* prior to its effect on sodium transport[94] which could be blocked by actinomycin D, which inhibits DNA-dependent RNA synthesis, and puromycin, which inhibits protein synthesis. Insulin was observed not only to increase amino acid incorporation into isolated rat diaphragm, but it also enhanced the synthesis of RNA, probably both messenger RNA and particle RNA.[338] Moreover, hydrocortisone was reported to stimulate the synthesis of nuclear RNA in the liver in adrenalectomized rats within 30 minutes, and after another lag period of about 30 minutes tyrosine transaminase began to accumulate.[157] Similarly, estrogen acted on uterine cells by stimulating RNA synthesis prior to a sustained increase in protein synthesis.[133] But the failure of actinomycin D to depress the hormone stimulated protein synthesis, while suppressing the response of

RNA synthesis led to the suggestion that the initial event in the hormone action is an activation of protein synthesis which initiates increased RNA synthesis followed by the sustained rise in protein synthesis. Selectivity of accumulation of hormones in tissue was indicated from the work with tritiated hexestrol, which after subcutaneous injection was localized in those organs that are known to respond to it.[124]

8.5. AGE EFFECT

The influence of age on cell function and proliferation, if not adequately taken into account, may give rise to conflicting results.

Young animals, prior to the stage of full development, have, of course, a relatively greater number of cells proliferating than the adults. On the basis of H^3-thymidine incorporation at various ages of an animal, stable cell populations, growing cell populations, and renewing cell populations are identifiable (see Table 5.3).[185] The decrease of the proliferative activity of growing cell populations with advancing age was demonstrated, for example, in the testes of mice, where the amount of H^3-thymidine incorporated at any time declined until an age of about 7 weeks was reached.[289]

In normal adults, cell proliferation is a sign of functional renewal and not of growth, and with progressing age cell renewal also is retarded. A decrease in the number of cells incorporating H^3-thymidine in mouse kidney, in both tubules and corpuscles, was thus observed with increasing age to 13 months.[190] Bucher et al.[43] demonstrated the influence of age on the incorporation of H^3-thymidine by regenerating rat liver. In young growing rats the first peak of synchronized cells was sharply defined at about 18 hours after hepatectomy; in adults the incorporation of thymidine not only diminished but the number of DNA-synthesizing cells rose less synchronously over longer periods of time, from about 13 to 33 hours after hepatectomy. Age differences determine the degree of response also to varying amounts of liver which is removed.[44] Hence, tracer data from regenerating liver may be not reproducible if the age of the animal and the amount of tissue removed is not considered. In the skeleton, Tonna[324,325] found that the turnover of structural, protoplasmic proteins did not differ in old mice and young, but the turnover rate of amino acids utilized for protein formation for the bone matrix was diminished in all skeletal cell types of older mice, except perhaps for osteoblasts of the metaphyseal endosteum.

It must be remembered that tracer data from animals of various ages may be influenced by changes in the "soluble pool," as discussed in Section 4. Particularly with labeled thymidine small alterations in the size of the intracellular or extracellular pools are of great consequence. Changes in the relationship of the pools for thymidine and uridine were observed with varying age of *Ilyanassa* embryos.[66] Cells *in vitro* (L cells) showed a declining activity of uridine kinase but not of uridine phosphorylase with progressing age of the subculture.[169] Total nucleic acid content and nucleotide content in cells are known to alter with age.[60] For example, in the brain and muscle of very young rats, the DNA and RNA concentrations are relatively high, but they were shown first to drop sharply and subsequently more slowly with increasing age. In the liver, however, DNA and RNA concentrations rose after birth, then declined rapidly at first and more slowly thereafter, whereas in old age the RNA value appeared to increase again somewhat.[88] On the other hand, incorporation of H^3-cytidine into liver led to a lower RNA specific activity in young rats and mice than in old animals.[286,339] The difference was diminished greatly by giving the tracer in a higher concentration, which points to the soluble pool size being smaller in older animals.[339]

8.6. Temperature Effect

Among the various factors which influence cellular metabolism and cellular kinetics, the temperature must always be considered, especially in plants, single cell and organ cultures, and microbial systems. This needs no further comment here except to say that the mitosis appears to be the most sensitive stage of the cell cycle.[269] Also, in complex organisms with physiological temperature control, such as the mammals, unequal exposure of various organs to the external temperature is of consequence for cell metabolism and proliferation. This is exemplified by the kinetic behavior of some epidermis cells. Whereas the DNA-synthesis time in the mouse and rat is about 6–9 hours, it is 15–30 hours in cells in the ear epidermis.[251,303] The lower protection of the ear against temperature changes and the generally lower temperature in the ear tissue compared to most other tissue of the body was held responsible for the exceptionally long DNA-synthesis times and cell-cycle times.[303] In various plant species (*Vicia faba, Zea mays, Tradescantia,* and *Pisum sativum*) an increase of the temperature from 4° to 25°C caused a concomitant rise of the DNA–RNA ratio in the nuclei of the growing cells.[194]

Concluding this short summary, the reader should be well aware of the possible influences of metabolic and physiological regulation and control mechanisms which are universally prevalent, and at times may be overlooked in an experiment. Their proper anticipation will prevent duplication of effort and doubtful interpretation of data, if it does not lead to new discoveries.

9. The Metabolism of Water

The metabolism of water deserves a separate discussion since tritium is the usual label for tracing water, and it is preferred over deuterium because of the ease of isotopic measurement.

9.1. ROUTES OF ADMINISTRATION OF LABELED WATER

Accidental exposure to tritium often involves tritiated water of high specific activity, which is commonly encountered in the course of tracer studies with this isotope. Tritiated water is absorbed through the skin within a few minutes as shown by Pinson and Langham.[253] When man was exposed to vapors of tritiated water, the amount of activity absorbed through the skin was about equal to that entering the body through the lungs. During breathing, 98–99% tritium water vapor was absorbed and distributed in the body. The tritium activity in the venous blood after inhalation decreased with an initial half-time of 12 minutes. Inhaled tritium gas was partially metabolized in the body to tritiated water, which appeared in the urine within minutes. About 1000 times more tritium gas than tritiated water vapor was needed in rats to produce the same rate of accumulation of tritiated water in the body, as determined by measurements of urine activity.

For the study of water metabolism in animals, the tracer is usually administered by intravascular injection. Still, a complete absorption of tritiated water by the intestinal tract is also assured within about 45 minutes after ingestion.[253] Since tritiated water is distributed quickly throughout the organism while equilibrating with the body water constantly produced in the course of metabolism and since it is excreted readily, radiation hazards from tritiated water are relatively small compared to those, for example, from ^{3}H-thymidine.

9.2. DISTRIBUTION AND RENEWAL OF TOTAL BODY WATER

Water metabolism has been determined in many animal species, some of which are listed in Table 5.5.[276] In man, the water volumes measured with tritiated water are in the same range of values as those obtained by various other techniques,[276] and 60% of the body weight may be taken as the normal value for males, and 55% for females. Considerable changes in the values occur depending mainly on the relative amount of adipose tissue and bone. Thus, in infants, the body water was found to be about 85%, whereas it was about 47% in adults who were 86 years or older[327]; but females had slightly lower values than males.

Variations are also reported for the water turnover, with biological half-times ranging from less than 7 days to more than 10 days. In

TABLE 5.5

BODY WATER METABOLISM IN MAMMALS[a]

Species	Sex	Weight (g)	Dose (mc)	Route of administration	Exchangeable body water (% of body weight)[b, c]	Half-time (days)	Water loss (ml/day)
Mouse	F	21.4 (24)	0.708	ip	58.49 ± 3.97 (24)[c]	1.13 ± 0.14 (12)	7.22 ± 1.15 (12)
Rat	M	298 (12)	4.329	ip	59.61 ± 4.04 (11)	3.53 ± 0.40 (12)	34.54 ± 4.90 (11)
Dipo-domys[d]	F, M	93 (20)	0.850	ip	62.20 ± 2.35 (20)	11.82 ± 2.96 (10)	3.75 ± 0.95 (10)
Rabbit	F	3159 (4)	7.100	ip	58.35 ± 5.31 (4)	3.87 ± 0.21 (4)	338 ± 62 (4)
Dog	M	10,582 (5)	1.270	Oral	65.95 ± 1.42 (5)	5.14 ± 0.18 (5)	946 ± 124 (5)
Man	F, M	67,302 (5)	2.000	Oral	55.34 ± 5.31 (5)	9.46 ± 0.88 (5)	2,747 ± 519 (5)
Horse	M	398,533 (3)	142.1	iv	65.71 ± 0.72 (3)	8.41 ± 0.53 (3)	21,722 ± 3247 (3)

[a] Number in parentheses is the number of animals composing the average. Reproduced with permission of Richmond et al., J. Cell. Comp. Physiol.[276]

[b] From the derivative of $V_t = V_0 e^{-kt}$, when V_0 is the volume of exchangeable body water (ml), t is time 0, and k is the rate constant of the exponential function (fractional change per day).

[c] $x \pm \sqrt{\dfrac{(x - \bar{x})^2}{n - 1}}$.

[d] Kangaroo rats maintained in laboratory during experiment on dry pearled barley alone. No other sources of exogenous water were available.

normal man the half-time of body water is regarded to be 8–9 days,[340] with five-thirds of the 24-hour urine being the daily total water loss.

The distribution of the total body water in the human calculated from tritium data, according to Moore,[213] gave about 60% of the body weight to the extracellular space, 16.6% to the intracellular space, and 0.36% to the lung space. Immediately after injection of the tritiated water, the tracer appeared in the urine and the breath water rather parallel to the activity in the blood. The turnover was observed to consist of five components, one with a half-time of 20 minutes, then with a half-time of 3.6 hours, and subsequently with half-times of 4.6, 12, and 90 hours. Periodic variations of water metabolism have been described.[22] It is clear, of course, that the value for total body water and turnover may drastically alter in disease, injury, or upon nutritional influences. Changes

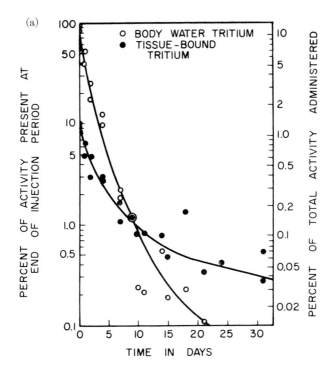

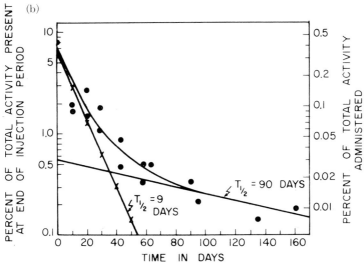

FIG. 5.9. Biological half-times of tritium bound to water, and that in tissue solids, after repeated injections of tritiated water in mice; (a) early, (b) late. Courtesy of Thompson, *J. Biol. Chem.*[321]

in the climate apparently had remarkably little influence on water turn-over in individuals adapted to the climate.[113]

9.3. TISSUE-BOUND TRITIUM FROM TRITIATED WATER

After administration of tritiated water, a fraction of the tritium exchanges with the hydrogen bound in the tissue solids. This exchange depends on the molecular positions of the hydrogen involved. Thus, in a single protein species, there are various categories of exchangeable hydrogen with exchange half-times from a few seconds to several hours, as was discussed in Chapter 2. In addition to direct exchange, tritium from water is also incorporated into tissue constituents by metabolism, detectable mainly in those positions on a molecule that do not let hydrogen exchange easily. One-third of the total hydrogen in the solids of lean tissue is considered exchangeable[305]; yet the value is considerably lower for adipose tissue.

The total amount of tritium bound by either direct exchange or via metabolism to the dry tissue solids of mice, 24 hours after a single administration of tritiated water, amounted to about 7% of the dose injected, and about 1.5% was bound metabolically.[305]

As to be expected, 10 days after a single or repeated administration of tritiated water, the tritium bound to the tissue solids (total mouse)

TABLE 5.6

TRITIUM RETENTION FROM COMBUSTION OF DRY TISSUES OF MICE[a]

	Tritiated water in body fluids (μc/liter)	
Tissue	50 Days after acute exposure to 1.4×10^5 μc/liter	32 Days after 5 months chronic exposure maintained at 2880 μc/liter
Brain	516	263
Skin	428	183
Muscle	310	135
Heart	—	94
Bone	277	91
Spleen, liver, thymus, lung	93	67[b]
G.I. tract	110	49
Fat	71	49
Kidney	126	48
Liver	—	27
Body water (urine)	4.0	4.2

[a] Reproduced with permission of Pinson and Langham, *J. Appl. Physiol.*[253]
[b] Value for spleen and thymus only.

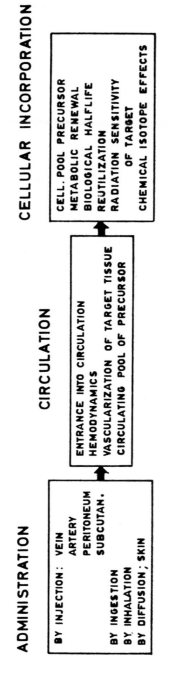

Fig. 5.10. Summarizing scheme of factors which influence the incorporation of labeled metabolic precursors.

exceeded that bound to water.[321] For both tritium fractions there were different biological half-times—the tritium bound to water decreased to 50% within 1.1 day, the remaining tritium bound in the tissue declined with two components having half-times of 9 and 90 days. Figure 5.9 shows these data. In another study in rats, the tritium activity of the tissue solids equaled the tritium bound to water at about 9–11 days after injection of tritiated water,[22] and the specific activities of both fractions were reported to decline subsequently with a half-time of about 10 days. The differences in the data referred to may be due to the difference in the schedule of tracer injection or the type of animal, or due to unequal analytical procedures. Nevertheless, it is obvious that, following an injection of tritiated water, a substantial amount of tritium is retained in the tissue solids for a considerably longer period of time than the initial biological half-time of tritiated water would indicate.

The distribution of tritium in various dry tissues in mice was examined following an acute and after continuous exposure (over 5 months) to tritiated water.[253] The data in Table 5.6 are expressed in microcuries per liter to allow a comparison with the tritium dose administered. It is clear that relatively minimal amounts of tritium remained bound to the various tissue solids 30–50 days after acute or chronic administration of the tracer.

The magnitude of the metabolic engagement of tritium-labeled water may apparently be altered because of changes primarily affecting total body water distribution and turnover. Thus, it was reported by Zuppinger and co-workers[349] that an injection of tritiated water at day 10 after 600 r X-rays to the total body led 2 days later to a 50% increase of tritium bound in dry brain and liver. When, however, the tritiated water was injected later than 10 days after irradiation, the amount of tritium in dry brain and liver fell below the control values. Extending these observations, it was reported that an indirect radiation effect caused an early reduced binding of tritium in shielded skin already between days 5 and 10 after irradiation.[350] In unshielded skin the reduction occurred around day 15.

10. Conclusion

The various general factors which one needs to take into account for the interpretation of data from tracer experiments are schematically summarized in Fig. 5.10. For many labeled compounds these factors are still little known.

REFERENCES

1. G. Acs, E. Reich, and S. Valanju, RNA Metabolism of *B. subtilis,* Effects of Actinomycin, *Biochim. Biophys. Acta,* **76:** 68–79 (1963).

2. S. J. Adelstein, C. P. Lyman, and R. C. O'Brien, Variations in the Incorporation of the DNA of Some Rodent Species, *Comp. Biochem. Physiol.,* **12**: 223–231 (1964).
3. J. Altman and S. L. Chorover, Autoradiographic Investigation of the Distribution and Utilization of Intraventricularly Injected Adenine-H³, Uracil-H³, and Thymidine-H³ in the Brains of Cats, *J. Physiol. (London),* **169**: 770–779 (1963).
4. J. Aschoff, Comparative Physiology: Diurnal Rhythms, *Ann. Rev. Physiol.,* **25**: 581–600 (1963).
5. B. M. Balfour, E. H. Cooper, and E. L. Alpen, Morphological and Kinetic Studies on Antibody Producing Cells in Rat Lymph Nodes, *Immunology,* **8**: 230–244 (1965).
6. R. N. Baney, J. J. Vasquez, and F. J. Dixon, Cellular Proliferation in Relation to Antibody Synthesis, *Proc. Soc. Exptl. Biol. Med.,* **109**: 1–4 (1962).
7. R. Baserga and E. Lisco, Duration of DNA Synthesis in Ehrlich Ascites Cells as Estimated by Double Labeling with C¹⁴- and H³-Thymidine and Autoradiography, *J. Natl. Cancer Inst.,* **31**: 1559–1571 (1963).
8. R. Baserga, The Relationship of the Cell Cycle to Tumor Growth and Control of Cell Division: A Review, *Cancer Res.,* **25**: 581–595 (1965).
9. J. R. Beckwith, A. B. Pardee, R. Austrian, and F. Jacob, Coordination of the Synthesis of the Enzymes in the Pyrimidine Pathway of *E. coli, J. Mol. Biol.,* **5**: 618–634 (1962).
10. P. R. Bell and K. Mühlethaler, Evidence for the Presence of Deoxyribonucleic Acid in the Organelles of the Egg Cells of *Pteridium aquilinum, J. Mol. Biol.,* **8**: 853–862 (1964).
11. A. Bendich, T. Wilczok, and E. Borenfreund, Circulating DNA as a Possible Factor in Oncogenesis, *Science,* **148**: 374–375 (1965).
12. K. Bensch, G. B. Gordon, and L. Miller, The Fate of DNA-Containing Particles Phagocytized by Mammalian Cells, *J. Cell Biol.,* **21**: 105–114 (1964).
13. F. D. Bertalanffy and C. Lau, Cell Renewal, *Intern. Rev. Cytol.,* **13**: 359–366 (1962).
14. F. D. Bertalanffy, R. Schachter, J. Ali, and J. C. Ingimundson, Mitotic Rate and Doubling Time of Intraperitoneal and Subcutaneous Ehrlich Ascites Tumor, *Cancer Res.,* **25**: 685–690 (1965).
15. L. E. Bertani, A. Häggmark, and P. Reichard, Enzymatic Synthesis of Deoxyribonucleotides. II. Formation and Interconversion of Deoxyuridine Phosphates, *J. Biol. Chem.,* **238**: 3407–3413 (1963).
16. P. A. Bianchi, J. A. V. Butler, A. R. Crathorn, and K. V. Shooter, The Thymidine Phosphorylating Kinases, *Biochim. Biophys. Acta,* **53**: 123–131 (1961).
17. P. A. Bianchi, Thymidine Phosphorylation and Deoxyribonucleic Acid Synthesis in Human Leukemic Cells, *Biochim. Biophys. Acta,* **55**: 547–549 (1962).
18. H. R. Bierman, Characteristic of Leukopietin G in Animals and Man, *Ann. N.Y. Acad. Sci.,* **113**: 753–765 (1964).
19. D. Billen, Alteration in Deoxyribonucleic Acid Synthesizing Capacity in Bacteria, an *in Vivo–in Vitro* Study, *Biochim. Biophys. Acta,* **55**: 960–968 (1962).
20. D. Billen, Alteration in the Sequence of Deoxyribonucleic Acid Synthesis by Thymidine Deprivation, *Exptl. Cell Res.,* **34**: 396–399 (1964).
21. P. Block, I. Seiter, and W. Oehlert, Autoradiographic Studies of the Initial Cellular Response to Injury, *Exptl. Cell Res.,* **30**: 311–321 (1963).
22. K. M. Bogdanov, M. I. Shalnov, and J. M. Stuckenberg, The Use of Tritium in

the Study of Periodic Biological Phenomena, Isotopes in Biochemistry and Physiology, *proc. 2nd Intern. Conf. Peaceful Use At. Energy, Geneva 1958* part 2, **25**: 215–222.

23. F. J. Bollum and V. R. Potter, Nucleic Acid Metabolism in Regenerating Rat Liver. VI. Soluble Enzymes Which Convert Thymidine to Thymidine-Phosphates and DNA, *Cancer Res.*, **19**: 561–565 (1959).

24. V. P. Bond, E. P. Cronkite, T. M. Fliedner, and P. K. Schork, Desoxyribonucleic Acid Synthesizing Cells in Peripheral Blood of Normal Human Beings, *Science*, **128**: 202–203 (1958).

25. V. P. Bond, T. M. Fliedner, E. P. Cronkite, J. R. Rubini, and J. S. Robertson, Cell Turnover in Blood and Blood Forming Tissues Studied with Tritiated Thymidine, in *The Kinetics of Cellular Proliferation* (F. Stohlman, Jr., ed.), pp. 188–200, Grune and Stratton, New York, 1959.

26. V. P. Bond, N. Odartchenko, H. Cottier, L. E. Feinendegen, and E. P. Cronkite, The Kinetics of the More Mature Erythrocytic Precursors Studied with Tritiated Thymidine, in *Erythropoiesis* (L. Jacobson and M. Doyle, eds.), pp. 173–183, Grune and Stratton, New York, 1962.

27. V. P. Bond, T. M. Fliedner, and J. O. Archambeau, *Mammalian Radiation Lethality*, Academic Press Inc., New York, 1965.

28. D. Bootsma, C. Budke, and O. Vos, Studies on Synchronous Division of Tissue Culture Cells Initiated by Excess Thymidine, *Exptl. Cell Res.*, **33**: 301–309 (1964).

29. D. Bootsma, Changes Induced in the First Post-Irradiation Generation Cycle of Human Cells Studied by Double Labeling, *Exptl. Cell Res.*, **38**: 429–431 (1965).

30. H. Borsook, C. L. Deasy, A. J. Haagen-Smit, G. Keighley, and P. H. Lowy, Metabolism of C^{14}-Labeled Glycine, L-Histidine, L-Leucine, and L-Lysine, *J. Biol. Chem.*, **187**: 839–848 (1950).

31. R. P. Boyce and R. B. Setlow, A Simple Method of Increasing the Incorporation of Thymidine into the Deoxyribonucleic Acid of *E. coli*, *Biochim. Biophys. Acta*, **61**: 618–620 (1962).

32. R. P. Boyce and P. Howard-Flanders, Release of Ultraviolet Light Induced Thymidine Dimers from DNA in *E. coli* K-12, *Proc. Natl. Acad. Sci. U.S.*, **51**: 293–300 (1964).

33. J. Brachet, Ribonucleic Acids and the Synthesis of Cellular Proteins, *Nature*, **186**: 194–199 (1960).

34. J. Brachet, Nucleo-cytoplasmic Interactions, in *The Cell* (J. Brachet and A. E. Mirsky, eds.), Vol. II, Academic Press Inc., New York, 1961.

35. J. Brachet and A. Miraux-Jonckheere, Les effets du beta mercapto éthanol sur l'incorporation des précurseurs des protéines et des acides nucléiques dans le foie et l'intestin de souris, *Exptl. Cell Res.*, **27**: 539–547 (1962).

36. J. Brachet and A. Ficq, Binding Sites of ^{14}C-Actinomycin in Amphibian Ovocytes and an Autoradiography Technique for the Detection of Cytoplasmic DNA, *Exptl. Cell Res.*, **38**: 153–159 (1965).

37. R. Braun, C. Mittermayer, and H. P. Rusch, Sequential Temporal Replication of DNA in *Physarum polycephalum*, *Proc. Natl. Acad. Sci. U.S.*, **53**: 924 (1965).

38. F. Bresciani, Duration and Rate of DNA Synthesis in the Mammary Gland of the C3H Mouse as Studied by Incorporation of H^3-Thymidine, *6th Intern. Congr. Biochem., New York, 1964.*

39. F. Bresciani, Effect of Ovarian Hormones on Duration of DNA Synthesis in Cells of the C3H Mouse Mammary Gland, *Exptl. Cell Res.*, **38**: 13–32 (1965).

40. B. J. Bryant, Reutilization of Lymphocyte DNA by Cells of Intestinal Crypts and Regenerating Liver, *J. Cell Biol.,* **18**: 515–523 (1963).

41. B. J. Bryant, *In Vivo* Utilization of the DNA Thymidine of Necrotized Liver Cells by Cells of Testis and Intestine, *Exptl. Cell. Res.,* **32**: 209–212 (1963).

42. B. J. Bryant, The Delayed Uptake of ³H-Thymidine by Ehrlich Ascites Tumor Cells, *Exptl. Cell Res.,* **37**: 490–504 (1965).

43. N. L. R. Bucher, M. N. Swaffield, and J. F. Ditroai, The Influence of Age upon the Incorporation of Thymidine-2-C¹⁴ into the DNA of Regenerating Rat Liver, *Cancer Res.,* **24**: 509–512 (1964).

44. N. L. R. Bucher and M. N. Swaffield, The Rate of Incorporation of Labeled Thymidine into the Deoxyribonucleic Acid of Regenerating Rat Liver in Relation to the Amount of Liver Excised, *Cancer Res.,* **24**: 1611–1625 (1964).

45. G. C. Budd and G. M. Mills, Labelled Cytoplasmic Organelles in *Allium cepa* Var. "White Lisbon" after Administration of Tritiated Thymidine, *Nature,* **205**: 524–525 (1965).

46. W. S. Bullough, Analysis of the Life Cycle in Mammalian Cells, *Nature,* **199**: 859–862 (1963).

47. W. S. Bullough, C. L. Hewett, and E. B. Laurence, The Epidermal Chalone: A Preliminary Attempt at Isolation, *Exptl. Cell Res.,* **36**: 192–200 (1964).

48. W. S. Bullough, Mitotic and Functional Homeostasis. A Speculative Review, *Cancer Res.,* **25**: 1683–1727 (1965).

49. J. Cairns, A Minimum Estimate for the Length of the DNA of *E. coli* Obtained by Autoradiography, *J. Mol. Biol.,* **4**: 407–409 (1962).

50. J. Cairns, The Bacterial Chromosome and Its Manner of Replication as Seen by Autoradiography, *J. Mol. Biol.,* **6**: 208–213 (1963).

51. J. Cairns, Forme et duplication de l'ADN, *Endeavor,* **22**: 141–145 (1963).

52. I. L. Cameron and R. C. Greulich, Evidence for an Essential Constant Duration of DNA Synthesis in Renewing Epithelia of the Adult Mouse, *J. Cell Biol.,* **18**: 31–40 (1963).

53. I. L. Cameron, Is the Duration of DNA Synthesis in Somatic Cells of Mammals and Birds a Constant? *J. Cell Biol.,* **20**: 185–188 (1964).

54. I. L. Cameron and G. Cleffmann, Initiation of Mitosis in Relation to the Cell Cycle Following Feeding of Starved Chickens, *J. Cell Biol.,* **21**: 169–174 (1964).

55. I. L. Cameron and G. E. Stone, Relation Between the Amount of DNA per Cell and the Duration of DNA Synthesis in Three Strains of *Tetrahymena pyriformis, Exptl. Cell Res.,* **36**: 510–514 (1964).

56. I. L. Cameron, Macromolecular Events Leading to Cell Division in *Tetrahymena pyriformis* after Removal and Replacement of Required Pyrimidines, *J. Cell Biol.,* **25**: 9–18 (1965).

57. A. Cantarow, T. L. Williams, and K. E. Paschkis, Hormonal and Nutritional Influence on the Incorporation of Uracil into Liver and Tumor RNA in the Rat, *Cancer Res.,* **22**: 1021–1025 (1962).

58. L. G. Caro and G. E. Palade, Protein Synthesis, Storage and Discharge in the Pancreatic Exocrine Cell. An Autoradiographic Study, *J. Cell Biol.,* **20**: 473–495 (1964).

59. S. M. Cattaneo, H. Quastler, and F. G. Sherman, DNA Synthesis in Irradiated Hair Follicles of the Mouse, *Radiation Res.,* **12**: 587–593 (1960).

60. E. Chargaff and J. N. Davidson, *The Nucleic Acids,* Academic Press Inc., New York, 1955.

61. J. H. Cherry, Association of Rapidly Metabolized DNA and RNA, *Science*, **146**: 1066–1068 (1965).

62. M. Chèvremont, E. Baeckeland, and S. Chèvremont-Comhaire, Contribution cytochimique et histoautoradiographique à l'étude du métabolisme et de la synthèse des ADN dans des cellules animales cultivées *in vitro*. II, *Biochem. Pharmacol.*, **4**: 67–78 (1960).

63. J. E. Cleaver and R. M. Holford, Investigations into the Incorporation of (^{3}H-) Thymidine into DNA in *L*-Strain Cells and the Formation of a Pool of Phosphorylated Derivatives During Pulse, *Biochim. Biophys. Acta*, **103**: 654–671 (1965).

64. J. F. Codington, R. Fecher, M. H. Maguire, R. Y. Thomson, and G. B. Brown, The Synthesis of Cytidine-2-C^{14}-ribosyl-H^3, *J. Am. Chem. Soc.*, **80**: 5164–5166 (1958).

65. S. S. Cohen, H. D. Barner, and T. Lichtenstein, The Conversion of a Phage Induced Ribonucleic Acid to Deoxyribonucleotides *in vitro*, *J. Biol. Chem.*, **236**: 1448–1457 (1961).

66. J. R. Collier, The Incorporation of Uridine into the Deoxyribonucleic Acid of the *Ilyanassa* Embryo, *Exptl. Cell Res.*, **32**: 442–447 (1963).

67. S. L. Commerford, Biological Stability of 5-Iodo-2′-deoxyuridine Labelled with Iodine-125 after Its Incorporation into the Deoxyribonucleic Acid of the Mouse, *Nature*, **206**: 949–950 (1965).

68. D. E. Coutois and W. F. K. Seymour, DNA-Turnover: Evidence from Studies of Steady State Bacterial Populations, *Biochem. Biophys. Res. Commun.*, **16**: 124–128 (1964).

69. D. H. Cormack and E. J. Ambrose, Cytological Studies of the Entry of Enzymes into Cells in Tissue Culture, *Exptl. Cell Res.*, **31**: 566–575 (1963).

70. H. Cottier, N. Odartchenko, L. E. Feinendegen, G. Keiser, and V. P. Bond, Autoradiographische Untersuchungen über die Entkernung der Erythroblasten nach *in vivo* Markierung mit Thymidine-^{3}H, *Schweiz. Med. Wochschr.*, **93**: 1061–1076 (1963).

71. H. Cottier, N. Odartchenko, G. Keiser, M. Hess, and R. D. Stoner, Incorporation of Tritiated Nucleosides and Amino Acids into Lymphoid and Plasmocytoid Cells during Secondary Response to Tetanus Toxoid in Mice, *Ann. N. Y. Acad. Sci.*, **113**: 612–626 (1964).

72. H. Cottier, N. Odartchenko, L. E. Feinendegen, and V. P. Bond, Possibilities and Limitations in the Use of Tritiated Thymidine for *in vivo* Cytokinetic Studies on Lymphoreticular Tissue, *First Intern. Conf. on The Thymus in Immunobiology* (Good and Gabrielson, eds.), pp. 332–340, Harper & Row, Hoeber Medical Division, New York, 1964.

73. H. Cottier, personal communication, 1964.

74. C. G. Craddock, G. S. Nakai, H. Fukuta, and L. M. Vanslager, Proliferative Activity of the Lymphatic Tissues of Rats as Studied with Tritium-Labeled Thymidine, *J. Exptl. Med.*, **120**: 389–412 (1964).

75. A. R. Crathorn and K. V. Shooter, Uptake of Thymidine and Synthesis of Deoxyribonucleic Acid in Mouse Ascites Cells, *Nature*, **187**: 614–615 (1960).

76. A. R. Crathorn and K. V. Shooter, The Incorporation of Thymidine into DNA and Effects of γ-Radiation. I. Experiments with Ascites Cells *in Vitro*, *Intern. J. Radiation Biol.*, **7**: 575–585 (1963).

77. W. A. Creasy and R. C. Haff, Studies on the Biochemistry and Pharmacology of 6-Uracil Methyl Sulfone, *Cancer Res.*, **23**: 462–467 (1963).

78. E. P. Cronkite, T. M. Fliedner, V. P. Bond, J. R. Rubini, G. Brecher, and H. Quaster, Dynamics of Hemopoietic Proliferation in Man and Mice Studied by Thymidine-H³ Incorporation into DNA, *Proc. 2nd Intern. Conf. Peaceful Uses At. Energy, Geneva* Part 2, **25**: 190–198 (1958).

79. E. P. Cronkite, T. M. Fliedner, V. P. Bond, J. R. Rubini, G. Brecher, and H. Quastler, Dynamics of Hemopoietic Proliferation in Man and Mice Studied by H³-Thymidine Incorporation into DNA, *Ann. N. Y. Acad. Sci.,* **77**: 803–820 (1959).

80. E. P. Cronkite, S. W. Greenhouse, G. Brecher, and V. P. Bond, Implication of Chromosome Structure and Replication on Hazard of H³-Thymidine and the Interpretation of Data on Cell Proliferation, *Nature,* **189**: 153–154 (1961).

81. E. P. Cronkite, T. M. Fliedner, S. A. Killmann, and J. R. Rubini, Tritium Labeled Thymidine (H³TdR): Its Somatic Toxicity and Use in the Study of Growth Rates and Potentials in Normal and Malignant Tissue of Man and Animals, in *Tritium in the Physical and Biological Sciences, Symp. Intern. At. Energy Agency,* **2**: 189–207 (1961).

82. N. K. Das, E. P. Siegel, and M. Alfert, Synthetic Activities during Spermatogenesis in the Locust, *J. Cell Biol.,* **25**: 387–395 (1965).

83. D. Davidson, RNA Synthesis in Roots of *Vicia faba, Exptl. Cell Res.,* **35**: 317–325 (1964).

84. V. Defendi and L. A. Manson, Analysis of the Life-Cycle in Mammalian Cells, *Nature,* **198**: 359–361 (1963).

85. L. Delmonte and R. A. Liebelt, Granulocytosis-Promoting Extract of Mouse Tumor Tissue: Partial Purification, *Science,* **148**: 521–523 (1965).

86. A. de Recondo, C. Frayssinet, and J. de Recondo, Incorporation de thymidine tritiée au niveau du cytoplasme de cellules hépatiques néoplasiques. Etude faite chez le Rat albinos, *Compt. Rend.,* **255**: 3471 (1962).

87. C. H. De Verdier and V. R. Potter, Alternative Pathways of Thymine and Uracil Metabolism in the Liver and Hepatoma, *J. Natl. Cancer Inst.,* **24**: 13–29 (1960).

88. A. Devi, M. A. Mukundan, U. Srivastava, and N. K. Sarkar, The Effect of Age on the Variations of Deoxyribonucleic Acid, Ribonucleic Acid, and Total Nucleotides in Liver, Brain, and Muscle of Rat, *Exptl. Cell Res.,* **32**: 242–250 (1963).

89. F. Devik and K. Halvorsen, Observations by Biochemical Analysis and Autoradiography on Labeled Deoxyribonucleic Acid in the Normal and Regenerating Liver of Mice, *Nature,* **97**: 148 (1963).

90. H. Diderholm, K. E. Fichtelius, and L. Linder, Availability Time of H³-Thymidine *in Vivo, Exptl. Cell Res.,* **27**: 431–435 (1962).

91. D. R. Dubbs and S. Kit, Effect of Halogenated Pyrimidines and Thymidine on Growth of *L*-cells and a Subline Lacking Thymidine Kinase, *Exptl. Cell Res.,* **33**: 19–28 (1964).

92. J. A. Dvorak and A. W. Jones, *In Vivo* Incorporation of Tritiated Cytidine and Tritiated Thymidine by the Cestode, *Hymenolepis microstoma, Exptl. Parasitol.,* **14**: 316–322 (1963).

93. S. Ebbe and F. Stohlman, Jr., Megacaryocytopoiesis in the Rat, *Blood,* **26**: 20–35 (1965).

94. I. S. Edelman, R. Bogoroch, and G. A. Porter, On the Mechanism of Action of Aldosterone on Sodium Transport: The Role of Protein Synthesis, *Proc. Natl. Acad. Sci. U.S.,* **50**: 1169–1177 (1963).

95. M. Edelman, J. A. Schiff, and H. T. Epstein, Studies of Chloroplast Development in *Euglena*, XII. Two Types of Satellite DNA, *J. Mol. Biol.*, **11**: 769–774 (1965).

96. C. R. Eidam and D. J. Merchant, The Plateau Phase of Growth of the *L-M*-Strain Mouse Cell in a Protein Free Medium, I. Pattern of Protein and Nucleic Acid Synthesis and Turnover, *Exptl. Cell Res.*, **37**: 132–139 (1965).

97. O. I. Epifanova, Autoradiographic Analysis of the Mitotic Cycle and of Cell Population Kinetics in the Uterine Epithelium of Mice, *Dokl. Biol. Sci. Sect.* (*English Transl.*), **149**: 358–360 (1963).

98. H. J. Evans, Uptake of H^3-Thymidine and Patterns of DNA Replication in Nuclei and Chromosomes of *Vicia faba*, *Exptl. Cell Res.*, **35**: 381–393 (1964).

99. P. M. Frearson, S. Kit, and D. R. Dubbs, Deoxythymidylate Synthetase and Deoxythymidine Kinase Activities of Virus-Infected Animal Cells, *Cancer Res.*, **25**: 737–744 (1965).

100. L. E. Feinendegen, V. P. Bond, W. W. Shreeve, and R. B. Painter, RNA and DNA Metabolism in Human Tissue Culture Cells Studied with Tritiated Cytidine, *Exptl. Cell Res.*, **19**: 443–459 (1960).

101. L. E. Feinendegen, V. P. Bond, and R. B. Painter, Studies on the Interrelationship of RNA Synthesis, DNA Synthesis and Precursor Pool in Human Tissue Culture Cells, Studied with Tritiated Pyrimidine Nucleosides, *Exptl. Cell Res.*, **22**: 381–405 (1961).

102. L. E. Feinendegen, V. P. Bond, and W. L. Hughes, RNA Mediation in DNA Synthesis in HeLa Cells Studied with Tritium Labeled Cytidine and Thymidine, *Exptl. Cell Res.*, **25**: 627–647 (1961).

103. L. E. Feinendegen, V. P. Bond, and R. M. Drew, Effect of RNA-ase and DNA-ase on Incorporation of Tritiated Pyrimidine Nucleosides into RNA and DNA in Human Cancer Cells (HeLa) in Culture, *Nature,* **191**: 1398–1399 (1961).

104. L. E. Feinendegen and V. P. Bond, Differential Uptake of H^3-Thymidine into the Soluble Fraction of Single Bone Marrow Cells Determined by Autoradiography, *Exptl. Cell Res.*, **27**: 474–484 (1962).

105. L. E. Feinendegen, N. Odartchenko, H. Cottier, and V. P. Bond, Kinetics of Megacaryocyte Proliferation, *Proc. Soc. Exptl. Biol. Med.*, **111**: 177–182 (1962).

106. L. E. Feinendegen and V. P. Bond, Observations on Nuclear RNA during Mitosis in Human Cancer Cells in Culture (HeLa-S₃), Studied with Tritiated Cytidine, *Exptl. Cell Res.*, **30**: 393–404 (1963).

107. L. E. Feinendegen, V. P. Bond, E. P. Cronkite, and W. L. Hughes, RNA Turnover in Normal Rat Bone Marrow, *Ann. N. Y. Acad. Sci.*, **113**: 727–741 (1964).

108. L. E. Feinendegen, V. P. Bond, and W. L. Hughes, I^{125}-Du(5-iodo-2'-deoxyuridine) in Autoradiographic Studies of Cell Proliferation, *Exptl. Cell Res.* **43**: 107–119 (1966).

109. L. E. Feinendegen, N. Odartchenko, H. Cottier, and V. P. Bond, unpublished data, 1962.

110. R. M. Fink and K. Fink, Relative Retention of H^3 and C^{14} Labels on Nucleosides Incorporated into Nucleic Acids of *Neurospora*, *J. Biol. Chem.*, **237**: 2889–2891 (1962).

111. H. Firket and W. G. Verly, Autoradiographic Visualization of Synthesis of DNA in Tissue Cultures with Tritium Labeled Thymidine, *Nature,* **181**: 274–275 (1958).

112. T. M. Fliedner, M. Kesse, E. P. Cronkite, and J. S. Robertson, Cell Proliferation in Germinal Centers of the Rat Spleen, *Ann. N. Y. Acad. Sci.,* **113:** 578–594 (1964).

113. M. Foy, The Biological Half-Life of Tritiated Water in the Mouse, Rat, Guinea Pig and Rabbit under Tropical Conditions and the Effect of Climate and Saline Drinking on the Biological Half-Life of Tritiated Water in the Rat, *J. Cell. Comp. Physiol.,* **64:** 279–282 (1964).

114. E. P. Frenkel, D. R. Korst, and C. J. D. Zarafonetis, The "Biologic Clock" Effect on Deoxyribonucleic Acid Synthesis, *IXth Congr. Intern. Soc. Hematol., Mexico, 1962.*

115. M. Friedkin, D. Tilson, and D. Roberts, Studies of Deoxyribonucleic Acid Biosynthesis in Embryonic Tissue with C^{14}-Thymidine, *J. Biol. Chem.,* **220:** 627–637 (1956).

116. F. Gavosto, A. Pileri, and G. Maraini, Incorporation of Thymidine Labeled with Tritium by Circulating Cells of Infectious Mononucleosis, *Nature,* **184:** 1691–1692 (1959).

117. S. Gelfant, Initiation of Mitosis in Relation to the Cell Division Cycle, *Exptl. Cell Res.,* **26:** 395–403 (1962).

118. G. A. Gentry, P. A. Morse, Jr., D. H. Ives, R. Gebert, and V. R. Potter, Pyrimidine Metabolism in Tissue Culture Cells Derived from Rat Hepatomas, II. Thymidine Uptake in Suspension Cultures Derived from the Novikoff Hepatoma. *Cancer Res.,* **25:** 509–516 (1965).

119. G. A. Gentry, P. A. Morse, Jr., and V. R. Potter, Pyrimidine Metabolism in Tissue Culture Cells Derived from Rat Hepatomas. III. Relationship of Thymidine to the Metabolism of other Pyrimidine Nucleosides in Suspension Cultures Derived from the Novikoff Hepatoma, *Cancer Res.,* **25:** 517–525 (1965).

120. G. B. Gerber and J. Remy-Defraigne, Synthese der Desoxyribonucleinsäure in der isolierten perfundierten Rattenleber, I. Der Einbau von ^{3}H-Thymidin in normale Leber und in Leber nach partieller Hepatektomie, *Z. Naturforsch.,* **18b:** 216–218 (1963).

121. G. B. Gerber, personal communication, 1964.

122. A. Gibor and S. Granick, Plastids and Mitochondria: Inheritable Systems, *Science,* **145:** 890–897 (1965).

123. A. Girgis and J. Vieuchange, Incorporation de thymidine radioactive dans des cellules de mammifères cultivées *in vitro, Ann. Inst. Pasteur,* **106:** 29–47 (1964).

124. R. F. Glascock and W. G. Hoekstra, Selective Accumulation of Tritium Labelled Hexoestrol by the Reproductive Organs of Immature Female Goats and Sheep, *Biochem. J.,* **72:** 673 (1959).

125. I. H. Goldberg, M. Rabinovitz, and E. Reich, Basis of Actinomycin Action, II. Effect of Actinomycin on the Nucleoside Tri-Phosphate-Inorganic Pyrophosphate Exchange, *Proc. Natl. Acad. Sci. U.S.* **49:** 226–229 (1963).

126. G. B. Gordon, L. R. Miller, and K. G. Bensch, Studies on the Intracellular Digestive Process in Mammalian Tissue Culture Cells, *J. Cell Biol.,* **25:** 41 (1965).

127. Ch. Gosse, J. B. LePecq, P. Defrance and C. Paoletti, Initial Degradation of Deoxyribonucleic Acid after Injection in Mammals, *Cancer Res.,* **25:** 877–883 (1965).

128. J. Gough, M. W. Elves, and M. C. G. Israels, The Formation of Macrophages from Lymphocytes *in Vitro, Exptl. Cell Res.,* **38:** 476–482 (1965).

129. R. Goutier, M. Goutier-Pirotte, and A. Raffi, Acid Deoxyribonuclease Activity and Labilization of Deoxyribonucleic Acid from Nucleoprotein in Thymus and Regenerating Liver after Whole Body Irradiation, *Intern. J. Radiation Biol.*, **8**: 51–58 (1964).
130. J. A. Grasso, J. W. Woodard, and H. H. Swift, Cytochemical Studies of Nucleic Acids and Proteins in Erythrocytic Development, *Proc. Natl. Acad. Sci. U.S.* **50**: 134–140 (1963).
131. R. C. Greulich, I. L. Cameron, and J. D. Trasher, Stimulation of Mitosis in Adult Mice by Administration of Thymidine, *Proc. Natl. Acad. Sci. U.S.*, **47**: 743–748 (1961).
132. J. B. Gurdon and D. D. Brown, Cytoplasmic Regulation of RNA Synthesis and Nucleolus Formation in Developing Embryos of *Xenopus laevis*, *J. Mol. Biol.*, **12**: 27–35 (1965).
133. T. H. Hamilton, Sequences of RNA and Protein Synthesis during Early Estrogen Action, *Proc. Natl. Acad. Sci. U.S.*, **51**: 83–89 (1964).
134. E. Hammersten, P. Reichard, and E. Saluste, Pyrimidine Nucleosides as Precursors of Pyrimidines in Polynucleotides, *J. Biol. Chem.*, **183**: 105 (1950).
135. C. V. Harding, A. Donn, and B. D. Srinivasan, Incorporation of Thymidine by Injured Lens Epithelium, *Exptl. Cell Res.*, **18**: 582–585 (1959).
136. C. V. Harding and B. D. Srinivasan, A Propagated Stimulation of DNA Synthesis and Cell Division, *Exptl. Cell Res.*, **25**: 326–340 (1961).
137. H. Harrington, Effect of Cytidine on Purine Nucleotide Formation in Ascites Tumor Cells *in Vitro*, *Biochim. Biophys. Acta*, **68**: 509–518 (1963).
138. E. A. Hell, R. J. Berry, and L. G. Lajtha, A Pitfall in High Specific Activity Tracer Studies, *Nature*, **185**: 47 (1960).
139. E. A. Hell and C. N. D. Cruickshank, The Effect of Injury upon the Uptake of H^3-Thymidine by Guinea Pig Epidermis, *Exptl. Cell Res.*, **31**: 128–139 (1963).
140. St. B. Hendricks, Metabolic Control of Timing, *Science*, **141**: 21–27 (1963).
141. G. R. Honig and M. Rabinovitz, Actinomycin D: Inhibition of Protein Synthesis Unrelated to Effect on Template RNA Synthesis, *Science*, **149**: 1504–1506 (1965).
142. M. Horikawa, Y. Doida, and T. Sugahara, Preliminary Studies of Cytosis in Mammalian Cells Cultured *in Vitro*, *Exptl. Cell Res.*, **32**: 404 (1963).
143. Y. Hotta and H. Stern, Molecular Facets of Mitotic Regulation. I. Synthesis of Thymidine Kinase, *Proc. Natl. Acad. Sci. U.S.*, **49**: 648–654 (1963).
144. Y. Hotta and H. Stern, Inducibility of Thymidine Kinase by Thymidine as a Function of Interphase Stage, *J. Cell Biol.*, **25**: 99–108 (1965).
145. A. Howard and S. R. Pelc, Synthesis of DNA in Normal and Irradiated Cells and Its Relation to Chromosome Breakage, *Heredity* (*Suppl.*), **6**: 261 (1953).
146. A. Howard and G. Douglas, Effect of X-irradiation on DNA Labelling in Cells Exposed During Synthesis, *Intern. J. Radiation Biol.*, **6**: 405–415 (1963).
147. W. L. Hughes, V. P. Bond, G. Brecher, E. P. Cronkite, R. B. Painter, H. Quastler, and F. G. Sherman, Cellular Proliferation in the Mouse as Revealed by Autoradiography with Tritiated Thymidine, *Proc. Natl. Acad. U.S.* **44**: 476–483 (1958).
148. W. L. Hughes, S. L. Commerford, D. Gitlin, R. C. Krueger, B. Schultze, V. Shah, and P. Reilly, Studies on Deoxyribonucleic Acid Metabolism *in vivo*. I. Cell Proliferation and Death as Measured by Incorporation and Elimination of Iododeoxyuridine, *Federation Proc.*, **23**: 640–648 (1964).
149. G. H. Huntley and L. G. Lajtha, The Radiosensitivity of the Processes of

DNA-Synthesis in Mouse Spleen, *Intern. J. Radiation Biol.,* **5**: 447–460 (1962).

150. T. Iwamura, Characterization of the Turnover of Chloroplast DNA in *Chlorella, Biochim. Biophys. Acta,* **61**: 472–474 (1962).

151. L. Jacobson and M. Doyle, eds., *Erythropoiesis,* Grune and Stratton, New York, 1962.

152. K. B. Jacobson and D. M. Prescott, The Nucleotide Pools for Thymidine and Cytidine in *Tetrahymena pyriformis, Exptl. Cell Res.,* **36**: 561–567 (1964).

153. F. Jacob and J. Monod, Genetic Regulatory Mechanisms in the synthesis of Proteins, *J. Mol. Biol.,* **3**: 318–356 (1961).

154. H. A. Johnson and V. P. Bond, A Method of Labeling Tissues with Tritiated Thymidine *in Vitro* and Its Use in Comparing Rates of Cell Proliferation in Duct Epithelium, Fibroadenoma, and Carcinoma of Human Breast, *Cancer,* **14**: 639–643 (1961).

155. M. D. Kamen, *Radioactive Tracers in Biology,* 3rd ed., Academic Press Inc., New York, 1957.

156. L. S. Kelly, Radiosensitivity of Biochemical Processes, in *Fundamental Aspects of Radoiosensitivity, Brookhaven Symp. Biol.,* **14**: 32–52 (1961).

157. F. T. Kenny and F. J. Kull, Hydrocortisone-stimulated Synthesis of Nuclear RNA in Enzyme Induction, *Proc. Natl. Acad. Sci. U.S.,* **50**: 493–499 (1963).

158. R. K. Kielley, Particle-Bound Thymidylate Kinase in Mouse Liver, a Possible Factor in the Control of DNA Synthesis, *Biochem. Biophys. Res. Commun.,* **10**: 249–253 (1963).

159. D. Kilander and A. Zetterberg, Quantitative Cytochemical Studies on Interphase Growth, I. Determination of DNA, RNA and Mass Content of Age Determined Mouse Fibroblasts *in Vitro* and of Intercellular Variation in Generation Time, *Exptl. Cell Res.,* **38**: 272–284 (1965).

160. S. A. Killmann, E. P. Cronkite, T. M. Fliedner, and V. P. Bond, Mitotic Indices of Human Bone Marrow Cells. I. Number and Cytological Distribution of Mitosis, *Blood,* **19**: 743 (1962).

161. S. A. Killmann, E. P. Cronkite, T. M. Fliedner, V. P. Bond, and G. Brecher, Mitotic Indices of Human Bone Marrow Cells. II. The Use of Mitotic Indices for Estimation of Time Parameters of Proliferation in Serially Connected Multiplicative Cellular Compartments, *Blood,* **21**: 141 (1963).

162. S. A. Killmann, Effect of Deoxyuridine on Incorporation of Tritiated Thymidine: Difference Between Normoblasts and Megaloblasts, *Acta Med. Scand.,* **175**: 483–488 (1964).

163. S. A. Killmann, Erythropoietic Response to Thymidine in Pernicious Anemia, *Acta Med. Scand.,* **175**: 489–497 (1964).

164. J. H. Kim and A. G. Perez, Ribonucleic Acid Synthesis in Synchronously Dividing Populations of HeLa Cells, *Nature,* **207**: 974–975 (1965).

165. B. F. Kimball and S. W. Perdue, Autoradiographic Study on the Conservation of Label from Ribonucleosides and Amino Acids in *Paramecium aurelia, Exptl. Cell Res.,* **38**: 660–669 (1965).

166. N. Kislev, H. Swift, and L. Bogorad, Nucleic Acids of Chloroplasts and Mitochondria in Swiss Chard, *J. Cell Biol.,* **25**: 327–344 (1965).

167. S. Kit, Acquisition of DNA Synthesizing Enzymes by Animal Cells Infected with Pox Viruses, *Exptl. Cell Res. (Suppl.),* **9**: 270–275 (1963).

168. S. Kit, D. R. Dubbs, L. J. Piekarski, and T. C. Hsu, Deletion of Thymidine Kinase Activity from *L*-cells Resistant to Bromodeoxyuridine, *Exptl. Cell Res.,* **31**: 297–312 (1963).

298   TRITIUM-LABELED MOLECULES IN BIOLOGY AND MEDICINE

169. S. Kit, Y. Valladares, and D. R. Dubbs, Effects of Age of Culture and Vaccinia Infection on Uridine Kinase Activity of L-cells, *Exptl. Cell Res.*, **34**: 257–265 (1964).
170. N. O. Kjelgaard and C. G. Kurland, The Distribution of Soluble and Ribosomal RNA as a Function of Growth Rate, *J. Mol. Biol.*, **6**: 341–348 (1963).
171. J. J. Klein, A. L. Goldstein, and A. White, Enhancement of *in vivo* Incorporation of Labeled Precursors into DNA and Total Protein of Mouse Lymphnodes after Administration of Thymic Extracts, *Proc. Natl. Acad. Sci. U.S.*, **53**: 812–817 (1965).
172. M. S. Kligerman, W. S. Heidenreich, and S. Green, Distribution of Tritiated Thymidine about a Capillary Sinusoid in a Transplanted Mouse Tumor, *Nature*, **196**: 282–283 (1962).
173. E. Koburg and W. Maurer, Autoradiographische Untersuchung mit H³-Thymidine über die Dauer der Deoxyribonukleinsäuresynthese und ihren zeitlichen Verlauf bei den Darmepithelien und anderen Zellarten der Maus, *Biochim. Biophys. Acta*, **61**: 229–242 (1962).
174. C. G. Konrad, Protein Synthesis and RNA Synthesis During Mitosis in Animal Cells, *J. Cell Biol.*, **19**: 267–277 (1963).
175. Ch. M. A. Kuypper and L. A. Smets, Role of the Medium in Radiation Effects on Cells Cultivated *in vitro*, *Naturwissenschaften*, **49**: 21–22 (1962).
176. W. J. Labordus-van-Breukelen and C. J. H. van den Brock, Labeling of Eggs by Injection of Tritiated Thymidine into *Asellus aquaticus* Females, *Nature*, **202**: 1020–1021 (1961).
177. A. Lacassagne and J.-S. Lattès, Répartition du polonium (injecté sous la peau) dans l'organisme de Rats porteurs de greffes cancéreuses, *Compt. Rend.*, **90**: 352–353 (1924).
178. A. Lahtiharju and H. Teir, Specific Increase in the Utilization of H³-Thymidine by Liver Cells in Hepatectomized Mice Following Injection of Autolytic Liver Tissue, *Exptl. Cell Res.*, **34**: 205–207 (1964).
179. L. G. Lajtha, R. Oliver, and F. Ellis, Incorporation of P³² and Adenine-C¹⁴ into DNA by Human Bone Marrow Cells *in Vitro*, *Brit. J. Cancer*, **8**: 367–379 (1954).
180. P. K. Lala, M. A. Maloney, and H. M. Patt, A Comparison of Two Markers of Cell Proliferation in Bone Marrow, *Acta Haematol.*, **31**: 1–8 (1964).
181. P. K. Lala, M. A. Maloney, and H. M. Patt, Measurement of DNA-Synthesis Time in Myeloid-Erythroid Precursors, *Exptl. Cell Res.*, **38**: 626–634 (1965).
182. L. F. Lamerton and R. J. M. Frey, eds., *Cell Proliferation*, A Guinness Symposium, Blackwell Scientific Publications, Oxford, 1963.
183. K. G. Lark, Cellular Control of DNA Biosynthesis, in *Molecular Genetics* (J. H. Taylor, ed.), Part I, pp. 153–206, Academic Press Inc., New York, 1963.
184. A. Larsson, Enzymatic Synthesis of Deoxyribonucleotides. VII. Studies on the Hydrogen Transfer with Tritiated Water, *Biochemistry*, **4**: 1984–1993 (1965).
185. C. P. Leblond, B. Messier, and B. M. Kopriwa, Thymidine-H³ as a Tool for the Investigation of the Renewal of Cell Populations, *Lab. Invest.*, **8**: 296 (1959).
186. S. M. Lehnert and S. Okada, DNA-Synthesis in Nuclei Isolated from Regenerating Rat Liver after Whole Body Irradiation, *Intern. J. Radiation Biol.*, **5**: 323–329 (1962).
187. E. M. Levine, Y. Becker, C. W. Boone, and H. Eagle, Contact Inhibition, Macromolecular Synthesis and Polyribosomes in Cultured Human Diploid Fibroblasts, *Proc. Natl. Acad. Sci. U.S.*, **53**: 350–355 (1965).

188. M. Lipkin, P. Sherlock, and B. Bell, Cell Proliferation Kinetics in the Gastro-intestinal Tract of Man. II. Cell Renewal in Stomach, Ileum, Colon, and Rectum, *Gastroenterology*, **45**: 721–729 (1964).
189. J. W. Littlefield and D. B. Dunn, The Occurrence and Distribution of Thymidine and Three Methylated Adenine Bases in Ribonucleic Acids from Several Sources, *Biochem. J.*, **70**: 642–661 (1958).
190. R. M. Litvak and R. Baserga, An Autoradiographic Study of the Uptake of H^3-Thymidine by Kidney Cells of Mice at Different Ages, *Exptl. Cell Res.*, **33**: 540–552 (1964).
191. M. R. Loran and T. T. Crocker, Population Dynamics of Intestinal Epithelia in the Rat Two Months after Partial Resection of the Ileum, *J. Cell Biol.*, **19**: 285–291 (1963).
192. R. A. McGrath, R. W. Williams, and R. B. Setlow, Increased ^{3}H-Thymidine Incorporation into DNA of Irradiated Slime Mould, *Intern. J. Radiation Biol.*, **8**: 373–380 (1964).
193. R. A. McGrath, W. M. Leach, and J. G. Carlson, Cell Stages Refractory to Thymidine Incorporation Induced by X-Rays, *Exptl. Cell Res.*, **37**: 39–44 (1965).
194. J. McLeish, Quantitative Relationship between Deoxyribonucleic and Ribo-nucleic Acid in Isolated Plant Nuclei, *Proc. Royal Soc.* (*London*), **B158**: 261–278 (1963).
195. O. Maløe and P. C. Hanawalt, Thymine Deficiency and the Normal DNA-Replication Cycle I., *J. Mol. Biol.*, **3**: 144–155 (1961).
196. M. A. Maloney and H. M. Patt, Neutrophil Life Cycle with Tritiated Thymi-dine, *Proc. Soc. Exptl. Biol. Med.*, **98**: 801–803 (1958).
197. G. Marin and M. A. Bender, Survival Kinetics of HeLa-S₃ Cells after Incorpora-tion of H^3-Thymidine or H^3-Uridine, *Intern. J. Radiation Biol.*, **7**: 221–233 (1963).
198. G. Marin and M. A. Bender, A Comparison of Mammalian Cell Killing by Incorporated H^3-Thymidine and H^3-Uridine, *Intern. J. Radiation Biol.*, **7**: 235–244 (1963).
199. J. C. Marsh and S. Perry, Thymidine Catabolism by Normal and Leukemic Human Leukocytes, *J. Clin. Invest.*, **43**: 267–278 (1964).
200. Y. Maruyama, Re-utilization of Thymidine during Death of a Cell, *Nature*, **201**: 93–94 (1964).
201. M. L. Mendelsohn, F. C. Dohan, Jr., and H. A. Moore, Jr., Autoradiographic Analysis of Cell Proliferation in Spontaneous Breast Cancer of CH₃ Mouse. I. Typical Cell Cycle and Timing of DNA Synthesis, *J. Natl. Cancer Inst.*, **25**: 477 (1960).
202. M. L. Mendelsohn, The Kinetics of Tumor Cell Proliferation, in *Cellular Radiation Biology*, The Williams and Wilkins Company, 1965, pp. 498–513.
203. M. Meselson and F. W. Stahl, The Replication of DNA in *Escherichia coli*, *Proc. Natl. Acad. Sci. U.S.*, **44**: 671 (1958).
204. B. Miletic, Z. Kucan, and L. Sasel, Synthesis of Deoxyribonucleic Acid in X-Irradiated Bacteria Treated with Chloramphenicol, *Nature*, **202**: 311–312 (1964).
205. O. L. Miller, Jr., G. E. Stone, and D. M. Prescott, Autoradiography of Soluble Materials, *J. Cell Biol.*, **23**: 654–658 (1964).
206. J. Mitchell, Autoradiographic Studies on Nucleic Acid and Protein Metabolism

in Lymphoid Cells. I. Differences amongst Members of the Plasma Cell Sequence, *Australian J. Exptl. Biol. Med. Sci.*, **42**: 347–362 (1964).

207. J. M. Mitchell, Autoradiographic Studies of Nucleic Acid and Protein Metabolism in Lymphoid Cells. II. The Stability and Actinomycin Sensitivity of Rapidly Formed RNA and Protein, *Australian J. Exptl. Biol. Med. Sci.*, **42**: 363–372 (1964).

208. J. M. Mitchison, Patterns of Synthesis of RNA and Other Cell Components during the Cell Cycle of *Schizosaccharomyces pombe*, *J. Cell. Comp. Phys.*, **62**: (Suppl. 1) 1–13 (1963).

209. J. M. Mitchison and J. E. Cummins, Changes in the Acid Soluble Pool during the Cell Cycle of *Schizosaccharomyces pombe*, *Expl. Cell Res.*, **35**: 394–401 (1964).

210. J. M. Mitchison and P. R. Gross, Selective Synthesis of Messenger RNA in a Fission Yeast during a Stepdown, and Its Relation to the Cell Cycle, *Exptl. Cell Res.*, **37**: 259–277 (1965).

211. J. Monod, J. Wyman, and J. P. Changeux, On the Nature of Allosteric Transitions: A Plausible Model, *J. Mol. Biol.*, **12**: 88–118 (1965).

212. J. Monod, J. P. Changeux, and F. Jacob, Allosteric Proteins and Cellular Control Systems, *J. Mol. Biol.*, **6**: 306–329 (1963).

213. R. Moore, A Comparison of HTO in Plasma and Expired Water Vapor, *Health Phys.*, **7**: 161–169 (1962).

214. N. R. Morris and G. A. Fishcher, Studies Concerning the Inhibition of Cellular Reproduction by Deoxyribonucleosides. I. Inhibition of the Synthesis of Deoxycytidine by a Phosphorylated Derivative of Thymine, *Biochim. Biophys. Acta*, **68**: 84–92 (1963).

215. N. R. Morris, P. Reichard, and G. A. Fischer, Studies Concerning the Inhibition of Cellular Reproduction by Deoxyribonucleosides. II. Inhibition of the Synthesis of Deoxcytidine by Thymidine, Deoxyadenosine and Deoxyguanosine, *Biochim. Biophys. Acta*, **68**: 93–99 (1963).

216. P. A. Morse, Jr. and V. R. Potter, Pyrimidine Metabolism in Tissue Culture Cells Derived From Rat Hepatomas. I. Suspension Cell Cultures Derived From the Novikoff Hepatoma, *Cancer Res.*, **25**: 499–508 (1965).

217. E. B. Mourad, Evidence for Cytoplasmic DNA in Root Cells of *Nicotiana*, *J. Cell Biol.*, **24**: 267–276 (1965).

218. H. S. Moyed and H. E. Umbarger, Regulation of Biosynthetic Pathways, *Physiol. Rev.*, **42**: 444–466 (1962).

219. O. Mühlbock and P. Emmelot, *Cellular Control Mechanisms and Cancer*, Elsevier Press, Amsterdam, 1964.

220. G. S. Nakai and C. G. Craddock, Acid-Soluble Nucleotides in Leukemic Cells, *Cancer Res.*, **25**: 575–587 (1965).

221. M. K. K. Nass, S. Nass, and B. A. Afzelius, The General Occurrence of Mitochondrial DNA, *Exptl. Cell Res.*, **37**: 516–539 (1965).

222. H. Naora and H. Naora, Some Observations on the Regulatory Control of the Multiplication of Mouse Hepatic Cells, *Exptl. Cell Res.*, **33**: 151–154 (1964).

223. A. Newton, P. P. Dendy, C. L. Smith, and P. Wildy, A Pool-size Problem Associated with the Use of Tritiated Thymidine, *Nature*, **194**: 886 (1962).

224. V. Nigon and S. Gillot, L'incorporation de la thymidine au cours de l'ovogénèse et du développement embryonnaire chez la *Drosophile*, *Exptl. Cell Res.*, **33**: 29–38 (1964).

225. M. C. Niu, Glucose-6-Phosphatase: Re-examination of the RNA-Induced Activity in Mouse Ascites Tumor Cells, *Science*, **148**: 513–516 (1965).

226. J. Nonnenmacher-Godet and E. C. Dougherty, Incorporation of Tritiated Thymidine in the Cells of *Caenorhabditis briggsae* (Nematode) Reared in Axenic Culture, *J. Cell Biol.*, **22**: 281–290 (1964).
227. O. F. Nygaard and R. L. Potter, Effect of X-radiation on DNA Metabolism in Various Tissues of the Rat. I. Incorporation of C^{14}-Thymidine into DNA during the First 24 Hours Post-Irradiation, *Radiation Res.*, **10**: 462–476 (1959).
228. N. Odartchenko, V. P. Bond, L. E. Feinendegen, and H. Cottier, Kinetics of Erythrocytic Precursor Proliferation in Dog, in *Cell Proliferation*, a Guinness Symposium (L. F. Lamerton and R. J. M. Frey, eds.), pp. 172–178. Blackwell Scientific Publications, Oxford, 1963.
229. N. Odartchenko, H. Cottier, L. E. Feinendegen, and V. P. Bond, Evaluation of Mitotic Time *in vivo*, Using Tritiated Thymidine as a Cell Marker: Successive Labeling with Time of Separate Mitotic Phases, *Exptl. Cell Res.*, **35**: 402–411 (1964).
230. N. Odartchenko, H. Cottier, L. E. Feinendegen, and V. P. Bond, Mitotic Delay in More Mature Erythroblasts of the Dog, Induced *in vivo* by Sublethal Doses of X-rays, *Radiation Res.*, **31**: 413–422 (1964).
231. W. Oehlert, D. Kramsch, and V. Beck, The Degradation of Ergastoplasmic Structures and Its Effect on the DNA Synthesis, *Exptl. Cell Res.*, **31**: 435–438 (1963).
232. R. Okazaki and A. Kornberg, Deoxythymidine Kinase of *Escherichia coli*. I. Purification and Some Properties of the Enzyme, *J. Biol. Chem.*, **239**: 269–274 (1964).
233. R. Okazaki and A. Kornberg, Deoxythymidine Kinase of *Escherichia coli*. II. Kinetics and Feedback Control, *J. Biol. Chem.*, **239**: 275–284 (1964).
234. M. Owen and S. McPherson, Cell Population Kinetics of an Osteogenic Tissue. II. *J. Cell Biol.*, **19**: 33–44 (1963).
235. R. B. Painter, F. Forro, and W. L. Hughes, Distribution of Tritium Labeled Thymidine in *E. coli* during Cell Multiplication, *Nature*, **181**: 328–329 (1958).
236. R. B. Painter, R. M. Drew, and W. L. Hughes, Inhibition of HeLa Growth by Intranuclear Tritium, *Science*, **127**: 1244–1245 (1958).
237. R. B. Painter, R. M. Drew, and B. G. Giauque, Further Studies on Deoxyribonucleic Acid Metabolism in Mammalian Cell Cultures, *Exptl. Cell Res.*, **21**: 98–105 (1960).
238. R. B. Painter and R. E. Rasmussen, A Pitfall of Low Specific Activity Radioactive Thymidine, *Nature*, **201**: 409–410 (1964).
239. R. B. Painter, R. M. Drew, and R. E. Rasmussen, Limitations in the Use of Carbon-Labeled and Tritium-Labeled Thymidine in Cell Culture Studies, *Radiation Res.*, **21**: 355–366 (1965).
240. W. J. Peacock, Chromosome Duplication and Structure as Determined by Autoradiography, *Proc. Natl. Acad. Sci. U.S.*, **49**: 793–801 (1963).
241. S. R. Pelc, Metabolic Activity of DNA as Shown by Autoradiography, *Lab. Invest.*, **8**: 225 (1959).
242. S. R. Pelc, Labelling of DNA and Cell Division in So-called Non-dividing Tissues, *J. Cell Biol.*, **22**: 21–28 (1964).
243. S. R. Pelc and T. C. Appleton, Distribution of Tritiated Thymidine in Various Tissues, *Nature*, **205**: 1287–1289 (1965).
244. S. Perry and J. C. Marsh, Uptake of Tritiated Thymidine by Leukemic Cells: Effect of Various Leukocyte Preparations, *Proc. Soc. Exptl. Biol. Med.*, **115**: 51–54 (1964).

245. R. O. Peterson and R. Baserga, Route of Injection and Uptake of Tritiated Precursors, *Arch. Pathol.*, **77**: 582–586 (1964).
246. D. Pettjohn and P. C. Hanawalt, Evidence for Repair-Replication of UV Damaged DNA in Bacteria, *J. Mol. Biol.*, **9**: 395–410 (1964).
247. G. W. Philpott and A. J. Coulombre, Lens Development. II. The Differentiation of Embryonic Chick Lens Epithelial Cells *in vitro* and *in vivo*, *Exptl. Cell Res.*, **38**: 635–644 (1965).
248. M. Pieber-Perretta, W. Rudolph, M. Perretta, and H. Hodgson, Effect of Erythropoietine on (^{14}C) Formate Incorporation into Rat Bone Marrow RNA, *Biochim. Biophys. Acta*, **95**: 360–362 (1965).
249. C. Pilgrim and W. Maurer, Autoradiographische Bestimmung der DNS-Verdopplungszeit verschiedener Zellarten von Maus und Ratte bei Doppelmarkierung mit ^{3}H und ^{14}C-Thymidine, *Naturwissenschaften*, **49**: 1–4 (1962).
250. C. Pilgrim, W. Erb, and W. Maurer, Diurnal Fluctuations in the Numbers of DNA Synthesizing Nuclei in Various Mouse Tissues, *Nature*, **199**: 863 (1963).
251. C. Pilgrim and W. Maurer, Autoradiographische Untersuchung über die Konstanz der DNS-Verdopplungsdauer bei Zellarten von Maus und Ratte durch Doppelmarkierung mit H-3- und C-14-Thymidin, *Exptl. Cell Res.*, **37**: 183–199 (1965).
252. C. Pilgrim, K. J. Lennartz, K. Wegener, S. Hollweg, and W. Maurer, Autoradiographische Untersuchung über tageszeitliche Schwankungen des H-3-Index und des Mitose-Index bei Zellarten der ausgewachsenen Maus, des Ratten-Fetus sowie bei Ascites Tumor Zellen, *Z. Zellforsch.*, **68**: 138–154 (1965).
253. E. Pinson and W. H. Langham, Physiology and Toxicology of Tritium in Man, *J. Appl. Physiol.*, **10**: 108–126 (1957).
254. W. S. Plaut, On the Incorporation of Thymidine in the Cytoplasm of *Amoeba proteus*, *Biochem. Pharmacol.*, **4**: 79–83 (1960).
255. V. Pohl and J. Quertier, Groupes sulfhydriles et morphogénèse. IV - Effets du beta mercapto éthanol et de l'acide-alpha-lipoique sur le métabolisme des acides nucléiques chez les embryons de Batracien et de Poulet, *J. Embryol. Exptl. Morphol.*, **11**: 293 (1963).
256. E. C. Pollard, M. J. Ebert, C. Miller, K. Kolacz, and T. F. Barone, Ionizing Radiation, Effect of Irradiated Medium on Synthetic Processes, *Science*, **147**: 1045–1047 (1965).
257. E. Ponder, The Cell Membrane and Its Properties, in *The Cell* (J. Brachet and A. E. Mirsky, eds.), Vol. II, Academic Press Inc., New York, 1961.
258. J. Post, C. Y. Huang, and J. Hoffman, The Replication Time and Pattern of the Liver Cell in the Growing Rat, *J. Cell Biol.*, **18**: 1–12 (1963).
259. J. Post and J. Hoffman, The Replication Time and Pattern of Carcinogen-Induced Hepatoma Cells, *J. Cell Biol.*, **22**: 341 (1964).
260. R. L. Potter, Discussion of Availability Time of Labeled DNA-precursors, in *Kinetics of Cellular Proliferation* (F. Stohlman, Jr., ed.), pp. 113–115, Grune Stratton, New York, 1959.
261. V. R. Potter, *Nucleic Acid Outlines*, Burgess Publishing Company, Minneapolis, Minnesota, 1960.
262. V. R. Potter, Feedback Inhibition of Thymidine Kinase by Thymidine Triphosphate, *Exptl. Cell Res.*, **9** (Suppl.): 259–261 (1963).
263. R. L. Potter and O. F. Nygaard, The Conversion of Thymidine to Thymine-Nucleotides and Deoxyribonucleic Acid *in Vivo*, *J. Biol. Chem.*, **238**: 2150–2155 (1963).
264. D. M. Prescott and M. A. Bender, Synthesis of RNA and Protein During

Mitosis in Mammalian Tissue Culture Cells, *Exptl. Cell Res.,* **26:** 260–268 (1962).

265. H. Quastler and F. G. Sherman, Cell Population Kinetics in the Intestinal Epithelium of the Mouse, *Exptl. Cell Res.,* **17:** 420–438 (1959).

266. M. Rabinovitz and W. S. Plaut, Cytoplasmic DNA Synthesis in *Amoeba proteus.* II. On the Behavior and Possible Nature of the DNA-containing Elements, *J. Cell Biol.,* **15:** 535–540 (1962).

267. M. Rabinovitz, J. Sinclair, L. DeSalle, R. Haselkorn, and H. H. Swift, Isolation of Deoxyribonucleic Acid from Mitochondrai of Chick Embryo Heart and Liver, *Proc. Natl. Acad. Sci. U.S.,* **53:** 1126–1133 (1965).

268. A. V. Rake and A. F Graham, Kinetics of Incorporation of Uridine-C^{14} into *L*-Cells RNA, *Biophys J.,* **4:** 267–284 (1964).

269. P. N. Rato and J. Engelberg, HeLa Cells: Effect of Temperature on the Life Cycle, *Science,* **148:** 1092–1094 (1965).

270. D. S. Ray and P. C. Hanawalt, Satellite DNA Components in *Euglena gracilis* Cells Lacking Chloroplasts, *J. Mol. Biol.,* **11:** 760–768 (1965).

271. P. Reichard and B. Estborn, Utilization of Desoxyribosides in the Synthesis of Poynucleotides, *J. Biol. Chem.,* **188:** 839–846 (1951).

272. P. Reichard, The Biosynthesis of Deoxyribonucleic Acid by the Chick Embryo. II. Metabolism of $O^2:2'$-cyclouridine, *J. Biol. Chem.,* **234:** 2719–2722 (1959).

273. A. B. Reiskin and M. L. Mendelsohn, A Comparison of DNA Synthesis in Induced Carciomata and Their Normal Counterpart, *Proc. Am. Assoc. Cancer Res.,* **3:** 353 (1962).

274. A. B. Reiskin and M. L. Mendelsohn, A Comparison of the Cell Cycle in Induced carcinomas and Their Normal Counterpart, *Cancer Res.,* **24:** 1131–1136 (1964).

275. M. Revel, H. H. Hiatt, and J.-P. Revel, Actinomycin D: An Effect on Rat Liver Homogenates Unrelated to Its Action on RNA Synthesis, *Science,* **146:** 1311–1313 (1965).

276. C. R. Richmond, W. H. Langham, and T. T. Trujillo, Comparative Metabolism of Tritiated Water by Mammals, *J. Cell. Comp. Physiol.,* **59:** 45–53 (1962).

277. W. O. Rieke, The *in Vivo* Reutilization of Lymphocytic and Sarcoma DNA by Cells Growing in the Peritoneal Cavity, *J. Cell Biol.,* **13:** 205–216 (1962).

278. S. H. Robinson and G. Brecher, Delayed Incorporation of Tritiated Thymidine into DNA, *Science,* **142:** 392 (1963).

279. J. R. Rubini, E. P. Cronkite, V. P. Bond, and T. M. Fliedner, The Metabolism and Fate of Tritiated Thymidine in Man, *J. Clin. Invest.,* **39:** 909–918 (1960).

280. J. R. Rubini, S. Keller, A. Eisentraut, and E. P. Cronkite, *In Vitro* Metabolism of H^3-Thymidine, in *Tritium in the Physical and Biological Sciences, Symp. Intern. At. Energy Agency,* **2:** 247–267 (1961).

281. J. R. Rubini, S. Keller, L. Wood, and E. P. Cronkite, Incorporation of Tritiated Thymidine into DNA after Oral Administration, *Proc. Soc. Exptl. Biol. Med.,* **106:** 49–52 (1961).

282. J. R. Rubini, S. Keller, and M. S. McCall, Inhibition of Tritiated Thymidine Incorporation into DNA by Alkaline Phosphatase Preparations, *Cancer Res.,* **24:** 655–661 (1964).

283. R. R. Rueckert and G. C. Muller, Studies on Unbalanced Growth in Tissue Culture. I. Induction and Consequences of Thymidine Deficiency, *Cancer Res.,* **20:** 1584 (1960).

284. J. Runnström, The Animalizing Effect of α-Lipoic Acid on Sea Urchin Eggs, *Exptl. Cell Res.,* **11:** 660 (1956).

285. R. Sager and Z. Ramanis, The Particulate Nature of Nonchromosomal Genes in *Chlamydomonas, Proc. Natl. Acad. Sci. U.S.*, **50**: 260 (1963).
286. H. V. Samis, Jr., V. J. Wulff, and J. A. Falzone, Jr., The Incorporation of (^{3}H) Cytidine into Ribonucleic Acid of Liver nuclei of Young and Old Rats, *Biochim. Biophys. Acta,* **91**: 223–232 (1964).
287. T. Samorajski and B. H. Marks, Localization of Tritiated Norepinephrine in Mouse Brain, *J. Histochem. Cytochem.,* **10**: 392–399 (1963).
288. H. Sampson, A. Katoh, Y. Hotta, and H. Stern, Metabolically Labile Deoxyribonucleic Acid, *Proc. Natl. Acad. Sci. U.S.*, **50**: 459–463 (1963).
289. L. D. Samuels and W. E. Kisieleski, Toxicological Studies of Tritiated Thymidine, *Radiation Res.,* **18**: 620–632 (1963).
290. A. A. Sandberg, Y. Kiguchi, and L. H. Crosswhite, Mitotic Ability of Leukemic Leukocytes in Chronic Myelocytic Leukemia, *Cancer Res.,* **24**: 1468–1473 (1964).
291. J. L. Sanders, G. V. Dalrymple, and C. D. Robinette, Retention of Labeled Deoxyribonucleic Acid Following Irradiation: A Statistical Consideration, *Nature,* **201**: 206–207 (1964).
292. S. K. Sarkar and R. K. Poddar, Non-conservation of H^3-Thymidine Label in the DNA of Growing Yeast Cells, *Nature,* **207**: 550–551 (1965).
293. G. Schmidt, Metabolism of Nucleic Acids, *Ann. Rev. Biochem.,* **33**: 667–728 (1964).
294. B. Schultze and W. Oehlert, Autoradiographic Investigation of Incorporation of H^3-Thymidine into Cells of the Rat and Mouse, *Science,* **131**: 737–738 (1960).
295. B. Schultze, W. Oehlert, and W. Maurer, Vergleichende Autoradiographische Untersuchung mit H-3-, C-14-, und S-35-markierten Aminosäuren zur Grösse des Eiweiss Stoffwechsels einzelner Gewebe und Zellarten bei Maus, Ratte und Kaninchen, *Beitr. Pathol. Anat. Allgem. Pathol.,* **122**: 406–431 (1960).
296. H. L. Segal and Y. S. Kim, Glucocorticoid Stimulation of the Biosynthesis of Glutamic Alanine Transaminase, *Proc Natl. Acad. Sci. U.S.,* **50**: 912–918 (1963).
297. N. Sestan, Diurnal Variation of ^{14}C-Leucine Incorporation into Proteins of Isolated Rat Liver Nuclei, *Naturwissenschaften,* **151**: 371 (1964).
298. R. B. Setlow and W. L. Carrier, The Disappearance of Thymine Dimers from DNA: An Error-correcting Mechanism, *Proc. Natl. Acad. Sci. U.S.,* **51**: 226–231 (1964).
299. R. B. Setlow, W. L. Carrier, and F. J. Bollum, Pyrimidine Dimers in UV-Irradiated Poly dI-dC, *Proc. Natl. Acad. Sci. U.S.,* **53**: 111–117 (1965).
300. D. Shemin and D. Rittenberg, Some Interrelationships in General Nitrogen Metabolism, *J. Biol. Chem.,* **153**: 401 (1944).
301. D. C. Shepard, Production and Elimination of Excess DNA in Ultraviolet-Irradiated *Tetrahymena, Exptl. Cell Res.,* **38**: 570–579 (1965).
302. F. G. Sherman and H. Quastler, DNA Synthesis in Irradiated Intestinal Epithelium, *Exptl. Cell Res.,* **19**: 343–360 (1960).
303. F. G. Sherman, H. Quastler, and D. R. Wimber, Cell Population Kinetics in the Ear Epidermis of Mice, *Exptl. Cell Res.,* **25**: 114–119 (1961).
304. R. T. Sims, The Incorporation and Fate of H^3-Tyrosine in the Hair Cortex of Rats Observed by Radioautography, *J. Cell Biol.,* **22**: 403–412 (1964).
305. W. F. Siri and J. Evers, Tritium Exchange in Biological Systems, in *Tritium in the Physical and Biological Sciences, Symp. Intern. At. Energy Agency,* **2**: 71–84 (1961).

306. J. E. Sisken and R. Kinosita, Timing of DNA Synthesis in the Mitotic Cycle *in Vitro, J. Biophys. Biochem. Cytol.,* **9:** 509–518 (1961).
307. J. E. Sisken and L. Morasca, Intrapopulation Kinetics of the Mitotic Cycle, *J. Cell Biol.,* **25:** 179–189 (1965).
308. R. N. Staroscik, W. H. Jenkins, and M. L. Mendelsohn, Availability of Tritiated Thymidine after Intravenous Administration, *Nature,* **202:** 456–458 (1964).
309. C. G. Steel, The Use of Direct Tritium Assay Techniques in Studies with Tritiated Thymidine, in *Tritium in the Physical and Biological Sciences, Symp. Intern. At. Energy Agency,* **2:** 349–358 (1961).
310. M. Steinert, Mitochondria Associated with the Kineto Nucleus of *Trypanosoma mega, J. Biophys. Biochem. Cytol.,* **8:** 542 (1969).
311. P. A. Stewart, H. Quastler, M. R. Skougaard, D R. Wimber, M. F. Wolfsberg, C. A. Perotta, B. Ferbel, and M. Carlough, Four-Factor Model Analysis of Thymidine Incorporation into Mouse DNA and the Mechanism of Radiation Effects, *Radiation Res.,* **24:** 521–537 (1965).
312. C. R. Stocking and E. M. Gifford, Incorporation of Thymidine into Chloroplasts of *Spirogyra, Biochem. Biophys. Res. Comm.,* **1:** 159–164 (1959).
313. F. Stohlman, Jr., ed., *The Kinetics of Cellular Proliferation,* Grune and Stratton, New York, 1959.
314. G. E. Stone and D. M. Prescott, Cell Division and DNA Synthesis in *Tetrahymena pyriformis,* Deprived of Essential Amino Acids, *J. Cell Biol.,* **21:** 275–281 (1964).
315. G. E. Stone, O. L. Miller, Jr., and D. M. Prescott, H³-Thymidine Derivative Pools in Relation to Macromolecular DNA Synthesis in *Tetrahymena pyriformis, J. Cell Biol.,* **25:** 171–177 (1965).
316. A. N. Stroud, A. M. Brues, and B. R. Svoboda, DNA Synthesis in Mammalian Kidney Cells in Tissue Culture after Single and Periodic Doses of Irradiation, *Ann. New York Acad. Sci.,* **95:** 942–959 (1961).
317. S. T. Takats and R. M. S. Smellie, Thymidine Degradation Products in Plant Tissues Labeled with Tritiated Thymidine, *J. Cell Biol.,* **17:** 59–66 (1963).
318. J. H. Taylor, P. S. Woods, and W. L. Hughes, The Organization and Duplication of Chromosomes as Revealed by Autoradiographic Studies Using Tritium Labeled Thymidine, *Proc. Natl. Acad. Sci. U.S.,* **43:** 122–128 (1957).
319. J. H. Taylor, Nucleic Acid Synthesis in Relation to the Cell Division Cycle, *Ann. N.Y. Acad. Sci.,* **90:** 409 (1960).
320. T. Terasima and L. J. Tolmach, Growth and Nucleic Acid Synthesis in Synchronously Dividing Populations of HeLa Cells, *Exptl. Cell Res.,* **30:** 344–362 (1963).
321. R. C. Thompson, Studies of Metabolic Turnover with Tritium as a Tracer, *J. Biol. Chem.,* **197:** 81–87 (1952).
322. E. A. Tonna and E. P. Cronkite, Cellular Response to Fracture Studied with Tritiated Thymidine, *J. Bone Joint Surgery,* **43A:** 352–362 (1961).
323. E. A. Tonna and E. P. Cronkite, The Effects of Extraperiosteal Injections of Blood Components on Periosteal Cell Proliferation, *J. Cell Biol.,* **23:** 79 (1964).
324. E. A. Tonna, An Autoradiographic Evaluation of the Aging Cellular Phase of Mouse Skeleton Using Tritiated Glycine, *J. Gerontol.,* **19:** 198–206 (1964).
325. E. A. Tonna, Protein Synthesis and Cells of the Skeletal System, in *The Use of Radioautography in Investigating Protein Synthesis, Symp. Intern. Soc. Cell*

Biol., Montreal, 1964, (C. P. Leblond and K. B. Warren, ed.), pp. 215–244, Academic Press, Inc., New York, 1965.

326. J. E. Trosko, E. H. Y. Chu, and W. L. Carrier, The Induction of Thymine Dimers In Ultraviolet-Irradiated Mammalian Cells, *Radiation Res.,* **24:** 667–672 (1965).

327. F. A. O. Udekwu, D. D. Kozoll, and K. A. Meyer, Determination of Total Body Water with Tritium Oxide (H_2^3O). *J. Nucl. Med.,* **4:** 60–69 (1963).

328. H. E. Umbarger, Intracellular Regulatory Mechanisms, *Science,* **145:** 674–679 (1965).

329. J. Van't Hoff and A. H. Sparrow, A Relationship between DNA Content, Nuclear Volume, and Minimum Mitotic Cycle Time, *Proc. Natl. Acad. Sci. U.S.,* **49:** 897–902 (1963).

330. J. Van't Hoff and H. K. Ying, Simultaneous Marking of Cells in Two Different Segments of the Mitotic Cycle, *Nature,* **202:** 981–983 (1964).

331. A. Vorbrodt, T. Wilczok, K. Schneiberg, and T. Gorki, Autoradiographic studies of the Fate of Heterologous DNA after Injection into Mice, *Neoplasma,* **10:** 355–359 (1963).

332. S. R. Wagle, The Influence of Growth Hormone, Cortisol and Insulin on the Incorporation of Amino Acids into Protein, *Arch. Biochem. Biophys.,* **102:** 373–378 (1963).

333. R. I. Walker and I. Fowler, Granulocyte Inhibition of Human Peripheral Blood Lymphocytes Grown *in Vitro, Exptl. Cell Res.,* **38:** 379–385 (1965).

334. N. K. Wessels, Effects of Extraepithelial Factors on the Incorporation of Thymidine by Embryonic Epidermis, *Exptl. Cell Res.,* **30:** 36–55 (1963).

335. A. J. Whaba and M. Friedkin, The Enzymatic Synthesis of Thymidylate. I. Early Steps in the Purification of Thymidylate Synthetase of *Escherichia coli, J. Biol. Chem.,* **237:** 3794–3801 (1962).

336. D. E. Wimber and H. Quastler, A C^{14}- and H^3-Thymidine Double Labeling Technique in the Study of Cell Proliferation in *Tradescantia* Root Tips, *Exptl. Cell Res.,* **30:** 8–22 (1963).

337. D. R. Wolstenholme and W. S. Plaut, Cytoplasmic DNA Synthesis in *Amoeba proteus.* III. Further Studies on the Nature of the DNA-Containing Elements, *J. Cell Biol.,* **22:** 505–512 (1964).

338. I. G. Wool and A. J. Munro, An Influence of Insulin on the Synthesis of a Rapidly Labeled RNA by Isolated Rat Diaphragm, *Proc. Natl. Acad. Sci. U.S.,* **50:** 918–923 (1963).

339. V. J. Wulff, H. Quastler, F. G. Sherman, and H. V. Samis, Jr., The Effect of Specific Activity of H^3-Cytidine on Its Incorporation into Tissues of Young and Old Mice, *J. Gerontol.,* **20:** 34–40 (1965).

340. K. F. Wylie, W. A. Bigler, and G. R. Grove, Biological Half Life of Tritium, *Health Physics,* **9:** 911–914 (1963).

341. N. Xeros, Deoxyriboside Control and Synchronization of Mitosis, *Nature,* **194:** 682–683 (1962).

342. Y. L. Yammamoto, L. E. Feinendegen, and V. P. Bond, Effect of Radiation on the RNA Metabolism of the Central Nervous System, *Radiation Res.,* **21:** 36–45 (1964).

343. C. H. Yoon and D. J. Sabo, Bases for Failure to Induce Transformation *in Vivo* with Exogenous, Homologous DNA in Mice. Autoradiographic Investigation of Incorporation of Exogenous DNA labeled with H^3-Thymidine into Germ Cells, *Exptl. Cell Res.,* **34:** 599–602 (1964).

344. Y. Yotsuyanagi and C. Guerrier, Mise en évidence par les techniques cytochimques et la microscopie électronique d'acid désoxyribonuclique dans les mitochondries et les proplastes d'*Allium cepa, Compt. Rend.,* **260**: 2344–2347 (1965).

345. R. W. Young, Regional Differences in Cell Generation Time in Growing Rat Tibia, *Exptl. Cell Res.,* **26**: 562–567 (1962).

346. G. Zajicek, A. Rosin, and J. Gross, Tritiated Thymidine as Tracer in DNA Metabolism and Cell Dynamics of Experimental Myeloid Leukemia, in *Tritium in the Physical and Biological Sciences, Symp. Intern. At. Energy Agency,* **2**: 291–300 (1961).

347. G. Zajicek, N. Bernstein, A. Rosin, and J. Gross, Studies on the *in Vitro* Incorporation of Tritiated Thymidine into Ascites Tumor Cells, *Exptl. Cell Res.,* **31**: 390–396 (1963).

348. G. Zajicek and J. Gross, Studies on the Radiobiological Effect of H^3-Thymidine on the DNA Turnover in Landschütz Ascites Tumor Cells, *Exptl. Cell Res.,* **34**: 138–143 (1964).

349. A. Zuppinger, G. Poretti, P. Zaoralek, and H. Aebi, Stahlenbedingte Störungen des Tritium Einbaues in die organische Zellsubstanz, *Strahlentherapie,* **118**: 42–45 (1962).

350. A. Zuppinger, G. Poretti, K. Schwarz, P. Zaoralek, and H. Aebi, Disturbances in the Tritium Content in Organs after Irradiation, *Radiol. Clin.,* **32**: 402–410 (1963).

CHAPTER 6

The Toxicity of Tritium

1. Introduction

Tritium-labeled compounds are not only effectively and widely used as metabolic tracers but also serve as unique tools for irradiating and killing single cells selectively with the short-range tritium β-particles. It is obviously necessary for the dose of a given tritiated compound in tracer experiments in biological systems not to exceed toxic levels.

The biological toxicity of tritium is due mainly to the β-particle emitted in the course of transmutation to He^3 and may also be elicited by direct chemical consequences of the transmutation. This has been referred to briefly in Chapters 1 and 2. Thus, the β-particle produces ions and excited molecules along its tract; then subsequent molecular reactions involve radicals; and bond rupture, configurational changes, fragmentations, and polymerizations may occur. In addition, the decay of tritium adds a positive charge to the daughter helium, which itself is chemically inert. The sudden change of charge may excite the carrier molecule sufficiently for inducing intramolecular bonds to split.[122] The helium capturing an electron when expelled from the molecule leaves an electron deficiency, e.g., a positively charged ion which can then capture a hydroxyl group or another electron donor. The recoil energy imparted to the nucleus at the moment of tritium decay is about 0–3 ev, probably too small to split a molecular bond. Because of the very short range of the tritium β-particle in matter, a distinction in a biological system between the radiation effect and the transmutation effect is difficult, whereas this is relatively easy in case of isotopes which not only emit a higher energy radiation than tritium but also impart a higher recoil energy to the transmuted nuclide. For example, in case of C^{14} transmutation, the maximum recoil energy of the resulting nitrogen nucleus is 6.9 ev,[111] enough to split a bond. It is 5.1 ev for P^{33} decay and 77.3 ev for P^{32}, and both isotopes decay to sulfur, an advantage for distinguishing between the recoil and chemical transmutation effect.[5]

Although the initial molecular events in radiation interaction have been recognized in pure chemical systems, they are very difficult to explore in complex biological material. In principle, the events in both systems are, of course, identical. For the sake of convenience rather than of accuracy, the primary radiation effects in biological systems frequently are expressed in terms of ion pairs per unit tract length of the trajecting electromagnetic or particle radiation, reflecting the "linear energy transfer" (LET), which expresses the rate of energy loss in electron volts per unit track length. The denser the ionizations per total dose absorbed, the greater are the toxic effects in biological systems.[72]

Chemical kinetic isotope effects do not contribute to tritium toxicity because the amount of isotope necessary to cause a generalized disturbance of metabolism is above the dose level at which serious radiation effects occur. The toxicity of the nonradioactive deuterium, nevertheless, is due to its "interference in the delicately synchronized net of chemical reactions in the cell," as discussed by Rittenberg.[97]

An evaluation of tritium toxicity must exclude possible metabolic alterations caused by the molecule to which tritium is bound. Thus, it was noted in Chapter 5 that, for example, thymidine in relatively low concentrations may already saturate the respective enzymes in the incorporation pathway and consequently affect the equilibrium of pyrimidine interconversions. With rising concentrations it may retard cell growth and cause cell death. Such toxic manifestations must be distinguished from radiation effects particularly when the H^3-thymidine is used in low specific activity.

Studies on the radiotoxicity of tritium date back to the early 1950's, after tritiated water became available for tracer work. More recently, the increasing use of tritiated nucleic acid precursors prompted intensified studies on the radiobiological effect of tritium incorporated into or close to the genetic material. Since the tritium β-radiation produces relatively dense and localized ionizations, dosimetry is difficult, and there will be a discussion in this chapter about the fact that a "relative biological effectiveness" (RBE value) for the tritium β-particle must be carefully defined in order to have any general meaning. The tritium toxicity varies with different experimental designs, largely with the different metabolic pathways and intracellular sites of incorporation of the molecule to which the isotope is attached. Since tritium has a long half-life of about 12.3 years, it is usually the biological half-life which determines the accumulated radiation dose.

In this chapter the experimental evidence for tritium toxicity will be briefly reviewed according to the type of tritiated molecule used in a specific biological system. In order to comprehend the diverse data, dosimetric problems with regard to tritium will be referred to first. Suggestions as to the tritium dose that should be employed for tracer studies will be offered in context of health physics problems at the end of the chapter.

2. The Problem of Dosimetry

2.1. LINEAR ENERGY TRANSFER

The range distribution of the β-particles from tritium in biological material was discussed in Chapter 1. It was emphasized that low-energy β-absorption is determined by the number of electrons per unit volume matter and that considerable scattering of the particles must be taken into account. A tritium β-particle of average energy (about 5.6 kev) travels approximately 0.9 μ in biological material of unit density and a maximum distance of about 6 μ is reached by less than 1% of the particles. About 80% of the particles are absorbed within 1 μ. It was also emphasized in Chapters 1 and 4 that densities are not strictly uniform in cells, hence the range values may differ for various sub-cellular structures. For convenience in calculations, wet biological material is usually assumed to be homogeneous with a density equal to water.

A β-particle loses energy by interacting with molecules along its track, causing molecular excitations and ionizations. The energy in electron volts absorbed per unit track length is expressed as linear energy transfer (LET). Since biological radiation effects are due to ionizations in most instances, the term LET is often substituted by the number of ion pairs per unit track length. In order to appraise the amount of energy absorbed in biological material containing tritium, two aspects must be considered: one is the ionization density along a single track; the other is the range spectrum of the tracks. The total energy absorbed per single track length is easily obtained from a fitting range-energy equation for an absorbing material of a given density (see Chapter 1). A tritium β-particle of average energy hence loses 5.6–5.7 kev over a distance of about 0.9 μ in biological material.

The energy absorbed from the particle per single ionization along the track is not known with certainty, but it is customary to compare it to the ionization energy of water, which is about 30 ev. Apelgot and Duquesne[4] adopted a value of 42 ev per ionization on the basis of the electron density of water (3.3 × 10^{23} cm^{-3}) and calculated with it the energy loss (LET) along an average tritium β-track in water, as indicated in Table 6.1. The table shows that in water 39 ev/0.01 μ is lost over the first 0.1-μ length of track; thereafter the energy loss

TABLE 6.1

CALCULATED ENERGY LOSS ALONG THE TRACK OF TRITIUM β-PARTICLE OF AVERAGE ENERGY (5.7 kev), IN WATER[a]

Track increment (μ)	Average energy of the β-particle at the end of track distance (kev)	Average energy loss over track increment (ev per mμ)	Average energy loss over total distance of track (ev)
0	5.70	3.9	0
0.010	5.66	3.9	39
0.015	5.64	3.9	58.5
0.02	5.62	3.9	78
0.05	5.50	3.9	195
0.10	5.31	4.18	390
0.2	4.89	4.3	808
0.3	4.46	4.9	1238
0.4	3.97	5.5	1728
0.6	2.82	—	2878

[a] Straight particle projectory assumed. Reproduced with permission of Apelgot and Duquesne, *Intern. J. Radiation Biol.*[4]

per unit track length increases. For DNA having 5.28×10^{23} electrons per cm³, 60 ev were estimated to be absorbed per ion pair.[4] The average β-track would be correspondingly shorter by a factor of about 0.7 in DNA. A value of 25 ev per ionization in X-irradiated DNA was chosen by Emmerson and Howard-Flanders.[38] It is thus deduced that a tritium β-particle of average energy, ranging approximately 0.9 μ in biological material (water) and 0.7 μ in chemically pure DNA only, produces approximately 90–200 ion pairs over this distance. For the tritium β-particle of maximum energy the ion density over the first unit track length is reduced to about one-third. Thus, within the immediate sphere around the disintegrating tritium, the ionization density is inversely proportional to the energy of the particle. It should be recalled that the most frequent tritium β-particles have energies of 2–3 kev. The tritium β-particles thus yield a higher LET close to the decaying nuclide than, for instance, C¹⁴ β-particles (maximum energy 0.185 Mev).

The considerable density of ionizations localized to the vicinity of the disintegrating tritium causes the radiobiological effects to vary with the position of this nuclide in a cell. Thus, ionization "packages" in the cell nucleus affect particularly the genetic material. According to Lea[72] the frequency of chromosome breaks rises about fivefold in a σ-shaped curve as a function of increase of linear density of ions, from about 10 to 10,000/1 μ. A hundred ionizations per micron, as produced by one single tritium-β, can therefore easily cause a chromosomal break.

To illustrate this point further, inactivation *in vitro* by X-rays of transforming DNA was achieved already by one ion pair per 5×10^5 molecular weight.[29] In terms of electron volts, 100 ev caused breaking of 6 or 7 hydrogen-bond pairs in DNA in 0.1% aqueous solution, largely due to attack by radicals, and 14 or 15 broken hydrogen-bond pairs were reported to result in a scission of the DNA chain under conditions of the experiments.[106] In *E. coli*, 1.2 ionizations in DNA per 2×10^8 molecular weight caused 6% of the DNA in the bacterium to break down.[38] In addition, it must be considered that one-half of the total injuries per bacterium appeared to be due to interaction of free radicals.[61]

2.2. Absorbed Dose

Radiation absorbed in matter is conventionally expressed in the unit of the rad, which equals 100 ergs (62.5×10^{12} ev) absorbed by 1 g of substance. Since the unit of the rad is valid only for that volume of substance that actually absorbs the energy, it can be used with tritium only if the nuclide is distributed truly uniformly (see Chapter 1). For expressing the energy deposited from a single tritium β-particle, for example, in an animal cell, the unit of the rad is meaningless and inapplicable.

For small spherical volumes with diameters in the range of the β-track various dose estimates were given. Thus, Robertson and Hughes[98,99] calculated, for material of unit density, that 53.5 rads are absorbed on an average from tritium β-particles within a sphere of 0.5-μ radius (0.52 μ^3) surrounding the disintegrating nuclide. From a particle with an energy of 2–3 kev, 82.5 rad would be delivered to this volume. Lajtha[69] and Oliver and Lajtha[70,84] held that about 168 rad were absorbed from an average-energy tritium β-particle within a sphere of 1-μ diameter around the point source. Strauss[111] expressed the radiation absorbed in units of roentgen-equivalent physical (rep = 93 ergs/g) in matter of unit density for spheres with varying radii around tritium: in a sphere with a radius of 0.01 μ, an average energy of 1.5×10^5 rep would be deposited per single β-particle; with a radius of 0.1 μ, 1490 rep would result; with a radius of 1 μ, 22.6 rep would result; and with a radius of 10 μ, only 0.023 rep would be delivered.

Apelgot and Duquesne[4] calculated the average energy deposited in bacteria and chose for that purpose spheres of various diameters containing tritium distributed uniformly with a specific activity of 1 $\mu c/\mu^3$. The diameters of the spheres calculated did not exceed the maximum β-track length. Thus, in a spherical volume of water having

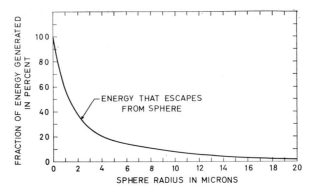

FIG. 6.1. Relative deposition of energy from tritium β-particles in spherical volumes, containing tritium distributed uniformly. Courtesy of J. S. Robertson, Brookhaven National Laboratory, Medical Department, Upton, New York.[100]

a 0.1-μ radius, approximately 10^9 ev or 10^{-3} erg per minute per microcurie tritium per cubic micron are deposited (1 ev $= 1.6 \times 10^{-12}$ erg). It is clear that in terms of rads the value of absorbed energy becomes relatively large. Thus, a bacterium with a volume of 4.2 μ^3 containing tritium uniformly distributed absorbs about 14 rad per β-particle of averge energy.

If tritium is distributed uniformly within a substance of unit density, 1 mc delivers 12.14 rad per hour (see Chapter 1). It is obvious that the amount of energy absorbed in a biological traget containing tritium depends on the relative size of the target with regard to the length of the particle track. Those structures larger than several microns in diameter may absorb the total energy of a tritium β-particle originating in the center of the structure. On the other hand, tritium positioned close to a cell wall has apparently a 50% chance of irradiating the environment of the target rather than the target itself. For instance, tritium positioned in the peripheral shell of a nucleus of an animal or plant cell may irradiate adjacent cytoplasm as much as the nucleus. The same situation pertains to bacteria[67] and phage.[14] Radiation isodose curves are helpful in approximating the amount of energy absorbed over a specific distance delineating the radius of a sphere.[4,52,99] A convenient function is plotted in Fig. 6.1, according to Robertson.[100] This graph correlates the radius of a material sphere of unit density, for example, of a cell nucleus containing tritium to the energy that escapes from the sphere in per cent of total energy generated. With this information, absorbed dose, for instance, to a spherical cell nucleus, can be estimated rather easily with the conventional β-absorption formula, provided the tritium is distributed uniformly. Accordingly,

$$\frac{A \times E \times k}{m \times 100} = \text{dose in rads per unit time}$$

where A = disintegrations per nucleus per unit time. This value may be obtained by radiochemical and autoradiographic analysis or by correction of autoradiographic data for β-absorption (see Section 7.1); E, average value for energy of the tritium β (5.6 × 10^{-3} Mev); k = 1.602 × 10^{-6} (ergs/mev); m = mass of the nucleus in grams, usually obtained from volume assuming unit density; and 100 = factor for converting ergs/gram to rads. If the cell nucleus has a diameter of 2 μ, 37% of the total energy generated escapes the nucleus. For a 4 μ-radius, the loss is only 20%.

For instance, if a nucleus of 4-μ radius contains 1 mc of tritium per gram, e.g., 270 × 10^{-12} mc per nucleus or about 35 tritium disintegrations per hour, the dose to the nucleus will be about 12 rad per hour minus 20% for "edge effect," resulting in 9.7 rad per hour.

The assumption of uniform distribution of tritium in the target can be ascertained by autoradiographic examination. For instance, cell nuclei labeled with H^3-thymidine show a seemingly random distribution of grains when the cell is in interphase, despite the fact that the contracted chromosomes during mitosis exhibit labeling concentration in certain chromosomal segments. Since the duration of mitosis is short in comparison with the length of interphase, uniform tritium distribution after H^3-thymidine labeling is, in most instances, a valid assumption for dose calculation. On the other hand, nuclear tritium after RNA labeling is often localized mainly in the nucleoli throughout most of interphase, and calculation of absorbed dose to the entire nucleus on the basis of uniform tritium distribution is, of course, not permitted.

2.3. RELATIVE BIOLOGICAL EFFECTIVENESS

The term "relative biological effectiveness" (RBE) expresses the ratio of a dose of standard radiation, usually X- or γ-radiation, to produce a specific biological effect to the dose of an unknown radiation required to yield the same biological effect. The more toxic the unknown radiation, the higher is the RBE value. Maximum permissible doses are conventionally expressed in terms of rem, which is equal numerically to the RBE value × rad.

Because of the relatively high linear energy transfer within the immediate vicinity of a disintegrating tritium nuclide, the resulting toxic effects in biological systems vary with the radiosensitivity of the structure containing the tritium. For example, a cell nucleus is more radiosensitive than the cytoplasm,[16,79,81,118,120,121,128] and different cell

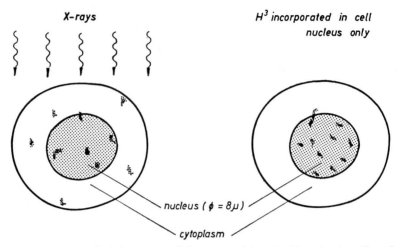

Fig. 6.2. The absorbed dose to a cell from β-particles of tritium in the cell nucleus is localized mainly to the nucleus, contrary to the random absorption from X- or γ-rays. The ionization "packages" from the tritium β-particles are comparable to those produced by the photo- and Compton electrons generated by 250 kvp X-rays.

types have various sensitivities,[7,26] which are probably also determined by the nucleotide content in the nuclei.[63] It is the discrete energy absorption to selected targets within an organism which makes the determination of the relative biological effectiveness against a standard radiation difficult. This is illustrated in Fig. 6.2.

A comparison of the relative toxicity of the tritium β-radiation with that of other types of radiation requires adequately defined units of measurement. It is obvious from the foregoing discussion that the rad can serve this purpose provided specific circumstances prevail, for example, in the case of a uniform distribution of tritium in the respective target. Moreover, it is important to consider the low and changing dose rate from incorporated tritium when the standard radiation is designed. Otherwise RBE values cannot be determined.

RBE values for tritiated water have been proposed. With weight reduction of spleen and thymus[125] or death[49] in mice chosen as parameters, the β-radiation delivered from tritiated water was found to be about 1.4[125] to 1.7[49] times more effective than a comparable energy absorbed over several days from γ-rays (Co[60]). These values are meaningful with respect to the total animal, but they are based on the assumption of uniform distribution of tritiated water within the animal organism. Uniform distribution, however, actually does not exist since the bones take up less water than soft tissue. If the inhomogeneous water distribution is considered, the RBE value from the tritium β-radiation must be lower. In fact, if a correction factor of 0.8 is applied and if the γ-radiation from Co[60] would be replaced as standard by 250 kvp X-rays, the RBE value would be close to 1.[16] An attempt at investigating the literature data on tritium effects from H[3]-thymidine in mammalian cells also led to the suggestion that the RBE value for the tritium β-radiation is probably 1 if 250 kvp X-rays are used as standard.[16] The same conclusion was reached from work with bacteria.[6] The important statement that one can consider the tritium β-spectrum to be comparable to the spectrum of Compton and photoelectrons generated in matter by 250 kvp X-rays can now be made (see also Fig. 6.2).

It is, however, obvious that a single maximum permissible burden of tritium (or tritium-labeled compound) in an organism cannot be recommended as generally valid for all labeled compounds. An extreme example is the comparison of toxicity of tritiated water and H[3]-thymidine. The latter being concentrated in the cell nucleus was found to be about 1000 times more toxic than the tritiated water in comparable doses in HeLa cells in culture.[86] It has been estimated that under various conditions in the total animal body H[3]-thymidine, because of its selective incorporation into DNA, may deliver a dose to the chromosomes of proliferating cells from 50 to 50,000 times greater than that delivered from tritiated water administered to the animal in an equal amount of microcuries.[57]

2.4. CONCLUSION

Since the radiation absorbed from the tritium β-particles cannot be expressed easily in most instances in conventional terms of comparative dosimetry, predictions as to the degree of toxicity to be expected from a certain dose of a tritiated compound are frequently vague. Radiation effects from tritium in living systems must be determined experimentally for each class of tritiated compounds.

The following sections will briefly survey the information now available on the biological toxicity of tritium-labeled compounds. Early and delayed effects have been examined mainly with tritiated water and tritiated nucleosides, especially thymidine. Some data have also become known from work with tritiated amino acids. Despite the attempts presented here, integrating the various data to common expressions which allow predictions to be made and hence to become useful information for further research still appears to be a task for the future.

3. Toxicity of Tritium-Labeled Water

3.1. SINGLE CELLS

Toxicity of tritium was first studied in unicellular organisms. In 1951, Powers and Shefner[94] reported on the lethality of the progeny of single *Paramecium aurelia* grown for 2 days in a nutrient medium containing tritiated water 1–100 mc/ml. The fact that an increasing lethality with increasing dose of tritiated water was observed only after autogamy, 3–5 days after the tritium was incorporated by the single progenitor *Paramecium*, suggested a radiation effect mainly to the nuclear material and not to the cytoplasm of the cells. The data were compatible with the fact that β-radiation was the sole cause of the lethality without addition from a transmutation effect by helium. The dose of tritium necessary to produce the observed effects was clearly very large, being about 1–100 mc, compared with the dose sufficient to produce biological effects in mammals, as will be seen below.

The predominant role of the nucleus in radiosensitivity also in mammalian cells is obvious from the experiments by Painter and collaborators[86] who compared the relative toxicity of tritiated water and of H³-thymidine incorporated into DNA in HeLa tissue culture cells. Five millicuries of tritiated water per milliliter of medium for 48 hours caused the number of cells in the culture to decrease to approximately one-half; but only 1–2000 times less radioactivity from H³-thymidine specific activity 500 mc/mmole) for 24 hours, followed by 48 hours culturing in regular medium, was necessary to produce the same effect. A dose of tritiated water 100 times higher than that of H³-thymidine added to the culture medium was reported to yield the same degree of depression of antibody synthesis by probably also inhibiting cell proliferation.[37] The H³-thymidine was added in an amount of 25 μc/ml and had a specific activity of 1.5 c/mmole. In a careful study on induction of chromosomal aberrations, Dewey *et al.*[31] described the radiation dose from tritiated water to be about 1.2 times more effective than the same dose of Co⁶⁰ γ-radiation, which would yield a RBE value close to 1 if 250 kvp X-rays were the standard radiation. Moreover, the authors found that the β-particle from tritium bound to thymidine was less effective than that bound to water, on the basis of equal dose. These latter findings were discussed in the context of comparable data and are not readily explained.[16] Perhaps the tritium distribution was not really uniform. Sanders *et al.*[103] compared the dose–effect relationships (cell killing) of tritium radiation delivered only to the nucleus from H³-thymidine of low specific activity (280 mc/mmole) and from tritiated water at various dose levels and found tritium bound to thymidine to be relatively more toxic than tritiated water at comparable dose levels in the nucleus. It was postulated that the discrepancy was a result of some mechanism in addition to the β-radiation from H³-thymidine. The toxicity of even low concentration of nonradioactive thymidine on cell growth,[87] however, explains the different responses without invoking other mechanisms, for example, a transmutation effect. In addition, the effects were examined 48 and 72 hours after beginning of exposure, while the intranuclear tritium content was compared at 30 hours. During the interval, H^3-thymidine probably continued to be incorporated and concentrated in the proliferating cells.

The effect on cell growth in culture by continuous irradiation from increasing doses of tritiated water and the effect of trypsinization on such irradiated cultures was reported by Nias and Lajtha.[83] One millicurie of tritiated water per milliliter arrested growth at about day 4, while 0.1 mc began to cause growth inhibition at about day 9. The latter concentration corresponds to 1.2 rad per hour.

Differential effects of radiation from tritium on nucleus and cytoplasm were evaluated with tritiated water also in experiments with chick embryo cells infected with rickettsiae.[54] Eleven to 180 mc of tritiated water were injected into the eggs containing infected embryos. It was observed that the growth of *R. mooseri* (typhus) in the cytoplasm was accelerated, whereas the growth of *R. akari* (spotted fever) in the cell nuclei was inhibited after injection of more than 22 mc of tritiated water. Since rickettsiae grow well in an environment having low metabolic activity, the experiments were interpreted to indicate an increase of metabolism in the nuclei of the embryo cells with concomitant metabolic depression in the cytoplasm upon irradiation injury. The dosimetry in these experiments is certainly difficult. It was shown, however, that pratically all the tritium was retained as tritiated water in the eggs up to 8 days after the injection.

Examining the initial chemical events responsible for the radiation toxicity from tritium, Brüggemann and Giesecke[22] exposed bacteria from the bovine rumen under anaerobic condition to increasing doses of tritiated water equivalent to 75,000–300,000 rad. With highest doses to the bacterial flora in the resting stage, a stimulating effect was observed on cell division and production of volatile fatty acids. But when oxygen was present during the irradiation, a strong reduction in the number of viable cells subsequently occurred, which indicated the involvement of oxidizing radicals as secondary radiation products in causing lethality. In yeast cells, 2.5 mc of tritiated water per milliliter of medium for 17 hours caused a slowdown of growth and an increased respiratory quotient. Both effects could be abolished by cysteamine. In control experiments, however, the dose of cysteamine required for inhibition already caused metabolic toxicity. Therefore it was suggested that radiation effects observed were only partially due to interactions of free radicals.[51]

TABLE 6.2

LETHAL EFFECT OF TRITIATED WATER IN MICE[a]

Tritiated water injected ip (mc/g of body weight)	Half-time of total-body water (hours)	Mortality at day 30 (%)
0.70	45.5	7
0.84	46.9	32
0.98	50.3	81
1.13	52.1	94
1.41	58.3	100

[a] Reproduced with permission of Furchner, *Radiation Res.*[49]

3.2. ANIMAL ORGANISMS

Tritiated water in a single dose of 1 mc per gram weight caused lethality to 50% within 30 days in mice.[21] The animals became ill on the second day after injection, and water consumption fell drastically. Furchner[49] observed an even higher mortality. After a single injection of 1.41 mc tritiated water per gram weight, all mice died within 30 days, as shown in Table 6.2. It is noteworthy that the water turnover diminished with an increasing dose of tritiated water, probably due to decreased food and water consumption by the sick animals.

4. Toxicity of Tritium-Labeled Thymidine

Tritium incorporated with thymidine into DNA in the nucleus of multiplying cells irradiates mainly the nucleus and genetic material. Within the group of resulting radiation effects, besides mitotic delay and lethality, chromosomome changes and delayed manifestations such as mutations and tumor induction are hence of prevailing interest. Microorganisms, insects, plants, and animals have been studied for these effects; the respective data and their interpretation are presented below. Related information contrasting with H[3]-thymidine toxicity or bearing on the problem of genetic damage caused by other tritiated nucleosides and tritiated amino acids will be cited also. The question of transmutation effect is treated in a separate section later in this chapter.

4.1. MICROORGANISMS—SURVIVAL AND MUTATIONS

In most cases a simple exponential dose–effect relationship is characteristic for irradiated microorganisms when tested for viability. This indicates lack of repair or "single hit" of radiation injury in these systems. Such characteristic survival curves are also obtained with tritium as a radiation source incorporated by the cells (see Fig. 6.3). Dose accumulation from incorporated tritium is usually allowed by storing

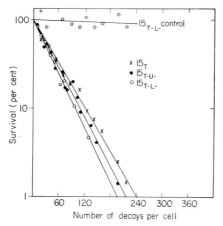

FIG. 6.3. Survival of *E. coli;* three mutants requiring thymine (T-), thymine plus uracil (T-U-), and thymine plus leucine (T-L-), as a function of the number of tritium decays per cell after labeling with H³-thymidine and storage at 4°C prior to viability test. Courtesy of Person and Lewis, *Biophys. J.*[88]

the labeled organisms for various periods of time in a medium deficient in growth factors, or at low temperatures, at which metabolism is arrested, before a viability test by planting on nutrient agar is performed. The viable cells produce clones on the agar at 37°C and can thus be counted. From the number of cells killed by a certain number of isotope disintegrations the killing efficiency or inactivation probability α can be calculated according to Hershey *et al.*[58]

$$-\frac{dS}{dt} = \alpha\lambda N^*S$$

where S is the number of surviving cells at time t, N^* is the number of tritium nuclides per cell at time t, and λ is the decay constant. The α value thus gives the probability of a lethal effect per single disintegration.

In experiments with a mutant of *E. coli*, requiring thymine and resistant to streptomycin, Latarjet *et al.*[71] found that a killing efficiency of tritium incorporated with thymidine was 0.0041 at 0°C, probably totally due to the β-particle without contribution from a transmutation effect,[1] which, however, was predominant in the case of C¹⁴ and P³².[2,5] When the bacteria labeled with H³-thymidine were stored at −196°C prior to the viability test, the killing efficiency was only approximately 0.0005, regardless of the specific activity of the tritiated thymidine incorporated by the cells.[1,3] Assuming 80 ions pairs per first 0.63 μ of the β-particle track, Apelgot[1] calculated that at a storage temperature of

$-196°C$ approximately 42.8×10^{15} ion pairs per gram of DNA led to a 37% survival, whereas at $0°C$ about 5.4×10^{15} ion pairs were necessary. It was subsequently found that the values varied with the purity of the water used for the medium, regardless of whether the bacteria were irradiated with the tritium β-particle or X-rays.[6] The killing efficiency was lowest after storage in triple distilled water. Addition to the triple distilled water of 10^{-5} M calcium ions abolished the effect and was held therefore to be the contaminant mainly responsible in single distilled water for the higher killing efficiency of both types of radiation. In addition, the α-values for both altered to the same extent in the presence of cysteamine. These observations indicated that a tritium transmutation effect was of no importance with regard to cell killing.

Investigating the temperature dependence of the α-value, Person and Lewis[88] reported evidence for a latent killing effect when the bacteria were stored in the frozen state after H^3-thymidine labeling. Long-lived radicals in the frozen bacteria were probably responsible. The latent killing was observed only when the cells, after storage in the frozen state, were stored in liquid at $37°C$ for an additional period of time prior to the viability test, and the increase in lethality was greater than that expected from the dose delivered in the bacteria during liquid storage. Besides storage temperature, the composition of the medium during storage appeared to influence the α value also.[88]

The surviving $E.\ coli$ population shows an increasing number of new mutants with rising lethality. Thus, for a culture inactivated to 1.5% survival after storage at $-78°C$, one in 5000 viable cells was a mutant.[88] It was calculated that with an α value of about 0.02 for H^3-thymidine one out of 10^6 tritium disintegrations resulted in the production of the specific mutation of lactose to nonlactose fermentation. Lubin[75] selected more than 15 mutants of $E.\ coli$ among the 1.0 to 0.1% survivors after treatment with H^3-thymidine. The accumulation of mutants among the surviving bacteria indicates selectivity. Indeed, Rachmeler and Pardee[95] suggested strongly the exclusive responsibility of the β-particle for viability loss in $E.\ coli$, but a transmutation effect seemed to be operative in producing mutations such as loss of β-galactosidase-forming ability. Thus, tritium disintegrations in the DNA were much more effective than those in RNA or proteins. When, by mating, bacteria were prepared which carried DNA-tritium, except in the chromosomal region containing the specific cistron for β-galactosidase formation, viability but not enzyme formation was sensitive to the tritium disintegration.

Although in the above experiments the killing efficiencies of H^3-thymidine were similar to those of H^3-uridine (RNA plus DNA precursor), in reports on tritiated amino acids[89,90] the respective α values differed, the higher ones being listed for H^3-thymidine, while the lower were for H³-histidine. This change in killing efficiency with the molecular species as tritium carrier, e.g., the different effect of tritium bound to protein compared to that bound to total nucleic acids, was held to indicate that a transmutation effect was an additional factor in viability loss.[89] It was subsequently calculated, however, that the differences can be explained by the unequal geometry of source and target position in the bacterium.[67] A similar situation applies to the phage T4 where the energy absorbed in DNA from tritium bound to DNA was calculated to be 2.6 times that deposited in the DNA from tritium bound to the protein.[14] On this basis, the respective killing efficiencies in T4 phage from tritium in DNA or protein were entirely attributed to radiation damage without addition from a transmutation effect.[91] Extending the investigations on genetic effects, Person and Bockrath[90] examined the sensitivity in the chromosome of the genetic locus for arginine requirement in *E. coli* and found tritium bound to the total nucleic acids (mainly RNA) considerably more effective than that incorporated into DNA or protein. The respective data expressed in units of revertant bacteria per surviving bacteria per tritium disintegration in RNA:DNA: protein had a ratio of 6.7:2.4:1.0 (with 1.0 being 0.28×10^{-8}). The predominance of RNA-bound tritium (from H³-uridine or uracil) in reverting the mutant despite nearly equal distribution in the bacteria of protein-tritium appeared to indicate a specific involvement of RNA in the reversion process, mediated by a local molecular phenomenon in addition to the β-irradiation. A cytosine "hot spot" in DNA was also considered as a possible cause.

4.2. ANIMAL CELLS IN CULTURE; SURVIVAL

The consequences of the initial physicochemical events produced by ionizing radiation are considerably more complex in more highly developed cells than in microorganisms. This is expressed in the survival kinetics of irradiated cells. Cell death is not a simple exponential function of the radiation dose absorbed; it follows rather a "multiple hit" curve characterized by a rising probability of death by equal increases in dose increments (see Fig. 6.4). Sublethal doses may retard the proliferation of the cell[123] or may cause delayed or late manifestations of radiation damage,[25] and the integrated disturbances of organ function in an animal may lead to "radiation illness." [7,15,25,26] Cells in culture are particularly suited for studying radiation lethality without interference from secondary factors known to influence and coordinate cellular function in an intact organism. Loss of viability of cells in culture and of ascites tumor cells in response to toxic doses of H³-thymidine will be discussed in this section.

Soon after H³-thymidine became available as a tracer, its toxic effects

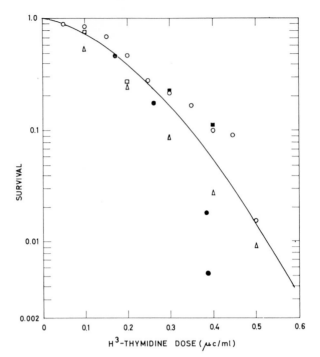

F𝗂𝗀. 6.4. Survival of HeLa-S₃ cells tested by cloning technique follows a multi-hit curve after labeling with H³-thymidine in rising doses; the total amount of thymidine remained 0.001 μm/ml at all dose levels. Courtesy of Marin and Bender, *Intern. J. Radiation Biol.*[78]

were investigated by Painter and collaborators[86] in tissue culture cells (HeLa-S₃). When H³-thymidine (specific activity 500 mc/mmole) was added to the culture cells in amounts of 1.25–2.55 μc/ml of medium for 24 hours, a 50–65% depression in cell count resulted within 48 hours. A similar effect was obtained by incubating cells in parallel with 1000–5000 μc of tritiated water per milliliter of medium for 48 hours. These results suggested clearly that the radiation insult to the nucleus was responsible for the cell death and that tritiated thymidine was about 1000 times more toxic than an equal dose of tritiated water. Subsequent experiments by Drew and Painter[32] showed that increasing lethality expressed in terms of depression of clone-forming ability resulted from H³-thymidine (specific activity 1.88 c/mmole) in doses above 0.02 μc/ml of medium for 24 hours. The LD_{37} value obtained was about 0.07–0.08 μc/ml of medium. The formation of atypical cell forms and giant cells was also observed. Two microcuries of H³-thymidine per milliliter of medium were tolerated when added to clone-forming cells for not longer than 30 minutes, but increasing cell death occurred with prolonged exposure time. Below an exposure time of 30 minutes, a dose of 0.02 μc/ml of a specific activity of even 5.1 c/mmole had no effect on viability.[34] A correlation of colony-forming ability, number of unlabeled cells per clone, and mean grain count of the labeled cells after various durations of exposure to H[3]-thymidine showed the survival of cell clones in the cultures to depend on the presence of unlabeled cells.[33] With the assumption of a 10% autoradiographic efficiency (see Chapter 4), disintegrations per minute per labeled cell can be calculated from the cellular grain count obtained after 2 hours of autoradiographic exposure. Thus, after a 3-hour incubation of the cells with H[3]-thymidine (2 μc/ml), 4.1 disintegrations per minute were delivered to the cell and its entire progeny, if any, until death, which occurred within the 12-day period of observation. At this dose level the number of clones was depressed to only 85.9% of control owing to the presence of unlabeled cells in the clones. In these experiments an increasing mitotic delay was also seen in response to a prolonged exposure to H[3]-thymidine. Thus, a mitotic delay of 1 hour may have occurred after the 3-hour exposure, it must have been at least 4 hours for the 6-hour exposure, and at least 7 hours for an exposure of 9 hours. It follows from the corresponding grain counts, assuming an autoradiographic efficiency of about 10%, that about four disintegrations per minute for 3 hours caused a definite mitotic delay. It should be recalled that radiation-induced delay in the proliferation rate occurs mainly or exclusively in the premitotic (G_2) phase.[17,116] Osgood[85] also recognized the severe effects exerted by 1 μc of tritiated thymidine (specific activity, 360 mc/mmole) on the survival and the morphology of lymphocytes in culture (culture J-111-Cl-1551).

Marin and Bender[78] investigated the survival kinetics of HeLa-S_3 cells by first exposing them to H[3]-thymidine for 15–16 hours prior to transfer into Petri dish cultures for the clone-formation test. Thus, all cells were labeled. The total amount of thymidine per culture remained constant at 0.001 μmole/ml, with increasing radioactivity up to 0.6 μc/ml of medium. Figure 6.4 shows the resulting viability loss with increasing dose of H[3]-thymidine. With a dose of about 0.21 μc/ml survival was depressed to about 37%. Taking into account reduction of radiation dose-rate with cell division, the authors constructed a model for the expected survival kinetics and fitted it to the experimental data. It was concluded that the observed killing effect was entirely attributable to the β-radiation. The effect from X-irradiation or the labeled cells was just additive to the effect of the tritium β-radiation, and it was suggested that the viability loss was determined by the radiation dose delivered to the nucleus. The same conclusion was reached from similar experiments with

Chinese hamster cells labeled with H^3-uridine, a precursor for RNA and DNA, or with H^3-thymidine.[79] Indeed, the contribution of cytoplasmic irradiation after H^3-thymidine incorporation to the nuclear irradiation in causing cell death was very small if there was any. In an attempt to express the survival data as a function of incorporated tritium per cell nucleus, autoradiograms were prepared from H^3-thymidine-labeled Chinese hamster cells prior to the clone-formation test. With an autoradiographic efficiency of 7%, determined by the authors, it was calculated that, on the average, 1.33 disintegrations per minute per nucleus from H^3-thymidine depressed clone formation to 37%, and 2.1 disintegrations per minute reduced survival to 10%.[79]

Ascites tumor cells were tested *in vivo* by Licso *et al.*[73] Tritiated thymidine with a specific activity of 360 mc/mmole was injected into the peritoneal cavity of mice where the tumor cells resided. The dose ranged from 0.1 to 10 μc/g of weight six times every 4 hours. The tumor growth was tested at various times up to 12 days after H^3-thymidine injection and was seen to be inhibited in proportion to the dose injected. Even at the highest dose level the number of tumor cells was reduced by not more than about 43%. An increasing number of abnormal cells, such as giant cells or pyknotic cells, appeared with higher doses. The proportion of larger cells relatively poor in RNA fell in favor of a relative increase of smaller cells with a higher RNA content. It was interesting to note that the effects obtained with 10 μc/g of weight were similar to those after X-irradiation with 600–1000 r.

Zajicek and Gross[127] showed that DNA breakdown resulted when the dose administered to 10^8 cells exceeded 0.7 μc in ascites tumor cells labeled *in vitro* with H^3-thymidine of high specific activity, 2.7 c/mmole. The labeled catabolites from DNA partially accumulated in the acid-soluble fraction. These data must be regarded in the context of the metabolic instability of ascites tumor cells under *in vitro* conditions.

4.3. ANIMAL ORGANISMS—SURVIVAL AND PROLIFERATION

In 60-hour-old chick embryos, the inoculation of 50 μc of H^3-thymidine (specific activity 1.9 c/mmole) caused only a transient cytological injury recognizable from 12 hours on after administration of the labeled compound,[104] and there was no immediate cessation of mitosis. When the treated embryos were, however, observed for a longer period of time, hatching appeared to be somewhat delayed and longer. Still, the proportion of embryos having muscular or neuronal defects or those which did not hatch at all was only slightly higher than that in the control group.[105] The actual amount of H^3-thymidine incorporated by the embryonic cells from the inoculum of 50 μc was not determined, but it was found to be less injurious than 200 r from X-irradiation at a rate of 150 r/minute.

Lymphocytes are known to be particularly sensitive to radiation. Cronkite et al.[27] examined the number of pyknotic lymphocytes circulating in the blood of rats following injection of various doses of H³-thymidine (specific activity, 1.9 c/mmole). A toxic effect was demonstrated with doses higher than 5 μc/g of body weight. By extrapolation, 25 μc/g of weight were found to be approximately equivalent to a total-body dose of 75 r from X-rays. Repeated injections of 0.5 μc/g of weight every 12 hours to a total of 18 μc, however, did not cause pyknosis in circulating lymphocytes.

Rapidly proliferating cells such as intestinal epithelial cells are particularly suitable for studying effects on the duration of the cell's generation time. Duodenal crypt cells in mice began to show a delay in the generation time about 8 hours after injection of 10 μc of H³-thymidine per gram of weight (specific activity 360 mc/mmole.)[48] The initial labeling indices of interphase cells were identical after injection of various doses from 0.1 to 10 μc/g of weight. It was also reported that nonlabeled thymidine in amounts equivalent to 100–500 μc of H³-thymidine of a specific activity of 360 mc/mmole, i.e., 66–330 μg per mouse, caused an increase 1 hour after intraperitoneal administration in the number of duodenal crypt cells with Feulgen-positive extranuclear bodies. This is interesting in view of the small size of the effective thymidine pool in the total mouse, estimated to be approximately 0.05 μmole, i.e., about 12 μg,[59] as discussed in Chapter 5.

A low tolerance to tritiated thymidine (specific activity 1.9 c/mmole) by spermatogonia in mice was reported by Johnson and Cronkite.[62] When the testes were examined 4 days after a single injection of 1 μc or more per gram of body weight, the fraction of spermatogonia surviving was decreased as indicated in Table 6.3. The effect of a dose of 0.5 μc was questionable. In comparison with equivalent data after total-body exposure to γ-radiation from Co⁶⁰, the effect observed after 1 μc of H³-thymidine per gram of weight was held comparable to that of less than 5 r of γ-radiation, 5 μc corresponded to 10 r, and 10 μc, to 20 r as shown in Table 6.3. Cell killing was shown to be directly dependent on the amount of H³-thymidine incorporated and retained in the testes, which again depended on dose and specific activity of H³-thymidine injected.[101] Kisieleski et al.[66] found a lower effect per dose of H³-thymidine injected compared with that reported by Johnson and Cronkite[62] probably because of the lower specific activity of 360 mc/mmole. An attempt was made to correlate the effect to the amount of tritium incorporated per cell. The latter was calculated from the tritium content per total organ

TABLE 6.3

EFFECT OF TRITIATED THYMIDINE ON MOUSE SPERMATOGONIA[a]

Single dose of H³Tdr (µc/g of body weight)	Radiation from Co⁶⁰ (r)	Fraction of spermatogonia surviving
0	—	1.00
0.5	—	0.97
1.0	5	0.93
5.0	10	0.75
10.0	20	0.65
20.0	—	0.44

[a] Animals were sacrificed 4 days after injection. Reproduced with permission of Johnson and Cronkite, *Radiation Res.*[62]

and from an estimate of the respective number of spermatogonia per organ. It was thus shown that 0.107 µc of H³-thymine per testis (50 mg wet weight) over a period of 10 days, or 0.131 µc for 8 days, resulted in a significant reduction in the number of resting primary spermatocytes (spermatogonia). This would correspond to an average dose-rate of about 17–19 disintegrations per cell per day leading to an accumulated exposure of about 150–170 disintegrations per nucleus for minimal effect.

Regenerating liver, with its active cell proliferation nearly synchronized beginning approximately 18–20 hours after partial hepatectomy, is a suitable test organ for studying radiation effects of H³-thymidine. When 20 hours after partial hepatectomy 1 µc of H³-thymidine (specific activity 360 mc/mmole) per gram of body weight was injected in rats, the mitotic index dropped within 6 hours, the rate of increase of liver mass retarded at 12 hours, and mitotic abnormalities were obvious by 24 hours.[56] All three changes were apparently transitory. No toxic effect was observed after an injection of 0.3 µc/g of weight. The mitotic abnormalities appearing after injection of 1 µc of H³-thymidine per gram of weight were comparable to those reported to occur after 150 r from X-rays.

In the liver of rats the cellular ploidy (the number of chromosome sets per cell) shows a characteristic frequency distribution according to age. The ploidy distribution in liver cells of 3-week-old rats was changed within 24 hours after an intraperitoneal injection of 100 µc of H³-thymidine, e.g., about 2 µc/g of weight (specific activity 360 mc/mmole).[93] This early manifestation of injury changed further, so that 2 weeks later the ploidy distribution was similar to the one of control animals 2 years old. Unexplained in these experiments is the observation that many more nuclei were apparently involved in the ploidy changes than were labeled in the corresponding autoradiograms. Perhaps the autoradiographic efficiency was not optimal, or tritium was lost from the liver during the preparative steps for autoradiography. In addition to the alterations of ploidy there were morphological changes in the cytoplasm during the first 2 days such as vacuolization and reduction in the RNA content of the cells. A metabolic effect of the thymidine must be considered here too.

Various organs in the mouse showed an increased turnover rate of DNA when labeled with high doses of H^3-thymidine.[50] Thus after an injection of 10 μc H^3-thymidine per gram of weight (specific activity 4.4 c/mmole), the rate of decline of DNA-H^3 in skin, intestine, spleen, kidney, and testis, probably also in liver and muscle, exceeded that of the respective DNA labeled with C^{14}-thymidine in low dose. The data were interpreted to indicate cell death due to the radiation from tritium. When the dose of H^3-thymidine was reduced to 1 μc/g of weight, an effect was still found in testis and kidney. Whether cell loss is selective or occurs at random can be recognized by comparing the regression rates of DNA specific activity with the DNA per unit weight of the organ.[102]

In normal bone marrow of rats, the regression rate of DNA specific activity after H^3-thymidine injection was found to be lower than the true DNA renewal rate in the cell population because of thymidine reutilization.[46] This was briefly discussed in Chapter 5. When H^3-thymidine was injected in a dose of 1 μc per gram of body weight (specific activity 1.9 c/mmole), the regression rate of the DNA specific activity was not enhanced but further reduced,[16] partly because of a slow down in cell proliferation. This was indicated by a significant drop in the mitotic index between 12 and 18 hours after H^3-thymidine injection.[47] The labeling index, the mean grain count of the labeled cells, and the autoradiographic efficiency factor were determined for these preparations, and it was calculated that, on the average, 1.2 disintegrations per hour per nucleus occurred.[16] Since the grain count per single cell varied by a factor of 3–4 from the mean value, and since the β-absorption in the different cell types (e.g., the autoradiographic efficiency) is expected to vary also, the calculated dose of 1.2 disintegrations per cell per hour may accordingly be higher or lower, perhaps by a factor of 4, for individual cells. Thus, it is deduced that between 20 and 100 tritium disintegrations per nucleus were necessary for the mitotic delay observed. In addition, cytological abnormalities were observed at day 3 after H^3-thymidine injection. Assuming a diameter of 8 μ for the average bone-marrow cell, 1.2 tritium disintegrations per hour yield an accumulated dose of less than 30 rads until the retardation of cell proliferation became recognizable at about 18 hours after H^3-thymidine injection. Cell killing was also observed in a leukemic patient after 10 injections over a 5-

day period of 0.25 μc H³-thymidine per gram of body weight.[53] No alterations were observed with single doses of 0.5 μc or less.

Toxicity of H³-thymidine to bone-marrow transplants was demonstrated by Smith *et al.*[108] After high doses of 20 or 40 μc H³-thymidine per gram of body weight in mice, divided over 40 hours or 11 days, the marrow, when injected into recipients sublethally irradiated, partially lost the capacity to restore the hemopoietic system as measured by the number of circulating granulocytes and lymphocytes. The degree of restoration depended on the dose of H³-thymidine and on the number of bone-marrow cells transplanted. With an injection per animal of 1.8 × 10⁶ cells, the recovery proceeded equally well whether the donor cells were treated with H³-thymidine or not.

Using as parameter the colony-forming ability of transplanted cells in the spleens of irradiated mice,[117] Becker *et al.*[11] incubated cells of regenerating or fetal liver and adult marrow and spleen, prior to transplantation, *in vitro* for 20 minutes with H³-thymidine (specific activity 6.7 and 14.9 c/mmole) in amounts of as much as 600 μc per milliter of cell suspension. Colony-forming cells in the phase of DNA synthesis at the time of incubation were killed by this procedure. Thus, it was deduced from the recovery yield of spleen colonies that 40–65% of the colony-forming cells from the liver but scarcely any such cells from the bone marrow and spleen were in the phase of DNA synthesis during the *in vitro* exposure. On the other hand, when the donor cells were labeled *in vivo* over a period of 24 hours by repeated injections of H³-thymidine in doses of several millicuries (specific activity 13–19 c/mmole), Bruce and Meeker[20] observed a decrease to 20% survival of colony-forming cells from normal bone marrow. This would indicate that nearly 80% of these immature cells passed through DNA synthesis or a part of it during a 24-hour period. Perhaps this might not represent the physiological situation, since induction of resting "stem cells" into DNA synthesis by a stimulus from the damaged tissue could have occurred during the 24-hour labeling period *in vivo*.

4.4. PLANTS—GROWTH AND DEVELOPMENT

Seedlings and rootlets grow by developing lateral structure in serial sequence, and cell proliferation is most active in their distal portions; yet cell elongation contributes to the lengthening of the developing structures. The cells in the region of proliferative activity—for example, in the meristem—incorporate H³-thymidine readily and can thus be killed selectively by a sufficiently high dose of the tracer, leaving the cells of more quiescent zones functionally intact. Plants have also been used to study radiation effects on chromosomes, as will be discussed in a separate section below.

Stein and Quastler[109,110] exposed rootlings (from *Zea* and *Pisum*) to H³-thymidine, 50 μc/ml of nutrient medium for 8–24 hours (specific activity 1.9 c/mmole) and observed the effects on subsequent development and growth. It was assumed that about 1/10 of the dose was incorporated by the roots. The youngest portion of the roots failed in developing lateral roots, but in older portions lateral roots did not appear to be severely affected. Primary roots continued to grow and later gave rise to lateral roots despite 100% labeling of their pericycle cells. These new lateral roots showed a compensatory increase in growth. Thus, lateral root development appeared to be most sensitive at the stages of early differentiation. Indeed, McQuade and Friedkin[76] found that the lateral roots which developed after treatment with a toxic dose of H³-thymidine in onion seedlings compensated functionally and fully, and the seedlings grew in the greenhouse like the control seedlings. A similar functional recovery was reported from the studies on seedlings of *Allium cepa*,[23] which were labeled with H³-thymidine prior to the meristem getting fully involved in proliferation.

Radiation injury from incorporated H³-thymidine in wheat seedlings accounted for a relatively high incidence of phenotypic abnormalities of the seedlings.[77] However, plants which developed from embryos to adults after H³-thymidine incorporation or from seedlings with epicotyls cut back prior to treatment with H³-thymidine showed a low yield of chromosome aberrations in pollen mother cells. Less than half of the plants with such aberrations had, in addition, phenotypic changes. The low yield of aberrations was mainly due to a sufficient number of cells remaining undamaged in the embryos and to the relatively low incorporation of H³-thymidine by the central cells of the growing points in the seedlings over a period of 24 hours. Increase of the exposure time to H³-thymidine resulted in a higher aberration frequency in the adult plants.

Marked mitotic inhibition and probably cell death was observed in root meristems of *Vicia faba* when the specific activity of H³-thymidine in the nutrient medium for 10 hours exceeded 90 mc/mmole with a dose of 0.65–3 μc/ml.[82] Similar are the results in *Tradescantia paludosa*,[124] where the mitotic index dropped when 1 μc of H³-thymidine (specific activity, 360 mc/mmole) was given for 8 hours. Also working with *Vicia faba*, Krause and Plaut[68] examined the toxicity of H³-thymidine by its effect on the incorporation of thymidine labeled with C¹⁴. When the seedlings were exposed to 6 μc of H³-thymidine plus C¹⁴-thymidine per milliliter of nutrient medium (final specific activity, 16 mc/mmole),

C^{14}-thymidine was incorporated in a greater amount than in the controls which were exposed to C^{14}-thymidine alone, 1 $\mu c/ml$ (specific activity, 2.7 mc/mmole). The authors emphasized that H^3-thymidine may not always measure the normal pathway of the unlabeled precursor.

4.5. CHROMOSOMES

Radiation effects on chromosomes may be generally classified into chromosome-type aberrations, chromatid-type aberrations, and subchromatid-type aberrations. The first two are visually recognizable in cytologically adequate chromosome preparations of cells in metaphase. In order to understand the induction mechanism of the various types of aberrations it is necessary to recall that chromosomal replication is semiconservative. This was discussed briefly in Chapter 5. Chromosome reproduction and radiation-induced aberrations have been reviewed by Taylor[115] and Evans.[40]

The frequency of chromosome-type aberrations and chromatid-type aberrations, as studied after X-irradiation, seems to depend on the stage of the cell's cycle at the time of irradiation. Thus, it appears that irradiation of cells prior to commencement of DNA synthesis results in a higher yield of chromosome-type aberrations; however, changes in the chromatids are predominant and more frequent in those cells irradiated during and after DNA synthesis.[41] The increase of chromatid aberration yield in the premitotic phase (G_2) was shown to be due to a separation of chromatid and to an increase in the number of sites where breaks can occur, and not to a greater sensitivity of the chromosome strands to radiation.[18,19] With respect to repair, it was reported for Chinese hamster cells that chromosomal breaks or chromatid breaks produced in G_1 phase may repair within 5 minutes, during which time exchanges can occur. In cells which were irradiated during the phase of DNA synthesis, however, breaks remained open for at least 1 hour and probably longer. Because of this failure of restitution and reunion of two breaks in chromosomes after strand separation, a larger number of exchanges was found in cells irradiated in the postmitotic (G_1) phase than in cells irradiated later in the cell cycle.[30,60] Indeed, considering the theoretical probability for a chromosomal break or chromatid break in a cell containing tritium-labeled DNA, it is surprising to find close to a thousand tritium decays required for one aberration that can be seen in metaphase.[31] Repair is obviously extensive. In this section aberrations of the chromosome- and chromatid-type induced by incorporated H^3-thymidine will be discussed.

Shortly after submitting the model for chromosome duplication (see Chapter 5), Taylor in 1958[114] reported on chromatid exchanges in cells of *Bellevalia romana* after H³-thymidine labeling, which confirmed the model of chromosome duplication. Although sister chromatid exchanges were frequent, half-chromatid exchanges (exchanges between two homologous chromatids) were not seen. The frequency of exchanges was obviously proportional to the length of the chromosome. Following the second interphase after exposure of the seedlings to H³-thymidine for 6–10 hours (specific activity 300–400 mc/mmole, 2.5–5.0 μc/ml) the frequency of exchanges was lower than observed after the first interphase. A toxic effect of the incorporated H³-thymidine was considered to be responsible, especially since the reduction in exchange frequency at the second mitosis may perhaps be explained by a reduction in radiation dose per cell to one-half with cell division.

Various types of chromatid aberrations were described by Bender et al.[12] in human leukocytes after H³-thymidine labeling, 1 μc/ml of culture medium for 30 minutes (specific activity, 3 c/mmole). While some of these aberrations were known from work with X-rays, others were observed specifically after H³-thymidine treatment such as interstitial deletions and achromatic lesions which were rarely produced after X-irradiation; and double gaps had not been seen previously. Isochromatid deletions were seen most frequently. Tritiated uridine also caused aberrations but no interstitial deletions. There obviously was no correlation between the local labeling intensity and the site of aberration, a finding supporting the radiation effect, with little or no contribution from a transmutation effect, being held responsible for the chromatid breaks. This was confirmed by Marin and Prescott[80] who, in addition, examined sister chromatid exchanges as a function of the dose of H³-thymidine. There was no statistically significant alteration in the exchange rate despite a hundredfold rise in the amount of H³-thymidine. These authors therefore proposed that sister chromatid exchanges are not caused by tritium radiation in Chinese hamster cells in culture. But the exchange rate was slightly increased following X-irradiation with 50 r.

Plaut[92] argued that breaks within substructures of a chromatid, perhaps with subsequent faulty rejoining of the strands, may be more frequent than chromatid exchanges or aberrations and may remain unrecognizable as such by the techniques used. The ionization energy of the electron from tritium, of course, would be quite sufficient for causing such effects which, if not repaired, are manifested perhaps in genetic or somatic mutations.

The frequency of chromosome breaks observed as chromosome fragments at anaphase of mitosis were analyzed by Wimber[124] in work with roots of *Tradescantia paludosa*. The roots were placed for various lengths of time in nutrient medium containing H³-thymidine, 1–2 μc/ml, specific

TABLE 6.4

FREQUENCY OF CHROMOSOMAL ABERRATIONS AND MICRONUCLEATED CELLS IN ONION ROOTLETS[a]

Dose of H^3Tdr $\mu c/ml$ of nutrient (medium for 18 hours)	Equivalent amount of Tdr ($\mu mole/ml$)	Cells with chromosomal aberrations (%)	Number of micronucleated cells per meristem
20.0	22.5×10^{-3}	99.5	++++
2.0	2.25×10^{-3}	27.3	214
1.0	1.13×10^{-3}	6.9	14
0.67	0.75×10^{-3}	2.0	12
0.5	0.56×10^{-3}	4.1	10
0.2	0.22×10^{-3}	2.5	6

[a] Reproduced with permission of McQuade and Friedkin, *Exptl. Cell Res.*[76]

activity, 360 mc/mmole). One microcurie of H^3-thymidine per milliliter caused an abrupt onset of mitotic delay at 8 hours, i.e., a retardation of the generation time of the labeled cells probably in the G_2-phase. The number of chromosomal fragments per 100 cells in anaphase rose from 31 to 72 when the exposure time of the roots to H^3-thymidine was extended from 4 to 8 to 56 hours and was correlated to the labeling intensity as represented by the autoradiographic grain count. There was a linear relationship between tritium content and number of fragments in anaphase. With an assumed 143 decays in the total nucleus giving rise to one silver grain overlying the section of the nucleus, approximately 3.3 tritium decays per hour over a period of 1–2 days caused one fragment in 100 anaphases.

Similar experiments were carried out with onion rootlets.[76] The corresponding data are shown in Table 6.4. The specific activity was 890 mc/mmole, and the exposure time was 18 hours. At a dose of 20 $\mu c/ml$ practically all anaphases had aberrant chromosomes and micronuclei were extremely frequent. In addition, it was reported that C^{14}-thymidine (position 2) with comparable doses to the cell nuclei gave aberration frequencies similar to those observed with H^3-thymidine. But thymidine labeled with C^{14} in the methyl group instead of in position 2 of the thymine ring caused a twofold rise in aberration frequency. This impressive difference which depends on the molecular position of the C^{14} probably reflects a transmutation effect in addition to the radiation effect and emphasizes the importance of properly selecting a tracer.

The dependence of the frequency of chromosomal breaks (anaphase aberrations) and the degree of mitotic delay on the amount of tritium incorporated was also demonstrated by Natarajan[82] in meristem cells of *Vicia fava* grown for 10 hours in H^3-thymidine, specific activity from

45 to 360 mc/mmole, 0.37 to 3 μc/ml of nutrient medium. The frequency of anaphase breaks rose with an increase in dose and specific activities higher than 90 mc/mmole, and mitotic delay was obvious at the highest dose level 24 hours after treatment. The effects were comparable to those induced by 5.4–75 r of X-rays.

The frequency of chromosomal fragments and chromatid exchanges obviously declined with time after limited exposure to H^3-thymidine.[76,77, 82,114] This phenomenon of recovery may, in part, be due to repair. It may also result from selective death of heavily labeled cells or cells with a large number of aberrations. In addition, it apears to reflect a reduction of the radiation dose with consecutive cell divisions. The latter was discussed in theory by Cronkite et al.[28] and referred to in Chapter 5.

Chromosomal aberrations (breaks and chromatid exchanges) were chosen as the end point for comparative dosimetric studies with tritiated water, H^3-thymidine, and Co^{60} γ-radiation in Chinese hamster cells.[31] Two aberrations were observed to be caused by 3500 tritium decays for H^3-thymidine, while only 1780 disintegrations per nucleus were needed when tritium was bound to water. The latter corresponded to 490 rads, while 520 rads were needed from Co^{60}. This difference in effectiveness was absent at the level of one aberration per cell. These data were discussed in Section 3.1, and it was considered that perhaps some specific situation might have been responsible for this seemingly unequal biological effectiveness of the tritium β-radiation.

4.6. GENETIC MUTATIONS

The increased frequency of mutations in tritiated DNA of microorganisms has been discussed in Section 3.2. The tritium β-particle, similar to other types of radiations, causes an increased mutation rate in higher organisms also; for example, in Drosophila melanogaster, the classic test object of geneticists.

Genetic effects of H^3-thymidine in Drosophila were studied by Kaplan and Sisken.[64] Larvae of Drosophila were kept on an agar medium containing approximately 100 μc/ml of H^3-thymidine (specific activity, 1.9 c/mmole) until pupae appeared. On the first day after reaching adult stage on normal medium, males were selected and mated with normal females. There were 3.9% lethal chromosomes in the progency compared to 0.24% in the control group. Some males were found to carry several mutations after treatment with H^3-thymidine. The frequency of sex-linked recessive lethals was highest 12–13 days after adult male flies were injected with the labeled precursor.[112]

Extending these findings, Kaplan et al.[65] correlated the occurrence of

TABLE 6.5

LETHAL MUTATIONS IN *Drosophila melanogaster* INDUCED BY TRITIATED THYMIDINE[a]

Brood	Dominant lethals (%)	Sperm bundles labeled (%)	Labeled sperm per bundle	Average grain count per sperm head
1	65.6	100	<64–64	22.8 ± 4.7
2	69.1	100	64	36.4 ± 5.3
3	23.9	50	16–32	6.3 ± 3.3
4	6.8	20	1–4	2.3 ± 1.0
Control	∼3.0	—	—	—

Brood	Sex-linked recessive lethals (%)	Sperm bundles labeled (%)	Average grain count per sperm head
1	2.4	100	26.7 ± 18.8
2	5.2	100	40.8 ± 4.2
3	1.3	64	11.2 ± 6.2

[a] Reproduced with permission of Kaplan *et al.*, *Genetics*.[65]

mutations with the amount of H³-thymidine incorporated. With successive broods the labeling intensity of the sperms decreased concomitantly with the frequency of lethal mutations. This is shown in Table 6.5. Furthermore, the sex-linked recessive lethals were mapped on the chromosome and a nonrandom distribution was found which was different from that observed after X- or γ-irradiation. This specific distribution was interpreted to reflect the varying frequency with which thymine bases occur along the length of the X-chromosome, and a transmutation effect may perhaps be responsible. A nonrandom frequency distribution of specific mutations was also described by Strömnaes and Kvelland.[113] The mutations were studied in broods from males labeled by injection of H³-thymidine, 0.08 μc per fly (specific activity, 2.7 c/mmole). After mating the males six times for 3-day periods, the sixth brood had significantly higher frequency of minute flies and flies with hemithorax than any other group, but mosaic females appeared most frequently in brood 3.

Genetic mutations have also been produced in mammals by H³-thymidine. Greulich[55] let mice freely drink water containing H³-thymidine (specific activity, 890 mc/mmole; concentration, 2 μc/ml) until 245–300 μc of tritium were consumed over a period of 24–32 days. The first offspring of pairs with one normal partner, male or female, were phenotypically normal. Later mating between litters or between males of the first offspring and normal females led to an increased incidence of stillbirth, monsters, and male sterility. Interbreeding the first "normal" off-spring gave an incidence of stillbirth and neonatal death of approximately 70%. An attempt was made by Bateman and Chandley[9] to correlate the frequency of dominant lethal mutations in mice to the tritium content of the sperm estimated from autoradiographic data. After six intraperitoneal injections over a period of 2 days to a total dose of 300 μc of H³-thymidine, 34% of the sperms were labeled on the 30th day and 100% on the 32nd day. Hence, from the fourth week on males were mated. From the frequency of intrauterine death and from the average labeling intensity of the respective sperm, it was estimated that it required approximately 25 grains per sperm in an autoradiographic exposure time of 3 weeks to produce one lethal mutation. If one assumes for the sperm an autoradiographic efficiency of 10%, 250 disintegrations may have occurred in the labaled DNA over a period of 3 weeks or close to 400 disintegrations in 32 days; that is, about 12 disintegrations per day per sperm and consequently perhaps twice as many per immature spermatocyte if dose reduction with cell division is considered. At any rate, it is likely that less than 1% of the tritium disintegrations yielded one lethal mutation. In view of the lethal effect of about 150 tritium disintegrations per cell over 8 days, calculated for mouse spermatogonia by Kisieleski et al.,[66] the mutation yield may perhaps express selection within the group of surviving spermatogonia.

4.7. TUMOR FREQUENCY

To test carcinogenetic effects of H³-thymidine long-term experiments must be set up. The first results of such experiments were reported by Lisco et al.[74] and Baserga et al.[8] Various doses of H³-thymidine (0.1–10 μc/g of body weight) and C¹⁴-thymidine (0.02–2 μc/g of weight) were injected into mice of various ages.[8] The specific activities were 360 mc/mmole for H³-thymidine and 3 mc/mmole for C¹⁴-thymidine. Both isotopes were found to shorten the life span, depending on the dose injected and on the age of the animals at the time of injection. There was evidence of carcinogenesis since even a single dose of 1 μc of H³-thymidine per gram of body weight injected at the age of 6–7 months suggested an increased appearance of tumors about 18 months later, close to the 50% life expectancy. Newborn mice were not affected by 0.1 μc. More tumors developed when the mice were injected as young adults than later in life. In a single dose, 10 μc of tritiated thymidine per gram of weight produced tumors less frequently than when administered in six divided doses over 8 days. Among the tumors were thymic lymphomas and nonthymic disseminated lymphomas, salivary gland tumor, and carcinoma of skin, lung, and liver. On the other hand, in some of the control groups of animals the incidence of tumors was higher than in those having received H³-thymidine, depending on the age of the animal.

Zajdela[126] also observed an increased incidence of leukemias (lymphomas), hepatomas, ovarian tumors, and pulmonary adenomas in mice after 8 μc of H³-thymidine (specific activity, 3 c/mmole) injected in five divided doses every 12 hours beginning at the age of 30 days. The animals were observed until death or until the age of 20 months. During a shorter period of observation to 250 days, Cottier et al.[24] did not observe a significant rise in tumor frequency in mice after the following treatments at the age of 6 weeks: H³-thymidine, 3 × 10 μc/g of body weight at weekly intervals (specific activity, 1.9 c/mmole); H³-cytidine in the same dose and with the same schedule used for H³-thymidine, but with a specific activity of 1 c/mmole; H³-thymidine and H³-cytidine combined, with doses and injection schedule the same as above. However, γ-irradiation of Co⁶⁰ to the total body, 160 r three times at weekly intervals, increased significantly the frequency of thymic lymphomas.

These preliminary data point out that on long-term observations H³-thymidine may be carcinogenic even if used in amounts often chosen for tracer studies. Yet, further evidence is needed. For assessing the carcinogenesis of H³-thymidine it is to be considered that H³-thymidine in DNA is eventually lost from the organism with maturing cells except for DNA breakdown products in reutilization. Only those few quiescent and nonproliferating cells which happened to synthesize DNA at the time of H³-thymidine availability may retain the label for a prolonged period of time. Thus, the chance for late somatic radiation effects from incorporated H³-thymidine is expected to be small.

5. Toxicity of Tritium-Labeled Nucleosides Other than Thymidine and of Tritium-Labeled Amino Acids

The toxicity of tritium bound to nucleic acid precursors other than thymidine expectedly varies with the site of incorporation, the rate of renewal of the labeled macromolecule, and the extent of interconversion and reutilization of catabolites (see Chapter 5). In both microorganisms and higher cells the site of incorporation with respect to the cell nucleus or the nuclear and cellular wall determines the dose to the radiation-sensitive nucleus, as discussed in Section 2.2 of this chapter.

Ribonucleosides serve as precursors mainly for RNA and to a lesser degree also for DNA, but in any case they are first incorporated for the major part, if not exclusively, into the cell nucleus. Incorporated into RNA, the label subsequently transfers from the nucleus to the cytoplasm. Although thymidine (the deoxyriboside) is incorporated into DNA only during a limited period of the generation time (cell-cycle time), ribonucleosides (RNA precursors) are incorporated into nucleic acids throughout interphase, but less efficiently or not at all during mitosis. Some of the RNA precursors remain available for DNA synthesis in the cell for at least one generation time. The respective time sequences have been studied particularly in HeLa cells in culture.[42-45]

Two predictions can be made from the incorporation pattern of nucleosides other than thymidine. One is that the toxicity of H³-RNA nucleosides per dose administered may at times be larger than that per identical dose of H³-thymidine because more cells may be affected by H³-RNA precursors. The other prediction is that the toxicity of H³-nucleosides incorporated by the single cells is lower than that of a comparable amount of H³-thymidine because of only a transient contact of RNA-tritium with the nucleus known to be the main site of cellular radiosensitivity.

In principle, a similar reasoning applies to predicting the degree of toxicity of H³-amino acids. A labeled amino acid which would be incorporated and would remain in the cell nucleus and cytoplasm a similar length of time as an RNA precursor is expected to exert the same degree of toxicity as the tritiated RNA precursor. But since protein synthesis in most cell types occurs mainly in the cytoplasm, and since most species of protein molecules renew rapidly, toxicity of tritium bound to amino acids is expected to be lower than that of H³-nucleosides.

Despite the small diameter of microorganisms, differences in viability loss per amount of incorporated tritium bound to nucleic acids and protein were found. Tritiated leucine,[95] H³-proline,[90] and H³-histidine[89] were all less toxic in *E. coli* than H³-nucleosides and led to a killing efficiency (α-value) of approximately one-half the value obtained for H³-uridine and H³-thymidine.[89,90,95] Although the values for H³-thymidine and H³-uridine probably lay within the limits of statistical variation, the lower killing efficiency of the tritium in protein was probably due to geometrical factors.[67] Essentially similar differences were found in phage T4, where the α value of tritium in DNA was 2.5 times greater than for tritium in protein. Again, the relative energy absorption to the phage DNA calculated from the two sources differed by a factor of 2.6.[14] It was concluded therefore that the killing efficiency was entirely accounted for by the radiation damage and that a transmutation effect was not involved.[91]

Figure 6.5 illustrates the relative toxicity of H³-cytidine and H³-thymidine in HeLa-S₃ cells in culture. Both precursors had a specific activity of 1 c/mmole and were used in comparable dose ranges for 24 hours before the development of clones in regular culture conditions was

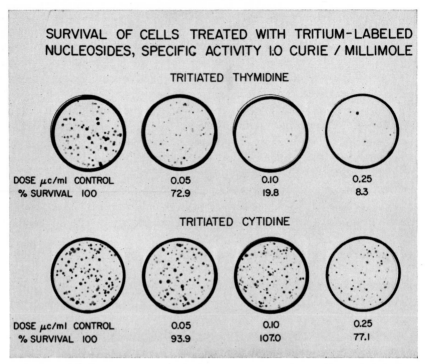

FIG. 6.5. Comparable survival of clones of HeLa-S₃ cells after labeling for 24 hours with H³-thymidine and H³-cytidine in various doses with identical specific activity. Courtesy of R. M. Drew, Brookhaven National Laboratory, Medical Department, Upton, New York.[35]

observed. Up to 0.1 µc of H³-cytidine per milliliter of medium had no significant effect on viability, whereas at the same dose level H³-thymidine depressed survival to 19.8%.[35]

Marin and Bender[79] showed the survival kinetics of Chinese hamster fibroblasts in culture after exposure to H³-uridine to follow a "multi hit curve" similar to the effect of H³-thymidine (see Fig. 6.6). The viability loss after H³-uridine incorporation was due to tritium situated in the cell nucleus with the contribution from tritium in the cytoplasm being negligible, at best. Hence, more H³-uridine was tolerated by the cells than H³-thymidine when both precursors were allowed to be incorporated by all cells of the culture. When, thus, on the average about 1.3 disintegrations per minute per cell from H³-thymidine depressed survival to 37%, approximately 1.7 disintegrations per minute per cell from H³-uridine caused the same effect. The exact value for total dose accumulated during the cloning experiment, before the cells actually died, is not known.

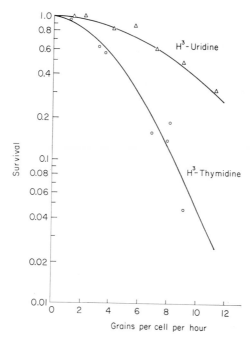

Fig. 6.6. Survival of Chinese hamster fibroblasts tested by cloning technique as a function of tritium incorporated from H³-thymidine and H³-uridine. The incorporated tritium is expressed in the number of autoradiographic silver grains produced per cell per hour. The autoradiographic efficiency test in these cells showed 14.3 disintegrations per grain for H³-thymidine, 10 disintegrations per grain for H³-uridine, which is distributed throughout the entire cell. Courtesy of Marin and Bender, *Intern. J. Radiation Biol.*[79]

Chromosome damage as a result of incorporation of H³-uridine in human leukocytes in culture was reported by Bender *et al.*[12] After 1 μc/ml of medium for 30 minutes (specific activity 1.29 c/mmole) and subsequent normal culture condition, various chromatid aberrations were described, somewhat different from those after H³-thymidine incorporation (specific activity 3 c/mmole). Isochromatid deletions occurred most frequently; interstitial deletions were not observed after H³-uridine treatment, but occurred after H³-thymidine incorporation. The total breaks numbered 24–29 per 100 mitoses, 24 and 60 hours after treatment with H³-uridine, only half that many occurred after H³-thymidine labeling.

6. Transmutation Effect

The recoiling nucleus of He³ after tritium decay has a maximum energy of about 3 ev and thus is probably incapable of rupturing a molecular bond, in contrast to the situation in which isotopes emit higher energy radiation. But the sudden acquisition of a positive charge may add sufficient excitation energy to the carrier molecule for occurrence of chemical effects.[122] Moreover, the inert helium probably splits off the postively charged molecule which may then bind, for instance, a free hydroxyl ion. Although chemical transmutation effects are well known,[122] the mechanism of such effects is difficult to explore in living matter, but biological manifestations have been suggested[5] for P^{32} and P^{33} and also for tritium.

Rachmeler and Pardee[95] probably differentiated a tritium transmutation effect in *E. coli* from the β-radiation effect. The *E. coli* chromosome was labeled with H^3-thymidine except for the genetic region carrying specificity for β-galactosidase formation. This specific tritium distribution was achieved by mating. Testing these bacteria for viability and enzyme formation, the authors found that the latter remained unaffected despite increasing viability loss with increasing number of tritium disintegrations. Moreover, when *E. coli* labeled in the entire DNA was compared with *E. coli* labeled mainly in the RNA, the viability was equally sensitive in both. However, the enzyme-forming capacity was less affected when the bacteria were labeled in the RNA.

A transmutation effect was considered by Person and Brockrath[90] when they investigated the effect of tritium on the reversion of arginine dependence of *E. coli*. Tritiated uridine or uracil, H^3-thymidine, H^3-proline, and H^3-histidine were used. The data were expressed in units of revertant bacteria per surviving bacteria per tritium decay. Tritium bound mainly to RNA was significantly more effective in yielding reverted mutants among the survivors than was tritium bound to DNA or protein. A local molecular phenomenon involving RNA was postulated to operate in this effect, but other mechanisms may still have been involved.

No clear indication of transmutation effects from tritium in higher cells has become known. But they could be excluded from gross responsibility for chromatid aberrations since the labeling intensity of chromosomal segments did not coincide with the site of the breaks.[12,80] Since transmutation effects are considered expressions of localized molecular reactions insufficient for causing death but capable of inducing mutations, they should become recognizable also in higher cells with proper genetic techniques. An approach in this direction is the work with *Drosophila* of Kaplan *et al.*[65] referred to in Section 4.6 of this chapter.

7. Permissible Dose; Health Physics Problems

7.1. EXPRESSION OF DOSE

Biological manifestations of tritium toxicity may be compared directly with effects of other types of radiation in terms of "relative biological effectiveness," if it is possible to express the dose absorbed by a target from the tritium β-particle in appropriate terms, for example, in rads. This requires that tritium is distributed uniformly within the material investigated. Calculation of absorbed dose was treated in Section 2.2. Direct comparison of the toxicities of different tritium-labeled compounds is feasible if the doses can be simply expressed in disintegrations per labeled structure. This approach is common in work with microorganisms where the probability of lethal effect per decay is described by the α value, as discussed in Section 4.1.

The information on tritium toxicity in higher cells thus far is incomplete for expressing the effect as a function either of the number of tritium disintegrations per target or of absorbed dose. For the latter the geometry of the source with respect to the target must be known. Most data are available, as they were referred to above, in terms of effect per dose of tritium administered, and the amount of tritium incorporated and retained by the target tissue and the target geometry was often not established.

A direct approach to check the amount of tritium incorporated into a cell utilizes the autoradiographic technique. But there are considerable difficulties in converting grain counts per cell in a smear or a section to total isotope content in the structure. This was discussed in Chapter 4. There are two ways of finding the appropriate autoradiographic efficiency factor necessary for converting the data on grain counts into disintegrations. One is to measure structural thickness in terms of milligrams per square centimeter per single cell, for example, with an interference microscope, and to calculate the number of disintegrations per autoradiographic silver grain from the respective degree of self-absorption of the β-particles. The other possibility lies in correlating data of radiochemical analysis with autoradiographic data on labeling index and grain count. If the total number of cells analyzed is known, the total tritium content per unit cells is easily related to the autoradiographic data on labeling intensity and percentage of labeled cells. Thus, an average efficiency factor for all labeled cells is obtained.

Proper appraisal of absorbed dose in comparison to a standard radiation must further include the low dose rate from the incorporated tritium. A radiation dose delivered at a low rate over a long period of time is less toxic than when the same dose is administered within a few minutes.[10] This dose-rate factor is not known for tritium, but in case of H³-thymidine incorporated into DNA, the rate diminishes with each cell division. From the various reports discussed in the preceding sections it appears likely that in mammalian cells minimal effects may be induced by an accumulated dose of less than 100 tritium disintegrations per cell nucleus over a period of about 1 day.[16,47] This corresponds to less than 30 rad for a cell nucleus of 4-μ radius.

Taking these variables into account by appropriate estimates, a review of the data on toxicity of H^3-thymidine led to the proposal that the tritium β-particle is as effective as 250 kvp X-rays, i.e., the RBE is approximately 1.[16] It was consequently deduced that the ionization from the tritium β-particle in a cell nucleus occurs indeed at random and no fraction of the nuclear volume would be insensitive to radiation. It also follows that the absorbed dose in the cell nucleus is responsible for the degree of effect with little or no contribution from the dose absorbed in the cytoplasm. The data further provided an argument in favor of the theory that direct cellular injury rather than abscopal mechanisms determined mammalian radiation lethality.[15] Further experiments on tritium β-dosimetry are required to establish that these points are generally valid for mammalian cells.

7.2. DOSE LIMITS SUGGESTED FOR TRACER EXPERIMENTS

Definite biological effects were seen to become manifest within about 24 hours after administration of 1 μc of H^3-thymidine per gram of body weight[16,56,62]; no such effects have been reported for doses below that level. However, late somatic effects and mutations appeared to require larger doses. It is hence suggested that the dose of H^3-thymidine be restricted for long-term tracer experiments in animals to 0.1 μc per gram of body weight. This is sufficient to produce adequate autoradiograms for light microscopic work. For short-term tracer experiments with rapidly dividing cells higher doses may be chosen, but they should not exceed 1.0 μc per gram of weight. For cells in tissue culture it should be recalled that 0.02 μc of H^3-thymidine per milliliter of medium (specific activity, 1.88 c/mmole) given for a period of 24 hours caused lethality in HeLa cells,[82] but 2 μc/ml for 30 minutes did not obviously induce cell killing.[34]

Because of mutagenic properties H^3-thymidine should not be used at all as a tracer in a man of reproductive age and with a normal life expectancy.

In plants, 1 μc of H^3-thymidine (specific activity, 360 c/mmole) per milliliter of nutrient solution appeared to be potentially toxic if the exposure time exceeded a few hours.[124] At 8 hours, mitotic delay was obvious. The yield of chromosomal aberrations may increase with 0.5 μc of H^3-thymidine (specific activity, 890 mc/mmole) per milliliter nutrient solution for 18 hours. Consequently, the dose should be considerably lower for tracer experiments.

In comparison with H^3-thymidine, tritiated ribonucleosides and tritiated amino acids administered at equal dose should be considered around 30% less toxic (see Section 5), and tritiated water may be a thousand times less effective[86] than H^3-thymidine given at equal doses.

7.3. Maximum Permissible Dose

Since tritiated water is distributed in the animal body rather uniformly, a "relative biological effectiveness" (RBE value) may be defined for it. Thus, a value of about 1.7 has been suggested by Furchner[49] with γ-radiation from Co^{60} used as the standard. This RBE pertains to total body irrespective of the RBE value for the β-radiation per se which, as discussed in Section 2.3 of this chapter, is close to 1 with 250 kvp X-rays as standard. With the RBE of 1.7 for the total organism, tolerable doses for man may be calculated from the basic recommendations of the International Commission of Radiation Protection and the National Committee on Radiation Protection.[119]

The permissible doses are expressed in rem (RBE value × rad). Thus, in adults 0.1 rem is permissible per week, based on the formula for accumulated dose (whole-body, head, trunk): 5 × (age − 18) rem. Over a period of 30 years, 150 rem may be accumulated, or 5 rem per year.

For tritiated water, a dose of 0.029 μc per gram of body weight, i.e., 2 mc per adult man (70 kg), delivers on the average per total body 0.1 rem per week. With a biological half-life for total-body water of 8.5 days, 7.5% of the total-body water renews daily, of which 60% is assumed to be excreted with urine. Since 150 μc of 2 mc total dose would thus be replaced per day, about 90 μc would appear as urinary activity. Assuming 2 liters of urine produced per day, about 45 μc tritiated water per liter of urine is the maximum permissible excretion indicating a chronic exposure to 2 mc per day.

A dose of 2 mc of tritiated water is delivered over 24 hours by inhalation of air containing about 0.14 μc/liter, or 150 μc is incorporated when the air contains 0.01 μc/liter.

A single administration of about 2.5 mc of tritiated water to man (70 kg) leads to a dose accumulation of 0.1 rem over a period of a week, and about 110 μc would be excreted with total urine or about 55 μc/liter on the day following the single administration.

Considering the accumulation of tritiated metabolites in cells, especially that of H^3-thymidine in DNA with the concomitant possibility of late somatic and genetic effects, tritium-labeled compounds should not be given as tracers to man, unless the life expectancy is limited and fertility is excluded. Further data on long-term experiments are needed to better assess the mutagenic and carcinogenic properties of H^3-thymidine and other tritiated precursors until valid recommendations as to permissible dose are possible.

7.4. POTENTIAL HAZARDS FROM TRITIUM

Tritium is an occupational hazard mainly as tritiated water of high specific activity or as tritium gas. Both are commonly used for labeling molecules with tritium.

All high specific activity compounds must be kept in closed vessels or under an appropriate exhaust hood so that vapors do not contaminate the whole room. It should be considered that tritiated water of high specific activity produces volatile decomposition products which keep a closed container under slight positive pressure. Stopcock grease that has been in contact with tritium gas, for example, in the glass apparatus for labeling molecules according to Wilzbach's method should be disposed of carefully. If there is a chance during manipulation for a high specific activity compound to contaminate the skin, rubber gloves should be worn. The work bench is best draped with disposable paper for easy decontamination.

Oral pipetting of solutions containing tritium may be dangerous, even if done with care. For instance, 5–70 mμliter of water vapor are inhaled per operation using pipets of 0.1–5 ml volume.[13] Since pure tritiated water has 3×10^6 mc/ml, 15–210 mc may be inhaled with each single pipetting.

Tritium contamination cannot be detected by ordinary gas counters, and special designs and equipment are necessary (see Chapter 3). Appropriate instruments for monitoring surfaces[36] or air[36,39] are commercially available. It is easy to use a small disc of filter paper or membrane for wiping a surface; the discs can be monitored subsequently by an appropriate gas counter or, more conveniently, by liquid scintillation counting. If exposure has been doubtful, a urine examination of individuals involved may give information on the dose incorporated. This is easy with tritium gas or tritiated water (see Section 7.3.), but is uncertain with tritiated metabolites unless the excretion pattern in the urine is known. For instance, one half of the H³-thymidine administered to humans is catabolized within less than 1 hour, and tritiated water is the major labeled catabolic end product. Thus, the rate of excretion of tritium in the urine may be used to estimate closely the dose of H³-thymidine received.

Tritium disposal should be handled, of course, as dangerous radioactive waste, although a rare load of small amounts, in the order of microcuries, may be regarded harmless because of dilution in the sewage. Local conditions of waste collection and disposal must be observed. Industrial plants or laboratories using tritium in large amounts must be equipped with appropriate hoods and air filters in addition to adequate provision for waste collection to control health hazards.[36,96,107]

REFERENCES

1. S. Apelgot, Inactivation de bactéries *Escherichia coli* marquées par la thymidine tritiée, in *Tritium in the Physical and Biological Science, Symp. Intern. At. Energy Agency,* **2:** 167–178 (1961).
2. S. Apelgot and R. Latarjet, Marquage d'un acide déoxyribonucléique bactérien par le radiophosphore, le radiocarbone et le tritium: comparaison des effets létaux, *Biochim. Biophys. Acta,* **55:** 40–55 (1962).
3. S. Apelgot, B. Ekert, R. Latarjet, and N. Rebeyrotte, Radiochemische Untersuchungen an Nukleinsäuren, *Strahlentherapie,* **118:** 54–66 (1962).
4. S. Apelgot and M. Duquesne, Energie dissipée par le thitium dans des microorganismes, *Intern. J. Radiation Biol.,* **7:** 65–74 (1963).
5. S. Apelgot and R. Latarjet, Comparaison des "suicides" d'une bactérie marquée par les phosphores radioactifs 32 et 33, *Intern. J. Radiation,* **10:** 165–175 (1966).
6. S. Apelgot, personal communication, 1965.
7. Z. M. Bacq and P. Alexander, *Fundamentals of Radiobiology,* Pergamon Press, New York, 1961.
8. R. Baserga, H. Lisco, and W. Kisieleski, Further Observations on Induction of Tumors in Mice with Radioactive Thymidine, *Proc. Soc. Exptl. Biol. Med.,* **110:** 687–690 (1962).
9. A. J. Bateman and A. C. Chandley, Mutations Induced in the Mouse with Tritiated Thymidine, *Nature,* **193:** 705–106 (1962).
10. J. L. Bateman, V. P. Bond, and J. S. Robertson, Dose-Rate Dependence of Early Radiation Effects in Small Animals, *Radiology,* **79:** 1008–1014 (1962).
11. A. J. Becker, E. A. McCulloch, L. Siminovitch, and J. E. Till, The Effect of Differing Demands for Blood Cell Production on DNA Synthesis by Hemopoietic Colony-Forming Cells of Mice, *Blood,* **26:** 296–308 (1965).
12. M. A. Bender, P. C. Gooch, and D. M. Prescott, Aberrations Induced in Human Leukocyte Chromosomes by H^3-labeled Nucleosides, *Cytogenetics,* **1:** 65–74 (1962).
13. B. Bloom, The Hazard of Orally Pipetting Tritium Oxide, *J. Lab. Clin. Med.,* **55:** 164 (1960).
14. R. C. Bockrath, Jr., Regional Energy Deposits from Localized Tritium Calculated in Non-spherical Models, *Meeting Biophys. Soc., San Francisco, 1965,* p. 44.
15. V. P. Bond, T. M. Fliedner, and J. O. Archambeau, *Mammalian Radiation Lethality,* Academic Press Inc., New York, 1965.
16. V. P. Bond and L. E. Feinendegen, Intranuclear ³H-Thymidine: Dosimetric, Radiobiological and Radiation Protection Aspects, *Health Phys.,* **12:** 1007–1020 (1966).
17. D. Bootsma, Changes Induced in the First Post-Irradiation Generation Cycle of Human Cells Studied by Double Labeling, *Exptl. Cells Res.,* **38:** 429–431 (1965).
18. J. G. Brewen, Studies on the Frequencies of Chromatid Aberrations Induced

by X-rays at Different Times of the Cell Cycle of *Vicia faba, Genetics,* **50**: 101–107 (1964).

19. J. G. Brewen, Cell Cycle and Radiosensitivity of the Chromosomes of Human Leukocytes, *Intern. J. Radiation Biol.,* **9**: 391–397 (1965).

20. W. R. Bruce and B. E. Meeker, Comparison of the Sensitivity of Normal Hematopoietic and Transplanted Lymphoma Colony-Forming Cells to Tritiated Thymidine, *J. Natl. Cancer Inst.,* **34**: 849–857 (1965).

21. A. M. Brues, A. N. Stroud, and L. Rietz, Toxicity of Tritium Oxide to Mice, *Proc. Soc. Exptl. Biol. Med.,* **79**: 174–176 (1952).

22. J. Brüggemann and D. Giesecke, Studies on the Influence of Tritium Radiation on Anaerobic Bacteria from the Bovine Rumen, in *Tritium in the Physical and Biological Sciences, Symp. Intern. At. Energy Agency,* **2**: 179–187 (1961).

23. F. A. L. Clowes, Effects of Beta Radiation on Meristems, *Exptl. Cell Res.,* **25**: 529–534 (1961).

24. H. Cottier, E. P. Cronkite, E. A. Tonna, and N. O. Nielsen, Leukemogenic Effect of Whole Body Co⁶⁰-Gamma-Irradiation Compared with H³-thymidine and H³-cytidine: Preliminary Report on the Development of Thymic Lymphomas in C 57 BL/6J Mice, in *Cellular Basis and Aetiology of Late Somatic Effects of Ionizing Radiation,* pp. 27–34, Academic Press Inc., New York, 1962.

25. H. Cottier, *Strahlenbedingte Lebensverkürzung,* Springer Verlag, Berlin-Göttingen-Heidelberg, 1961.

26. E. P. Cronkite and V. P. Bond, *Radiation Injury in Man,* Charles C Thomas, Springfield, Illinois, and Blackwell Scientific Publication, Ltd., Oxford, England, 1960.

27. E. P. Cronkite, T. M. Fliedner, S. A. Killmann, and J. R. Rubini, Tritium Labeled Thymidine (H³TdR): Its Somatic Toxicity and Use in the Study of Growth Rates and Potentials in Normal and Malignant Tissue of Man and Animals, in *Tritium in the Physical and Biological Sciences, Symp. Intern. At. Energy Agency,* **2**: 189–207 (1961).

28. E. P. Cronkite, S. W. Greenhouse, G. Brecher, and V. P. Bond, Implication of Chromosome Structure and Replication on Hazard of H³-thymidine and the Interpretation of Data on Cell Proliferation, *Nature,* **189**: 153–154 (1961).

29. F. M. Defilippes and W. R. Guild, Irradiation of Solutions of Transforming DNA, *Radiation Res.,* **11**: 38–53 (1959).

30. W. C. Dewey and R. M. Humphrey, Restitution of Radiation-Induced Chromosomal Damage in Chinese Hamster Cells Related to the Cell's Life Cycle, *Exptl. Cell Res.,* **35**: 262–276 (1964).

31. W. C. Dewey, R. M. Humphrey, and B. A. Jones, Comparisons of Tritiated Thymidine, Tritiated Water, and Co⁶⁰ Gamma Rays in Inducing Chromosomal Aberrations, *Radiation Res.,* **24**: 214–238 (1965).

32. R. M. Drew and R. B. Painter, Action of H³-thymidine on the Clonal Growth of Mammalian Cells, *Radiation Res.,* **11**: 535–544 (1959).

33. R. M. Drew and R. B. Painter, Further Studies on the Clonal Growth of HeLa-S₃ Cells Treated with H³-thymidine, *Radiation Res.,* **16**: 303–311 (1962).

34. R. M. Drew and R. B. Painter, personal communication, 1964.

35. R. M. Drew, personal communication, 1963.

36. G. E. Driver, Tritium Survey Instruments, *Rev. Sci. Instr.,* **27**: 300–303 (1957).

37. R. W. Dutton, Importance of Cell Division for Antibody Production in an *in Vivo* System, *Nature,* **192**: 462–463 (1961).

38. P .T. Emmerson and P. Howard-Flanders, Post-Irradiation Degeneration of DNA

Following Exposure of Ultraviolet-Sensitive and -Resistant Bacteria to X-rays, *Biochem. Biophys. Res. Commun.,* **18:** 24–19 (1965).

39. B. C. Eutsler, G. L. Evans, R. D. Hiebert, R. N. Mitchell, M. C. Robbins, and R. J Watts, Instruments for Monitoring Tritium in the Atmosphere, *Nucleonics,* **149:** 114–117 (1956).
40. H. J. Evans, Chromosome Aberrations Induced by Ionizing Radiations, *Intern. Rev. Cytol.,* **13:** 221–322 (1962).
41. H. J. Evans and J. R. K. Savage, The Relation between DNA Synthesis and Chromosome Structure as Resolved by X-ray Damage, *J. Cell Biol.,* **18:** 525–540 (1963).
42. L. E. Feinendegen, V. P. Bond, W. W. Shreeve, and R. B. Painter, RNA and DNA Metabolism in Human Tissue Culture Cells Studied with Tritiated Cytidine, *Exptl. Cell Res.,* **19:** 443–459 (1960).
43. L. E. Feinendegen, V. P. Bond, and R. B. Painter, Studies on the Interrelationship of RNA Synthesis, DNA Synthesis and Precursor Pool in Human Tissue Culture Cells Studied with Tritiated Pyrimidine Nucleosides, *Exptl. Cell Res.,* **22:** 381–405 (1961).
44. L. E. Feinendegen, V. P. Bond, and W. L. Hughes, RNA Mediation in DNA Synthesis in HeLa Cells Studied with Tritium Labeled Cytidine and Thymidine, *Exptl. Cell Res.,* **25:** 627–647 (1961).
45. L. E. Feinendegen and V. P. Bond, Observations on Nuclear RNA during Mitosis in Human Cancer Cells in Culture (HeLa-S₃) Studied with Tritiated Cytidine, *Exptl. Cell Res.,* **30:** 393–404 (1963).
46. L. E. Feinendegen, V. P. Bond, E. P. Cronkite, and W. L. Hughes, RNA Turnover in Normal Rat Bone Marrow, *Ann. N.Y. Acad. Sci.,* **113:** 727–741 (1964).
47. L. E. Feinendegen, V. P. Bond, and W. L. Hughes, unpublished data, 1964.
48. R. J. M. Fry and S. Lesher, Some Aspects of Toxicity of Tritiated Thymidine, *Radiation Res,* **14:** 466–467 (1961).
49. J. Furchner, Relative Biological Effectiveness of Tritium Beta-particles and Co⁶⁰-gamma-rays Measured by Lethality in CF₁ Mice, *Radiation Res.,* **6:** 483–490 (1957).
50. K. H. Garder and F. Devik, Studies on the Incorporation of Tritiated Thymidine in Deoxyribonucleic Acid in Mouse Tissues and on Its Radiation Effects, *Intern. J. Radiation Biol.,* **6:** 157–172 (1963).
51. G. Giovannozzi-Sermanni, R. Masironi, and I. Cacciavi, Physiological Effects of Tritiated Water on *Rhodo-Torula-Gracilis* as Influenced by Cystamine, *Intern. J. Radiation Biol.,* **5:** 485–491 (1962).
52. C. R. Goodheart, Radiation Dose Calculation in Cells Containing Intranuclear Tritium, *Radiation Res.,* **15:** 767–773 (1961).
53. M. L. Greenberg, A. D. Ghanana, E. P. Cronkite, L. M. Schiffer, and P. A. Strykmans, Detection of Cytocidal Effects of Tritiated Thymidine (H³TdR) During a Study of Cell Proliferation in a Case of Acute Lymphocytic Leukemia, *Clin. Res.,* **13:** 274 (1965).
54. D. Greiff, The Effects of Beta Rays (H³) on the Growth of Rickettsiae and Influenza Virus, in *Tritium in the Physical and Biological Sciences, Symp. Intern. At. Energy Agency,* **2:** 155–165 (1961).
55. R. C. Greulich, Deleterious Influence of Orally Administered H³-Thymidine on Reproduction Capacity of Mice, *Radiation Res.,* **14:** 83–95 (1961).
56. J. W. Grisham, Inhibitory Effect of Tritiated Thymidine on Regeneration of the Liver in the Young Rat, *Proc. Soc. Exptl. Biol. Med.,* **105:** 555–558 (1960).

57. W. R. Guild, Hazards from Isotopic Tracers, *Science,* **128**: 1308 (1958).

58. A. D. Hershey, M. D. Kamen, J. W. Kennedy, and H. Gest, The Mortality of Bacteriophage Containing Assimilated Radioactive Phosphorus, *J. Gen. Physiol.,* **34**: 305–319 (1951).

59. W. L. Hughes, S. L. Commerford, D. Gitlin, R. C. Krueger, B. Schultze, V. Shah, and P. Reilly, Deoxyribonucleic Acid Metabolism *in Vivo:* I. Cell Proliferation and Death as Measured by Incorporation and Elimination of Iododeoxyuridine, *Federation Proc.,* **23**: 640–648 (1964).

60. T. C. Hsu, W. C. Dewey, and R. M. Humphrey, Radiosensitivity of Cells of Chinese Hamster *in Vitro* in Relation to the Cell Cycle, *Exptl. Cell Res.,* **27**: 441–452 (1962).

61. I. Johansen and P. Howard-Flanders, Macromolecular Repair and Free Radical Scavenging in the Protection of Bacteria Against X-rays, *Radiation Res.,* **24**: 184–200 (1965).

62. H. A. Johnson and E. P. Cronkite, The Effect of H³-Thymidine of Mouse Spermatogonia, *Radiation Res.,* **11**: 825–831 (1959).

63. H. S. Kaplan and L. E. Moses, Biological Complexity and Radiosensitivity, *Science,* **145**: 21–25 (1965).

64. W. D. Kaplan and J. E. Sisken, Genetic and Autoradiographic Studies of H³-thymidine in Testes of *Drosophila melanogaster, Experientia,* **16**: 67–69 (1960).

65. W. D. Kaplan, H. D. Gugler, K. K. Kidd, and V. E. Tinderholt, Non-random Distribution of Lethals Induced by Tritiated Thymidine in *Drosophila melanogaster, Genetics,* **49**: 701–714 (1964).

66. W. E. Kisieleski, L. D. Samuels, and P. C. Hiley, Dose-Effect Measurements of Radiation Following Administration of Tritiated Thymidine, *Nature,* **202**: 458–459 (1964).

67. A. L. Koch, A Distributional Basis for the Variation in Killing Efficiencies by Different Tritiated Compounds Incorporated into *Escherichia coli, Radiation Res.,* **24**: 398–411 (1965).

68. M. Krause and W. S. Plaut, An Effect of Tritiated Thymidine on the Incorporation of Thymidine into Chromosomal Deoxyribonucleic Acid, *Nature,* **188**: 511–512 (1960).

69. L. G. Lajtha, On DNA Labeling in the Study of the Dynamics of Bone Marrow Cell Populations, in *Kinetics of Cellular Proliferation* (F. Stohlman, Jr., ed.), pp. 173–182, Grune & Stratton, Inc., New York, 1959.

70. L. G. Lajtha and R. Oliver, The Application of Autoradiography in the Study of Nucleic Acid Metabolism, *Lab. Invest.,* **8**: 214–221 (1959).

71. R. Latarjet, B. Ekert, S. Apelgot, and N. Rebeyrotte, Etudes radiobiochimiques sur l'ADN, *J. Chim. Phys.,* **58**: 1046 (1961).

72. D. E. Lea, *Actions of Radiations of Living Cells,* Cambridge University Press, London and New York, The Macmillan Company, New York, 1947.

73. H. Lisco, E. T. Nishimura, R. Baserga, and W. E. Kisieleski, Effect of H³-thymidine on the Growth of Ehrlich Ascites Tumor *in Vivo, Lab. Invest.,* **10**: 435–443 (1961).

74. H. Lisco, R. Baserga, and W. E. Kisieleski, Induction of Tumors in Mice with H³-thymidine, *Nature,* **192**: 571–572 (1961).

75. M. Lubin, Selection of Auxotrophic Bacterial Mutants by Tritium Labeled Thymidine, *Science,* **129**: 838–839 (1959).

76. H. A. McQuade and M. Friedkin, Radiation Effects of H³-thymidine and Thymidine-C¹⁴, *Exptl. Cell Res.,* **21**: 118–125 (1960).

77. H. A. McQuade, Induction of Aberrations in Meiotic Chromosomes of Wheat by Means of Thymidine-H³, *Radiation Res.*, **20**: 451–465 (1963).
78. G. Marin and M. A. Bender, Survival Kinetics of HeLa-S₃ Cells after Incorporation of H³-thymidine or H³-uridine, *Intern. J. Radiation Biol.*, **7**: 221–233 (1963).
79. G. Marin and M. A. Bender, A Comparison of Mammalian Cell Killing by Incorporated H³-thymidine and H³-uridine, *Intern. J. Radiation Biol.*, **7**: 235–244 (1963).
80. G. Marin and D. M. Prescott, The Frequency of Sister Chromatid Exchanges Following Exposure to Varying Doses of H³-thymidine or X-rays, *J. Cell Biol.*, **21**: 159–167 (1964).
81. T. R. Munro, Alpha Radiation of Parts of Single Cells in Tissue Culture. IV. Irradiation of Chick Fibroblasts During Metaphase and Anaphase, *Exptl. Cell Res.*, **18**: 76–99 (1959).
82. A. T. Natarajan, Chromosome Breakage and Mitotic Inhibition Induced by H³-thymidine in Root Meristems of *Vicia faba, Exptl. Cell Res.*, **22**: 275–281 (1961).
83. A. H. W. Nias and L. G. Lajtha, Continuous Irradiation with Tritiated Water of Mammalian Cells in a Monolayer, *Nature,* **202**: 613–614 (1964).
84. R. Oliver and L. G. Lajtha, Hazard of Tritium as a DNA Label in Man, *Nature,* **186**: 91–92 (1960).
85. E. E. Osgood, in Discussion: Leukocyte Production and Survival, in *Kinetics of Cellular Proliferation* (F. Stohlman, Jr., ed.)., Grune & Stratton, New York, 1959.
86. R. B. Painter, R. M. Drew, and W. L. Hughes, Inhibition of HeLa Growth by Intranuclear Tritium, *Science,* **127**: 1244–1245 (1958).
87. R. B. Painter, R. M. Drew, and R. E. Rasmussen, Limitations in the Use of Carbon-Labeled and Tritium-Labeled Thymidine in Cell Culture Studies, *Radiation Res.*, **21**: 355–366 (1964).
88. S. Person and L. Lewis, Effects of Decay of Incorporated H³-thymidine on Bacteria, *Biophys. J.*, **2**: 451–463 (1962).
89. S. Person, Comparative Killing Efficiencies for Decays of Tritiated Compounds Incorporated into *E. coli, Biophys. J.*, **3**: 183–187 (1963).
90. S. Person and R. C. Bockrath, Jr., Differential Mutation Production by the Decay of Incorporated Tritium Compounds in *E. coli, Biophys. J.*, **4**: 355–365 (1964).
91. S. Person, F. D. Funk, and R. C. Bockrath, The Mechanism of Lethality by Tritium Decay in T₄-Coliphage, *Meeting Biophys. Soc., San Francisco, 1965,* p. 44.
92. W. S. Plaut, The Effect of Tritium on the Interpretation of Autoradiographic Studies on Chromosomes, *Lab. Invest.,* **8**: 286–293 (1959).
93. J. Post and J. Hoffmann, Some Effects of H³-thymidine as a DNA Label in the Rat Liver, *Radiation Res.*, **14**: 713–720 (1961).
94. E. L. Powers and D. Shefner, Tritium Induced Effects in *Paramecium aurelia, Proc. Soc. Exptl. Biol. Med.*, **78**: 493–497 (1951).
95. M. Rachmeler and A. B. Pardee, Loss of Viability and Beta-galactosidase-forming Ability as a Consequence of Tritium Decay in *E. coli, Arch. Biochim. Biophys.,* **68**: 62–67 (1963).
96. W. C. Reinig and E. L. Albenesius, Control of Tritium Health Hazards at the Savannah River Plant, *Am. Ind. Hyg. Assoc. J.,* **24**: 276 (1963).

97. D. Rittenberg, The Effect of Isotopic Substitution on the Living Cell, *J. Chim. Phys.*, **60**: 318–322 (1963).

98. J. S. Robertson and W. L. Hughes, Theoretic Considerations of the Radiation Dose from Discrete Tritium Sources, *Radiology*, **68**: 102 (1957).

99. J. S. Robertson and W. L. Hughes, Intranuclear Irradiation with Tritium-Labeled Thymidine, *Proceedings 1st Natl. Biophys. Conf. New Haven*, pp. 278–283. Yale University Press, 1959.

100. J. S. Robertson, personal communication, 1965.

101. L. D. Samuels and W. E. Kisieleski, Toxicological Studies of Tritiated Thymidine, *Radiation Res.*, **18**: 620–632 (1963).

102. J. L. Sanders, G. V. Dalrymple, and C. D. Robinette, Retention of Labeled Deoxyribonucleic Acid Following Irradiation: A Statistical Consideration, *Nature*, **201**: 206–207 (1964).

103. P. C. Sanders, D. F. Petersen, and W. H. Langham, The Influence of Intranuclear Irradiation on the Growth of HeLa Cells in Agitated Fluid Medium, *Ann. New York Acad. Sci.*, **95**: 969–974 (1961).

104. M. E. Sauer and B. E. Walker, Radiation Injury Resulting from Nuclear Labeling with H^3-thymidine in the Chick Embryo, *Radiation Res.*, **14**: 633–642 (1961).

105. M. E. Sauer, B. E. Walker, and M. Schneider, Development of Hatching of Chick Embryos Given Early Treatment with H^3-thymidine, *Texas Rept. Biol. Med.*, **20**: 279–283 (1962).

106. G. Scholes, J. F. Ward, and J. J. Weiss, Mechanism of the Radiation Induced Degradation of Nucleic Acids, *J. Mol. Biol.*, **2**: 379–391 (1960).

107. Séminaire sur la protection contre les dangers du tritium. Health Physics Society, section française, Service central de protection contre les rayonnements ionisants, Paris, 1964.

108. W. W. Smith, G. Brecher, F. Stohlman, Jr., and J. Cornfield, Toxicity of Tritiated Thymidine to Bone Marrow Transplants, *Radiation Res.*, **16**: 201–207 (1962).

109. O. L. Stein and H. Quastler, The Effect of H^3-thymidine on the Morphogenesis of Lateral Roots, in *Tritium in the Physical and Biological Sciences, Symp. Intern. At. Energy Agency*, **2**: 149–153 (1961).

110. O. L. Stein and H. Quastler, Effect of H^3-thymidine on the Morphogenesis of Lateral Roots in *Zea mays, Radiation Res.*, **21**: 212–222 (1964).

111. B. S. Strauss, The Genetic Effect of Incorporated Radioisotopes: The Transmutation Problem, *Radiation Res.*, **8**: 234–247 (1948).

112. O. Strömnaes, Mutagenic Effect of C^{14}- and H^3-labelled DNA Precursors Injected into *Drosophila melanogaster* Males, *Can. J. Genet. Cytol.*, **4**: 440–446 (1962).

113. O. Strömnaes and I. Kvelland, The Induction of Minute Mutations in *Drosophila* with Tritium Labeled Thymidine, *Genetics*, **48**: 1559–1565 (1963).

114. J. H. Taylor, Sister Chromatid Exchanges in Tritium Labeled Chromosomes, *Genetics*, **43**: 515–529 (1958).

115. J. H. Taylor, Chromosome Reproduction, *Intern. Rev. Cytol.*, **13**: 39–74 (1962).

116. J. E. Till, Radiation Effects on the Division Cycle of Mammalian Cells *in Vitro*, *Ann. N. Y. Acad. Sci.*, **95**: 911–919 (1961).

117. J. E. Till and E. A. McCulloch, A Direct Measurement of the Radiation Sensitivity of Normal Mouse Bone Marrow Cells, *Radiation Res.*, **14**: 213–222 (1961).

118. H. Ulrich, Radiation Effects on Nucleus and Cytoplasm and Their Dependence upon Oxygen, *Radiation Res.*, **9**: 196–197 (1958).

119. *Natl. Bur. Std. (U.S.) Handbook* **85** (March 31, 1964); *Radiation Protection, Recommendations of the International Commission on Radiological Protection,* ICRP Publication 6, Pergamon Press, New York, 1964.

120. R. C. Von Borstel and S. Wolff, Photoreactivation Experiments on the Nucleus and Cytoplasm of the *Habrobracon* Egg, *Proc. Natl. Acad. Sci. U.S.,* **41:** 1004–1009 (1955).

121. R. C. Von Borstel and R. W. Rogers, Alpha-Particle Bombardment of the *Habrobracon* Egg. II. Response of the Cytoplasm, *Radiation Res.,* **8:** 248–253 (1958).

122. S. Wexler, Dissociation of Molecules by Nuclear Decay of Constituent Atoms, in *Chemical Effects of Nuclear Transformations, Symp. Intern. At. Energy Agency, Prague, 1960,* pp. 115–145.

123. G. F. Whitmore and J. E. Till, Quantitation of Cellular Radiobiological Responses, *Ann. Rev. Nucl. Sci.,* **14:** 347–374 (1964).

124. D. E. Wimber, Chromosome Breakage Produced by H^3-labeled Thymidine in *Tradescantia paludosa, Proc. Natl. Acad. Sci. U.S.,* **45:** 839–846 (1959).

125. F. C. V. Worman, The Relative Biological Effectiveness of Tritium Beta-rays in Producing Splenic and Thymic Weight Loss in Mice, U.S. At. Energy Comm. Document LA-1641 (1954).

126. F. Zajdela, personal communication, 1964.

127. G. Zajicek and J. Gross, Studies on the Radiobiological Effect of H^3-thymidine on the DNA Turnover in Landschütz Ascites Tumor Cells, *Exptl. Cell Res.,* **34:** 138–143 (1964).

128. R. E. Zirkle and R. E. Bloom, Irradiation of Parts of Individual Cells, *Science,* **117:** 487–493 (1953).

Supplementary List of References

The number of individuals using tritium as a marker in biological experimentation appears to be constantly rising, and the literature consequently is enormous. Selected reports were used to illustrate in the preceding chapters advantages and problems to be reckoned with in using tritium-labeled molecules. Additional references are given below with the principle aim of aiding those who wish to start on a new project and want to know more about the application of tritium as a tracer in their field of interest. This supplementary list of references is vastly incomplete, partly because it was compiled mainly from those papers which appeared within a few years prior to July 1964. Even so, it should be helpful in conjunction with the references of the preceding chapters to give an initial perspective and orientation on authors, subjects, and laboratories. A sequence of papers on one research project carried out by one group of scientists is represented in this list usually by the most recent communication prior to July 1964. Collective reports from proceedings of specific seminars and symposia and respective books were already referred to and are therefore not included here again. Omissions and errors are difficult to avoid and the reader is asked to pardon such inadequacy, the responsibility for which rests with the author.

The list is divided into 11 groups of subjects; the first four groups are comprised of papers on work with H^3-thymidine. Within each group the reports are listed alphabetically by the last name of the senior author.

I. The Use of H^3-Thymidine in Studies on the Mechanism of DNA Synthesis and Its Control

II. The Use of H^3-Thymidine in Studies on Chromosomal DNA

III. The Use of H^3-Thymidine in Studies on Cellular Proliferation

IV. The Use of H^3-Thymidine in Studies on Transfer and Reutilization of DNA Label

V. The Use of Tritium-Labeled Nucleosides Other than Thymidine in Studies on Nucleic Acid Synthesis and Metabolism

VI. The Use of Tritium-Labeled Amino Acids and Proteins

VII. The Use of Tritium-Labeled Hormones

VIII. The Use of Tritium-Labeled Vitamins

IX. The Use of Tritium-Labeled Carbohydrates and Lipids

X. The Use of Tritium-Labeled Alkaloids and Drugs

XI. Methods and Technical Aspects in Using Tritium as a Label

I. The Use of H^3-Thymidine in Studies on the Mechanism of DNA Synthesis and Its Control

E. K. Adrian, Jr. and B. E. Walker, Incorporation of Thymidine-H^3 by Cells in Normal and Injured Mouse Spinal Cord, *J. Neuropathol. Exptl. Neurol.*, **21**: 597–609

(1962).   H. W. Altman, E. Stöcker, and W. Thoenes, Über Chromatin und DNS Synthese im Nukleolus, electronenmikroskopische, autoradiographische und licht-mikroskopische Untersuchungen an Leberzellen von Ratten, Z. Zellforsch. Mikroskop. Anat., 59: 116–133 (1963).   M. Aronson and S. S. Elberg, Detection of Inclusion Bodies Containing DNA by Means of Autoradiography, Nature, 192: 981–982 (1961).   S. Bader, R. M. Goodman, and D. Spiro, Chromosome Fine Structure and Localization of DNA and RNA in Human Cells, J. Cell Biol., 19: 84A (1963).   M. R. Banerjee, Functional Properties of the Acentric Chromosome Fragments of Mouse Leukemia Cells, Exptl. Cell Res., 34: 351–359 (1964).   H. J. Barr, An Effect of Exogenous Thymidine on the Mitotic Cycle, J. Cellular Comp. Physiol., 61: 119–127 (1963).   R. Baserga, G. C. Henegar, W. E. Kisieleski, and H. Lisco, Uptake of Tritiated Thymidine by Human Tumors in vivo, Lab. Invest., 11: 360–364 (1962).   R. M. Behki and W. C. Schneider, Incorporation of H³-thymidine into DNA of Isolated Nuclei, Biochim. Biophys. Acta, 68: 34–44 (1963).   L. F. Belanger and B. B. Migicovsky, Bone Cell Formation and Survival in H³-thymidine-labeled Chicks under Various Conditions, Anat. Record, 145: 385–390 (1963).   R. E. Beltz, Comparison of the Effect of X-radiation on the Elevation of Thymidine Kinase and Thymidylate Synthetase during Liver Regeneration, Biochem. Biophys. Res. Commun., 9: 78–83 (1962).   C. Biagini, P. G. Paleani Vettori, and R. Z. Bignami, Recovery of Mice Thymus after X-rays and 15 MeV Electrons. Comparative Study of the Cell Population Using Tritiated Thymidine, in Tritium in the Physical and Biological Sciences, Symp. Intern. At. Energy Agency, Vienna, 2: 373–379 (1961).   P. A. Bianchi, A. R. Crathorn, and K. V. Shooter, Thymidine Kinase and DNA Synthesis in Normal and Regenerating Rat Liver, Biochim. Biophys. Acta, 61: 728–735 (1962).   P. A. Bianchi, Thymidine Kinases in Human Tumours, Biochem. J., 81: 21–22 (1961).   P. A. Bianchi, Thymidine Kinases in Normal and Malignant Tissues, Biochem. J., 81: 20–21 (1961).   P. A. Bianchi, A. R. Crathorn, and K. V. Shooter, The Use of Tritium Labelled Thymidine in Studies on the Synthesis of Deoxyribonucleic Acids, in Tritium in the Physical and Biological Sciences, Symp. Intern. At. Energy Agency, Vienna, 2: 270–276 (1961).   F. J. Bollum and V. R. Potter, Nucleic Acid Metabolism in Regenerating Rat Liver. VII. Effect of X-radiation on Enzymes of DNA Synthesis, Cancer Res., 20: 138–143 (1959).   V. P. Bond, T. M. Fliedner, E. P. Cronkite, J. R. Rubini, G. Brecher, and P. K. Schork, Proliferative Potentials of Bone Marrow and Blood Cells Studied by in vitro Uptake of H³-thymidine, Acta Haematol., 21: 1–15 (1959).   V. P. Bond, J. R. Rubini, T. M. Fliedner, and E. P. Cronkite, Study of the Effect of Therapy on Cells in the Blood of Leukemic Patients Capable of Incorporating H³-thymidine, J. Lab. Clin. Med., 59: 412–418 (1962).   E. Borenfreund and A. Bendich, A Study of the Penetration of Mammalian Cells by Deoxyribonucleic Acid, J. Biophys. Biochem. Cytol., 9: 81–91 (1961).   T. R. Breitman, The Feedback Inhibition of Thymidine Phosphokinase, Biochim. Biophys. Acta, 67: 153–155 (1963).   S. M. Cattaneo, H. Quastler, and F. G. Sherman, DNA Synthesis in Irradiated Hair Follicles of the Mouse, Radiation Res., 12: 587–593 (1960).   R. S. Chang and H. Liepins, A Study of the Mechanism of DNA and Thymine Degradation in Cultured Human Cells Infected with a Lipo-virus, J. Exptl. Med., 115: 967 (1962).   R. S. Chang and H. Vetrovs, Loss of Radioactivity from Labeled DNA of Primary Human Ammion Cells, Science, 139: 1211–1212 (1963).   M. Chèvremont, E. Baeckeland, and J. Frederic, Contribution cytochimique et histoautoradiographique à l'étude du métabolisme et de la synthèse des acides désoxyribonucleiques dans les cellules animales cultivées in vitro. I. Etudes cytophotométrique et histautoradiographiques des ADN dans des fibroblastes traités par le Myleran, *Biochem. Pharmacol.*, **4:** 57–66 (1960).   M. Chèvremont, E. Baeckeland, and S. Chèvremont-Comhaire, Contribution à l'étude du métabolisme et de la synthèse cytoplasmique d'acides désoxyribonucléiques en culture de tissus, *Bull. Acad. Roy. Med. Belg.*, **25:** 349–367 (1960).   M. Chèvremont, Le mécanisme de l'action antimitotique, *Pathol. Biol.*, **9:** 973–1004 (1961).   E. H. Cooper, DNA-synthesis in the Thoracic Duct Lymphocytes of Rats during Recovery from Sub-lethal Irradiation, *Int. J. Rad. Biol.*, **1:** 43–51 (1959).   J. Côté, W. Oehlert, and F. Büchner, Autoradiographische Untersuchungen zur DNS-Synthese während der experimentellen Kanzerisierung der Ratte durch Diäthylnitrosamin, *Beitr. Pathol. Anat. Allgem. Pathol.*, **127:** 450–473 (1962).   S. Dales, The Uptake and Development of Vaccinia Virus in Strain L Cells Followed with Labeled Viral Deoxyribonucleic Acid, *J. Cell Biol.*, **18:** 51 (1963).   N. K. Das and M. Alfert, Accelerated DNA Synthesis in Onion Root Meristem During X-irradiation, *Proc. Natl. Acad. Sci. U. S.*, **47:** 1–6 (1961).   N. K. Das, Synthetic Capacities of Chromosome Fragments Correlated with Ability to Maintain Nucleolar Material, *J. Cell Biol.*, **15:** 121–130 (1962).   V. Defendi and D. Kritchevsky, A. Histoautoradiographic Study of DNA Synthesis in Tissue Cultures of Chicken Embryo Liver Cells Infected with RPL-12 Lymphomatosis Virus, *J. Biophys. Biochem. Cytol.*, **7:** 201–202 (1960).   F. Gavosto, G. Maraini, and A. Pileri, Radioautographic Investigations on DNA and Protein Metabolism in 2 cases of Di Guglielmo's Disease, *Blood*, **16:** 1122–1132 (1960).   F. Gavosto, G. Maraini, and A. Pileri, Nucleic Acid and Protein Metabolism in Acute Leukemia Cells, *Blood*, **16:** 1555–1563 (1960).   F. Gavosto, Nucleic Acid and Protein Metabolism of Bone Marrow Cells Studied by Means of Tritium Labeled Precursors, *in Tritium in the Physical and Biological Sciences, Symp. Intern. At. Energy Agency, Vienna*, **2:** 238–246 (1961).   G. B. Gerber, W. G. Aldridge, T. R. Koszalka, and G. Gerber, Biochemical and Autoradiographic Studies on DNA Metabolism in Vitamin E-deficient Hamsters, *J. Nutr.* **78:** 307–319 (1962).   G. B. Gerber, G. Gerber, K. I. Altman, and L. H. Hempelman, The Catabolism of Nucleic Acids in the Rat. IV. The Replacement of Desoxyribonucleic Acid in the Irradiated Rat, *Intern. J. Radiation Biol.*, **6:** 17–22 (1963).   G. B. Gerber, W. G. Aldridge, G. Gerber, K. I. Altman, and L. H. Hempelman, The Catabolism of Nucleic Acids, V. Autoradiographic Studies on the Replacement of DNA in Normal and X-irradiated Rats, *Intern. J. Radiation Biol.*, **6:** 23–38 (1963).   A. M. Girgis, Etude autoradiographique de l'incorporation de la thymidine tritiée en fonction du temps dans l'acide désoxyribonucléique des cellules HeLa cultivées *in vitro*, *Compt. Rend.*, **256:** 2037–2040 (1963).   R. Goutier, L. Baugnet-Mahieu, and M. Semal, Effets de l'irradiation totale et de l'AET sur l'activité des kinases de la thymidine dans le foie en régénération. *Arch. Intern. Physiol. Biochim.*, **71:** 130–131 (1963).   R. Goutier and I. Bologna, Localisation intracellulaire dans le foie de rat, d'un facteur inhibiteur de la synthèse du DNA *in vitro*, *Biochim. Biophys. Acta*, **72:** 40–47 (1963).   E. D. Gray and R. M. S. Smellie, On the Intramolecular Location of Deoxyribonucleotides Incorporated into DNA by Extracts of Ascites Tumor Cells, *Biochim. J.*, **72:** 16 (1959).   A. J. Hale, The Leucocyte as a Possible Exception to the Theory of DNA Constancy, *J. Pathol. Bacteriol.*, **85:** 311–326 (1963).   P. C. Hanawalt and D. S. Ray, Isolation of the Growing Point in the Bacterial Chromosome, *Proc. Natl. Acad. Sci. U. S.*, **52:** 125–132 (1964).   H. Harrington, Effect of X-irradiation on the Priming Activity of DNA, *Proc. Natl. Acad. Sci. U. S.*, **51:** 59–66 (1964).   M. Hayashi, M. N. Hayashi, and S. Spiegelman, Restriction of *in vivo* Genetic Transcription to One of the Complimentary Strands of DNA, *Proc. Natl. Acad. Sci. U. S.*, **50:** 664–672 (1963).   M. Hayashi, M. N. Hayashi, and S. Spiegelman, DNA Circularity and the

Mechanism of Strand Selection in the Generation of Genetic Messages, *Proc. Natl. Acad. Sci. U. S.*, **51**: 251–359 (1964).   D. H. Ives, P. A. Morse, Jr., and V. R. Potter, Feedback Inhibition of Thymidine Kinase by Thymidine Triphosphate, *J. Biol. Chem.*, **238**: 1467–1474 (1963).   M. Izawa, V. G. Allfrey, and A. E. Mirsky, The Relationship between RNA Synthesis and Loop Structure in Lampbrush Chromosomes, *Proc. Natl. Acad. Sci. U. S.*, **49**: 544–551 (1963).   E. V. Jensen, E. Ford and C. Huggins, Depressed Incorporation of Thymidine-H[3] into Deoxyribonucleic Acid Following Administration of 7,1-dimethylbenz(a)anthracene, *Proc. Natl. Acad. Sci. U. S.*, **50**: 454–459 (1963).   B. Källén and K. Valmin, DNA Synthesis in the Embryonic Chick Central Nervous System, *Z. Zellforsch. Mikroskop. Anat.*, **60**: 491–496 (1963). R. C. King and R. G. Burnett, Autoradiographic Study of Uptake of Tritiated Glycine, Thymidine, and Uridine by Fruit Fly Ovaries, *Science*, **129**: 1674–1675 (1959). S. Kit, L. J. Piekarski, and D. R. Dubbs, Induction of Thymidine Kinase by Vaccinia-Infected Mouse Fibroblasts, *J. Mol. Biol.*, **6**: 22–33 (1963).   S. Kit and D. R. Dubbs, Biochemistry of Vaccinia Infected Mouse Fibroblasts (Strain L-M). IV, H[3]-thymidine Uptake into DNA of Cells Exposed to Cold Shock, *Exptl. Cell Res.*, **31**: 397–406 (1963).   J. L. van Lancker, Inhibition of Incorporation of H[3]-thymidine in Tissue Homogenate after Total Body Doses of X-radiation, *Biochim. Biophys. Acta*, **33**: 587–588 (1959).   J. L. van Lancker, Metabolic Alterations after Total Body Doses of X-radiation. I. The Role of Regenerating Liver Nuclei and Cytoplasm in the Inhibition due to X-radiation of Incorporation of H[3]-thymidine into DNA, *Biochim. Biophys. Acta*, **45**: 57–62 (1960).   K. G. Lark, T. Repko, and E. J. Hoffman, The Effect of Amino Acid Deprivation on Subsequent Deoxyribonucleic Acid Replication, *Biochim. Biophys. Acta*, **76**: 9–24 (1963).   S. M. Lehnert and S. Okada, Nuclear Factors Involved in the Radiation-induced Depression of DNA Synthesis of Deoxyribonucleic Acid, *Nature*, **199**: 1108–1109 (1963).   N. de Lesdain and C. Paoletti, Evolution de la radioactivité de l'acide desoxyribonucleique chez la souris après administration de thymidine tritiee, *Compt. Rend.*, **253**: 1701–1703 (1962).   A. Lima-de-Faria, Metabolic DNA in *Tipula oleracea*, *Chromosoma*, **13**: 47–59 (1962). A. Lima-de-Faria and J. Reitalu, Heterochromatin in Human Male Leukocytes, *J. Cell Biol.*, **16**: 315–322 (1963).   A. Lindner, T. Kutkam, K. Sankaranarayanan, R. Rucker, and J. Arradondo, Inhibition of Ehrlich Ascites Tumor with 5-fluoruracil and Other Agents, *Exptl. Cell Res.*, *Suppl.*, **9**: 485–508 (1963).   V. C. Littau, V. G. Allfrey, J. H. Frenster, and A. E. Mirsky, Active and Inactive Regions of Nuclear Chromatin as Revealed by Electron Microscope Autoradiography, *Proc. Natl. Acad., Sci. U. S.* **52**: 93–100 (1964).   J. W. Littlefield, DNA-synthesis in Partially Synchronized L-cells, *Exptl. Cell Res.*, **26**: 318–326 (1962).   B. W. Looney, R. C. Campbell, and B. E. Holmes, The Effect of Irradiation on the Replication of Deoxyribonucleic Acid in Hepatocytes, *Proc. Natl. Acad. Sci. U. S.*, **46**: 698–708 (1960).   W. B. Looney, Some Limitations of Labeled Compounds in Radiobiological Investigations of Deoxyribonucleic Acid (DNA) synthesis, *Ann. N. Y. Acad. Sci.*, **95**: 975–983 (1961). O. Maaløe, Role of Protein Synthesis in the DNA Replication Cycle in Bacteria, *J. Cellular Comp. Physiol.*, **62**: (Suppl. 1): 31–44 (1963).   R. M. Maenza and C. V. Harding, Disappearance of H[3]-thymidine and H[3]-water from the Anterior Chamber of the Rabbit Eye, *Nature*, **196**: 786–787 (1962).   J. A. McCarter and H. Quastler, Note on the Effect of a Carcinogenic Hydrocarbon on the Synthesis of Deoxyribonucleic Acid, *Biochim. Biophys. Acta*, **55**: 552–553 (1962).   W. E. Magee and O. V. Miller, Dissociation of the Synthesis of Host and Viral Deoxyribonucleic Acid, *Biochim. Biophys. Acta*, **55**: 818–826 (1962).   J. Minowada, Effect of X-irradiation on DNA-synthesis in Polyoma Virus-infected Cultures. Autoradiographic Studies, *Exptl. Cell Res.*, **33**: 161–175 (1964).   G. C. Mueller, Molecular Events in Replication of Nuclei,

Exptl. Cell Res. Suppl., **9**: 144–149 (1963). R. M. Nakamura, D. S. Miyada, and D. L. Moyer, Interrelationship of the Thyroid Gland to Liver Regeneration in Rats as Studied by Tritiated Thymidine Incorporation, *Exptl. Cell Res.*, **34**: 410–413 (1964). B. R. Nebel, C. J. Murphy, and H. J. Lindner, Autoradiographic Study with Tritiated Thymidine of Mouse Testis after 320 r and after 1000 r of Acute Localized X-irradiation. *Radiation Res.*, **13**: 126–136 (1960). O. F. Nygaard and R. L. Potter, Effect of X-radiation on DNA Metabolism in Various Tissues of the Rat. II. Recovery after Sublethal Doses of Radiation. III. Retention of Labeled DNA in Normal and Irradiated Animals, *Radiation Res.*, **12**: 120–130 (1960). S. Okada, Incorporation of Tritium Labeled Thymidine and Tritium Labeled Deoxycytidylic Acid into Deoxyribonucleic Acid after Irradiation of the Deoxyribonucleic Acid Primer with γ-rays, *Nature*, **185**: 193–194 (1960). E. E. Osgood, Radiobiologic Observations on Human Hemic Cells *in vivo* and *in vitro*, *Ann. N. Y. Acad. Sci.*, **95**: 828–838 (1961). R. B. Painter and W. L. Hughes, Nucleic Acid Metabolism and the Lethal Effect of Radiation on Cultured Human Cells (HeLa), *Ann. N. Y. Acad. Sci.*, **95**: 960–968 (1961). R. B. Painter, The Direct Effect of X-irradiation on HeLa-S3 DNA Synthesis, *Radiation Res.*, **16**: 846–859 (1962). R. B. Painter and R. E. Rasmussen, Organization of the Deoxyribonucleic Acid Replicating System in Mammalian Cells as Revealed by the Use of X-radiation and Bromuracil-deoxyriboside, *Nature*, **201**: 162–165 (1964). C. Pelling, Application of Tritiated Compounds to the Midge *Chironomus* and Some Aspects of the Metabolism of Salivary Gland Chromosomes, in *Tritium in the Physical and Biological Sciences, Symp. Intern. At. Energy Agency, Vienna*, **2**: 327–334 (1961). W. Plaut and L. A. Sagan, Incorporation of Thymidine in the Cytoplasm of *Amoeba proteus*, *J. Biophys. Biochem. Cytol.*, **4**: 843–844 (1958). W. F. Powell, The Effects of Ultraviolet Irradiation and Inhibitors of Protein-Synthesis on the Initiation of Deoxyribonucleic Acid Synthesis in Mammalian Cells in Culture. I. The Overall Process of Deoxyribonucleic Acid Synthesis, *Biochim. Biophys. Acta*, **55**: 969–978 (1962). D. M. Prescott, F. J. Bollum, and B. C. Kluss, Is DNA Polymerase a Cytoplasmic Enzyme? *J. Cell Biol.*, **13**: 172–174 (1962). D. M. Prescott, R. F. Kimball, and R. F. Carrier, Comparison between the Timing of Micronuclear and Macronuclear DNA-synthesis in *Euplotes eurystomus*, *J. Cell Biol.*, **13**: 175–176 (1962). M. Rabinovitch and W. Plaut, Cytoplasmic DNA-synthesis in *Amoeba proteus*, I. On the Particulate Nature of the DNA Containing Elements, *J. Cell Biol.*, **15**: 525–534 (1962). W. M. Rigal, Uptake and Incorporation of H^3-thymidine *in vitro* Culture, *Nature*, **192**: 768 (1961). J. Seed, Action of Radiation on Synthesis of DNA in Normal and Tumour Strain Cells, *Nature*, **192**: 944–945 (1961). R. W. Seed and I. H. Goldberg, Biosynthesis of Thyroglobulin: Relationship to RNA-template and Precursor Protein, *Proc. Natl. Acad. Sci. U. S.*, **50**: 275–282 (1963). R. B. Setlow, P. A. Swenson, and W. L. Carrier, Thymine Dimers and Inhibition of DNA Synthesis by Ultra-Violet Irradiation of Cells, *Science*, **142**: 1464–1466 (1963). V. C. Shah, Autoradiographic Studies of the Effects of an Antibiotics, Amino Acid Analogue, and Nucleases on the Synthesis of DNA in Cultured Mammalian Cells, *Cancer Res.*, **23**: 1137–1147 (1963). A. J. Shatkin and N. P. Salzman, Deoxyribonucleic Acid Synthesis in Vaccinia Virus Infected HeLa-Cells, *Virology*, **19**: 551–560 (1963). J. E. Sisken, The Synthesis of Nucleic Acids and Proteins in the Nuclei of *Tradescantia* Root Tips, *Exptl. Cell Res.*, **16**: 602–614 (1959). J. Sisken, T. A. Okada, and E. Roberts, Autoradiographic Studies of Antimitotic Action of Maleuric Acid, *Proc. Soc. Exptl. Biol. Med.*, **101**: 461–463 (1959). C. L. Smith, Effect of Alpha Particle and X-ray Irradiation on DNA-synthesis in Tissue Cultures, *in Tritium in the Physical and Biological Sciences, Symp. Intern. At. Energy Agency, Vienna*, **2**: 381–391 (1961). H. H. Smith, B. H. Kugelman, S. L. Commerford, and W. Szybalski, Incorporation of

5-iododeoxyuridine into DNA of Plant Cells, *Proc. Natl. Acad. Sci. U. S.* **49:** 451–457 (1963).   C. P. Stanners and J. E. Till, DNA Synthesis in Individual L-strain Mouse Cells, *Biochim. Biophys. Acta*, **37:** 406–419 (1960).   T. O. Swallen, A Radioautographic Study of the Lesions of Fowl Pox Using H^3-thymidine, *Am. J. Pathol.*, **42:** 485–491 (1963).   J. H. Taylor, Tritium and Autoradiography in Cell Biology, *in Tritium in the Physical and Biological Sciences, Symp. Intern. At. Energy Agency, Vienna*, **2:** 221–228 (1961).   T. Terasima and L. J. Tolmach, X-ray Sensitivity and DNA-synthesis in Synchronous Populations of HeLa Cells, *Science*, **140:** 490–492 (1963).   E. C. Theil and S. Zamenhof, Possible Turnover of DNA with an Increased 6-methylamino-purine Content, *Nature*, **199:** 599–600 (1963).   A. Tsuya, V. P. Bond, T. M. Fliedner, and L. E. Feinendegen, Cellularity and DNA-synthesis in Bone Marrow Following Total and Partial Body Irradiation, *Radiation Res.*, **14:** 618–632 (1961).   S. M. Weissman, R. M. S. Smellie, and J. Paul, Studies on the Biosynthesis of DNA by Extracts of Mammalian Cells. IV. The phosphorylation of Thymidine, *Biochim. Biophys. Acta*, **45:** 101–110 (1960).   A. M. Zimmerman, Incorporation of H^3-thymidine in the Eggs of *Arbacia punctulata*. A Pressure Study, *Exptl. Cell Res.*, **31:** 39–51 (1963).

II. The Use of H^3-Thymidine in Studies on Chromosomal DNA

L. Atkins, P. D. Taft, and K. P. Dalal, Asynchronous DNA Synthesis of Sex Chromatin in Human Interphase Nuclei, *J. Cell. Biol.*, **15:** 390–393 (1962).   S. Bader, O. J. Miller, and B. B. Mukherjee, Observations on Chromosome Duplication in Cultured Human Leukocytes, *Exptl. Cell Res.*, **31:** 100–112 (1963).   S. Bell and S. Wolff, Studies on the Mechanism of the Effect of Fluorodeoxyuridine on Chromosomes, *Proc. Natl. Acad. Sci. U.S.*, **51:** 195–202 (1964).   J. Cairns, Proof that the Replication of DNA Involves Separation of the Strands, *Nature*, **194:** 1274 (1962).   G. M. Donnelly and E. H. Newcomer, Autoradiographic Patterns in Cultured Leukocytes of the Domestic Fowl, *Exptl. Cell Res.*, **30:** 363–368 (1963).   P. J. Fitzgerald, A. Adams, and F. V. Gunz, Chromosome Studies in Adult Acute Leukaemia, *J. Natl. Cancer Inst.*, **32:** 395–417 (1964).   F. Gavosto, L. Pegoraro, and A. Pileri, Possibilité de marquer, a l'aide de précurseurs tritiés, les chromosomes de cellules leucémiques chez l'homme, *Rev. Franc. Etudes Clin. Biol.*, **8:** 920–923 (1963).   F. Gavosto, A. Pileri, and L. Pegoraro, DNA Metabolism in Acute Leukemia Chromosomes. *IXth Congr. Europ. Soc. Hematol., Lisbon, 1963*.   F. Gavosto, A. Pileri, L. Pegoraro, and A. Momigliano, *In vivo* Incorporation of Tritiated Thymidine in Acute Leukaemia Chromosomes, *Nature*, **200:** 807–809 (1963).   J. L. German, DNA Synthesis in Human Chromosomes, *Trans. N.Y. Acad. Sci.*, **24:** 395–407 (1962).   J. German, The Pattern of DNA Synthesis in the Chromosomes of Human Blood Cells, *J. Cell. Biol.*, **20:** 37–55 (1964).   C. W. Gilbert, S. Muldal, L. G. Lajtha, and J. Rowley, Time Sequence of Human Chromosome Duplication, *Nature*, **195:** 869–873 (1962).   M. M. Grumbach, A. Morishima, and J. H. Taylor, Human Sex Chromosome Abnormalities in Relation to DNA Replication and Heterochromatinization, *Proc. Natl. Acad. Sci. U.S.*, **49:** 581–589 (1963).   A. Haque, Differential Labeling of *Trillium* Chromosomes by H^3-thymidine at Low Temperatures, *Heredity*, **18:** 129–133 (1963).   M. Hayashi, M. N. Hayashi, and S. Spiegelman, Replicating Form of a Single Stranded DNA Virus: Isolation and Properties, *Science*, **140:** 1313–1316 (1963).   A. Howard and D. L. Dewey, Nonuniformity of Labeling Rate during DNA Synthesis, *Exptl. Cell Res.*, **24:** 623 (1961).   L. F. Lacour and S. R. Pelc, Effect of Colchicine on the Utilization of Thymidine Labeled with Tritium during Chromosomal Reproduction, *Nature*, **183:** 1455–1457 (1959).   L. G. Lajtha, Time Sequence of Human Chromosome Duplication, *IXth Congr. Europ. Soc. Hematol., Lisbon, 1963*, Karger, Basel, 1964. A. Lima-de-Faria, Differential Uptake of Tritiated Thymidine into Hetero- and Euchromatin in *Melanoplus* and *Secale*, *J. Biophys. Biochem. Cytol.*, **6**: 457–466 (1959). A. Lima-de-Faria, J. Reitalu, and S. Bergman, Das Muster der DNS-Synthese in den Chromosomen des Menschen, *Hereditas*, **47**: 695–701 (1961). R. A. McGrath, X-ray Induced Incorporation of Tritiated Thymidine into Deoxyribonucleic Acid of Grasshopper Neuroblast Chromosomes, *Radiation Res.*, **19**: 526–537 (1963). O. J. Miller, B. B. Mukherjee, S. Bader, and A. C. Christakos, Autoradiographic Studies of X-chromosome Duplication in an XO/X-isochromosome X Mosaic Human Female, *Nature*, **200**: 918–919 (1963). V. Monesi, Autoradiographic Study of DNA Synthesis and the Cell Cycle in Spermatogonia and Spermatocytes of Mouse Testis Using Tritiated Thymidine, *J. Cell Biol.*, **14**: 1–18 (1962). P. S. Moorhead and V. Defendik Asynchrony of Synthesis in Chromosomes of Human Diploid Cells, *J. Cell Biol.*, **16**: 202–207 (1963). A. Morishima, M. M. Grumbach, and J. H. Taylor, Asynchronous Duplication of Human Chromosomes and the Origin of Sex Chromatin, *Proc. Natl. Acad. Sci. U. S.*, **48**: 756–763 (1962). B. B. Mukherjee and A. K. Sinha, Single Active Hypothesis: Cytological Evidence for Random Inactivation of X-chromosomes in a Female Mule Complement, *Proc. Natl. Acad. Sci. U. S.*, **51**: 252–259 (1964). B. B. Mukherjee, O. J. Miller, W. R. Breg, and S. Bader, Chromosome Duplication in Cultured Leucocytes from Presumptive XXX and XXXX Y Human Subjects, *Exptl. Cell Res.*, **34**: 333–350 (1964). S. Muldal, C. W. Gilbert, L. G. Lajtha, J. Lindsten, J. Rowley, and W. Fraccaro, Tritiated Thymidine Incorporation in an Isochromosome for the Long Arm of the X Chromosome in Man, *Lancet*, **20**: 861–863 (1963). R. B. Painter, Asynchronus Replication of HeLa-S₃ Chromosomal Deoxyribonucleic Acid, *J. Biophys. Biochem. Cytol.*, **11**: 484–488 (1961). C. Pelling, Application of Tritiated Compounds to the Midge *Chironomus* and Some Aspects of the Metabolism of the Salivary Gland Chromosomes, in *Tritium in the Physical and Biological Sciences, Symp. Intern. At. Energy Agency, Vienna*, **2**: 327–334 (1961). W. Plaut, On the Replicative Organization of DNA in the Polytene Chromosome of *Drosophila melanogaster*, *J. Mol. Biol.*, **7**: 632–635 (1963). D. M. Prescott and M. A. Bender, Autoradiographic Study of Chromatid Distribution of Labeled DNA in Two Types of Mammalian Cells *in vitro*, *Exptl. Cell Res.*, **29**: 430–442 (1963). D. M. Prescott and M. A. Bender, Synthesis and Behavior of Nuclear Proteins during the Cell Life Cycle, *J. Cellular Comp. Physiol.*, **62**: (Suppl. 1): 175–194 (1963). R. Rolfe, Changes in the Physical State of DNA during the Replication Cycle, *Proc. Natl. Acad. Sci. U.S.*, **49**: 386–392 (1963). J. Rowley, S. Muldal, C. W. Gilbert, L. G. Lajtha, J. Lindsten, M. Fraccaro, and K. Kaiser, Synthesis of Deoxyribonucleic Acid on the X-chromosome of an XXXY-male. *Nature*, **197**: 251–252 (1963). E. Stubblefield and G. C. Mueller, Molecular Events in the Reproduction of Animal Cells. II. The Focalized Synthesis of DNA in the Chromosomes of HeLa Cells, *Cancer Res.*, **22**: 1091–1099 (1962). J. H. Taylor, The Duplication of Chromosomes, *Sci. Am.*, **198**: 36 (1958). J. H. Taylor, Asynchronus Duplication of Chromosomes in Cultured Cells of Chinese Hamster, *J. Biophys. Biochem. Cytol.*, **7**: 455–464 (1960). J. H. Taylor, Duplication of Chromosomes and Related Events in the Cell Cycle, in *Cell Physiology of Neoplasia*, pp. 547–575, The University of Texas Press, Austin, 1960. J. H. Taylor, Tritium and Autoradiography in Cell Biology, in *Tritium in the Physical and Biological Sciences, Symp. Intern. At. Energy Agency, Vienna*, **2**: 221–228 (1961). R. H. Taylor, W. F. Haut, and J. Tung, Effects of Fluorodeoxyuridine on DNA Replication, Chromosome Breakage and Reunion, *Proc. Natl. Acad. Sci. U. S.*, **48**: 190–198 (1962). J. H. Taylor, DNA Synthesis in Relation to Chromosome Reproduction and the Reunion of Breaks, *J. Cellular Comp.*

Physiol., **62** (Suppl. 1): 73–86 (1963).   J. H. Taylor, Effects of Inhibitors of Thymidylate Synthetase on Chromosome Breakage and Reunion, *Exptl. Cell Res. Suppl.*, **9**: 99–106 (1963).   J. H. Taylor, The Arrangement of Chromosomes in the Mature Sperm of the Grasshopper, *J. Cell Biol.*, **21**: 286–289 (1964).   D. W. Wimber, Asynchronous Replication of Deoxyribonucleic Acid in Root Tip Chromosomes of *Tradescantia paludosa*, *Exptl. Cell Res.*, **23**: 402–407 (1961).   D. E. Wimber and W. Prensky, Autoradiography with Meiotic Chromosomes of the Male Newt (*Triturus viridescens*) using H³-thymidine, *Genetics*, **48**: 1731–1738 (1963).   P. S. Woods, H. Gay, and A. Sengrün, Organization of the Salivary-Gland Chromosome as Revealed by the Pattern of Incorporation of H³-thymidine, *Proc. Natl. Acad. Sci. U.S.*, **47**: 1486–1493 (1961).   J. Woodard and H. Swift, The DNA Content of Cold Treated Chromosomes, *Exptl. Cell Res.*, **34**: 131–137 (1964).   H. Yoshikawa and N. Sueoka, Sequential Replication of the *Bact. subtilis* Chromosome, II. Isotopic Transfer Experiments, *Proc. Natl. Acad. Sci. U.S.*, **49**: 806–813 (1963).

III. The Use of H³-Thymidine in Studies on Cellular Proliferation

R. J. Ancill, Thymidylic Acid Synthesis and the Regulation of Cellular Proliferation in the Bone Marrow, *Biochim. Biophys. Acta*, **76**: 135–137 (1963).   M. Atlas, V. P. Bond, and E. P. Cronkite, Deoxyribonucleic Acid Synthesis in the Developing Mouse Embryo Studied with Tritiated Thymidine, *J. Histochem. Cytochem.*, **8**: 171–181 (1960).   R. Baserga and R. Gold, The Uptake of Tritiated Thymidine by Newly Transplanted Ehrlich Ascites Tumor Cells, *Exptl. Cell Res.*, **31**: 576–585 (1963).   H. Baumgärtel, H. G. Hansen, and J. Meissner, Versuche zur zytologischen Autoradiographie am lymphatischen System, *Acta Haematol.*, **22**: 363–376 (1960).   R. Barer and S. Joseph, The Action of X-rays and Chlorambucil on the Cytoplasmic Solid Concentration of Lymphocytes, *Exptl. Cell Res.*, **19**: 51–64 (1960).   M. A. Bender and D. M. Prescott, DNA Synthesis and Mitosis in Cultures of Human Peripheral Leukocytes, *Exptl. Cell Res.*, **27**: 221–229 (1962).   A. L. Burnett, R. Baird, and F. Diehl, Method of Introducing H³-thymidine into the Tissues of Hydra, *Science*, **138**: 825–826 (1962).   R. W. Caffrey, W. O. Rieke, and N. B. Everett, Radioautographic Studies of Small Lymphocytes in the Thoracic Duct of the Rat, *Acta Haematol.*, **28**: 145–154 (1962).   E. E. Capello, T. Makinodan, and W. D. Gude, Fate of H³-thymidine Labeled Spleen Cells in *in vivo* Cultures during Secondary Antibody Responses, *J. Immunol.*, **89**: 1–7 (1962).   M. Chèvremont, La préparation à la mitose. Quelques modalités de son inhibition par des substances antimitotiques, *Chemotherapia*, **2**: 191–209 (1961).   E. H. Cooper and A. J. Hale, Correlated Quantitative Cytochemical and Radioautographic Studies on DNA Synthesis, *Biochem. J.*, **85**: 28p (1962).   C. G. Craddock and G. S. Nakai, Leukemic Cell Proliferation as Determined by *in vitro* DNA Synthesis, *J. Clin. Invest.*, **41**: 360–369 (1962).   E. P. Cronkite, V. P. Bond, T. M. Fliedner, and S. A. Killmann, The Use of Tritiated Thymidine in the Study of Haemopoietic Cell Proliferation, *Ciba Found. Symp. Haemopoiesis: Cell Prod. Regulation, 1961*.   E. P. Cronkite, C. R. Jansen, H. Cottier, K. Rai, and C. R. Sipe, Lymphocyte Production Measured by Extracorporeal Irradiation, Cannulation, and Labeling Techniques, *Ann. N.Y. Acad. Sci.*, **113**: 566–577 (1964).   G. Curry and A. Gotlieb, Use of Tritiated Thymidine to Control by Autoradiography the Blood Cyto-differentiation *in vitro* of Chicken Embryonary Spleen Explants, *Compt. Rend.*, **157**: 1043–1045 (1963).   D. R. Davies and D. E. Wimber, Studies of Radiation-Induced Changes in Cellular Proliferation, Using Double Labeling Autoradiographic Technique, *Nature*, **200**: 29–32 (1963).   F. Devik, Studies on the Duration of DNA-synthesis and Mitosis in Irradiated and

SUPPLEMENTARY LIST OF REFERENCES 363

Regenerating Epidermis Cells in Mice, by Means of Tritium Labeled Thymidine, *Intern. J. Radiation Biol.*, **5**: 59–60 (1962).   B. S. Dornfest, J. LoBue, E. S. Handler, A. S. Gordon, and H. Quastler, Mechanisms of Leukocyte Production and Release. II. Factors Influencing Leukocyte Release from Isolated Perfused Rat Legs, *J. Lab. Clin. Med.*, **60**: 777–787 (1962).   A. Evensen, Significance of Mitotic Duration in Evaluating Kinetics of Cellular Proliferation, *Nature*, **195**: 718–719 (1962).   N. B. Everett, W. O. Reinhardt, and J. M. Yoffey, The Appearance of Labeled Cells in the Thoracic Duct Lymph of the Guinea Pig after the Administration of Tritiated Thymidine, *Blood*, **15**: 82–94 (1960).   N. B. Everett, R. W. Caffrey, and W. O. Rieke, Recirculation of Lymphocytes, *Ann. N. Y. Acad. Sci.*, **113**: 887–897 (1964). N. B. Everett, R. W. Caffrey, and W. O. Rieke, Radioautographic Studies of the Effect of Irradiation on the Long Lived Lymphocytes of the Rat, *Radiation Res.*, **21**: 383–393 (1964).   T. M. Fliedner, E. P. Cronkite, and V. P. Bond, Das Studium der Proliferatiosadynamik der Myelopoese unter Verwendung der Einzelzellautoradiographie, *Fol. Haematol*, **6**: 1–3 (1961).   T. M. Fliedner, E. D. Thomas, L. M. Meyer, and E. P. Cronkite, The Fate of Transfused H³-thymidine Labeled Bone Marrow Cells in Irradiated Recipients, *Ann. N.Y. Acad. Sci.*, **114**: 510–526 (1964). T. M. Fliedner, V. P. Bond, and E. P. Cronkite, Structural, Cytological and Autoradiographic (H³-thymidine) Changes in the Bone Marrow Following Total Body Irradiation, *Am. J. Pathol.*, **38**: 599–623 (1961).   P. J. Fitzgerald, Autoradiographic Labeling of Pancreatic Acinar Cells with *H³*-thymidine during Degeneration and Regeneration, *Can. Med. Assoc. J.*, **88**: 480–482 (1963).   J. K. Ford and R. W. Young, Cell Proliferation and Displacement in the Adrenal Cortex of Young Rats Injected with Tritiated Thymidine, *Anat. Record*, **146**: 125–137 (1963).   R. C. Fraser, Autoradiographic Analysis of DNA and RNA Synthesis in the Red Blood Cells of the Developing Chick Embryo, *Exptl. Cell Res.*, **33**: 473–480 (1964).   R. J. M. Fry, S. Lesher, and H. I. Kohn, A Method for Determining Mitotic Time, *Exptl. Cell Res.*, **25**: 469–471 (1961).   S. Fujita and S. Miyake, Selective Labeling of Cell Groups and Its Application to Cell Identifications, *Exptl. Cell Res.*, **28**: 158–161 (1962).   S. Fujita, M. Hovii, T. Tanimura, and H. Nishimura, H³-thymidine Autoradiographic Studies on Cytokinetic Responses to X-ray Irradiation and to Thio-TEPA in the Neural Tube of Mouse Embryos, *Anat. Record*, **149**: 37–48 (1964).   F. Gavosto, A. Pileri, and G. Maraini, Incorporazione de timidana marcata con tritio negli elementi del midullo osseo normale e leucemico. Indagini autoradiografiche, *Haematologica*, **44**: 977–992 (1959).   G. B. Gerber, K. I. Altman, and L. H. Hempelman, The Catabolism of Nucleic Acids in the Rat. IV. The Replacement of Desoxyribonucleic Acid in the Irradiated Rat, *Intern. J. Radiation Biol.*, **6**: 17–22 (1963).   G. B. Gerber, W. G. Aldridge, G. Gerber, K. I. Altman, and L. H. Hempelman, The Catabolism of Nucleic Acids. V. Autoradiographic Studies on the Replacement of DNA in Normal and X-irradiated Rats, *Intern. J. Radiation Biol.*, **6**: 23–38 (1963).   E. M. Gifford, Incorporation of H³-thymidine into Nuclei of Shoot Apical Meristems, *Science*, **131**: 360 (1960).   E. M. Gifford, Incorporation of H³-thymidine into Shoot and Root Apices of *Ceratopteris thalictroides*. *Am. J. Botany*, **47**: 834–837 (1960).   S. Gothie, R. Moricard, and R. Cartier, Utilisation de la thymidine tritiée pour l'étude des phénomènes de prolifération cellulaire normale et cancéreuse (microscopie optiques et électronique), *Compt. Rend.*, **157**: 74–75 (1963).   J. W. Grisham, A Morphologic Study of DNA-synthesis and Cell Proliferation in Regenerating Rat Liver, Autoradiography with Thymidine-H³, *Cancer Res.*, **22**: 842–849 (1962).   C. W. Gurney, L. G. Lajtha, and R. Oliver, A Method for Investigation of Stem Cell Kinetics, *Brit. J. Haematol.*, **8**: 461–466 (1963).   M. G. Hanna, Jr., An Autoradiographic Study of the Germinal Center in Spleen White Pulp during Early Intervals of the Immune Response, *Lab. Invest.*, **13**: 95–104 (1964).   P. F. Harris and J. H. Kugler, Cells which Synthesize DNA in Guinea Pig Bone Marrow during Recovery from Whole Body X-irradiation, *Nature*, **184**: 1883–1884 (1959).   W. Hilscher and W. Maurer, Autoradiographische Bestimmung der Dauer der DNS Verdopplung und ihres zeitlichen Verlaufes bei Spermatogonien der Ratte durch Doppelmarkierung mit C^{14}—und H^3-Thymidin, *Naturwissenschaften*, **49**: 352 (1962).   T. E. Hunt and E. A. Hunt, Radioautographic Study of Proliferation in the Stomach of the Rat Using Thymidine-H^3 and Compound 48/80, *Anat. Record*, **142**: 505–517 (1962). H. A. Johnson, W. E. Haymaker, J. R. Rubini, T. M. Fliedner, V. P. Bond, E. P. Cronkite, and W. L. Hughes, A Radioautographic Study of a Human Brain and Glioblastoma Multiforme after the *in vivo* Uptake of Tritiated Thymidine, *Cancer*, **13**: 636–642 (1960).   H. A. Johnson, Some Problems Associated with the Histological Study of Cell Proliferation Kinetics, *Cytologia*, **26**: 32–41 (1961).   S. A. Killmann, E. P. Cronkite, T. M. Fliedner, and V. P. Bond, Cell Proliferation in Multiple Myeloma Studied with H^3-thymidine *in vivo*, *Lab. Invest.*, **11**: 845–853 (1962).   S. A. Killmann, E. P. Cronkite, J. S. Robertson, T. M. Fliedner, and V. P. Bond, Estimation of Phases of the Life Cycle of Leucemic Cells from *in vivo* Labeling in Human Beings with Tritiated Thymidine, *Lab. Invest.*, **12**: 671–684 (1963).   E. Koburg and B. Schultze, Autoradiographische Untersuchungen mit H^3-thymidin über die Dauer der DNS Synthese, der Ruhephase und der Mitose bei proliferierenden Systemen wie den Epithelien des Darms, des Oesophagus und der Cornea der Maus, *Verhandl. Deut. Ges. Pathol.*, **45**: 103–107 (1961).   E. S. Kurtides, W. A. Rambach, H. L. Alt, and J. C. Wurster, Effect of Erythropoietin on H^3-thymidine Incorporation by the Rat Spleen, *J. Lab. Clin. Med.*, **61**: 23–33 (1963).   L. G. Lajtha, R. Oliver, and C. W. Gurney, Kinetic Model of a Bone Marrow Stem Cell Population, *Brit. J. Haematol.*, **8**: 4 2–460 (1962).   S. Lesher, A. N. Stroud, and A. M. Brues, The Effects of Chronic Irradiation on DNA Synthesis in Regenerating Mouse Liver, *Cancer Res.*, **20**: 1341–1346 (1960).   S. Lesher, R. J. M. Frey, and G. A. Sacher, Effects of Chronic Gamma Irradiation on the Generation Cycle of the Mouse Duodenum, *Exptl. Cell Res.*, **25**: 398–404 (1961).   A. G. Levis and A. de Nadai, Nucleic Acid and Protein Synthesis in Nitrogen Mustard Induced Giant Cells *in vitro*, *Exptl. Cell Res.*, **33**: 207–215 (1964). A. Lima-de-Faria and K. Borum, The Period of DNA Synthesis Prior to Meiosis in the Mouse, *J. Cell Biol.*, **14**: 381–388 (1962).   M. Lipkin and H. Quastler, Cell Retention and Incidence of Carcinoma in Several Portions of the Gastrointestinal Tract, *Nature*, **194**: 1198–1199 (1962).   W. B. Looney, Some Limitations of Labeled Compounds in Radiobiological Investigations of Deoxyribonucleic Acid (DNA) Synthesis, *Ann. N.Y. Acad. Sci.*, **95**: 975–983 (1961).   E. A. McCulloch and J. E. Till, The Sensitivity of Cells from Normal Mouse Bone Marrow to Gamma Radiation *in Vitro* and *in Vivo*, *Radiation Res.*, **16**: 822–832 (1962).   R. A. McDonald and G. K. Mallory, Autoradiography Using Tritiated Thymidine Detection of New Cell Formation in Rat Tissues, *Lab. Invest.*, **8**: 1547 (1959).   P. Maldagne, P. Hong-Que, and J. Maisin, Etude autoradiographique de l'incorporation de thymidine tritiée chez le rat, *in Tritium in the Physical and Biological Sciences, Symp., Intern. At. Energy Agency, Vienna*, **2**: 361–372 (1961).   M. A. Maloney, C. L. Weber, and H. M. Patt, Myelocyte–metamyelocyte Transition in the Bone Marrow of the Dog, *Nature*, **197**: 150–152 (1963).   H. J. Mankin, Localization of Tritiated Thymidine in Articular Cartilage of Rabbits. III. Mature Articular Cartilage, *J. Bone Joint Surg.*, **54a**: 529–540 (1963). Y. Maruyama, An Isotopic Method for Determination of Cell Generation Time, *Nature* **198**: 1197–1198 (1963).   A. M. Mauer and V. Fisher, Comparison of the Proliferative Capacity of Acute Leukemia Cells in Bone Marrow and Blood, *Nature*, **193**: 1085–1086 (1962).   M. L. Mendelsohn, Autoradiographic Analysis of Cell

Proliferation in Spontaneous Breast Cancer of C3H Mouse II. Growth and Survival of Cells Labeled with Tritiated Thymidine, *J. Natl. Cancer Inst.*, **25**: 485–500 (1960). M. L. Mendelsohn, Chronic Infusion of Tritiated Thymidine into Mice with Tumors, *Science*, **135**: 213–215 (1962). M. L. Mendelsohn, Autoradiographic Analysis of Cell Proliferation in Spontaneous Breast Cancer of C3H Mouse. III. The Growth Fraction, *J. Natl. Cancer Inst.*, **28**: 1015–1029 (1962). M. L. Mendelsohn, Cell Proliferation and Tumour Growth, in *The Guinness Symposium on Cell Proliferation*, Blackwell Scientific Publications, Oxford, 1963. B. Messier and C. P. Leblond, Cell Proliferation and Migration as Revealed by Radioautography after Injection of H³-thymidine into Male Rats and Mice, *Am. J. Anat.*, **247**: 85 (1960). H. S. Micklem and C. E. Ford, Proliferation of Injected Lymphnode and Thymus Cells in Lethally Irradiated Mice, *Transplant. Bull.*, **26**: 436 (1960). J. Mitchell, W. McDonald, and G. J. V. Nossal, Autoradiographic Studies of the Immune Response. 3. Differential Lymphopoiesis in Various Organs, *Australian J. Exptl. Biol. Med. Sci.*, **41**: 411–422 (1963). V. Monesi, Autoradiographic Study of DNA Synthesis and the Cell Cycle in Spermatogonia of Mouse Testis Using H³-thymidine, *J. Cell Biol.*, **14**: 1–18 (1962). J. S. Natarian and J. D. Feldman, Passive Transfer of Contact Sensitivity by Tritiated Thymidine Labeled Lymphoid Cells, *J. Exptl. Med.*, **117**: 775–780 (1963). H. Noetzel and J. Rox, Autoradiographische Untersuchungen über Zellteilung und Zellentwicklung im Gehirn der erwachsenen Maus und des erwachsenen Rhesus Affen nach Injektion von radioaktivem Thymidin, *Acta Neuropathol.*, **3**: 326–342 (1964). G. J. V. Nossal, J. Mitchell, and W. McDonald, Autoradiographic Studies on the Primary Response, *Australian J. Exptl. Biol. Med. Sci.*, **41**: 423–436 (1963). G. J. V. Nossal, J. Mitchell, and W. McDonald, Autoradiographic Studies of the Immune Response. 3. Differential Lymphopoiesis in Various Organs. 4. Single Cell Studies on the Primary Response, *Australian J. Exptl. Biol. Med. Sci.*, Spec. Suppl. August, 1963, pp. 411–435. N. Odartchenko, H. Cottier, L. E. Feinendegen, and V. P. Bond, Mitotic Delay in More Mature Erythroblasts of the Dog. Induced *in Vivo* by Sublethal Doses of X-rays, *Radiation Res.*, **21**: 413–422 (1964). D. G. Osmond and N. B. Everett, Nucleophagocytosis in Bone Marrow, *Nature*, **196**: 488–489 (1962). D. G. Osmond and N. B. Everett, Radioautographic Studies of Bone Marrow Lymphocytes *in vivo* and in Diffusion Chamber Cultures, *Blood*, **23**: 1–17 (1964). R. B. Painter and J. S. Robertson, Effect of Irradiation and Theory of Role of Mitotic Delay on the Time Course of Labeling HeLa-S3 Cells with H³-thymidine, *Radiation Res.*, **11**: 206–217 (1959). R. B. Painter and R. M. Drew, Studies on Deoxyribonucleic Acid Metabolism in Human Cancer Cell Cultures (HeLa). I. The Temporal Relationships of Deoxyribonucleic Acid Synthesis to Mitosis and Turnover Time, *Lab. Invest.*, **8**: 278–285 (1959). R. B. Painter and W. L. Hughes, Nucleic Acid Metabolism and the Lethal Effect of Radiation on Cultures of Human Cells (HeLa). *Ann. N.Y. Acad. Sci.*, **95**: 960–968 (1961). W. Parrish and R. G. Kleinfeld, Maturation of Transplantable Leukemic Cells Cultivated *in vivo* in Diffusion Chambers, *Cancer Res.*, **23**: 1164–1168 (1963). C. R. Partanen, The Validity of Auxin-induced Divisions in Plants as Evidence of Endopolyploidy, *Exptl. Cell Res.*, **31**: 597–599 (1963). H. Peters, T. Levy, and M. Crone, DNA Synthesis in Oocytes of Mouse Embryos, *Nature*, **195**: 915–916 (1962). T. I. Poliakova, A Study of Physiological Regeneration and Cellular Cycle in the Epithelium of *Rana temporaria* Carried out with the Aid of H³-thymidine, *Dokl. Akad. Nauk. SSSR*, **145**: 910–912 (1962). K. A. Porter and E. H. Cooper, Recognition of Transformed Small Lymphocytes by Combined Chromosomal and Isotopic Labels, *Lancet*, **7251**: 317–319 (1962). T. T. Puck, Life Cycle Analysis of Mammalian Cells *in vitro*, *J. Cell Biol.*, **19**: 57A (1963). H. Quastler, Effects of Irradiation on Intestinal Mucosal Cell Population, *Federation*

Proc., **22:** 1330–1333 (1963).   E. L. Reid, Autoradiographic Analysis of Uptake of Tritiated Thymidine and S³⁵ Cystine by Cultured Human Cervical Explants Undergoing Metaplasia, *J. Natl. Cancer Inst.*, **32:** 1059–1073 (1964).   W. O. Rieke, R. W. Caffrey, and N. B. Everett, Rates of Proliferation and Interrelationships of Cells in the Mesenteric Lymph Node of the Rat, *Blood*, **22:** 674–689 (1963).   D. A. Rigas, Kinetics of Isotope Incorporation into Desoxyribonucleic Acid (DNA) of Tissues: Life Span and Generation Time of Cells, *Bull. Math. Biophys.*, **20:** 33–70 (1958). D. A. Rigas, Isotope Incorporation into the DNA and Its Use in Studies of Leukokinetics, *Ann. N.Y. Acad. Sci.*, **113:** 954–962 (1964).   R. Schindler, Biochemical Studies of the Division Cycle of Mammalian Cells: Evidence for the Premitotic Period, *Biochem. Pharmacol.*, **12:** 533–538 (1963).   J. C. Schooley, Autoradiographic Observations of Plasma Cell Formation, *J. Immunol.*, **86:** 331–337 (1961).   J. L. Sirlin, The Labeling of Mouse Spermatozoa by Adenine-C¹⁴ and Thymidine-H³, *Exptl. Cell Res.*, **15:** 250 (1958).   E. A. Tonna, The Cellular Complement of the Skeletal System Studied Autoradiographically with Tritiated Thymidine (H³Tdr) during Growth and Aging, *J. Biophys. Biochem. Cytol.*, **9:** 813–824 (1961).   E. A. Tonna and E. P. Cronkite, A Study of the Persistence of the H³-thymidine Label in the Femora of Rats, *Lab. Invest.*, **13:** 161–171 (1964).   A. Tsuya, V. P. Bond, T. M. Fliedner, and L. E. Feinendegen, Cellularity and Deoxyribonucleic Acid Synthesis in Bone Marrow after Total and Partial-Body Irradiation, *Radiation Res.*, **14:** 618–632 (1961).   B. E. Walker, Mast Cell Turnover in Adult Mice, *Nature*, **192:** 980–981 (1961).   B. E. Walker, The Origin of Myeloblasts and the Problem of Dedifferentiation, *Exptl. Cell Res.*, **30:** 80–92 (1962).   K. Wegener, S. Hollweg, and W. Maurer, Autoradiographische Bestimmung der DNS Verdopplungszeit und anderer Teilphasen des Zell-Zyklus bei fetalen Zellarten der Ratte, *Z. Zellforsch. Mikroskop. Anat.*, **63:** 309–326 (1964).   N. K. Wessels, DNA Synthesis, Mitosis, and Differentiation in Pancreatic Acinar Cells *in vitro*, *J. Cell Biol.*, **20:** 415–433 (1964).   D. R. Wimber and L. F. Lamerton, Cell Population Studies on the Intestine of Continuously Irradiated Rats, *Radiation Res.*, **18:** 137–146 (1963).   J. M. Yoffey, N. B. Everett, and W. O. Reinhardt, Cellular Migration Streams in the Hemopoietic System, in *Kinetics of Cellular Proliferation* (F. Stohlman, Jr., ed.), Grune and Stratton, New York, 1959.   J. M. Yoffey, Further Problems of Lymphocyte Production, *Ann. N.Y. Acad. Sci.*, **113:** 867–886 (1964).   M. H. Young and W. A. J. Crane, Effect of Hydrocortisone on the Utilization of Tritiated Thymidine for Skeletal Growth in the Rat, *Ann. Rheumatic Diseases*, **23:** 163–168 (1964).   W. Zeman, Disturbances of Nucleic Acid Metabolism Preceding Delayed Radionecrosis of Nervous Tissue, *Proc. Natl. Acad. Sci. U.S.* **50:** 626–630 (1963).

IV. The Use of H³-Thymidine in Studies on Transfer and Reutilization of DNA Label

E. L. Alpen, E. H. Cooper, and H. Barkley, Effects of Ionizing Radiation on Rat Lymphoid Tissue *in vivo*, *Intern. J. Radiation Biol.* **2:** 425–439 (1960).   R. Baserga and W. E. Kisieleski, Comparative Study of the Kinetics of Cellular Proliferation of Normal and Tumorous Tissues with the Use of Tritiated Thymidine. I. Dilution of the Label and Migration of Labeled Cells, *J. Natl. Cancer Inst.*, **28:** 331–339 (1962). E. Borenfreund and A. Bendich, A Study of the Penetration of Mammalian Cells by DNA's *J. Biophys. Biochem. Cytol.*, **8:** 81–91 (1961).   B. J. Bryant, Reutilization of Leukocyte DNA by Cells of Regenerating Liver, *Exptl. Cell Res.*, **27:** 70–79 (1962). M. Chorazy, A. Bendich, E. Borenfreund, O. L. Ittensohn, and D. J. Hutchison, Uptake of Mammalian Chromosomes by Mammalian Cells, *J. Cell. Biol.*, **19:** 71–77 (1963).

M. Eder, H. Wrba, and H. H. Muth, Autoradiographische Untersuchungen zum Nukleinsäure-Stoffwechsel bei der Umwandlung von Ascitestumoren, *Naturwissenschaften*, **50**: 46 (1963). K. E. Fichtelius and H. Diderholm, Autoradiographic Analysis of the Accumulation of Lymphocytes in Wounds, *Acta Pathol. Microbiol. Scand.*, **52**: 11–17 (1962). K. E. Fichtelius and O. Goth, Re-utilization of Deoxyribonucleic Acid from Cells Other than Leucocytes, *Nature*, **200**: 587–588 (1963). S. M. Gartler, Demonstration of Cellular Uptake of Polymerised DNA in Mammalian Cell Cultures, *Biochem. Biophys. Res. Commun.*, **3**: 127 (1960). M. Hill and V. Drasil, Nuclear Uptake of DNA Fragments after Injection of P^{32}-labeled Thymocytes in Lethally Irradiated Mice, *Exptl. Cell Res.*, **21**: 569–582 (1960). M. Hill, Uptake of DNA: A Special Property of the Cell Nucleus, *Nature*, **189**: 916–917 (1961). M. Hill, Intercellular Passage of H^3-thymidine Labeled DNA from Donor Lymphocytes to Recipient Bone Marrow Cells, *Exptl. Cell Res.*, **28**: 21–26 (1962). M. Hill and J. Jakubickova, Intercellular Passage of DNA as Revealed in Bone Marrow Autoradiographs, *Exptl. Cell Res.*, **26**: 541–551 (1962). R. C. Krueger, D. Gitlin, S. L. Commerford, J. Stein, and W. L. Hughes, Iododeoxyuridine (IDU) as a Tracer of DNA metabolism *in vivo*, *Federation Proc.*, **19**: 307 (1960). S. Lacks, Molecular Fate of DNA in Genetic Transformation of Pneumococcus, *J. Mol. Biol.*, **5**: 119–131 (1962). L. Ledoux, M. Callebaut, P. Charles, and A. Leonard, Sur la possibilité d'un transfert d'acide désoxyribonucléique dans la système génital de la souris, *Arch. Intern. Physiol. Biochim.*, **70**: 309–313 (1962). T. Miyake, Exchange of Genetic Material between *Salmonella typhimurium* and *E. coli* K-12, *Genetics*, **47**: 1047–1052 (1962). J. S. Natarian and J. D. Feldman, Passive Transfer of Transplantation Immunity, I. Tritiated Lymphoid Cells. II. Lymphoid Cells in Millipore Chambers, *J. Exptl. Med.*, **115**: 1083–1093 (1962). E. Ottolenghi and R. D. Hotchkiss, Release of Genetic Transforming Agent from Pneumococcal Cultures during Growth and Disintegration, *J. Exptl. Med.*, **116**: 491–519 (1962). A. Popovic, A. Becarevic, D. Kanazir, N. Stosic, and V. Pautic, Fate of Tritiated Native Liver DNA Injected into Lethally Irradiated Rats, *Nature*, **198**: 165–167 (1963). T. Tsumita and M. Iwanaga, Fate of Injected DNA in Mice. *Nature*, **198**: 1088–1089 (1963). A. Vorbrodt, T. Wilczok, K. Schneiberg, and T. Gorki, Autoradiographic Studies of the Fate of Heterologous DNA after Injection into Mice, *Neoplasma*, **10**: 355–359 (1963).

V. The Use of Tritium-Labeled Nucleosides Other Than Thymidine in Studies on Nucleic Acid Synthesis and Metabolism

V. G. Allfrey and A. E. Mirsky, Evidence for the Complete DNA Dependence of RNA Synthesis in Isolated Thymus Nuclei, *Proc. Natl. Acad. Sci. U.S.*, **48**: 1590–1596 (1962). M. Amano and C. P. Leblond, Comparison of the Specific Activity Time Curves of Ribonucleic Acid in Chromatin, Nucleolus and Cytoplasm, *Exptl. Cell Res.*, **20**: 250–253 (1960). P. Barlett and S. Shelata, Mechanism of Aminonucleoside Induced Nephrosis in the Rat. I. Metabolism of Tritiated Aminonucleoside, *Proc. Soc. Exptl. Med.*, **102**: 499–503 (1959). G. C. Barr and J. A. V. Butler, Biosynthesis of Nucleic Acid in *Bacillus megaterium*. 2. The Formation of Ribonucleic Acid by Nuclear Material *in vitro*, *Biochem. J.*, **88**: 252–259 (1963). G. C. Barr and J. A. V. Butler, Histones and Gene Function, *Nature*, **199**: 1170–1172 (1963). R. Baserga, A Study of Nucleic Acid Synthesis in Ascites Tumor Cells by Two Emulsion Autoradiography, *J. Cell Biol.*, **12**: 633–637 (1962). K. K. F. Bautz, Physical Properties of Messenger RNA of Bacteriophage T$_4$, *Proc. Natl. Acad. Sci. U.S.*, **49**: 68–74 (1963). M. A. Bender and D. M. Prescott, DNA Synthesis and Mitosis in Cultures of Human Peripheral Leukocytes, *Exptl. Cell Res.*, **27**: 221–229 (1962). L. E. Bertani, A. Häggmark, and P. Reichard, Synthesis of Pyrimidine Deoxyribonucleoside Diphosphates with Enzymes from *Escherichia coli*, *J. Biol. Chem.*, **236**: 67–68 (1961).   N. Bieliavsky and R. Tencer, Incorporation of H³-uridine into Amphibian Eggs, *Nature*, **185**: 401 (1960).   K. Bier, Synthese, Intercellulärer Transport, und Abban von Ribonukleinsäure im Ovar der Stubenfliege *Musca domestica*, *J. Cell Biol.*, **16**: 436–440 (1963).   B. B. Biswas and R. Abrams, Incorporation of Nucleoside Triphosphates into Ribonucleic Acid with a Particulate Fraction of Disrupted Thymus Nuclei, *Biochim. Biophys. Acta*, **55**: 827–836 (1962).   C. W. Bodemer, Distribution of Ribonucleic Acid in the Regenerating Urodele Limb as Determined by Autoradiographic Localization of Uridine-H³, *Anat. Record*, **142**: 457–467 (1962).   R. Bogoroch and B. V. Siegel, Some Metabolic Properties of the Nucleolus as Demonstrated by Recent Radioisotope Experiments, *Acta Anat.*, **45**: 265–287 (1961).   F. J. Bollum, Intermediate States in Enzymatic DNA Synthesis, *J. Cellular Comp. Physiol.*, **62** (Suppl. 1): 61–71 (1963).   V. P. Bond, L. E. Feinendegen, E. Heinze, and H. Cottier, Distribution of Transfused Tritiated Cytidine-Labeled Leukocytes and Red Cells in the Bone Marrow of Normal and Irradiated Rats, *Ann. N.Y. Acad. Sci.*, **113**: 1009–1019 (1964).   E. V. Boudnitskaya, M. Brunfaut, and M. Errera, Effects of X-rays on RNA and RNA Metabolism in HeLa Cells, *Biochim. Biophys. Acta*, **80**: 567–573 (1964). R. Byrne, J. G. Levine, H. A. Bladen, and M. W. Nirenberg, The *in vitro* Formation of a DNA-ribosome Complex, *Proc. Natl. Acad. Sci. U.S.*, **52**: 140–148 (1964).   I. L. Cameron and D. M. Prescott, RNA and Protein Metabolism in the Maturation of the Nucleated Chicken Erythrocyte, *Exptl. Cell Res.*, **30**: 609–612 (1963).   J. Carneiro and P. A. Abrahamson, Effects of Thioacetamide on Protein and Ribonucleic Acid Metabolism of Rat Liver Cells. A Radioautographic Study, *Z. Zellforsch. Mikroskop. Anat.*, **61**: 813–823 (1964).   P. Y. Cheng, Modification of Labeling of "Messenger Ribonucleic Acid" Produced by Viral Infection, *Biochim. Biophys. Acta*, **61**: 318–320 (1962).   P. Y. Cheng, Sedimentation and Autoradiographic Analysis of Rapidly Labeled RNA's in Human Amnion Cells, *Biophys. J.*, **2**: 465–482 (1962).   L. Cheong, M. A. Rich, and M. L. Eidinoff, Introduction of the 5-Halogenated Uracil Moiety into Deoxyribonucleic Acid of Mammalian Cells in Culture, *J. Biol. Chem.*, **235**: 1441–1447 (1960).   M. Chèvremont and E. Baeckeland, Etude histoautoradiographique de l'incorporation d'uridine tritiée en culture de tissus dans des fibroblastes normaux ou soumis à l'action de substances antimitotiques, *Arch. Biol.*, **72**: 461–484 (1961). M. Chèvremont, Le mécanisme de l'action antimitotique, *Pathol. Biol.*, **9**: 973–1004 (1961).   M. I. H. Chipchase and M. L. Birnstiel, Synthesis of Transfer RNA by Isolated Nuclei, *Proc. Natl. Acad. Sci. U.S.*, **49**: 692–699 (1963).   N. K. Das, Synthetic Capacities of Chromosome Fragments Correlated with Their Ability to Maintain Nucleolar Material, *J. Cell. Biol.*, **15**: 121–130 (1962).   N. K. Das, Chromosomal and Nucleolar RNA Synthesis in Root Tips during Mitosis, *Science*, **140**: 1231–1233 (1963).   M. L. Eidinoff, L. Cheong, and M. A. Rich, Incorporation of Unnatural Pyrimidine Bases into Deoxyribonucleic Acid of Mammalian Cells, *Science*, **129**: 1550–1551 (1959).   M. Errera and M. Brunfaut, Observations of Mitotic Figures in Pulse Labeled HeLa Cells, *Exptl. Cell. Res.*, **33**: 105–111 (1964).   L. E. Feinendegen and V. P. Bond, Zur RNS Synthese im Chromatin und im Nucleolus der menschlichen Krebszelle HeLa-S₃ in Kultur, *Atomkernenergie*, **9**: 283–293 (1964).   R. M. Fink, Utilization of H³-uracil and Formation of 5-ribosyluracil in *Neurospora*, *J. Biol. Chem.*, **238**: 1764–1766 (1963).   H. Firket and P. Granboulan, Electron Microscope Autoradiographs of Tritiated Uridine Incorporation, *J. Roy. Microscop. Soc.*, **81**: 227–228 (1963).   M. Fishman, R. A. Hamerstrom, and V. P. Bond, *In vitro* Transfer of Macrophage RNA to Lymphnode Cells, *Nature*, **198**: 549–551 (1963).   P. J. Fitzgerald and K. Vinijchaikul, Nucleic Acid Metabolism of Pancreatic Cells as Revealed by Cytidine-H^3 and Thymidine-H^3, *Lab Invest.*, **8**: 319–328 (1959). R. C. Fraser, Autoradiographic Analysis of DNA and RNA Synthesis in Red Blood Cells of the Developing Chick Embryo, *Exptl. Cell Res.*, **33**: 473–480 (1964). P. Galbraith, W. J. Mitus, M. Gollerkevi, and W. Dameshek, The "Infectious Mononucleosis Cell." A Cytochemical Study, *Blood*, **22**: 630–638 (1963). F. Gavosto, G. Maraini, and A. Pileri, Nucleic Acids and Protein Metabolism in Acute Leukemia Cells, *Blood*, **16**: 1555–1561 (1960). F. Gavosto, Nucleic Acids and Protein Metabolism of Bone Marrow Cells Studied by Means of Tritium Labeled Precursors, *in Tritium in the Physical and Biological Sciences, Symp. Intern. At. Energy Agency, Vienna*, **2**: 237–246 (1961). M. Geuskens, Accumulation nucléolaire d'acide ribonucleique (RNA) dans l'oocyte d'astérie, *Exptl. Cell Res.*, **30**: 322–330 (1963). M. Girard, S. Penman, and J. E. Darnell, The Effect of Actinomycin on Ribosome Formation in HeLa cells, *Proc. Natl. Acad. Sci. U.S.*, **51**: 205–211 (1964). G. N. Godson and J. A. V. Butler, Biosynthesis of Nucleic Acids in *Bacillus megaterium*. 3. Biosynthesis of Ribonucleic Acid *in vivo*, *Biochem. J.*, **88**: 259–266 (1963). L. Goldstein and J. Micou, On the Primary Site of Nuclear RNA Synthesis, *J. Biophys. Biochem. Cytol.*, **6**: 301–304 (1959). C. C. Gordon and O. L. Stein, The Use of H^3-uridine as a Marker in Studies of Fungal Life Cycles, *Radiation Botany*, **2**: 7–8 (1962). M. P. Gordon, O. M. Intrieri, and G. B. Brown, Nucleosides Labeled with Tritium in the Ribosyl Group, *J. Am. Chem. Soc.*, **80**: 5161–5164 (1958). A. F. Graham and A. V. Rake, RNA Synthesis and Turnover in Mammalian Cells Propagated *in vitro*, *Ann. Rev. Microbiol.*, **17**: 139–166 (1963). P. R. Gross and G. H. Cousineau, Macromolecule Synthesis and the Influence of Actinomycin on Early Development, *Exptl. Cell Res.*, **33**: 368–395 (1964). H. Harrington, The Effect of X-irradiation on the Progress of Strain U-12 Fibroblasts through the Mitotic Cycle, *Ann. N.Y. Acad. Sci.*, **95**: 901–910 (1961). H. Harrington, Effect of X-irradiation on the Priming Activity of DNA, *Proc. Natl. Acad. Sci. U.S.*, **51**: 59–66 (1964). H. Harris, H. W. Fischer, A. Rodgers, T. Spencer, and J. W. Watts, An Examination of the Ribonucleic Acids in the HeLa Cell with Special Reference to Current Theory about the Transfer of Information from Nucleus to Cytoplasm, *Proc. Roy. Soc. (London)*, **B157**: 177–198 (1963). H. Harris, Rapidly Labeled Ribonucleic Acid in the Cell Nucleus, *Nature*, **198**: 184–185 (1963). H. Harris and L. F. La Cour, Site of Synthesis of Cytoplasmic Ribonucleic Acid, *Nature*, **200**: 227–229 (1963). M. Mayashi, S. Spiegelman, N. C. Franklin, and S. E. Luria, Separation of the RNA Message Transcribed in Response to a Specific Inducer, *Proc. Natl. Acad. Sci. U.S.*, **49**: 729–736 (1963). S. A. Henderson, Differential Ribonucleic Acid Synthesis of X- and Autosomes during Meiosis, *Nature*, **200**: 1235 (1963). T. C. Hsu, Differential Rate in RNA Synthesis between Euchromatin and Heterochromatin, *Exptl. Cell Res.*, **27**: 332–334 (1962). M. Izawa, V. G. Allfrey, and A. E. Mirsky, The Relationship between RNA Synthesis and Loop Structure in Lampbrush Chromosomes, *Proc. Natl. Acad. Sci. U.S.*, **49**: 544–551 (1963). M. Izawa, V. G. Allfrey, and A. E. Mirsky, Composition of the Nucleus and Chromosomes in the Lampbrush Stage of the Newt Oöcyte, *Proc. Natl. Acad. Sci. U.S.*, **50**: 811–817 (1963). J. Jacob and J. L. Sirlin, Synthesis of RNA *in Vitro* Stimulated in Dipteran Salivary Glands by 1,1,3-tricyano-2-amino-1-propene, *Science*, **144**: 1011–1012 (1964). E. Kellenberger, K. G. Lark, and A. Bolle, Aminoacid Dependent Control of DNA Synthesis in Bacteria and Vegetative Phage, *Proc. Natl. Acad. Sci. U.S.*, **48**: 1860–1868 (1962). R. F. Kimball and S. W. Perdue, Quantitative Cytochemical Studies on Paramecium. V. Autoradiographic Studies of Nucleic Acid Syntheses, *Exptl. Cell Res.*, **27**: 405–415 (1962). R. F. Kimball and D. M. Prescott, RNA and Protein Synthesis in Amacronucleate *Paramecium aurelia*, *J. Cell Biol.* **21**: 496–497 (1964). R. C. King, Autoradiographic Study of Uptake of Tritiated Glycine, Thymidine, and

Uridine by Fruit Fly Ovaries, *Science*, **129**: 1674–1675 (1959).   J. S. Krakow, C. Coutsogeorgopoulos, and E. S. Canellakis, Studies on the Incorporation of Deoxyribonucleotides and Ribonucleotides into Deoxyribonucleic Acid, *Biochim. Biophys. Acta*, **55**: 639–650 (1962).   P. L. Kuempel and A. B. Pardee, The Cycle of Bacterial Duplication, *J. Cellular Comp. Physiol.*, **62**(*Suppl. 1*): 15–30 (1963).   L. F. La Cour, Behaviour of Nucleoli in Isolated Nuclei, *Exptl. Cell Res.*, **34**: 239–242 (1964).   L. Ledoux and R. Huart, Nucleic Acids and Protein Metabolism of Barley Seedlings. IV. Translocation of Ribonucleic Acids, *Biochim. Biophys. Acta*, **61**: 185–196 (1962). A. G. Levis, L. Spanio, and A. de Nadai, Radiomimetic Effects of a Nitrogen Mustard on Survival, Growth, Protein and Nucleic Acid Synthesis of Mammalian Cells *in vitro*, *Exptl. Cell Res.*, **31**: 19–30 (1963).   A. G. Levis and A. de Nadai, Nucleic Acid and Protein Synthesis in Nitrogen Mustard Induced Giant Cells *in vitro*, *Exptl. Cell Res.*, **33**: 207–215 (1964).   H. B. Levy, Effect of Actinomycin D on HeLa Cell Nuclear RNA Metabolism, *Proc. Soc. Exptl. Biol. Med.*, **113**: 886–889 (1963).   A. Lindner, T. Kutkam, K. Sankaranarayanan, R. Rucker, and J. Arradondo, Inhibition of Ehrlich Ascites Tumor with 5-fluoruracil and Other Agents, *Exptl. Cell Res., Suppl.*, **9**: 485–508 (1963).   A. Linnartz-Niklas, K. Hempel, and W. Maurer, Autoradiographische Untersuchung über den Eiweiss und RNS-Stoffwechsel tierischer Zellen während der Mitose, *Z. Zellforsch. Mikroskop. Anat.*, **62**: 443–453 (1964).   O. Maløe, Role of Proteinsynthesis in the DNA Replication Cycle in Bacteria, *J. Cellular Comp. Physiol.*, **62** (Suppl. 1): 31–44 (1963).   H. J. Mankin, Localization of H^3-cytidine in Articular Cartilage of Immature and Adult Rabbit after Intra-articular Injection, *Lab. Invest.*, **12**: 543–548 (1963).   A. di Marco, M. Gaetani, and R. Silvestrini, Autoradiographic Studies on the Incorporation of Labeled Precursor in the AH 130 Ascites Hepatoma Cells and in the Liver from DAB-fed Wistar Rats, *Acta Unio Intern. Contra Cancrum*, **19**: 555–559 (1963).   P. I. Marcus and E. Robbins, Viral Inhibition in the Metaphase-arrest Cell, *Proc. Natl. Acad. Sci. U.S.*, **50**: 1156–1164 (1963).   D. Mazia, Synthetic Activities Leading to Mitosis, *J. Cellular Comp. Physiol.*, **62** (Suppl. 1): 123–140 (1963).   J. Mitchell and G. J. V. Nossal, Ribonucleic Acid Metabolism in the Plasma Cell Sequence, *Nature*, **197**: 1121–1122 (1963). J. M. Mitchison and K. G. Lark, Incorporation of H^3-adenine into RNA during the Cell Cycle of *Schizosaccharomyces pombe*, *Exptl. Cell Res.*, **28**: 452–455 (1963).   M. Nemer, Old and New RNA in the Embryogenesis of the Purple Sea Urchin, *Proc. Natl. Acad. Sci. U.S.*, **50**: 230–235 (1963).   W. Oehlert, Autoradiographische Untersuchungen zur Ribonukleinsäure-Synthese in den verschiedenen Strukturen der Zelle, *Beitr. Pathol. Anat. Allgem. Pathol.*, **124**: 311–350 (1961).   R. B. Painter, Nucleic Acid Metabolism in HeLa-S_3 Cells after X-ray Induced Mitotic Delay, *Radiation Res.*, **13**: 726–736 (1960).   C. Pelling, Chromosomal Synthesis of Ribonucleic Acid as Shown by Incorporation of Uridine Labeled with Tritium, *Nature*, **184**: 655–656 (1959). C. Pelling, Application of Tritiated Compounds to the Midge *Chironomus* and Some Aspects of the Metabolism of the Salivary Gland Chromosomes, *in Tritium in the Physical and Biological Sciences, Symp. Intern. At. Energy Agency, Vienna*, **2**: 327–334 (1961).   C. Pelling, Ribonukleinsäure-Synthese der Riesenchromosomen, Autoradiographische Untersuchungen an *Chironomus Tentans*, *Chromosoma*, **15**: 71–122 (1964).   R. P. Perry, Role of the Nucleolus in Ribonucleic Acid Metabolism and Other Cellular Processes, *Natl. Cancer Inst. Monograph* **14**: 73–87.   R. P. Perry, The Cellular Sites of Synthesis of Ribosomal and 4 sRNA, *Proc. Natl. Acad. Sci. U.S.*, **48**: 2179–2186 (1962).   P. Pinheiro, C. P. Leblond, and B. Droz, Synthetic Capacity of Reticulocytes as Shown by Radioautography after Incubation with Labeled Precursors of Protein or RNA, *Exptl. Cell Res.*, **31**: 517–537 (1963).   D. M. Prescott and R. F. Kimball, Relation between RNA, DNA, and Protein Synthesis in the Replicating Nucleus of Euplotes, *Proc. Natl. Acad. Sci. U.S.*, **47**: 686–693 (1961). D. M. Prescott, Symposium: Synthetic Processes in the Cell Nucleus. II. Nucleic Acid and Protein Metabolism in the Macronuclei of Two Ciliated Protozoa, *J. Histochem. Cytochem.*, **10**: 145–153 (1962). D. M. Prescott and M. A. Bender, Synthesis and Behavior of Nuclear Proteins during the Cell Life Cycle, *J. Cellular Comp. Physiol.*, **62** (Suppl. 1): 175–194 (1963). W. H. Prusoff, J. W. Cramer, M. K. Y. Chu, and A. D. Welch, 5-Bromo-2′-deoxycytidine (BCDR). I. Studies on Metabolism *in vitro* and in mice, *Biochem. Pharmacol.*, **8**: 324–326 (1961). P. Reichard, Z. N. Canellakis, and E. S. Canellakis, Regulatory Mechanism in the Synthesis of Deoxyribonucleic Acid *in vitro*, *Biochim. Biophys. Acta*, **41**: 558–559 (1960). J. H. Rho and M. I. Chipchase, Incorporation of Tritiated Cytidine into Ribonucleic Acid by Isolated Pea Nuclei, *J. Cell Biol.*, **14**: 183–192 (1962). G. T. Rudkin and P. S. Woods, Incorporation of H^3-cytidine and H^3-thymidine into Giant Chromosomes of *Drosophila* during Puff Formation, *Proc. Natl. Acad. Sci. U.S.*, **45**: 997–1003 (1959). B. Schultze and W. Maurer, Comparative Autoradiographic Study of the RNA and Protein Metabolism within the Various Tissues and Cells of the Mouse with Tritiated RNA Precursors and Labeled Amino Acids, *in Tritium in the Physical and Biological Sciences, Symp. Intern. At. Energy Agency, Vienna*, **2**: 229–236 (1961). B. Schultze and W. Maurer, Grösse der RNS-synthese in Nucleolus und Karyoplasma bei einigen Zellartender Maus, *Z. Zellforsch. Mikroskop. Anat.*, **60**: 387–391 (1963). R. W. Seed and I. H. Goldberg, Biosynthesis of Thyroglobulin: Relationship to RNA-template and Precursor Protein, *Proc. Natl. Acad. Sci. U.S.*, **50**: 275–282 (1963). J. L. Sirlin, Cell Sites of RNA and Protein Synthesis in the Salivary Gland of *Smittia* (*Chironomidae*). *Exptl. Cell Res.*, **19**: 177–179 (1960). J. L. Sirlin and J. Jacob, Function, Development and Evolution of the Nucleolus, *Nature*, **195**: 114–117 (1962). J. L. Sirlin, J. Jacob, and K. I. Kato, The Relation of Messenger to Nucleolar RNA, *Exptl. Cell Res.*, **27**: 355–359 (1962). J. L. Sirlin and N. A. Schor, Further Observations on Isolated Polytene Nuclei, *Exptl. Cell Res.*, **27**: 363–366 (1962). J. L. Sirlin, C. J. Tandler, and J. Jacob, The Relationship between the Nucleolus Organizer and Nucleolar RNA, *Exptl. Cell Res.*, **31**: 611–615 (1963). J. E. Sisken, The Synthesis of Nucleic Acids and Proteins in the Nuclei of *Tradescantia* Root Tips, *Exptl. Cell Res.*, **16**: 602–614 (1959). P. R. Srinivasan, Kinetics of Incorporation of 5-methyl-cytosine in HeLa Cells, *Biochim. Biophys. Acta*, **55**: 553–556 (1962). P. R. Srinivasan, A. Miller-Faurès, M. Brunfaut, and M. Errera, Kinetics of Pulse-Labeling of Ribonucleic Acid in HeLa Cells, *Biochim. Biophys. Acta*, **72**: 209–216 (1963). U. Stenram, Radioautographic Studies with H^3-methionine and H^3-cytidine on Protein Deficiency in Mice and Rats with Special Reference to Liver Cells, *Exptl. Cell Res.*, **26**: 485–492 (1962). U. Stenram, Effects of Diet on the Nucleolus, *Exptl. Cell Res. Suppl.* **9**: 176–181 (1963). A. R. Stevens, Electron Microscope Autoradiography of DNA and RNA Synthesis in *Euplotus eurystomas* (Abstr.), *J. Cell Biol.*, **19**: 67A (1963). E. Stöcker, Autoradiographische Untersuchungen zur Ribonukleinsäure und Eiweiss Synthese im nuklearen Funktionsformwechsel der exocrinen Pankreaszelle, *Z. Zellforsch. Mikroskop. Anat.*, **57**: 145–171 (1962). N. Sueoka and Ts'ai-Ying Cheng, Fractionation of Nucleic Acids with the Methylated Albumin Column, *J. Mol. Biol.*, **4**: 161–172 (1962). C. J. Tandler and J. L. Sirlin, Differential Uptake of Orthosphosphate and Ribonucleosides into Nucleolar Ribonucleic Acid, *Biochim. Biophys. Acta*, **80**: 315–324 (1964). J. H. Taylor, Autoradiographic Studies of Nucleic Acids and Proteins during Meiosis in *Lilium longiflorum*, *Am. J. Botany*, **46**: 477–484 (1959). J. H. Taylor, Duplication of Chromosomes and Related Events in the Cell Cycle, in *Cell Physiology of Neoplasia*, pp. 547–572, The University of Texas Press, Austin, Texas, 1960.   J. H. Taylor, DNA Synthesis in Relation to Chromosome Reproduction and the Reunion of Breaks, *J. Cellular Comp. Physiol.*, 62 (Suppl. 1): 73–86 (1963).   U. Torelli, G. Grossi, T. Artusi, and G. Emilia, RNA and Protein Synthesis in Normal Peripheral Mononuclear Leukocytes, *Acta Haematol.*, 30: 129–137 (1963).   P. O. P. Ts'o and P. Lu, Interaction of Nucleic Acids. I. Physical Binding of Thymine, Adenine, Steroids, and Aromatic Hydrocarbons to Nucleic Acids, *Proc. Natl. Acad. Sci. U.S.*, 51: 17–24 (1964).   F. de Bitry, Etude de l'action de la 5-flurodeoxyuridine sur la croissance et la morphogénèse de l'*acetabularia mediterranea*, *Exptl. Cell Res*, 25: 697–699 (1961).   F. de Vitry, Etude autoradiographique de l'incorporation de H^3-5-methylcytosine chez *acetabularia mediterranea*, *Exptl. Cell Res.*, 31: 376–384 (1963).   A. Wacker, S. Kirschfeld, and L. Träger, Über den Einbau Purin analoger Verbindungen in die Bakterien-Nukleinsäure, *J. Mol. Biol.*, 2: 241–242 (1960).   W. Wolberg and R. R. Brown, Autoradiographic Studies of *in vitro* Incorporation of Uridine and Thymidine by Human Tumor Tissue, *Cancer Res.*, 22: 1113–1119 (1962).   P. S. Woods and J. H. Taylor, Studies of Ribonucleic Acid Metabolism with Tritium Labeled Cytidine, *Lab. Invest.*, 8: 309–317 (1959).   P. S. Woods, RNA in Nuclear-Cytoplasmic Interaction, in *Brookhaven Symp. Biol.*, 12: 153–171 (1959).   P. S. Woods, Autoradiographic Studies of Ribonucleic Acid Metabolism with Tritium Labeled Cytidine, *in Tritium in the Physical and Biological Sciences, Symp. Intern. At. Energy Agency, Vienna*, 2: 335–346 (1961). V. J. Wulff, H. Quastler, and F. G. Sherman, The Incorporation of H^3-cytidine in Mice of Different Ages, *Arch. Biochem. Biophys.*, 95: 548–549 (1961).   V. J. Wulff, H. Quastler, and F. G. Sherman, An Hypothesis Concerning RNA Metabolism and Aging, *Proc. Natl. Acad. Sci. U.S.*, 48: 1373–1375 (1962).   T. Yamane and N. Sueoka, Conservation of Specificity between Amino Acid Acceptor RNA and Amino Acyl-sRNA Synthetase, *Proc. Natl. Acad. Sci. U.S.*, 50: 1093–1100 (1963).   S. A. Yankofsky and S. Spiegelman, Distinct Cistrons for the Two Ribosomal RNA Components, *Proc. Natl. Acad. Sci. U.S.*, 49: 538–544 (1963).   Y. Yasuda and T. Hirai, Incorporation of H^3-uracil into Tobacco Leaf Epidermis Infected with Tobacco Mosaic Virus, *Exptl. Cell Res.*, 34: 210–212 (1964).   L. C. T. Young and R. G. Stanley, Incorporation of H^3-nucleosides, Thymidine, Uridine, and Cytidine in Nuclei of Germinating Pine Pollen, *Nucleus*, 6: 83–90 (1963).   M. Zalokar, Primary Gene Product: Protein or RNA, *Proc. 10th Intern. Congr. Genet., Montreal, 1958*, 2: 330 (1959).   M. Zalokar, Nuclear Origin of RNA, *Nature*, 183: 1330 (1959).   M. Zalokar, Sites of Ribonucleic Acid and Protein Synthesis in *Drosophila*, *Exptl. Cell Res.*, 19: 184–186 (1960).   M. Zalokar, Sites of Protein and Ribonucleic Acid Synthesis in the Cell, *Exptl. Cell Res.*, 19: 559–576 (1960).   W. Zeman, Disturbances of Nucleic Acid Metabolism Preceding Delayed Radio-Necrosis of Nervous Tissue, *Proc. Natl. Acad. Sci. U.S.*, 50: 626–630 (1963).

VI. The Use of Tritium-Labeled Amino Acids and Proteins

K. A. Abraham and P. M. Bhargava, The Uptake of Radioactive Amino Acids by Spermatozoa. The Intracellular Sites of Incorporation into Proteins, *Biochem. J.*, 86: 308–313 (1963).   J. Altman, Differences in the Utilization of Tritiated Leucine by Single Neurones in Normal and Exercised Rats: An Autoradiographic Investigation with Microdensitometry, *Nature*, 199: 777–780 (1963).   R. B. Aronson, E. A. Popenoe, and D. D. van Slyke, The Formation of Collagen Hydroxylysine. Studies with Tritiated Lysine (Abstr.), *Federation Proc.*, 22: 229 (1963).   M. A. Bender and D. M. Prescott, DNA, RNA and Protein Synthesis and the Onset of Mitosis in Human Leukocytes *in vitro* (Abstr.), *Blood*, 20: 103 (1962).   J. P. Bentley and D.

S. Jackson, *In vivo* Incorporation of Labeled Amino Acids during Early Stages of Collagen Biosynthesis, *Biochem. Biophys. Res. Commun.*, **10**: 271–276 (1963). K. Bier, Autoradiographische Untersuchungen zur Dotterbildung, *Naturwissenschaften*, **49**: 332–333 (1962). D. P. Bloch and S. D. Brack, Evidence for the Cytoplasmic Synthesis of Nuclear histone during Spermiogenesis in the Grasshopper *Chortophaga viridi-fasciata* (de Geer), *J. Cell Biol.*, **22**: 327–340 (1964). W. Busanny-Caspari and M. Deimel, Untersuchungen mit H^3-markierten Aminosäuren zur Proteinsynthese in der regenerierten Rattenleber, *Z. Ges. Exptl. Med.*, **136**: 456–465 (1963). T. J. Byers, D. B. Platt, and L. Goldstein, The Cytonucleoproteins of Amebae. I. Some Chemical Properties and Intracellular Distribution, *J. Cell. Biol.*, **19**: 453–466 (1963); II. Some Aspects of Cytonucleoprotein Behavior and Synthesis, *J. Cell. Biol.*, **19**: 467–475 (1963). R. Byrne, J. G. Levin, H. A. Bladen, and M. W. Nirenberg, The *in vitro* Formation of a DNA-Ribosome Complex, *Proc. Natl. Acad. Sci. U.S.*, **52**: 140–148 (1964). I. L. Cameron and D. M. Prescott, RNA and Protein Metabolism in the Maturation of the Nucleated Chicken Erythrocyte, *Exptl. Cell Res.*, **30**: 609–612 (1963). J. Carneiro and C. P. Leblond, Role of Osteoblasts and Odontoblasts in Secreting the Collagen of Bone and Dentin as Shown by Radioautography in Mice Given Tritium Labeled Glycine, *Exptl. Cell Res.*, **18**: 291–300 (1959). J. Carneiro and P. A. Abrahamson, Effects of Thioacetamide on Protein and Ribonucleic Acid Metabolism of Rat Liver Cells. A Radioautographic Study, *Z. Zellforsch. Mikroskop. Anat.*, **61**: 813–823 (1964). A. N. Chatterjee and J. T. Park, Biosynthesis of Cell Wall Mucopeptide by a Particulate Fraction from *Staphylococcus aureus*, *Proc. Natl. Acad. Sci. U.S.*, **51**: 9–16 (1964). S. M. Chou and H. A. Hartmann, Autoradiographic Studies on the Axonal Protein Flow in IDPN-treated Rats. *Federation Proc.*, **22**: 316 (1963). P. Citoler and W. Maurer, Etude autoradiographique du métabolisme de protéines dans une hépatite spontanée chez la souris, *Presse Med.*, **71**: 83 (1963). P. Citoler and W. Maurer, Quelques apports de l'histo-autoradiographie à l'étude de la cellule normale et pathologique, *Presse Med.*, **71**: 84 (1963). E. H. Cooper, The Uptake of (^{3}H) Leucine into Human Lymphocytes *in vitro*, *Biochem. J.*, **78**: 21p (1961). E. M. Deuchar, Sites of Earliest Collagen-Formation in the Chick Embryo, as Indicated by Uptake of Tritiated Proline, *Exptl. Cell Res.*, **30**: 528–540 (1963). B. Droz and C. P. Leblond, Migration of Proteins along the Axons of the Sciatic Nerve, *Science*, **137**: 1047–1048 (1962). B. Droz, Dynamic Condition of Proteins in the Visual Cells of Rats and Mice as Shown by Radioautography with Labeled Amino Acids, *Anat. Record*, **145**: 157–168 (1963). W. Erb and K. Hempel, Vergleichende autoradiographische Untersuchung des Eiweissstoffwechsels in Nukleolus, Kern und Cytoplasma bei generativen und somatischen Zellen, *Ann. Histochim. Suppl.*, **2**: 71–76 (1962). W. Erb and W. Maurer, Autoradiographische Untersuchungen über den Eiweissstoffwechsel von Oocyten und Eizellen, *Z. Naturforsch.*, **17b**: 268–273 (1962). S. Fischer, G. F. Bruns, B. A. Lowy, and I. M. London, The effect of Exogenous RNA and DNA on Amino Acid Incorporation by Subcellular Fractions Prepared from Erythroid Tissues, *Proc. Natl. Acad. Sci. U.S.*, **49**: 219–225 (1963). A. S. Fox and S. H. Kang, Amino Acid Incorporation into Protein by Cell-free Preparations of *Drosophila melanogaster*, *Federation Proc.*, **22**: 303 (1963). F. Gavosto, G. Maraini, and A. Pileri, Radioautographic Investigations on DNA and Protein Metabolism in 2 cases of Di Guglielmo's Disease, *Blood*, **16**: 1122–1132 (1960). F. Gavosto, G. Maraini, and A. Pileri, Nucleic Acids and Protein Metabolism in Acute Leukemia Cells, *Blood*, **16**: 1555–1563 (1960). F. Gavosto, A. Pileri, and G. Maraini, Protein Metabolism in Bone Marrow and Peripheral Blood Cells, Evaluation of H^3-DL-leucine Uptake by a High Resolution Radioautographic Technique, *Proc. 7th Congr. Europ. Soc. Haema-*

tol. London, 1959, **2**: 380–385 (1960).   F. Gavosto, Nucleic Acids and Protein Metabolism of Bone Marrow Cells Studied by Means of Tritium Labeled Precursors, *in Tritium in the Physical and Biological Sciences, Symp. Intern. At. Energy Agency, Vienna*, **2**: 237–246 (1961).   K. Gerbaulet, J. Brückner, and W. Maurer, Autoradiographische Untersuchungen über den Einfluss einer Röntgen-Ganzkörperbestrahlung auf die Eiweiss-Syntheserate im Zellkern, *Naturwissenschaften*, **48**: 526 (1961).   P. R. Gross and G. H. Cousineau, Synthesis of Spindle-associated Proteins in Early Cleavage, *J. Cell Biol.*, **19**: 260–265 (1963).   K. Hempel, K. J. Lennartz, and W. Maurer, Autoradiographische Untersuchung zum Eiweisstoffwechsel im Kern und Cytoplasma der normalen und durch Buttergelb cancerisierten Leberzelle, *Beitr. Pathol. Anat. Allgem. Pathol.*, **126**: 381–394 (1962).   K. Hempel and M. Deimel, Untersuchungen zur gezielten Strahlentherapie des Melanoms und des chromaffinen Systems durch selektive H-3-Inkorporation nach Gabe von H-3-markiertem DOPA, *Strahlentherapie*, **121**: 22–45 (1963).   E. Helmreich, M. Kern, and H. N. Eisen, Observations on the Mechanism of Secretion of Gamma-Globulins by Isolated Lymph Node Cells, *J. Biol. Chem.*, **237**: 1925–1931 (1962).   D. J. Holbrook, J. E. Evans, and J. L. Irvin, Incorporation of Labeled Precursors into Proteins and Nucleic Acids of Nuclei of Regenerating Liver, *Exptl. Cell Res.*, **28**: 120–125 (1962).   J. K. Hoober and I. A. Berstein, Studies on the Mechanism of the Localized Incorporation of Glycine-H³ in Newborn Rat Epidermis, *Federation Proc.*, **22**: 238 (1963).   Y. Hotta and H. Stern, Synthesis of Messenger-like Ribonucleic Acid and Protein during Meiosis in Isolated Cells of *Trillium erectum*, *J. Cell Biol.*, **19**: 45–58 (1963).   W. S. S. Hwang, G. A. Tonna, and E. P. Cronkite, An Autoradiographic Study of the Mouse Incisor Using Tritiated Histidine, *Arch. Oral Biol.*, **8**: 377–385 (1963).   M. Isawa, V. G. Allfrey, and A. E. Mirsky, The Relationship between RNA Synthesis and Loop Structure in Lampbrush Chromosomes, *Proc. Natl. Acad. Sci. U.S.*, **49**: 544–551 (1963).   R. C. King and R. G. Burnett, Autoradiographic Study of Uptake of Tritiated Glycine, Thymidine, and Uridine by Fruit Fly Ovaries, *Science*, **129**: 1674–1675 (1959).   O. Klatt, A. N. Milner, and J. S. Stehlin, Jr., Studies on the *in vivo* Metabolism of L-Phenylalanine Mustard-H³ in Patients with Malignant Melanoma, *Proc. Am. Assoc. Cancer Res.*, **3**: 334 (1962).   E. Koburg, Autoradiographische Untersuchungen zum Eiweisstoffwechsel der Zellen des Knorpels und Knochens, *Beitr. Pathol. Anat. Allgem. Pathol.*, **124**: 108–135 (1961).   H. Kroeger, J. Jacob, and J. L. Sirlin, The Movement of Nuclear Protein from the Cytoplasm to the Nucleus of Salivary Cells, *Exptl. Cell Res.*, **31**: 416–423 (1963).   D. T. A. Lamport, Oxygen Fixation into Hydroxyproline of Plant Cell Wall Protein, *J. Biol. Chem.*, **238**: 1438–1440 (1963).   K. J. Lennartz, K. Hempel, and W. Maurer, Autoradiographische Untersuchung über die Anderung des Eiweisstoffwechsels im Kern und Cytoplasma bei Cancerisierung der Rattenleber durch Buttergelb, *Naturwissenschaften*, **48b**: 529 (1961).   A. G. Levis and A. de Nadai, Nucleic Acid and Protein Synthesis in Nitrogen Mustard Induced Giant Cells *in vitro*, *Exptl. Cell Res.*, **33**: 207–315 (1964).   A. G. Levis, L. Spanio, and A. de Nadai, Radiomimetic Effects of a Nitrogen Mustard on Survival, Growth, Protein and Nucleic Acid Synthesis of Mammalian Cells *in vitro*, *Exptl. Cell Res.*, **31**: 19–30 (1963).   A. Linnartz-Niklas, K. Hempel, and W. Maurer, Autoradiographische Untersuchungen über den Eiweiss und RNS-Stoffwechsel tierischer Zellen während der Mitose, *Z. Zellforsch. Mikroskop. Anat.*, **62**: 443–453 (1964).   A. Lindner, T. Kutkam, K. Sankaranarayanan, R. Rucker, and J. Arradondo, Inhibition of Ehrlich Ascites Tumor with 5-fluoruracil and Other Agents, *Exptl. Cell Res. Suppl.* **9**: 485–508 (1963).   F. Linneweh, M. Ehrlich, E. H. Graul, and H. Hundeshagen, Ueber den Aminosäuren-Transport bei phenylketonurischer Oligophrenie, *Klin. Wochsohr.*, **41**: 253–255 (1963).   M. Lipkin,

T. P. Almy, and H. Quastler, Stability of protein in intestinal epithelial cells, *Science*, 133: 1019–1021 (1961).   M. Lipkin, H. Quastler, and F. Muggia, Protein Synthesis in the Irradiated Intestine of the Mouse, *Radiation Res.*, 19: 277–285 (1963).   R. G. Martin, The First Enzyme in Histidine Biosynthesis: The Nature of Feedback Inhibition by Histidine, *J. Biol. Chem.*, 238: 257–268 (1963).   J. Mitchell and G. J. V. Nossal, Ribonucleic Acid Metabolism in the Plasma Cell Sequence, *Nature*, 197: 1121–1122 (1963).   H. G. Müller, Der Eiweissstoffwechsel der weiblichen Genitalorgane. Autoradiographische Untersuchungen mit isotopenmarkierten Aminosäuren an der weiblichen Ratte, *Strahlentherapie Sonderbände*, 47: 1–33 (1961).   H. G. Müller, Der Eiweisstoffwechsel der unbefruchteten und befruchteten Säugereizelle. Autoradiographische Untersuchungen mit isotopenmarkierten Aminosäuren, *Z. Ges. Exptl. Med.*, 135: 299–311 (1962).   L. R. Murrell and A. Lazarow, Organ Cultures of Fetal Endocrine Rat Pancreas on Liquid Medium, *Anat. Record*, 145: 264 (1963).   N. J. Nadler, S. K. Sarkar, and C. P. Leblond, Origin of Intracellular Colloid Droplets in the Rat Thyroid, *Endocrinology*, 71: 120–129 (1963).   N. J. Nadler, Synthesis and Release of Thyroid Hormones, *Federation Proc.*, 21: 628–629 (1962).   W. Noteboom and J. Gorski, Early Effects of Estrogen and Puromycin on Uterine Synthesis of Protein, RNA, and RNA Polymerase, *Federation Proc.*, 22: 329 (1963).   W. Oehlert and J. Hartje, Ueber die Umwandlung der Leberparenchymzelle in eine Krebszelle (Die Cancerisierung als progressive Transformation der DNS), *Naturwissenschaften*, 50: 358–359 (1963).   W. Oehlert, B. Schultze, and W. Maurer, Autoradiographische Untersuchung zur Frage der Eiweissynthese innerhalb des Kerns und des Cytoplasmas der Zelle, *Beitr. Pathol. Anat. Allgem. Pathol.*, 122: 289–312 (1960).   R. Pearlman and K. Bloch, N-Acetylamino Acids and Protein Synthesis, *Proc. Natl. Acad. Sci. U.S.*, 50: 533–537 (1963).   C. Pelling, Application of Tritiated Compounds to the Midge *Chironomus* and Some Aspects of the Metabolism of the Salivary Gland Chromosomes, in *Tritium in the Physical and Biological Sciences, Symp. Intern. At. Energy Agency, Vienna*, 2: 327–334 (1961).   A. Pileri, G. Maraini, and F. Gavosto, Interrelationship between RNA and Protein Metabolism in Human Normal Bone Marrow Cells, *Exptl. Cell Res.*, 20: 645–646 (1960).   P. Pinheiro, C. P. Leblond, and B. Droz, Synthetic Capacity of Reticulocytes as Shown by Radioautography after Incubation with Labeled Precursors of Protein or RNA, *Exptl. Cell Res.*, 31: 517–537 (1963).   D. Plester, E. Koburg, and K. Hempel, Autoradiographische Untersuchungen des Eiweissstoffwechsels der verschiedenen Gewebe des Innenohres, *Ann. Histochim.*, *Suppl.*, 2: 91–96 (1962).   K. A. Porter and E. H. Cooper, Transformation of Adult Allogeneic Small Lymphocytes after Transfusion into Newborn Rats, *J. Exptl. Med.*, 115: 997–1007 (1962).   D. M. Prescott and R. F. Kimball, Relation between RNA, DNA and Protein Synthesis in the Replicating Nucleus of *Euplotes*, *Proc. Natl. Acad. Sci. U.S.*, 47: 686–693 (1961).   D. M. Prescott, Turnover of Nuclear Proteins in Amoeba, *Science*, 140: 384 (1963).   D. M. Prescott, Synthetic Processes in the Cell Nucleus. II. Nucleic Acid and Protein Metabolism in the Macronuclei of Two Ciliated Protozoa, *J. Histochem. Cytochem.*, 10: 145–153 (1962).   J. P. Revel and E. D. Hay, An Autoradiographic Study of Collagen Synthesis by Cartilage Cells, *Anat. Record*, 145: 367 (1963).   A. N. Roberts and F. Haurowitz, Intracellular Localization and Quantitation of Tritiated Antigens in Reticuloendothelial Tissues of Mice during Secondary and Hyperimmune Responses, *J. Exptl. Med.*, 116: 407–422 (1962).   R. Ross and E. P. Benditt, A Comparison of the Utilization of Proline-H^3 in Healing Wounds as Seen by Electron Microscope-Autoradiography, *Federation Proc.*, 22: 190 (1963).   L. L. Ross and M. D. Gershon, Radioautographic Localization of H^3-hydroxytryptamine, *J. Cell. Biol.*, 19: 61 A (1963).   G. D. Roversi and R. Silvestrini, Study on the Protein Metabolism of the Evolutional Ovarian Follicle. Autoradiographic Research with H³-phenylalanine, *Exptl. Cell Res.*, **31**: 484–489 (1963).   B. A. Samal, L. E. Frazier, G. Monto, A. Slesers, Z. Hruban, and R. W. Wissler, Distribution of Tritium Labeled Beta-3-thienyl-L-alanine in Tissues of Adult Male Rats Bearing Murphy-Sturm Lymphosarcoma, *Proc. Soc. Exptl. Biol. Med.*, **112**: 442–445 (1963).   E. Sandborn, Amino Acid Incorporation in the Neurons of the Semilunar Ganglion of the Rat, *Anat. Record*, **145**: 280 (1963).   J. C. Schooley, Autoradiographic Observations of Plasma Cell Formation, *J. Immunol.*, **86**: 331–337 (1961).   L. Schreiner, Autoradiographische Untersuchungen zur Grösse des Eiweissstoffwechsels des peripheren Gleichgewichtsapparates beim Meerschweinchen, *Klin. Wochschr.*, **40**: 1016 (1962).   B. Schultze and W. Maurer, Comparative Autoradiographic Study of the RNA and Protein Metabolism within the Various Tissues and Cells of the Mouse with Tritiated RNA Precursors and Labeled Amino Acids, in *Tritium in the Physical and Biological Sciences, Symp. Intern. At. Energy Agency, Vienna*, **2**: 229–236 (1961).   M. R. Schwarz, Protein Synthesis in Rat Thoracic Duct Lymphocytes Studied with H³-precursors and Radioautography, *Anat. Record*, **145**: 282 (1963).   R. W. Seed and I. H. Goldberg, Biosynthesis of Thyroglobulin: Relationship to RNA-Template and Precursor Protein, *Proc. Natl. Acad. Sci. U.S.*, **50**: 175–182 (1963).   J. L. Sirlin, Cell Sites of RNA and Proteins Synthesis in the Salivary Gland of *Smittia* (*Chironomidae*), *Exptl. Cell Res.*, **19**: 177–180 (1960).   C. E. Slonecker, Studies on the Protein Fractions in Lymph of Immunized and Nonimmunized Rats, *Anat. Record*, **145**: 287 (1963). C. J. Smith and E. Herbert, Isolation of Oligonucleotides from the Acceptor End of Amino Acid Specific S-RNA, *Federation Proc.*, **22**: 230 (1963).   S. Sorof, E. M. Young, and P. L. Fetterman, Distribution of Incorporated Ethionine-ethyl-1-H³ in Electrophoretic Profiles of Soluble Liver Proteins during Hepato-carcinogenesis in the Rat, *Proc. Am. Assoc. Cancer Res.*, **3**: 362 (1962).   R. S. Speirs and E. E. Speirs, Cellular Localization of Radioactive Antigen in Immunized and Nonimmunized Mice, *J. Immunol.*, **90**: 561–575 (1963).   R. S. Speirs, The Action of Antigen upon Hypersensitive Cells, *Ann. N.Y. Acad. Sci.*, **113**: 819–824 (1964).   U. Stenram, Radioautographic Studies with Methionine-³H and Cytidine-³H on Protein Deficiency in Mice and Rats with Special Reference to Liver Cells, *Exptl. Cell Res.*, **26**: 485–492 (1962).   U. Stenram, Effects of Diet on the Nucleolus, *Exptl. Cell Res. Suppl.*, **9**: 176–181 (1963).   E. Stöcker and H. W. Altmann, Die Grösse des Nucleolus und die Nucleolus-Karyoplasma-Relation als Ausdruck synthetischer Aktivitäten. Autoradiographische Untersuchungen an Leberzellen normaler und Thioacetamid-behandelter Ratten, *Z. Krebsforsch.*, **65**: 351–377 (1963).   N. Stone and A. Meister, Function of Ascorbic Acid in the Conversion of Proline to Collagen Hydroxyproline, *Nature*, **194**: 555–557 (1962).   F. Suzuki, V. Rooze, and H. A. Barker, Studies on Glutamate Isomerase, *Federation Proc.*, **22**: 231 (1963).   D. J. L. Suck, Formation of Mitochondria in a Quantitative Radioautographic Study, *J. Cell Biol.*, **16**: 483–499 (1963).   E. W. Taylor, Relation of Protein Synthesis to the Division Cycle in Mammalian Cell Cultures, *J. Cell Biol.*, **19**: 1–18 (1963).   J. H. Taylor, Duplication of Chromosomes and Related Events in the Cell Cycle, in *Cell Physiology of Neoplasia*, The University of Texas Press, Austin, Texas, pp. 547–575, 1960.   E. A. Tonna and E. P. Cronkite, Utilization of Tritiated Histidine (H³HIS) by Skeletal Cells of Adult Mice, *J. Gerontol.*, **17**: 353–358 (1962).   E. A. Tonna, An Autoradiographic Examination of the Utilization of Tritiated Histidine by Cells of the Skeletal System, *Nature*, **193**: 1301–1302 (1962).   E. A. Tonna, E. P. Cronkite, and M. Pavelec, An Autoradiographic Study of the Localization and Distribution of Tritiated Histidine in Bone, *J. Histochem. Cytochem.*, **10**: 601–610 (1962).   E. A. Tonna, E. P. Cronkite, and M. Pavelec, A Serial Autoradiographic Analysis of H³-glycine

Utilization and Distribution in the Femora of Growing Mice, *J. Histochem. Cytochem.*, **11**: 720–733 (1963). U. Torelli, G. Grossi, T. Artusi, and G. Emilia, RNA and Protein Synthesis in Normal Peripheral Mononuclear Leukocytes, *Acta Haematol.*, **30**: 129–137 (1963). W. E. Truax and J. B. Bray, Synthesis of M Protein by Mouse Myeloma Tumor: Correlation of *in vitro* and *in vivo* Methods, *Blood*, **18**: 176–181 (1961). C. M. Tsung, W. G. Smith, F. R. Leach, and L. M. Henderson, Hydroxylysine Metabolism in *Streptococcus faecalis*, *J. Biol. Chem.*, **237**: 1194–1197 (1962). J. R. Warner, P. M. Knopf, and A. Rich, A Multiple Ribosomal Structure in Protein Synthesis, *Proc. Natl. Acad. Sci. U.S.*, **49**: 122–129 (1963). J. K. Weltman and D. W. Talmage, Selective Incorporation of Locally Synthesized Cysteine into Serum Albumin, *Federation Proc.*, **22**: 237 (1963). J. K. Whitehead, The Use of Isotopically Labeled Reagents in the Determination of Submicrogram Quantities of Amino Acids, *Biochem. J.*, **80**: 35P–36P (1961). T. Yamane and N. Sueoka, Conservation of Specificity between Amino Acid Acceptor RNA and Amino Acyl-sRNA Synthetase, *Proc. Natl. Acad. Sci. U.S.*, **50**: 1093–1100 (1963). B. A. Young, High-Resolution Radioautographic Localization of H^3-leucine Incorporated in the Rat Thyroid Gland, *Anat. Record*, **145**: 304 (1963). R. W. Young, Autoradiographic Studies on Post-natal Growth of the Skull in Young Rats Injected with Tritiated Glycine, *Anat. Record*, **143**: 1–13 (1962). M. Zalokar, Sites of Ribonucleic Acid and Protein Synthesis in *Drosophila*, *Exptl. Cell Res.*, **19**: 184–186 (1960). M. Zalokar, Sites of Protein and Ribonucleic Acid Synthesis in the Cell, *Exptl. Cell Res.*, **19**: 559–576 (1960). M. Zalokar, Kinetics of Amino Acid Uptake and Protein Synthesis in *Neurospora*, *Biochim. Biophys. Acta*, **46**: 423–432 (1961).

VII. The Use of Tritium-Labeled Hormones

C. R. Ayers, J. O. Davis, F. Lieberman, C. C. Carpenter, and M. Berman, The Effects of Chronic Hepatic Venous Congestion on the Metabolism of *dl*-aldosterone and *d*-aldosterone. *J. Clin. Invest.*, **41**: 884–895 (1962). B. H. Barbour and F. C. Barter, Angiotensin Labeled with I^{133} and with Tritium, *J. Clin. Endocrinol. Metab.*, **23**: 313–314 (1963). E. E. Baulieu, P. Robel, and P. Mauvais-Jarvis, Différences du métabolisme des androgènes chez l'homme et chez la femme, *Compt. Rend.*, **256**: 1016–1018 (1963). E. E. Baulieu, E. Wallace, and S. Lieberman, The Conversion *in vitro* of Δ^5-androstene-3β,17β-diol-17α-H^3 to Testosterone-17α-H^3 by Human Adrenal and Placental Tissue, *J. Biol. Chem.*, **238**: 1316–1319 (1963). S. Bergström, S. Lindstedt, and D. Sen, On the Preparation of Cholesterol Labeled with Tritium at Carbon Atoms 24 and 25 (Cholesterol-24,25-T$_2$). Bile Acids and Steroids 54, *Acta Chem. Scand.*, **11** (10): 1692–1694 (1957). E. G. Biglieri, S. Hane, P. E. Slaton Jr., P. H. Forsham, M. A. Herron, and S. Horita, *In Vivo* and *in Vitro* Studies of Adrenal Secretions in Cushing's Syndrome and Primary Aldosteronism, *J. Clin. Invest.*, **42**: 516–524 (1963). R. D. Bulbrook, B. S. Thomas, and B. W. Brooksbank, The Relationship between Urinary Androst-16-en-3α-ol and Urinary 11-Deoxy-17-oxosteroid Excretion, *J. Endocrinol.*, **26**: 149–153 (1963). A. M. Camacho and C. J. Migeon, Isolation, Identification, and Quantitation of Testosterone in the Urine of Normal Adults and in Patients with Endocrine Disorders, *J. Clin. Endocrinol. Metab.*, **23**: 301–305 (1963). C. A. Chidsey and D. C. Harrison, Studies on the Distribution of Exogenous Norepinephrine in the Sympathetic Neurotransmitter Store, *J. Pharmacol. Exptl. Therap.*, **140**: 217–223 (1963). C. A. Chidsey, R. L. Kahler, L. L. Kelminson, and E. Braunwald, Uptake and Metabolism of Tritiated Norepinephrine in the Isolated Canine Heart, *Circulation Res.*, **27**: 220–227 (1963). A. F. Clark and S. Solomon, Effect of Dehydroisoandrosterone on the *in vivo* Conversion of 17α-Hydroxypregnenolone to Urinary 11-Desoxy-17-ketosteroids, *J. Clin. Endocrinol, Metab.*, **23**: 481–488 (1963).   G. L. Cohn and P. J. Mulrow, Androgen Release and Synthesis *in vitro* by Human Adult Adrenal Glands, *J. Clin. Invest.*, **42**: 64–78 (1963). W. S. Coppage, Jr., D. P. Island, A. E. Cooner, and G. W. Liddle, The Metabolism of Aldosterone in Normal Subjects and in Patients with Hepatic Cirrhosis, *J. Clin. Invest.*, **41**: 1672–1680 (1962).   F. Chevallier, Etude du renouvellement du cholestérol des foies gras à l'aide de cholestérol tritiée, *in Tritium in the Physical and Biological Sciences, Symp. Intern. At. Energy Agency*, **2**: 413–417 (1961).   P. De Moor and O. Steeno, About the Existence in or on Erythrocytes of a Specific Cortisol Binding Agent, *J. Endocrinol.*, **26**: 301–302 (1963).   J. C. De Paepe, An Autoradiographic Study of the Distribution in Mice of Oestrogens Labeled with Carbon[14] and Tritium, *Nature*, **185**: 264–265 (1960).   J. Depaoli and K. B. Eik-Nes, Metabolism *in vivo* of (7α-H[3]) Pregnenolone by the Dog Ovary, *Biochim. Biophys. Acta*, **78**: 457–465 (1963).   N. Deshpande, R. D. Bulbrook, and F. G. Ellis, An Apparent Selective Accumulation of Testosterone by Human Breast Tissue, *J. Endocrinol.*, **25**: 555–556 (1963).   C. Donninger and G. Ryback, The Stereochemistry of Hydrogen Transfer Catalysed by Liver Alcohol Dehydrogenase: IR (I-H[3]) Geraniol as Substrate, *Biochem. J.*, **91**: 11p (1964).   K. B. Eik-Nes and M. Kekre, Metabolism *in vivo* of Steroids by the Canine Testes, *Biochim. Biophys. Acta*, **78**: 449–456 (1963).   J. Fishman, H. L. Bradlow, and T. F. Gallagher, Oxidative Metabolism of Estradiol, *J. Biol. Chem.*, **235**: 3104–3107 (1960).   J. M. Foy and H. Schnieden, The Effect of Malnutrition and Occluding the Hepatic Blood Supply on the Removal of H[3]-corticosteroids, *J. Endocrinol.*, **24**: 403–406 (1962).   W. Futterweit, N. L. McNiven, and R. I. Dorfman, Gas-Chromatographic Identification of Progesterone in Human Pregnancy Plasma, *Biochim. Biophys. Acta*, **71**: 474–476 (1963).   D. S. Gann, I. H. Mills, J. F. Cruz, A. G. T. Casper, and F. C. Bartter, On the Mechanism of Decrease of Aldosterone Secretion in the Dog, *Proc. Soc. Exptl. Biol. Med.*, **105**: 158–161 (1960).   A. M. Gawienowski, H. W. Knoche, and H. C. Moser, The Metabolism of C[14] and H[3] Labeled Diethylstilbesterol in the Rat, *Biochim. Biophys. Acta*, **65**: 150–152 (1962).   M. Goldstein and S. B. Gertner, Formation of a New Metabolite of Epinephrine and Norepinephrine in Liver and Kidney, *Nature*, **187**: 147–148 (1960). D. W. Gower, Biosynthesis of Androst-16-en-3α-ol from Dehydroepiandrosterone by Adrenocortical Slices, *J. Endocrinol.*, **26**: 173–174 (1963).   E. Gurpide, J. Mann, R. L. Vande Wiele, and S. Lieberman, A Discussion of the Isotope Dilution Method for Estimating Secretory Rates from Urinary Metabolites, *Acta Endocrinol.*, **39**: 213–222 (1962).   R. F. Glascock and W. G. Hoekstra, Selective Accumulation of Tritium Labeled Hexoestrol by the Reproductive Organs of Immature Female Goats and Sheep, *Biochim. J.*, **72**: 673–682 (1959).   M. Hayano, M. Gut, R. I. Dorfman, O. K. Sebek, and D. H. Peterson, Steric Considerations in the Enzymatic Course of the Hydroxylation of Steroids, *J. Am. Chem. Soc.*, **80**: 2336–2337 (1958).   G. Hertting and S. M. Hess, The Site of Binding of Injected H[3]-norepinephrine, *Experientia*, **18**: 214–215 (1962).   J. J. Hoet, P. Mahieu, P. Osinski, and G. C. Saba, New Acquisitions in the Field of Hypercortisolism Obtained with the Aid of Tritium-Labeled Cortisol, *Probl. Actuel. Endocrinol Nutr.*, **5**: 237–253 (1961).   W. Y. Huang and W. H. Pearlman, The Corpus Luteum and Steroid Hormone Formation. I. Studies on Luteinized Rat Ovarian Tissue *in vitro*, *J. Biol. Chem.*, **237**: 1060–1065 (1962). W. Y. Huang and W. H. Pearlman, The Corpus Luteum and Steroid Hormone Formation. II. Studies on the Human Corpus Luteum *in vitro*, *J. Biol. Chem.*, **238**: 1308–1315 (1963).   R. Hurter and J. D. N. Nabarro, Aldosterone Metabolism in Liver Disease, *Acta Endocrinol.*, **33**: 168–174 (1960).   C. Von Holt, I. Voelker, and L. Von Holt, Markierung von Insulin mit Tritium, *Biochim. Biophys. Acta*, **38**: 88–101 (1960).

P. A. Khairallah, I. H. Page, F. M. Bumpus, and R. R. Smeby, Angiotensin II: Its Metabolic Fate, *Science*, 138: 523–525 (1962). I. J. Kopin, Technique for the Study of Alternate Metabolic Pathways; Epinephrine Metabolism in Man, *Science*, 131: 1372–1374 (1960). I. J. Kopin and J. Axelrod, 3,4-Dihydroxyphenylglycol, A Metabolite of Epinephrine, *Arch. Biochem. Biophys.*, 89: 148 (1960). I. J. Kopin and E. K. Gordon, Metabolism of Administered and Drug-Released Norepinephrine-7-H^3 in the Rat, *J. Pharmacol. Exptl. Therap.*, 140: 207–216 (1963). D. Kritchevsky and V. Defendi, Persistence of Sterols Other than Cholesterol in Chicken Tissues, *Nature*, 192: 71 (1961). E. H. La Brosse and J. D. Mann, Presence of Metanephrine and Normetanephrine in Normal Human Urine, *Nature*, 185: 40 (1960). J. H. Laragh, Aldosterone in Fluid and Electrolyte Disorders: Hyper- and Hypoaldoteronism, *J. Chronic Diseases*, 11: 292–318 (1960). S. Lissistzky, M. T. Bénévent, J. Nunéz, C. Jacquemin, and J. Roche, Métabolisme de la L-thyronine marquée au tritium (^{3}H-thyronine) par le foie de rat, *Compt. Rend.*, 154: 267–270 (1960). M. R. Malinow, J. A. Moguilevsky, B. Lema, and G. E. Bur, Vascular and Extravascular Radioactivity after the Injection of Estradiol-6,7H^3 in the Human Being, *J. Clin. Endocrinol. Metab.*, 23: 306–310 (1963). P. Mlynaryk and J. B. Kirsner, Absorption and Excretion of 1,2-H^3-hydrocortisone in Regional Enteritis and Ulcerative Colitis, with a Note on Hydrocortisone Production Rates, *Gastroenterology*, 44: 257–260 (1963). P. Moor, K. de Heirwegh, J. F. Heremans, and M. Declerck-Raskin, Protein Binding of Corticoids Studied by Gel Filtration, *J. Clin. Invest.*, 41: 816–827 (1962). A. Nilsson, Demethylation of the Plant Oestrogen Biochanin A in the Rat, *Nature*, 192: 358 (1961). Y. Nishizuka, A. Ichiyama, S. Nakamura, and O. Hayaishi, A New Metabolic Pathway of Catechol, *J. Biol. Chem.*, 237: 268–270 (1962). J. Nunéz, C. Jacquemin, and J. Roche, Sur le métabolisme tissulaire des hormones thyroidiennes parquées par le tritium: désiodation des 3:5:3'-triiodo-DL-thyronine et 3:3':5-triiodo-L-thyronine, *Compt. Rend.*, 154: 544–547 (1960). J. Nunéz and C. Jacquemin, Sur la désiodation des hormones thyroidiennes tritiées, *Compt. Rend.*, 252: 802–804 (1961). J. Nunéz, J. Mauchamp, and J. Roche, On the Relationship between Iodotyrosines and Iodothyronines of Thyroglobuline Studied by *in vitro* Marking with I^{125} and H^3, *Compt. Rend.*, 157: 755–758 (1963). P. A. Osinski, Steroid 11β-ol Dehydrogenase in Human Placenta, *Nature*, 187: 777 (1960). F. G. Péron, Biosynthesis of Radioactive 18-Hydroxydeoxycorticosterone and 18-hydroxycorticosterone from 17α-H^3-Progesterone by Rat Adrenal Glands, *Endocrinology*, 70: 386–389 (1962). J. C. Porter, Secretion of Corticosterone in Rats with Anterior Hypothalamic Lesions, *Am. J. Physiol.*, 204: 715–718 (1963). L. T. Potter and J. Axelrod, Intracellular Localization of Catecholamines in Tissues of the Rat, *Nature*, 194: 581–582 (1962). L. T. Potter and J. Axelrod, Studies on the Storage of Norepinephrine and the Effects of Drugs, *J. Pharmacol. Exptl. Therap.*, 140: 199–206 (1963). J. Roche, J. Nunéz, and C. Jacquemin, Nature des produits de la désiodation des hormones thyroidiennes marquées simultanément par le tritium et l'iode radioactifs, *Biochim. Biophys. Acta*, 64: 475–486 (1962). A. W. Rogers and G. H. Thomas, Urinary Metabolites of Progesterone in the Rabbit, *Nature*, 193: 68–69 (1962). S. Rosell, I. J. Kopin, and J. Axelrod, Fate of H^3-noradrenaline in Skeletal Muscle before and Following Sympathetic Stimulation, *Am. J. Physiol.*, 205: 317–321 (1963). K. J. Ryan, The Conversion of Pregnenolone-7-^{3}H and Progesterone-4^{14}C to Oestradiol by a Corpus Luteum of Pregnancy, *Acta Endocrinol.*, 44: 81–89 (1963). M. P. Sambhi, B. A. Levitan, J. C. Beck, and E. H. Venning, The Rate of Aldosterone Secretion in Hypertensive Patients with Demonstrable Renal Artery Stenosis, *Metabolism*, 12: 498–506 (1963). W. R. Slaunwhite, Jr., H. Rosenthal, and A. A. Sandberg, Interactions of Steroids with Human Plasma Proteins, *Arch.*

380TRITIUM-LABELED MOLECULES IN BIOLOGY AND MEDICINE

Biochem. Biophys., **100**: 486–492 (1963).   S. Solomon, A. C. Carter, and S. Lieberman, The Conversion *in vivo* of 17-α-hydroxypregnenolone to Dehydroisoandrosterone and Other 17-ketosteroids, *J. Biol. Chem.*, **235**: 351–355 (1960).   P. Z. Thomas, E. Forchielli, and R. I. Dorfman, The Reduction *in vivo* of 17α-hydroxypregnenolone (3β,17α-dihydroxy-Δ⁵-pregnen-20-one) by Rabbit Skeletal Muscle, *J. Biol. Chem.*, **235**: 2797–2800 (1960).   S. Ullberg and G. Bengtsson, Autoradiographic Distribution Studies with Natural Oestrogens, *Acta Endocrinol.*, **43**: 75–86 (1963).   E. H. Venning and C. J. Lucis, Effect of Growth Hormone on the Biosynthesis of Aldosterone in the Rat, *Endocrinology*, **70**: 486–491 (1962).   E. Z. Wallace and S. Lieberman, Biosynthesis of Dehydroisoandrosterone Sulfate by Human Adrenocortical Tissue, *J. Clin. Endocrinol. Metab.*, **23**: 90–94 (1963).   S. F. Wang, F. S. Kawahara, and P. Talalay, The Mechanism of the Δ⁵-3-Ketosteroid Isomerase Reaction: Absorption and Fluoresence Spectra of Enzyme–Steroid Complexes. *J. Biol. Chem.*, **238**: 576–585 (1963).   H. Werbin, I. L. Chaikoff, and M. R. Imada, 5α-cholestan-3β-ol: Its Distribution in Tissues and Its Synthesis from Cholesterol in the Guinea Pig, *J. Biol. Chem.*, **237**: 2072–2077 (1962).   H. Werbin and I. L. Chaikoff, Loss of the 4-β hydrogen in the Conversion of (4-β-³H) Cholesterol to Cortisol by the Guinea-Pig Adrenal Gland Homogenate, *Biochim. Biophys. Acta*, **71**: 471–474 (1963).   L. G. Whitby, G. Hertting, and J. Axelrod, Effect of Cocaine on the Disposition of Noradrenaline Labeled with Tritium, *Nature*, **187**: 604–605 (1960).   H. Wilson, M. B. Lipsett, and S. G. Korenman, Evidence that 16 Androsten-3α-ol is not a Peripheral Metabolite of Testosterone in Man, *J. Clin. Endocrinol. Metab.*, **23**: 491–492 (1963).   H. P. Wolff, M. M. Torbica, J. Eisenburg, K. Ewe, M. Knedel, H. Jahrmärker, and R. Ködding, Eiweissmangelsyndrom bei exsudativer Enteropathie, *Klin. Wochschr.* **40**: 400–411 (1962).   H. P. Wolff and M. M. Torbica, Die Bestimmung des schwach gebundenen Aldosterons im Plasma Gesunder und Kranker, *Klin. Wochschr.*, **41**: 40–42 (1963).   R. J. Wurtman, E. W. Chu, and J. Axelrod, Relation between the Oestrous Cycle and the Binding of Catecholamines in the Rat Uterus, *Nature*, **198**: 547–548 (1963).   K. T. N. Yue and I. B. Fritz, Fate of Tritium-Labeled Carnitine Administered to Dogs and Rats, *Am. J. Physiol.*, **202**: 122–128 (1962).

VIII. THE USE OF TRITIUM-LABELED VITAMINS

M. Billeter and C. Martius, Über die Umwandlung von Phyllochinon (Vitamin K₁) in Vitamin K₂ (20) im Tierkörper, *Biochem. Z.*, **333**: 430–439 (1960).   R. L. Kisliuk, The Source of Hydrogen for Methionine Methyl Formation, *J. Biol. Chem.*, **238**: 397–400 (1963).   F. A. Klipstein, The Urinary Excretion of Orally Administered Tritium Labeled Folic Acid as a Test of Folic Acid Absorption, *Blood*, **21**: 626–639 (1963).   A. W. Norman and H. F. De Luca, The Preparation of H3-vitamins D₂ and D₃ and Their Localization in the Rat, *Biochem.*, **2**: 1160–1168 (1963). H. G. Schiefer and C. Martius, Über die Synthese von Vitaminen der K₂-Reihe und von Ubichinonen (aus Methyl-naphthochinon bzw. Dimethoxymethylbenzochinon) in Zellkulturen, *Biochem. Z.*, **333**: 454–462 (1960).   T. W. Sheehy, R. Santini, Jr., R. Guerra, R. Angel, and I. C. Plough, Tritiated Folic Acid as a Diagnostic Aid in Folic Acid Deficiency, *J. Lab. Clin Med.*, **61**: 650–659 (1963).   J. Simon-Reuss, H³-incorporation into Ascites Tumour and Tissue Culture Cells Exposed to Synkavit and Its Tritiated Analogue, *Acta Radiol.* **56**: 49–56 (1961).

IX. THE USE OF TRITIUM-LABELED CARBOHYDRATES AND LIPIDS

J. H. Balmain, S. J. Folley, and R. F. Glascock, Stimulation by Insulin of *in vitro* Fat Synthesis by Mammary Tissue Studied with Carbon¹⁴ and Tritium, *Nature*, **168**:

1083–1084 (1951). S. Bleecken and K. Schubert, Autoradiographische Untersuchung des Einbaues von tritiummarkiertem Cholesterin in *Mycobacterium smegmatis*, *Naturwissenschaften*, **49**: 141–142 (1962). F. Chevallier, Etude du renouvellement du cholestérol des foies gras à l'aide de cholesterol tritiée, in *Tritium in the Physical and Biological Sciences, Symp. Intern. At. Energy Agency, Vienna*, **2**: 413–417 (1961). M. Heimberg, I. Weinstein, H. Klausner, and M. L. Watking, Release and Uptake of Triglycerides by Isolated Perfused Rat Liver, *Am. J. Physiol.*, **202**: 353–358 (1962). L. Hellman, E. L. Frazell, and R. S. Rosenfeld, Direct Measurement of Cholesterol Absorption via the Thoracic Duct in Man, *J. Clin. Invest.*, **39**: 1288–1294 (1960). E. Joachim, Distribution of Tritium in Wilzbach Treated Cholesterol, *Experientia*, **18**: 360–362 (1962). R. G. Kallen and J. M. Lowenstein, The Stimulation of Fatty Acid Synthesis by Isocitrate and Malonate, *Arch. Biochem. Biophys.*, **96**: 188–190 (1962). D. J. L. Luck, Genesis of Mitochondria in *Neurospora crassa, Proc. Natl. Acad. Sci. U.S.*, **49**: 233–240 (1963). J. B. Marsh and A. T. James, The Conversion of Stearic to Oleic Acid by Liver and Yeast Preparations, *Biochim. Biophys. Acta*, **60**: 320–328 (1962). H. T. Navahava and P. Ozand, Studies of Tissue Permeability. IX. The Effect of the Insulin on the Penetration of 3-methylglucose-H^3 in Frog Muscle, *J. Biol. Chem.*, **238**: 40–49 (1963). R. E. Noble, R. L. Stjernholm, D. Mercier and E. Lederer, Incorporation of Propionic Acid into a Branched Chain Fatty Acid of the Preen Gland of the Goose, *Nature*, **199**: 600–601 (1963). J. A. Reid and R. H. Williams, Comparative Metabolic Studies of H^3 and C^{14} Labeled Stearic Acid, *Proc. Soc. Exp. Biol. Med.*, **105**: 151–153 (1960). B. Samuelsson and S. D. Goodman, Stereochemistry of the Hydrogen Transfer to Squalene during Its Biosynthesis from Farnesyl Pyrophosphate, *Biochem. Biophys. Res. Commun.*, **11**: 125–128 (1963). W. W. Shreeve, Diabetic *Ketosis, Ann. N.Y. Acad Sci.*, **104**: 772–786 (1963).

X. The Use of Tritium-Labeled Alkaloids and Drugs

C. P. Bianchi, Kinetics of Radio Caffeine Uptake and Release in Frog Sartorius, *J. Pharmacol. Exptl. Therap.*, **138**: 41–47 (1962). W. Bolt, F. Ritzl, R. Toussaint, and H. Nahrmann, Verteilung und Ausscheidung eines cytostatisch wirkenden, mit Tritium markierten *N*-Lost-Derivates beim krebskranken Menschen, *Arzneimittel-Forsch.*, **11**: 170–175 (1961). W. Bolt, F. Ritzl, and H. Nahrmann, Untersuchungen mit einem tritiummarkierten *N*-Lost-Derivat (Cyclophosphamid) in der Karzinombehandlung, *Nucl. Med.*, **2**: 251–264 (1962). R. F. Dawson, D. R. Christman, M. L. Solt, and A. P. Wolf, The Biosynthesis of Nicotine from Nicotinic Acid, Chemical and Radiochemical Yields, *Arch. Biochem. Biophys.* **91**: 14–50 (1960). V. F. Garagusi and R. E. Ritts, Tritiated Erythromycin in Tissues and Abscesses, *Arch. Pathol.* **77**: 587–593 (1964). W. S. Golder, A. J. Ryan, and S. E. Wright, The Urinary Excretion of Tritiated Butylated Hydroxyanisole and Butylated Hydroxytoluene in the Rat, *J. Pharm. Pharmacol.*, **14**: 268–271 (1962). D. Gröger, K. Mothes, H. Simon, H. G. Floss, and F. Weygand, Über den Einbau von Mevalonsäure in das Ergolinsystem der Clavin-Alkaloide, *Z. Naturforsch.*, **15b**: 141–143 (1960). M. J. Kline and M. I. Berlin, Measurement of Red Cell Survival with Tritiated Diisopropylfluorophosphate, *J. Lab. Ciln. Med.*, **60**: 826–832 (1962). D. Kurth, J. W. Athens, E. P. Cronkite, G. E. Cartwright, and M. M. Wintrobe, Leukokinetic Studies V. Uptake of Tritiated Diisopropylfluorophosphate by Leukocytes, *Proc. Soc. Exptl. Biol. Med.*, **107**: 422–426 (1961). C. Maggiolo and T. J. Haley, Brain Concentration of Reserpin-H^3 and Its Metabolites in the Mouse, *Proc. Soc. Exptl. Biol. Med.*, **115**: 149–151 (1964). J. R. Maisin and A. Leonard, Etude autoradiographique de la localisation de l'AET dans les tissus de la souris, *Compt. Rend.*, **157**: 203–206 (1963).   I. S. Pamukcu, J. Gerstein, R. Palma, and S. J. Gray, Localization of Tritiated Tetracycline in Mitochondria of Rat Liver Cells, *Proc. Soc. Exptl. Biol. Med.*, **113**: 575–578 (1963).   S. P. Rothenberg and R. Garcia, Impurities in Commercially Prepared Tritiated Folic Acid, *Nature*, **200**: 922 (1963).   I. A. Silver, D. B. Cater, D. H. Marrian, and B. Marshale, Tritiated Tetrasodium 2-methyl-1:4-Naphthaquinol Diphosphate for Treatment of Spontaneous Tumors in Animals, *Acta Radiol.*, **58**: 281–300 (1962).   S. B. Taubman, F. E. Young, and J. W. Corcoran, Antibiotic Glycosides, IV. Studies on the Mechanism of Erythromycin Resistance in *Bacillus subtilis*, *Proc. Natl. Acad. Sci. U.S.*, **50**: 955–962 (1963).   E. W. Taylor, Studies on the Mechanism of Inhibition of Mitosis by Colchizine, *J. Cell Biol.*, **19**: 70A (1963).   P. O. P. Ts'o and P. Lu, Interaction of Nucleic Acids, I. Physical Binding of Thymine, Adenine, Steroids, and Aromatic Hydrocarbons to Nucleic Acids, *Proc. Natl. Acad. Sci. U.S.*, **51**: 17–24 (1964).   P. O. P. Ts'o and P. Lu, Interaction of Nucleic Acids, II. Chemical Linkage of the Carcinogen 3,4-Benzpyrene to DNA Induced by Photoradiation, *Proc. Natl. Acad. Sci. U.S.*, **51**: 272–280 (1964).   E. F. Zimmerman and H. G. Mandel, Studies on the Actions of Pyrazolopyrimidines in Microorganisms. I. 4-Hydroxy-6-aminopyrazolopyrimidine, *Exptl. Cell Res.*, **33**: 130–137 (1964).   E. F. Zimmerman and H. G. Mandel, Studies on the Actions of Pyrazolopyrimidines in Microorganisms. II. 4-Aminopyrazolopyrimidine, *Exptl. Cell Res.*, **33**: 138–150 (1964).

XI. Methods and Technical Aspects of Using Tritium as a Label

E. C. Anderson and F. N. Hayes, Recent Advances in Low Level Counting Techniques, *Ann. Rev. Nucl. Sci.*, **6**: 303–316 (1956).   T. E. Banks, J. C. Crawhall, and D. G. Smyth, Some Techniques in the Assay of Tritium, T, *Biochem. J.*, **64**: 411–416 (1956).   D. Beale and J. K. Whitehead, The Determination of Sub-microgram Quantities of Amino Acids with H^3- and C^{14}-labelled 1-Fluoro-2,4-dinitrobenezne, *in Tritium in the Physical and Biological Sciences, Symp. Intern. At. Energy Agency, Vienna*, **1**: 179–190 (1961).   K. Becker, Photographische Bestimmung von Tritium im Wasser, *Atompraxis*, **7**: 358–360 (1961).   R. H. Benson and R. L. Maute, Liquid Scintillation Counting of Tritium. Improvements in Sensivitiy by Efficient Light Collection, *Anal. Chem.*, **34**: 1122–1214 (1962).   R. Bibron, Measurement of Weak Activities in Carbon-14 and Tritium by a Scintillation Method, *L'Onde Elect.*, **39**: 40–45 (1959).   E. H. Carter, Jr., and H. A. Smith, Separation and Detection of Hydrogen, Tritium Hydride, and Tritium at Low-Level Tritium Activities by Gas Chromatography, *J. Phys. Chem.*, **67**: 535–536 (1963).   P. S. Chen, Jr., Liquid Scintillation Counting of C^{14} and H^3 in Plasma and Serum, *Proc. Soc. Exptl. Biol. Med.*, **98**: 546–547 (1958).   D. R. Christman and C. M. Paul, Gas-Proportional Counting of Carbon-14 and Tritium and the Dry Combustion of Organic Compounds, *Anal. Chem.*, **32**: 131–132 (1960).   D. R. Christman, Tritium Counting in Glass Proportional Counting Tubes, *Chemist-Analyst*, **46**: 5–6 (1957).   P. A. Ciccarone, G. Thomas, and W. G. Verly, Determination of Tritium in a Proportional Counter. II. Preparation of Samples, *Nukleonik*, **1**: 329–332 (1959).   J. F. Dingman, W. W. Meyers, Y. Aqishi, and A. P. Wysocki, Specific Tritiation of Insulin, Oxytocin and Lysine Vasopressin (Abstr.), *47th Ann. Meeting Am. Soc. Exptl. Biol., Atlantic City, 1963.*   A. M. Downes and A. R. Till, Assay of Tritium, Carbon-14 and Sulphur-35 in Wool by Liquid Scintillation Counting, *Nature*, **197**: 449–450 (1963).   W. G. Duncombe, Scintillation Counting of Tritium in Solid Samples, *Biochem. J.*, **69**: 6P (1958).   S. W. Englander, A Hydrogen Exchange Method Using Tritium and Sephadex: Its Application to Ribonuclease, *Biochem.*, **2**: 798–807 (1963).

C. Evans and J. Herrington, Determination of Hydrogen in Sodium by Isotopic Dilution with Tritium, *Anal. Chem.*, **35**: 1907–1910 (1963). H. G. Forsberg, Liquid Scintillation Measurements, *Svensk Kem. Tidskr.*, **74**: 144–163 (1962). J. L. Garnett, W. K. Hannan, and S. W. Law, A Modified Tritium Gas Counting Procedure, *Anal. Chem. Acta*, **25**: 170–175 (1961). J. A. Gibson, Liquid Scintillation Counting of Tritium in Urine, *Phys. Med. Biol.*, **6**: 55–64 (1961). E. Gjone, H. G. Vance, and D. A. Turner, Direct Liquid Scintillation Counting of Plasma and Tissues, *Intern. J. Appl. Radiation Isotopes*, **9**: 95–97 (1960). M. Gut and M. Uskokovic, Incorporation of Tritium in Unsaturated Steroids: Pregnenolene-7α-H³ and Progesterone-7α-H³ of Very High Specific Activity, *Naturwissenschaften*, **47**: 40 (1960). J. A. Handler, A Liquid-Scintillation Method for Determining Tritium in the Tissues of Animals Dosed with Tritium-Labeled Vitamin A, *Analyst*, **88**: 47–55 (1963). E. Herczynska, Mesure de l'activite du tritium gazeux, *Nukleonika*, **4**: 381–388 (1959). E. Herczynska, Estimation of Tritio-methane in GM Counters, *Naturwissenschaften*, **46**: 169–170 (1959). T. Higashimura, T. Iawakura, and T. Sidei, Determination of H³ and C¹⁴ with a Liquid Scintillation Counter, *Oyo Butusri*, **29**: 20–27 (1960). T. S. Hodgson, G. E. Gordon, and M. E. Ackerman, Single-Channel Counter for Carbon-14 and Tritium, *Nucleonics*, **16**(7): 89–94 (1958). E. Joachim, Distribution of Tritium in Wilzbach Treated Cholesterol, *Experentia*, **18**: 360–362 (1962). E. Jones, J. R. Mallard, and C. J. Peachy, A Tritium Counter Designed for Routine Laboratory Use, *Phys. Med. Biol.*, **4**: 253–263 (1960). A. Karmen, I. McCaffrey, and R. L. Bowman, A Flow-through Method for Scintillation Counting of Carbon-14 and Tritium in Gas–Liquid Chromatographic Effluents, *J. Lipid Res.*, **3**: 372–377 (1962). Y. Kasida, M. Yamasaki, and T. Iwakura, C¹⁴ and H³ Measurement with Use of Liquid Scintillation Counters, *Radioisotopes (Tokyo)*, **10**: 27–37 (1961). H. Kawai and Y. Nishiwaki, Basic Consideration on the Method of Counting Low Energy β-particles with Liquid Scintillation, *Radioisotopes (Tokyo)*, **10**: 19–26 (1961). H. Kiefer and R. Manshart, Large Area Flow Counter Speed Radiation Measurement, *Nucleonics*, **19**(12): 51 (1961). F. Kohegyi, P. Fodor-Csanyi, and B. Levay, Liquid Scintillation Counting of Tritium with a Coincidence Circuit, *Magy, Kem. Folyoirat*, **67**: 413–414 (1961). A. A. Konstantimov and T. Vsesoyuz, Absolute Counting of β-particles. The Method of the Absolute Solid Angle and the "4 π-Counter" Method, *Nauchn. Issled., Inst. Metrol.*, **30**(90): 6–17 (1957). C. Mantescu and M. Fiti, Mesure du tritium et du carbone-14 en phase gazeuse, *Acad. Rep. Pupulare Romine Studii Cercetari Fiziol.*, **11**: 788–798 (1960). W. H. Melhuish, The Measurement of Carbon-14 and Tritium Activities in Gas-Filled Geiger Counters, *New Zealand J. Sci.*, **3**: 549–558 (1960). A. Ohno and W. Morimitsu, Measurement of Gaseous Tritium by a Proportional Counter, *Radioisotopes (Tokyo)*, **10**: 47–60 (1961). P. R. Payne and J. Done, The Routine Assay of Tritium in Water and Labelled Substances in the Range 20 to 10⁴ μμc. *Phys. Med. Biol.*, **3**: 16–26 (1958). G. Popjak, A. E. Lowe, and D. Moore, Scintillation Counter for Simultaneous Assay of H³ and C¹⁴ in Gas–Liquid Chromatographic Vapors, *J. Lipid Res.*, **3**: 364–371 (1962). V. Santoro, Determination of Tritium by Measurement of Radioactivity with High Precision with a Geiger-Muller Counter, *Gazz. Chim. Ital.*, **89**: 2102–2110 (1959). H. W. Scharpenseel, The Influence of Various Material Conditions on Measurement Yields in Liquid Scintillation Spectroscopy, *Atompraxis*, **7**: 178–181 (1961). P. E. Schulze and M. Wenzel, Determination of Molecular Weight of Unknown Natural Substances by Double Marking, *Proc. Conf. Methods Preparing Storing Marked Molecules, Brussels*, 1964, p. 1271. J. Sharpe and V. A. Stanley, Photomultipliers for Tritium Counting, *in Tritium in the Physical and Biological Sciences, Symp. Intern. At. Energy Agency, Vienna*, **1**: 211–229 (1961). R. S. Sigmond and K. G. Schjetne, Simple Low-Background Photon-Coincidence Detector for T. Liquid Scintillation Counting, *Appl. Sci. Res.*, **B9:** 93–101 (1961).   M. D. Silbert and R. H. Tomlinson, A Gas-Chromatographic Apparatus for the Study of the Hot Atom Chemistry of Organic Halides, *Can. J. Chem.*, **39:** 706–710 (1961). J. R. Tata and A. D. Brownstone, Synthesis of Tritium-Labelled Tyrosine, 3:5-Di-iodotyrosine and Thyroxine, *Nature*, **185:** 34–35 (1960).   T. Takeuchi, M. Saka-guchi, and M. Tatsuchima, Gas-Phase Counting of β-ray of Tritium and Its Application to the Study of Hydrogen Adsorption on Metal, *Radioisotopes (Tokyo)*, **10:** 106–111 (1961).   T. Tamnita, M. Iwanaga, and T. Komai, Studies on DNA's and Nucle-oproteins, II. Tritiation of DNA's, *J. Biochem. (Tokyo)*, **52:** 433–439 (1962).   G. N. Trusov and N. A. Aladzhalova, Determination of Tritium, *Zh. Anal. Khim.*, **15:** 238–239 (1960).   W. G. Verly, G. Hunebelle, and G. Thomas, Determination of Tritium in a Proportional Counter, *Nukleonik*, **1:** 325–329 (1959).

Author Index

Numbers in parentheses are reference numbers and indicate that an author's work is referred to although his name is not cited in the text. Numbers in italics show the page on which the complete reference is listed.

Subject Index

A

Aberrations
chromatid, 332–335
chromosome, 332–335
Absorption coefficient of tritium electrons, 7, 8, 223, *see also* Tritium, radiation from
Accelerators in production of tritium, 2, 3
Acetic acid, labeling of, with tritium, 41
Acetyl cholinesterase localization by labeled DFP in autoradiograms, 194
Acetylene, tritiated, in gas counting, 95–96, 99
Acid catalysis, labeling with tritium by, 39
Acids
differential histochemical extraction with, 191–193
liquid scintillation counting of, 107, 114, 136–140, 142–144
Acid-soluble pool, 242–259, 281–282
Acid-soluble substances
localization by autoradiography, 209–214, 248
loss of, during fixation, 186
Actinomycin D
inhibition of aldosterone action by, 280
of RNA synthesis by, 280
Adenosine triphosphate, effect on feedback by thymidine triphosphate, 251
Administration of labeled precursors, routes of, 238 (*see also* Precursors, labeled)
Adrenaline, in control of cell proliferation, 258, 275
Aerobacter aerogenes, DNA turnover in, 264
Aerosil in liquid scintillation counting of gel, 141

Age effect
on acid-soluble pool for thymidine, 281–282
for uridine, 282
on cell proliferation, 278, 281–282
on nucleic acid metabolism, 282
on tumor induction by tritiated thymidine, in mice, 337
on uridine kinase activity, 282
L-Alanine, tritium recoil technique in specific labeling of, 28
Albumin, serum, labeling with tritium, 32
Aldehydes-1-H^3, oxidation of, isotope effect, 20
Aldose-1-H^3 reaction, isotope effect, 20
Aldosterone action
inhibition by actinomycin D, 280
by puromycin, 280
intracellular localization of, 280
Algae in labeling with tritium by biosynthesis, 48
Alkaloids
paper chromatography of, 71
stability of tritium on, 54
Alkyl benzenes in liquid scintillation counting, 106, 108
Alpha particle, *see also* Helium-4
in lithium irradiation with neturons, 2, 3, 27–28
in tritium irradiation with deuterons, 2
Aluminum-2-ethyl-hexanoate in liquid scintillation counting of gel, 141
Aluminum stearate in liquid scintillation counting of gel, 141
Amino acids
cellular incorporation of, 245, 280
clearance from peripheral blood, 239
deprivation, effect on DNA synthesis, 258, 266

406

incorporation, hormone effect on, 280
nutrition effect on, 280
labeling with tritium, 42
liquid scintillation counting of, by
hyamine, 137–138
paper chromatography of, 70
radiation decomposition of, 59
stability of tritium in, biological, 51
chemical, 67
storage conditions of, 68
tracer dose, 345
tritiated
radiation decomposition of, 67
toxicity of, 322–323, 338–342
effect of cell geometry, 260–261,
339
Amino groups, histochemical measurement by autoradiography, 194
Ammonia, tritiated, in gas counting, 99
Androsterone, tritiated, metabolism of,
54
Anemia, megaloblastic, effect of thymidine on cell proliferation in,
254
H³-Aniline monohydrochloride in labeling proteins, 44
Anoxia, effect of, on beta radiation, in
bacteria, 319
Anthracene
in counting chromatographic effluents,
147
in counting tritium in paper chromatograms, 151–152
quenching in liquid scintillation
counting with, 143–144
in scintillation counting, 142–144, 147
Antibody, see also Proteins
tritiated, for localization of antigen
in autoradiograms, 194
tritium labeling of, 44, 48
Antigen localization by tritiated antibody, in autoradiograms, 194
Apurinic acid, formation of, 193
Aqueous solution in liquid scintillation
counting, 108, 136
Arginine dependence, E. coli, reversion
of, 322–323, 342
Argon in gas counting, 89
Arndt-Eistert reaction in labeling with
tritium, 42–43

Ascites tumor cells
radiation effect on, 326
toxicity of tritiated thymidine in, 326–327
Atropin, tritium labeling of, 31
Autoradiogram, see also Nuclear track
emulsion
artifacts in, 183
background, 171, 181–182, 220–222
coincidence error in, 218
darkroom for, 184–185
development of, 170–173
drying of, 185, 195–199
dry-mounting technique of, 209–214
efficiency of, 178, 179, 219–220, 223
electron microscopic, 201–209
evaluation of, 218–222
fading of final image in, 183
of latent image in, 179–181, 201
fixation of, 173–175
gelatin removal, 200–201, 208, 216
grain counting in, 218–224
grain size in, 164
histochemical techniques, 186–194
"infinite thickness" for tritium in, 178
labeling indices in, 221
nuclear track emulsion, application of,
for, 164–170, 194–214
photographic processing, 170–175
preparation of, 185–214
radiation dose calculation by, 343
resolution in, 176–178
self-absorption of tritium electrons in,
178–179, 223
specimen fixation, 186–191
specimen preparation, 186–194
specimen protection in, 200–203, 205–206, 208, 212, 214, 215
staining of, 191–193, 201–202, 214–218
storage of, 183–184, 196
water-soluble substances in, 209–214

B

Background in autoradiograms
bleaching of, 182
cause of, 181
correction for, 220–222
determination of, 220
development of, 171
variations in, 220